**Frontiers in
Bioinorganic Chemistry**

edited by
Antonio V. Xavier

Lectures presented at the
2nd International Conference on Bioinorganic Chemistry
15–19 April 1985, Algarve, Portugal

International Organizing Committee
I. Bertini
H.B. Gray
B.G. Malmström
J. Reedijk
H. Sigel
A.V. Xavier

© VCH Verlagsgesellschaft mbH, D-6940 Weinheim (Federal Republic of Germany), 1986

Distribution:
VCH Verlagsgesellschaft, Postfach 12 60/12 80, D-6940 Weinheim (Federal Republic of Germany)
USA und Canada: VCH Publishers, 303 N.W. 12th Avenue, Deerfield Beach FL 33442-1705 (USA)

ISBN 3-527-26460-4 (VCH Verlagsgesellschaft)
ISBN 0-89573-489-3 (VCH Publishers)

Preface

Bioinorganic chemistry, an interdisciplinary field "par excellence", has been defined as the science which brings inorganic chemistry into life, by recognizing the fundamental importance of life dependence on metal ions. Bioinorganic chemistry unifies research fields disparate as physics and medicine and brings together scientists working in all branches of the natural sciences.

Only recently established as a branch of science on its own, it has been growing fast both in terms of the number of scientists and the diversity of their original backgrounds. The significant development in the field as well as several conferences which were organized during the seventies prepared the way for a series of international conferences under the acronym of ICBIC (International Conferences on Bioinorganic Chemistry). The 1st ICBIC, organized by Ivano Bertini, was held in 1983 in Florence. Its success, which can be measured by the number of participants (well over four hundred), the wide number of nationalities represented, and the scientific work presented, is a convincing reflection of the coming of age of bioinorganic chemistry. However, although there is a "Journal of Inorganic Biochemistry", the literature in this field is, and probably will always be, quite scattered in different types of scientific journals (as to be expected of a truly interdisciplinary science). This prompted me to ask the invited speakers at the 2nd ICBIC (held in the Algarve, Portugal, in April of 1985) to write an article on their current research, so that a state-of-the-art report on bioinorganic chemistry could be made available to the scientific community. This copious and comprehensive book was the result, and I should like to thank all authors for their efforts.

The book illustrates the recent and exciting developments in bioinorganic chemistry, and in many respects indicates the scope and expectations for the even more significant developments expected in the near future. Developments in some new spectroscopic techniques, which will be instrumental for achieving a better understanding of the biological function of metal ions, are discussed in detail.

In conclusion, I would like to express my sincere thanks to the members of the International Scientific Committee of the 2nd ICBIC (I. Bertini, H.B. Gray, B.G. Malmström, J. Reedijk, and H. Sigel), the Organizing Committee (A.B.V.P. Aguiar, J.J.R. Fraústo da Silva, I. Moura, J.J.G. Moura, and L.F. Vilas-Boas) as well as the Conference Secretary, Margarida Martinez, and the last year chemistry students of the New University of Lisbon. Their help and dedication enabled me to hold the 2nd ICBIC, whose lectures form the basis of "Frontiers in Bioinorganic Chemistry".

Lisbon, October 1985   Antonio V. Xavier

Contents

Nickel-Biochemistry

Desulfovibrio gigas Hydrogenase: Catalytic Cycle and Activation Process

José J.G.Moura*, Miguel Teixeira*, Isabel Moura*, António V.Xavier* and Jean LeGall§

*Centro de Química Estrutural, U.N.L., Complexo I, I.S.T., Av. Rovisco Pais, 1000 Lisboa, Portugal.
§Department of Biochemistry, University of Georgia, Athens, Georgia 30602, U.S.A.

The metabolism of molecular hydrogen and the study of hydrogenases have figured centrally in the development of the present concepts regarding the biochemistry and the physiology of dissimilatory sulfate reduction. Two types of periplasmic hydrogenases have been characterized from *Desulfovibrio* species: one type containing nickel as well as iron-sulfur clusters, termed the [NiFe] hydrogenase and another type containing only iron-sulfur clusters, termed the [Fe] hydrogenase. The first type has been most extensively studied in *Desulfovibrio gigas* (1--5) and the second in *Desulfovibrio vulgaris* (6,7).

Desulfovibrio gigas [NiFe] hydrogenase (E.C. 1.12.2.1) has a molecular weight of 89 KD (63 and 26 KD subunits structure) and contains 1 gatm of nickel, 11 gatm of iron and 11--12 gatm of sulfide (1).

1 - NATIVE STATE

Iron-Sulfur centers

Mössbauer and EPR spectroscopic studies established that in the purified enzyme the iron-sulfur clusters are arranged in a $[Fe_3S_x]_{oxid}$ cluster (EPR active) and two $[Fe_4S_4]^{2+}$ clusters (EPR silent) (2). The

$[Fe_3S_x]_{ox}$ cluster is the origin of an almost isotropic EPR signal centered around g = 2.02, observable below 30 K. The Mössbauer parameters of the $[Fe_4S_4]$ clusters (quadrupole splitting of 1.16 mm/s and isomeric shift of 0.46 mm/s, at 4.2 K) are typical of 4Fe centers in the +2 oxidation level.

Nickel Center

    In the native preparations, a rhombic EPR signal with g-values at 2.31, 2.23 and 2.02 (Ni-signal A) is observed up to 120 K (Figure 1).

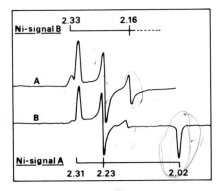

Fig. 1. EPR spectra of *D.gigas* [NiFe] hydrogenase, recorded in a
        Bruker ER-200 tt spectrometer, equipped with an Oxford
        Instruments continuous flow cryostat.
        A) and B) — Two different preparations of the enzyme.
        Temperature 100 K, modulation amplitude 1 mT, microwave
        power 2 mW, frequency 9.34 GHz.

This rhombic signal, assigned to nickel(III) accounts for 50–100% of the chemically detectable nickel depending on preparation. This assignment was confirmed by the observation of hyperfine coupling in [61]Ni isotopic replaced hydrogenase (3). A minor species can also be detected at g-values 2.33, 2.16 and ~2.0 (Ni-Signal B, Figure 1). The relative intensities of Ni-Signals A and B varies with preparation and can be altered by anaerobic redox cycling of the enzyme. This indicates that there exists different Ni(III) environments in the oxidized enzyme.

2 - INTERMEDIATE OXIDATION STATES (2)

$Y_2 \cdot 3/2$

The first event occuring during the anaerobic reduction of *D.gigas*·
hydrogenase with hydrogen is the disappearence of Ni-Signals A and B and
the isotropic g = 2.02 signal due to the $[Fe_3S_x]$ cluster. An EPR
silent state is then attained.   Further reduction of the enzyme under
H_2 atmosphere, is accompanied by the development of a new rhombic EPR
signal with g-values at 2.19, 2.16 and 2.02 (Ni-Signal C) (Figure 2-A).
This signal was attributed to a nickel species by the [61]Ni isotopic
substitution (3).

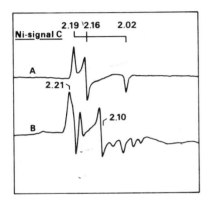

Fig. 2. EPR spectra of intermediate redox states of *D.gigas* [NiFe]
        hydrogenase, in the presence of hydrogen.   Experimental
        conditions as in Fig. 1.
        A) Temperature 77 K, microwave power 2 mW.
        b) Same as A, at 4.2 K, microwave power 2 mW.

During the course of the reductive experiment Ni-Signal C attains a
maximum intensity (40-60 % of the chemically detectable nickel). Longer
incubation time under H_2 yields an EPR silent state, when measured at
77 K.   At low temperature (below 15 K) EPR signals typical of $[Fe_4S_4]^{1+}$
clusters are observed (5).

At redox states of the enzyme such that Ni-Signal C develops, low
temperature studies reveal the presence of another EPR active species:
below 10 K, the shape of the EPR spectra changes drastically and a new
set of signals at g = 2.21, 2.10 and broad components at higher field
is clearly discernible at 4 K (Figure 2-B).   This set of g-values
exhibits different power dependence from that of Ni-Signal C (readily
saturated with low microwqve power, typical of a slow relaxation
species).   The origin of the "2.21" signals is under discussion. Since
these signals are only observable at low temperature with high micro-

wave power levels (fast relaxing species), they may originate from an
iron-sulfur center. Since the g-values appear to be too high, another
explanation is that they originate from the Ni-center weakly interacting with another paramagnetic center in the vicinity (e.g. iron-
-sulfur center).

3 - <u>MID-POINT REDOX POTENTIALS</u>

     Redox transitions were observed at -70 mV (measured by the disappear
ence of the 2.02 signal) and -220 mV (measured by the disappearence of
the Ni-Signal A)(Figure 3 - insert A).   Only the second redox transition
is pH dependent, with a slope of -60 mV per pH unit (7). Ni-Signal C
develops at a mid-point redox potential below -300 mV, reaches a
maximum around -350 mV and disappears below -400 mV (Figure 3).

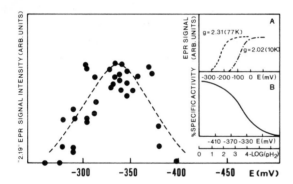

Fig. 3. EPR signal intensity (arbitrary units) of the Ni-Signal C in
        function of the redox potential.   EPR signals were measured at
        77 K.   No attempt was made to fit the experimental points to a
        Nernst equation.
        Insert A - Redox titration followed at g = 2.02 (10 K) and
        g = 2.31 (77 K) data from Rèference (2).
        Insert B - Activation profile of *D.gigas* [NiFe] hydrogenase at
        different partial pressures of hydrogen, data from Reference(7)

     Lissolo *et al*. (8) determined the activity of the enzyme as a
function of the redox potential.   Their study indicates that the hydro
genase activation is a one-electron process with a mid-point redox
potential around -340 mV (Figure 3, insert B).   This value correlates
with the appeerance of Ni-Signal C, suggesting that this signal may

represent an activated state of the enzyme.

4 - ACTIVATION PROCESS AND CATALYTIC CYCLE

The definition of the role of the nickel during the redox cycle of
[NiFe] hydrogenases requires the assignment of the oxidation states
involved, the characterization of the ligation mode of the nickel
center and the interaction between the redox centers in such a complex
enzyme.

The simplest interpretation of our redox data involves a redox scheme
that requires the transition from Ni(III) to Ni(0). However, nickel
chemistry shows that the very high and very low states are not stable
chemical species; very negative and very positive redox potentials
are associated with the transitions Ni(I)/Ni(0) and Ni(III)/Ni(II),
respectively. Also, the Ni(III)/Ni(II) chemistry offers a wide range
of versatile properties, namely: facile rearrangement of ligands, spin
and conformational equilibria as well as alteration of the type and
number of ligands in the nickel coordination sphere. The redox
properties of the Ni(III)/Ni(II) couple can be brought, in principle,
to physiological levels by preferential stabilization of the Ni(III)
state. Thus, the utilization of fewer redox states seems more realistic
in terms of the nickel chemistry.

Another important point to consider in the reactional mechanism of
hydrogenase is that the so-called "oxygen stable" [NiFe] hydrogenases
(e.g. *D.gigas* hydrogenase) are not fully active in the "as isolated"
state. Studies of the hydrogenase activity (7) indicate that the
enzyme must go through a lag phase as well as an activation one, in
order to be fully active. This complex phenomenum seems to involve the
removal of oxygen (lag phase) followed by a reduction step (activation
phase).

Taking into consideration the hydrogenase activity studies, the
plausibility of the Ni(III)/Ni(II) redox cycling scheme, and the
sequence of events observed by EPR spectroscopy upon exposure to H_2
atmosphere, a model is proposed for the mechanism of the [NiFe] hydrogenases in the context of both the catalytic and the activation
processes (Scheme 1).

The "as isolated" state is fully characterized. EPR and Mössbauer
studies in the enzyme "as isolated" (2) indicate that there is no
magnetic interaction between these four redox centers.

SCHEME 1

$$\begin{pmatrix} Ni(III) \\ [Fe_4S_4]^{2+} \\ [Fe_4S_4]^{2+} \\ [Fe_3S_x]_{ox} \end{pmatrix} \overset{H_2}{\underset{}{\rightleftharpoons}} \begin{pmatrix} Ni(III) \\ \updownarrow \\ [Fe_4S_4]^{1+} \\ [Fe_4S_4]^{2+} \\ [Fe_3S_x]_{red} \end{pmatrix} \overset{H_2}{\underset{}{\rightleftharpoons}} \begin{pmatrix} Ni(III)-H^- \\ [Fe_4S_4]^{1+}-H^+ \\ [Fe_4S_4]^{2+} \\ [Fe_3S_x]_{red} \end{pmatrix} \overset{}{\longrightarrow} \begin{matrix} Further \\ reduction \end{matrix}$$

Ni-Signal A   EPR silent   Ni-Signal C

Ni-Signal B   "2.21" EPR signal

$g = 2.02$

The active state of the enzyme is EPR silent. During this activation process, both the isotropic $g = 2.02$ and the nickel signal disappear. The loss of the $g = 2.02$ signal is attributed to the reduction of the $[Fe_3S_x]$ cluster, $E_o = -70$ mV (EPR silent $[Fe_3S_x]_{red}$).

In order to retain the Ni(III)/Ni(II) redox scheme, the disappearence of Ni-Signal A and/or Ni-Signal B requires a more complicated mechanism. We propose that one of the $[Fe_4S_4]$ clusters is reduced into a $[Fe_4S_4]^{1+}$ state (S = 1/2) and the reduced cluster is spin coupled with the Ni(III) center resulting in an EPR silent state. This proposal implies that the previously determined redox potential, -220 mV, for the disppearence of Ni-Signal A (2) is actually the mid-point redox potential for one of the $[Fe_4S_4]$ clusters. Such a mechanism is supported by the optical studies which indicate that the activation process involves the reduction of iron-sulfur clusters. Preliminary Mössbauer data (our unpublished results in collaboration with B.H.Huynh) also show that approximately one $[Fe_4S_4]$ cluster is reduced in the EPR silent state and it is possible to recognize the normal "signature" of the reduced 3Fe cluster.

The events which follow the EPR silent state are the appeerance of both the Ni-Signal C and the "$g = 2.21$" signal. In accordance with the heterolytic mechanism of hydrogen activation, we have proposed thta in the presence of the natural substrate a hydride intermediate state is obtained. The nickel center would be assigned to the hydride binding site and the $[Fe_4S_4]^{1+}$ cluster to the proton binding site. Breaking of the spin coupling between the Ni(III) and the $[Fe_4S_4]^{1+}$ cluster in this hydride intermediate, would originate Ni-Signal C [5]. Thus, this signal was assumed to represent the hydride-bound Ni(III) center and the $g = 2.21$ is attributed to the proton-bound $[Fe_4S_4]^{1+}$ cluster. An alternative explanation is that the $g = 2.19$ EPR signal is due to a transient Ni(III) state in a different coordination, resulting from the breaking of the coupling and the g = 2.21 is due to the interacting Ni(III) and $[Fe_4S_4]^{1+}$ centers bound to hydride and proton, respectively. Indeed, recent redox titrations (our unpublished results) show that the "g = 2.19" signal starts to develop well before the "g = 2.21" signal. The different coordination for the nickel "g = 2.19" state could be reached by adding S ligands (see discussion ref. [5]) which might be available from the reduction of dissulfide bridges. This would explain the appearence of a free radical signal before that of the "g = 2.19" signal.

5 - ACKNOWLEDGEMENTS

We thank Drs. T.Lissolo, B.H.Huynh, H.D.Peck,Jr., and D.V.DerVartanian for very interesting discussions. This research was supported by grants from Instituto Nacional de Investigação Científica, Junta Nacio nal de Investigação Científica e Tecnológica, AID Grant 936-5542-G-SS--4003-00 and NATO Grant 0341/83.

6 - REFERENCES

(1) J.LeGall, P.O.Ljungdhal, I.Moura, H.D.Peck,Jr., A.V.Xavier, J.J.G. Moura, M.Teixeira, B.H.Huynh, and D.V.DerVartanian, Biochem.Biophys. Res.Commun. 106 (1982) 610-616.

(2) M.Teixeira, I.Moura, A.V.Xavier, D.V.DerVartanian, J.LeGall, H.D. Peck,Jr., B.H.Huynh and J.J.G.Moura, Eur.J.Biochem. 130 (1985) 481--484.

(3) J.J.G.Moura, I.Moura, B.H.Huynh, H.J.Krüger, M.Teixeira, R.C. DuVarney, D.V.DerVartanian, A.V.Xavier, H.D.Peck,Jr. and J.LeGall, Biochem.Biophys.Res.Commun. 408 (1982) 1388-1393.

(4) J.J.G.Moura, M.Teixeira, I.Moura, A.V.Xavier and J.LeGall J.Mol. Cat. 23 (1984) 303-314.

(5) M.Teixeira, I.Moura, A.V.Xavier, B.H.Huynh, D.V.DerVartanian, J. LeGall and J.J.G.Moura J.Biol.Chem. (1985) in press.

(6) B.H.Huynh, M.H.Czechowski, H.J.Krüger, D.V.DerVartanian, H.D.Peck, Jr. and J.LeGall Proc.Natl.Acad.Sci.USA 81 (1984) 122-126.

(7) H.M.van der Westen, S.G.Mayhew and C.Veeger, FEBS Lett. <u>86</u> (1978) 122-126

(8) R.Cammack, D.Patil, R.Aguirre and E.C.Hatchikian, FEBS Lett. <u>142</u> (1982) 289-292.

(9) T.Lissolo, S.Pulvin and D.Thomas, J.Biol.Chem. <u>259</u> (1984) 11725- -11729.

On The Possible Redox States of Nickel and The Iron-Sulphur Cluster in Hydrogenase from *Chromatium vinosum*

S.P.J. Albracht, J.W. van der Zwaan, R.D. Fontijn and E.C. Slater.

Laboratory of Biochemistry, B.C.P. Jansen Institute, University of Amsterdam, P.O. Box 20151, 1000 HD Amsterdam (The Netherlands).

SUMMARY

EPR spectra of hydrogenase from Chromatium vinosum under various redox conditions indicate four distinct states of reduction. It is proposed that nickel can be present in the 3+, 2+, 1+ and possibly the zerovalent state. The coordination of Ni(I) is very sensitive to visible light. At temperatures below 77 K, light induces an irreversible dissociation of one of the ligands of nickel. The rate of this process in H_2O is 5.6 times faster than in ^2H_2O. It is concluded that hydrogen, possibly as H^-, is in the direct coordination sphere of Ni(I) and that nickel is the site of interaction of the enzyme with H_2. The line shapes of the Ni(I) signal at 25 K and 4.2 K are completely different. Analysis of X and Q-band spectra revealed that the change is caused by two-fold splitting from a rapidly relaxing paramagnet, presumably a reduced form of the iron-sulphur cluster. No EPR signal could be assigned to the cluster in this redox state yet.

1 INTRODUCTION

Hydrogenase from Chromatium vinosum as isolated in our laboratory
(1,2) is a hydrophylic enzyme with a molecular weight of 62 000. It
consists of one polypeptide and contains Ni(III) and an Fe-S cluster
which can both be detected with EPR. Purified preparations are inhomo-
geneous in the sense that they contain intact enzyme molecules, which
are fully active under assay conditions, as well as defect molecules,
with a very low activity. Enzymatic activity is related (2) to the
presence, in the isolated enzyme, of a complicated EPR signal between
$g=1.90$ and 2.05 which we have ascribed (3) to a $4Fe-4S^{3+}$ cluster
that is weakly spin-coupled to Ni(III). The corresponding nickel
signal in the $g=2.1$ to 2.3 region is also split by this interaction,
and the spin-relaxation rate of the Ni(III) ion is significantly
increased, so that it can be observed only below 25 K. Defect enzyme
molecules show two $S=1/2$ signals of equal intensities: (i) a rather
isotropic signal in the $g=2$ region ascribed to a 3Fe cluster and (ii)
a signal due to non-interacting low-spin Ni(III). The EPR spectra are
further complicated by the fact that in intact as well as defect
molecules two forms of nickel, called Ni-a and NI-b, have been found
(2). The ratio Ni-a/Ni-b varies from preparation to preparation but is
always the same in both forms of the enzyme within one batch. The
coordination of Ni-a in defect molecules is assumed to be identical to
that of Ni-a in intact enzyme, since the g values are identical (3).
The same holds for Ni-b.

The oxidized form of the intact enzyme does not readily react with
H_2. The enzyme gains activity only at low redox potentials (4). In
this paper we report on EPR studies with the enzyme at redox potentials down to -480 mV. A preliminary report has appeared elsewhere
(5).

2 MATERIALS AND METHODS

Growth of C.vinosum strain DSM 185 and the isolation and purification of hydrogenase were carried out as before (1,2). The enzyme was
dissolved in 50 mM Tris-HCl buffer (pH 7.4). Potentiometric titrations
were performed under Ar in the presence of a suitable mixture of
mediating dyes (6). Samples were anaerobically transferred into EPR
tubes, which were then immersed in cold (133 K) isopentane. Treatment
of the enzyme with H_2 and Ar or He was performed in Thunberg cells.
Illumination of samples was carried out by shining white light through
the irradiation grid of the microwave cavity, while the sample was

cooled by a stream of cold He gas. Recording, quantification and
simulation of EPR spectra were carried out as in (3).

3 RESULTS

A reductive titration of the enzyme under Ar revealed three stages
of reduction (See Fig. 1). In stage 1 (between -19 and -38 mV) we
observed the disappearence of all lines due to the interacting spin
pair of Ni(III) (arrows marked with 4) and the $[4Fe-4S]^{3+}$ cluster
(marked with 2). At the same time the signal of non-interacting
Ni(III) (arrows marked with 3) and of the 3Fe cluster (marked with 1)
increased in amplitude. During the second stage (between -38 and -247
mV) the signal of Ni(III) and the 3Fe cluster disappeared completely
with $E_{m,7.3}$ values of about -175 mV and -165 mV respectively. At still
lower potentials a signal with $g_{x,y}$=2.2 and 2.16 appeared (the strong
radical signal at g=2 is from mediating dyes).

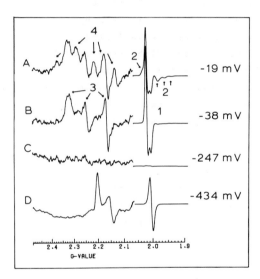

Fig. 1. EPR spectra of the enzyme at different potentials during a
redox titration at pH 7.3. The gain for the left-hand part of the
spectra A-C was 2.9 times that of D; the temperature was 16 K. the
relative gains for the right-hand part of the spectra A-C was 2 times
that of D; the temperature was 13 K.

The simplest interpretation of the changes is the following. First a
4Fe to 3Fe cluster transition is induced by reducing equivalents,

whereby the spin coupling with nickel is broken (stage 1). We have observed this phenomenon earlier (2). In stage 2 the Ni(III) and the 3Fe cluster are both reduced, whereas at lower potentials the divalent nickel is further reduced to Ni(I). The signal in Fig. 1D has been reported for two other nickel hydrogenases (7,8). Moura et al. (8), using ^{61}Ni, have shown that it is indeed due to nickel. Whenever we observed this signal during a titration it was noticd that the potential was unstable and drifted to higher values. Under H_2 the potential stabilized at about -480 mV (pH 7.8).

The signal could also be evoked by reaction of the enzyme with H_2 in the absence of mediators and then accounted for only 3% of the amount of nickel maximally observable in the oxidized enzyme. The intensity of the signal could be enhanced up to 13-fold by replacing the H_2 by Ar or He. This effect was already reported for the enzyme of Methanobacterium thermoautotrophicum (7). However, we found that extensive evacuation and gassing with He or Ar induced the complete removal of the Ni(I) signal (6). We discovered that the signal is very sensitive to light (Fig. 2). Starting with the signal induced by H_2 plus subsequent short treatment with He and freezing in the dark (Fig. 2A), illumination with white light at 22 K for several minutes (spectra B to D) induced gradual changes, finally resulting in the complete conversion into a new signal.

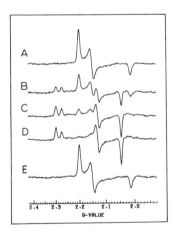

Fig. 2. Effect of illumination at 22 K on the EPR signal of Ni(I). A, before illumination; B, C and D, after 1, 3 and 6 min of illumination; E, the sample was thawed and frozen in the dark. Spectra were recorded with the same gain.

The total signal intensity did not change. the process was irreversible at low temperatures, but reversed at 200 K in about 10 min.
Thawing the sample and freezing in the dark had the same effect (Fig.
2E).

It is proposed that light causes the breakage of a bond between the
nickel ion and one of its ligands, resulting in considerable changes
in ligand field. When lyophylized enzyme dissolved in ^2H_2O (99.7%) was
used, we found that the rate of photodissociation decreased by a
factor of 5.6, relative to a control sample dissolved in H_2O. Since
the enzyme catalyses a rapid $H/^2H$ exchange reaction between the H_2 gas
and ^2H_2O (9), all exchangeable H atoms, including those introduced by
the reaction with H_2, will be replaced by deuterium. In view of the
large isotope effect on the rate of the photolytic process, it is
proposed that the light-sensitive bond is one between nickel and
hydrogen, possibly as a hydride ion. This strongly implies that Ni is
the site of interaction with H_2. Light sensitivity of Ni(I) was also
observed with the enzyme (10) from Wolinella succinogenes (J.W. van
der Zwaan, S.P.J. Albracht, G. Unden and A. Kröger, unpublished) and
is therefore expected to be a general property of Ni hydrogenases. The
line shapes of the Ni(I) signal of lyophylized enzyme dissolved in
^2H_2O (99.7%) or $H_2^{17}O$ (45%) showed no apparent differences. Likewise
no differences were seen between the signals of Ni(III) in these
preparations. This makes it unlikely that H or OH_2 are ligands to the
nickel in axial position. The rate of photodissociation was not
affected by the solvent $H_2^{17}O$.

It has been reported for the enzyme of Desulfovibrio gigas (11)
that at low temperatures (7 K) the signal, equivalent to that in Fig.
2A, broadens in a strange way and seems to be converted into another
signal. The Chromatium enzyme behaved similarly, but the transformation was found to be complete only at 4.2 K (Fig. 3). No further
changes were noticed down to 1.5 K. Spectra taken at 35 GHz revealed
that the changes were in fact a two-fold splitting of the original
signal caused by a coupling to a near-by spin, probably the Fe-S
cluster (Fig. 4). However, we could not yet identify a signal that
might represent this cluster. As a result of the coupling the
relaxation rate of the Ni(I) ion increased enormously: it was hard to
saturate the signal at 4.2 K. Above 25 K there is no apparent coupling
and the signal can be observed easily up to 100 K. The light-induced
signal shows a similar temperature dependence and a two-fold splitting
is here clearly observed in the X-band spectrum (not shown).

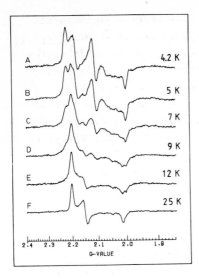

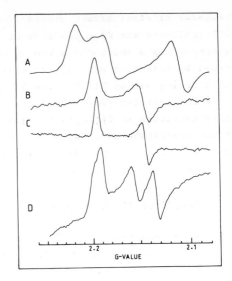

Fig. 3. Effect of temperature on the signal of Ni(I). Microwave power for A-E, 0.2 mW; for F, 0.7 mW. The gain in F was 0.95 times that in A-E.

Fig. 4. Comparison of X (9 GHz) and Q-band (35 GHz) spectra of Ni(I) at high and low temperature. A and B, X-band spectra at 4.2 K (0.2 mW) and 24 K (0.7 mW) respectively; C and D, Q-band spectra at 24 K (3.2 mW) and 10 K (3.2 mW) respectively. Spectra are plotted on the same $\underline{g}$ scale; only the $\underline{g}_{x,y}$ region is displayed.

4 DISCUSSION

4.1. The redox states of nickel.

The simplest interpretation of the redox titration data is that trivalent nickel is reduced to the EPR-undetectable divalent state, and then further to the monovalent state. Since at very low potentials practically no signal is observed, reduction to the zerovalent state might be considered. As this paper, presented at the Second International Conference on Bioinorganic Chemistry, was written after the conference, it is appropriate to include in this discussion some

proposals of other groups presented at the conference. Moura et al.
(12) explained the disappearance of the Ni(III) signal in the D. gigas
enzyme during a redox titration by spin-coupling to the S=1/2 system
formed by reduction of a 4Fe cluster. Reaction with H_2 would remove
the coupling making Ni(III) again EPR detectable, but now with a
different signature possibly due to hydride binding. At lower potentials reduction to Ni(II) was suggested. Evidence for a Ni(III) to
Ni(II) transition under H_2 also came from the shift of the K edge to
lower energy in X-ray absorption measurements (13). We cannot exclude
this explanation for the observations with the Chromatium enzyme.

4.2. Light-sensitivity of nickel(I)

From the experiments in ^2H_2O, where the rate of the photolytic
process was only 18% of that of a control experiment in H_2O, we
conclude that light induces the breakage of a nickel-hydrogen bond
present in the enzyme under H_2. This implies that H_2 reacts directly
with nickel. However, we found virtually no effect on the line widths
of the Ni(I) signal when H_2O was replaced by ^2H_2O. Only the width of
the g_y line decreased from 2.2 mT to 1.7 mT (6). This suggests that
the hydrogen atom is not present in axial position, the direction
where the unpaired electron is located (in contrast to what we
erroneously proposed earlier (6)). The breakage of a bond is indicated
by the great change in ligand field around the nickel (Fig. 2). Before
illumination the signal has one of its g values close to 2, indicating
the presence of the free electron in d_z2 orbital. After illumination
the smallest g value is 2.04, suggesting that the free spin resides
now in an orbital mainly with a d_{x2-y2} character. No hyperfine
splitting due to N nuclei was observed in any of the nickel spectra,
making the presence of this element in the direct coordination sphere
less likely, though not imposssible. Light had no effect on any of the
other EPR signals of the enzyme. Likewise the rate of the enzymatic
reaction was not affected.

4.3. The behaviour of the Fe-S cluster.

In recent studies, which will be presented in detail elsewhere
(14), we found that defect enzyme molecules can be converted to
intact, active ones by heating to 50 °C for 20 min in the presence of
5mM dithiolthreitol or 2-mercaptoethanol, under an H_2 atmosphere. When
cooled to 4 °C an oxygen-stable preparation was obtained. We could not
demonstrate any dependence on added Fe or S^{2-} ions. EPR spectra showed

that only active enzyme has the potential of forming a spin-coupled Ni(III)/$[4Fe-4S]^{3+}$ pair in the oxidized state. However, the Fe-S cluster in oxidized, intact enzyme can exist also as a $[3Fe-4S]^{+}$ cluster, as in the defect enzyme. In defect enzyme we have never observed a signal of a 4Fe cluster. Strictly speaking the classification as 3Fe or 4Fe cluster is only based on the (very different) EPR spectra (3) and the Fe and S^{2-} content (15); this remains to be verified with more direct methods.

It is difficult to say in what form and valence state the Fe-S cluster is present in the reduced enzyme. The observed splitting in the Ni(I) signal at 4.2 K indicates the presence of a paramagnetic cluster. If it were in a S=1/2 state, an EPR signal might be expected in the g=2 region, which we have not detected yet. The experiment in Fig. 3 was carried out with routinely prepared enzyme, where both the defect and intact forms were present. Thus we cannot yet say whether the signals are from enzyme molecules with a 3Fe or a 4Fe cluster. More might be learned from a comparison of preparations which are either completely transformed into the defect form or converted to the intact form. This is now under investigation.

ACKNOWLEDGEMENTS

We thank Dr.R. Cammack for a copy of his paper (11) prior to publication. This work was supported by the Netherlands Organization for the Advancement of Pure Research (Z.W.O.) under the auspices of the Netherlands Foundation for Chemical Research (S.O.N.).

5 REFERENCES

(1) H. van Heerikhuizen, S.P.J. Albracht, E.C. Slater and P.S. van Rheenen, Biochim. Biophys. Acta 657 (1981) 26-39.

(2) S.P.J. Albracht, M.C. Kalkman and E.C. Slater, Biochim. Biophys. Acta 724 (1983) 309-316.

(3) S.P.J. Albracht, J.W. van der Zwaan and R.D. Fontijn, Biochim. Biophys. Acta 766 (1984) 245-258.

(4) V.M. Fernandez, R. Munilla and A. Ballesteros, Arch. Biochem. Biophys. 215 (1982) 129-135.

(5) S.P.J. Albracht, J.W. van der Zwaan, R.D. Fontijn and E.C. Slater, Rev. Port. Quím 27 (1985) 66-67.

(6) J.W. van der Zwaan, S.P.J. Albracht, R.D. Fontijn and E.C. Slater, FEBS Lett. 179 (1985) 271-277.

(7) N. Kojima, J.A. Fox, R.P. Hausinger, L. Daniels, W.H. Orme-Johnson and C.T. Walsh, Proc. Natl. Acad. Sci USA 80 (1983) 378-382.

(8) J.J.G. Moura, I. Moura, B.H. Huynh, H.-J. Kruger, M. Teixeira, R.G. DuVarney, D.V. DerVartanian, P. Ljungdahl, A.V. Xavier, H.D. Peck, Jr. and J. LeGall, Biochem. Biophys. Res. Commun. 108 (1982) 1388-1393.

(9) A.I. Krasna, Methods Enzym. 53 (1978) 296-314.

(10) G. Unden, R. Bocher, J. Knecht and A. Kruger, FEBS Lett. 145 (1982) 230-234.

(11) R. Cammack, D.S. Patil and V.M. Fernandez, Biochem. Soc. Trans. (1985) in the press.

(12) J.J.G. Moura, M. Teixeira, I. Moura, A.V. Xavier and J. LeGall, Rev. Port. Quím. 27 (1985) 63-66.

(13) R.A. Scott, M. Czechowski, D.V. DerVatanian, J. LeGall, H.D. Peck, Jr. and I. Moura, Rev. Port. Quím. 27 (1985) 67-70.

(14) S.P.J. Albracht, R.D. Fontijn and J.W. van der Zwaan, Biochim. Biophys. Acta (1985) submitted for publication.

(15) P.H. Gitlitz and A.I. Krasna, Biochemistry 14 (1975) 2561-2568.

Nickel X-Ray Absorption Spectroscopy of *Methanobacterium thermoauto-trophicum* S-Methyl Coenzyme-M Reductase

Robert A. Scott,[a] Patricia L. Hartzell,[b] Ralph S. Wolfe,[b] Jean LeGall[c], Stephen P. Cramer[d]

[a]School of Chemical Sciences, University of Illinois, Urbana, Illinois 61801;
[b]Department of Microbiology, University of Illinois, Urbana, Illinois 61801;
[c]Department of Biochemistry, University of Georgia, Athens, Georgia 30602;
[d]Exxon Research and Engineering, Annandale, New Jersey 08801

SUMMARY

Ni XAS data of isolated F_{430} and F_{430} bound to protein C in the methylreductase system of <u>Methanobacterium thermoautotrophicum</u> indicate significant changes in the nickel first coordination sphere upon incorporation of F_{430} into methylreductase. These changes involve an increase in the average Ni-N distance of 0.1-0.2 Å. A plausible explanation is discussed which involves the planarization of an initially ruffled corphine ligand upon axial coordination of F_{430} to protein-derived ligands.

1 INTRODUCTION

It is only recently that nickel has been found to be a required component of a few different enzymes, including jack bean urease (1), several different hydrogen-ases (2-5), clostridial CO dehydrogenase (6), and the terminal methane-producing enzyme (S-methyl coenzyme-M reductase) of methanogenic bacteria (7). In urease, EXAFS results suggest a Ni first coordination sphere of <u>ca.</u> 6 (N,O)-containing ligands (8), whereas the Ni cofactor in methylreductase is known to be a Ni(II) tetrapyrrole called F_{430} (7). In as-isolated <u>Clostridium thermoaceticum</u> CO dehydrogenase, the Ni is EPR-silent, but upon substrate (CO) or product (HCO_3^-/CO_2) addition, a signal proposed to arise from Ni(III) interaction with a CO- or CO_2-derived radical species is observed (9). The Ni prosthetic group of this enzyme is apparently also acid-extractable as a low molecular weight cofactor (10). The Ni site(s) in the hydro-

genases is characterized by the presence of a rhombic Ni(III) EPR signal in some
oxidation states of the enzyme. There is also evidence for magnetic interaction between the Ni(III) site and the enzyme Fe-S cluster(s) for two of the hydrogenases
(2,3). In the Desulfovibrio gigas hydrogenase, H_2 reduction results in the disappearance of the Ni(III) EPR signal, apparently indicating reduction to Ni(II) and
implying participation of the nickel site in the hydrogenase activity. XAS techniques have been used to examine the Ni site in the oxidized hydrogenase from Methanobacterium thermoautotrophicum (Mt) and these studies indicate that the Ni first
coordination sphere is made up mainly of S-containing ligands (11). Our preliminary
results on the Desulfovibrio gigas hydrogenase are similar, in addition indicating a
Ni(III) → Ni(II) conversion upon H_2 reduction (12).

Even at this early stage of research on nickel metalloenzymes, it is clear that
this metal can take on a diverse set of structures and functions in biological systems. In addition, the various catalytic activities displayed involve small molecule reactions of considerable interest to chemists: H_2 oxidation, CO oxidation,
and CH_4 production from CO_2 and H_2. It will be very important to learn something
about the electronic and molecular structural changes at the nickel sites that accompany these catalytic conversions. For this reason, we have initiated a program of
XAS investigations of three nickel enzyme systems: the hydrogenase from Desulfovibrio gigas; the Clostridium thermoaceticum CO dehydrogenase and its Ni-containing cofactor; and the S-methyl coenzyme-M reductase enzyme and its Ni factor F_{430}. The
work described herein represents our preliminary studies on the methylreductase enzyme.

The final step in methanogenesis in Mt is the reduction of the methyl group of
S-methyl coenzyme-M (2-(methylthio)ethanesulfonate) to methane:

$$CH_3SCH_2CH_2SO_3^- + 2H^+ + 2e^- \rightarrow HSCH_2CH_2SO_3^- + CH_4$$

The enzyme that carries out this reaction, methylreductase, uses a nickel-containing
tetrapyrrole (a corphine) known as F_{430} for a prosthetic group. F_{430} can be removed
from the methylreductase protein and isolated in pure, concentrated form. We have
examined the Ni XAS of both isolated F_{430} and intact methylreductase in an effort to
probe the nature of the cofactor-protein and cofactor-substrate interactions.

2 EXPERIMENTAL

The methylreductase was purified from Methanobacterium thermoautotrophicum strain
ΔH grown on an atmosphere of H_2:CO_2::80:20 at 60°C. Freshly harvested cells were
passed through a French pressure cell at 16,000 psi under N_2 and the cell debris was
removed by centrifugation at 38,000 x g. The supernatant was loaded onto an anoxic
DEAE-52 cellulose column equilibrated with a 20 m$\underline{M}$ KP_i, pH = 7 buffer containing

10 mM β-mercaptoethanol. Washing this column with 100 mL of the loading buffer
eluted proteins with hydrogenase activity which were necessary to later reconstitute
the methanogenic activity. A linear gradient of the same buffer plus 0.1 to 0.5 $\underline{M}$
NaCl was used to elute the methylreductase activity (at 0.37 $\underline{M}$ NaCl). After dialysis to remove NaCl, the pooled methylreductase-containing fractions were adjusted to
1 $\underline{M}$ potassium acetate, 10 m$\underline{M}$ KP$_i$, pH = 6.8, and loaded on a phenyl Sepharose column
equilibrated with the same buffer. The methylreductase eluted in the void volume
and another protein required for reconstitution was removed by a wash step without
added salt. Further purification of methylreductase was achieved using a second
phenyl Sepharose column and finally a chelating Sepharose column charged with NiCl
and eluted with a linear gradient of 0 to 50 m$\underline{M}$ imidazole, pH = 7.5.

The methylreductase activity was determined by reconstituting the terminal step
of the methanogenic reaction and measuring CH$_4$ production _versus_ time. The reconstituted reaction mixture contained: 200 nmol S-methyl coenzyme-M (CH$_3$SCH$_2$CH$_2$SO$_3^-$);
4mM ATP; 20 mM magnesium acetate; 50 m$\underline{M}$ PIPES, pH = 6.2; saturating amounts of components A (hydrogenase activity), B (low molecular weight factor), and A2 (protein
separated from methylreductase on phenyl Sepharose); and a non-saturating amount of
methylreductase. These components were placed in vials inside a Coy anaerobic chamber, the vials stoppered, removed and gassed with H$_2$ for 10 minutes at 5 mL/min.
The reaction was initiated by transferring the vials to a 60°C heating block. At 5
minute intervals, 40 μL gas samples were removed and CH$_4$ determined by gas chromatography. The final specific activity of the methylreductase purified as described
was 6200 nmol CH$_4$-hr^{-1}-mg^{-1}.

The XAS data were collected at the Stanford Synchrotron Radiation Laboratory on
wiggler side station beam lines VII-3 or IV-3 under dedicated running at 3.0 GeV
(_ca._ 60 mA). The edge spectra were collected at high resolution (1 mm vertical aperture) using Si[220] monochromator crystals and each spectrum represents the average of _ca._ 3-4 15-minute scans over the Ni edge region (8320-8380 eV). The $\underline{Mt}$
methylreductase EXAFS data represent the average of a total of 23 30-minute scans on
three separate samples, two from Urbana and one from Athens, collected at lower resolution (2 mm vertical aperture) using the Si[220] crystals. All spectra were internally calibrated using a Ni foil (first inflection point of 8331.6 eV) and the
EXAFS data analysis was performed using amplitude and phase functions empirically
derived from model compounds by complex Fourier backtransformation (13). For Ni-S
interactions, [Ni(mnt)$_2$]$^{2-}$ (mnt ≡ maleonitriledithiolate) was used as a model, while
for Ni-N interactions, [Ni(en)$_3$]$^{2+}$ (en ≡ ethylenediamine) was used as a model.

3 RESULTS

Figure 1 compares the Ni K edge region of the XAS data for isolated F$_{430}$ and the
methylreductase enzyme (F$_{430}$ bound to protein C). It is apparent that significant

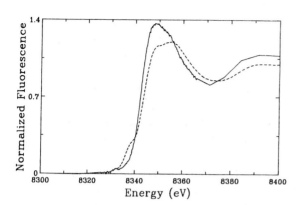

Figure 1. Fluorescence XAS data in the nickel edge region for isolated F_{430} (---) and methylreductase (unactivated, no additions) (——). The data were normalized to an edge height of unity by extrapolating a second-order, single region spline fit of the EXAFS region back to 8350 eV ($\underline{k}$=0). Differences between the two spectra are indicative of structural changes in the F_{430} Ni site upon incorporation into the protein.

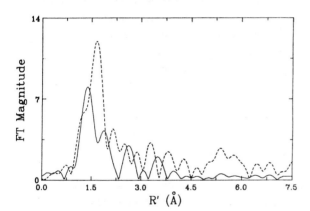

Figure 2. Fourier transforms (FTs) of Ni EXAFS data for isolated F_{430} (——) and methylreductase (---). The FT range for both sets of data was $\underline{k}$ = 3.5-12.5 $Å^{-1}$ and the original $\chi(\underline{k})$ data were $\underline{k}^3$ weighted. The positions of the major FT peaks indicate an overall increase in the average nickel-ligand distances upon incorporation of F_{430} into methylreductase.

structural differences exist at the nickel sites of these two samples. These structural differences are also reflected in the Fourier transforms (FTs) of the Ni EXAFS as shown in Figure 2. Upon incorporation of F_{430} into methylreductase, the first-shell amplitude increases substantially and the average first-shell Ni-ligand distance increases. In order to quantitate these effects, curve fitting was performed on the filtered first-shell contributions. The Fourier filter used for the F_{430} Ni EXAFS data is shown in Figure 3. The window function used for the filter includes the first two FT peaks but excludes the outer shell scattering due to the carbon framework on the corphine ligand (see Figure 3). This filtering results in the loss of the high frequency components observed at $\underline{k} \cong 5$ and 8 $Å^{-1}$ in the raw data.

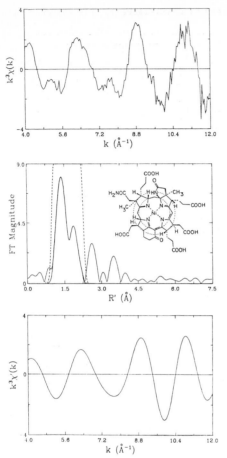

Figure 3. Fourier filtering of the first-shell peaks in the FT of Ni EXAFS data for isolated F_{430}. Top: Raw Ni EXAFS data collected by fluorescence excitation techniques. Center: FT ($\underline{k}$ = 3.5-12.5 Å^{-1}, $\underline{k}^3$ weighted) of EXAFS showing window used for filter (---). The two FT peaks beyond the window represent scattering by C, N atoms of the outer shells of the corphine ligand as indicated by dashed circles in the inset structure. Bottom: Fourier-filtered EXAFS ($\chi'(\underline{k})$) using the window indicated in the center frame. The curve-fitting was performed on this $\chi'(\underline{k})$ data.

The results of curve-fitting the filtered F_{430} data and filtered methylreductase data (generated in a completely analogous manner) are summarized in Table 1. For F_{430}, the obvious splitting in the FT was treated by performing two-shell fits with both shells assigned to N scatterers at different Ni-N distances. Two-shell fits using N and S scatterers were of much poorer quality. The refined fits resulted in the majority of N scatterers at 1.91 Å from the Ni with a second shell of lower co-ordination number at 2.14 Å from the Ni. The filtered methylreductase data could be fit to a single shell of N with an average Ni-N distance of 2.09 Å, but equally good fits with a second shell of N or S ligands (at reasonable distances) are obtained.

A plausible explanation for the overall expansion of the nickel coordination sphere upon insertion of F_{430} into the methylreductase protein comes from studies by Eschenmoser and coworkers on nickel corphinate models for F_{430}. Four-coordinate nickel corphinates exhibit an S_4 ruffling of the corphine ligand which serves to compress the nickel first coordination sphere (14) (<u>e.g.</u>, the Ni-N distance in a re-

Table 1. Results of curve fitting of filtered Ni EXAFS data.

Sample	Ni-N			Ni-N'			Ni-S			f(b)
	R (Å)	N	$\Delta\sigma^2$(a) ($Å^2$)	R (Å)	N	$\Delta\sigma^2$(a) ($Å^2$)	R (Å)	N	$\Delta\sigma^2$(a) ($Å^2$)	
F_{430}	2.14	(1)(c)	-0.0084	1.91	(3)	-0.0029				0.30
	2.14	(2)	-0.0054	1.91	(4)	-0.0018				0.30
methyl-	2.09	(6)	+0.0003							0.62
reduct-	2.14	(4)	-0.0047	2.00	(2)	-0.0058				0.57
ase	2.08	(4)	-0.0020				2.32	(1)	-0.0028	0.63

(a) Debye-Waller mean square amplitude measured relative to model compound.

(b) $f \equiv \{ \sum_{i=1}^{n} [\underline{k}^3(\chi_{obs}^{(i)} - \chi_{calc}^{(i)})]^2 / (N-1) \}^{\frac{1}{2}}$

(c) Coordination numbers (in parentheses) were not varied during optimizations.

lated "ruffled" nickel chlorin complex was found to be 1.92 Å (15)). Addition of
axial ligands typically results in a planar corphine ligand with longer Ni-N bonds
(e.g., the Ni-N distance in a hexacoordinate nickel porphyrin complex was found to
be 2.04 Å (16)). Thus, F_{430} may adopt a ruffled structure outside of the protein
with binding to fifth (and sixth?) ligands from the protein resulting in planarization of the corphine and lengthening of the Ni-N(pyrrole) bonds. Under this proposal, the static disorder observed in the F_{430} first shell may result from an
incomplete ruffling (three short Ni-N, one "normal" Ni-N bond lengths) due to the
asymmetric structure of the F_{430} corphinate ring system (17). The alternate description of the structure of isolated F_{430} which must be considered is a ruffled
corphinate that is axially coordinated (at longer distances) to two (N,O)-containing
ligands (e.g., H_2O). There is no evidence as yet that such a coordination geometry
is available to nickel corphinate complexes.

4 REFERENCES

(1) N. E. Dixon, C. Gazzola, R. L. Blakely, B. Zerner, J. Am. Chem. Soc. 97 (1975)
     4131-4133.

(2) S. P. J. Albracht, M. L. Kalkman, E. C. Slater, Biochim. Biophys. Acta 724
     (1983) 309-316.

(3) J. LeGall, P. O. Ljungdahl, I. Moura, H. D. Peck, Jr., A. V. Xavier, J. J. G.
     Moura, M. Teixera, B. H. Huynh, D. V. DerVartanian, Biochem. Biophys. Res.
     Commun. 106 (1982) 610-616.

(4) E.-G. Graf, R. K. Thauer, FEBS Lett. 136 (1981) 165-169.

(5) J. R. Lancaster, Jr., Science 216 (1982) 1324-1325.

(6) H. L. Drake, S.-L. Hu, H. G. Wood, J. Biol. Chem. 225 (1980) 7174-7180.

(7) W. L. Ellefson, W. B. Whitman, R. S. Wolfe, Proc. Natl. Acad. Sci. USA 79
     (1982) 3707-3710.

(8) L. Alagna, S. S. Hasnain, B. Piggott, D. J. Williams, Biochem. J. 220 (1984)
     591-595.

(9) S. W. Ragsdale, L. G. Ljungdahl, D. V. DerVartanian, Biochem. Biophys. Res.
     Commun. 108 (1982) 658-663.

(10) S. W. Ragsdale, J. E. Clark, L. G. Ljungdahl, L. L. Lundie, H. L. Drake, J.
     Biol. Chem. 258 (1983) 2364-2369.

(11) P. A. Lindahl, N. Kojima, R. P. Hausinger, J. A. Fox, B.-K. Teo, C. T. Walsh,
     W. H. Orme-Johnson, J. Am. Chem. Soc. 106 (1984) 3062-3064.

(12) R. A. Scott, S. A. Wallin, M. Czechowski, D. V. DerVartanian, J. LeGall, H. D.
     Peck, Jr., I. Moura, J. Am. Chem. Soc. 106 (1984) 6864-6865.

(13) R. A. Scott, Meth. Enzymol., in press.

(14) C. Kratky, A. Fässler, A. Pfaltz, B. Kräutler, B. Jaun, A. Eschenmoser, J.
     Chem. Soc., Chem. Commun. (1984) 1368-1371.

(15) A. Ulman, J. C. Galluci, D. Fisher, J. A. Ibers, J. Am. Chem. Soc. 102 (1980)
     6852-6854.

(16) J. F. Kirner, J. Garofalo, Jr., W. R. Scheidt, Inorg. Nucl. Chem. Lett. 11
     (1975) 107-112.

(17) A. Pfaltz, B. Jaun, A. Fässler, A. Eschenmoser, R. Jaenchen, H. H. Gilles, G.
     Diekert, R. K. Thauer, Helv. Chim. Acta 65 (1982) 828-865.

Bioenergetic Role of Nickel-Containing Proteins in Methanogens

Jack R. Lancaster, Jr., Stephen W. Carper, Billy P. Crider, Kevin Gillies, and
Kim R. Rogers

Department of Chemistry and Biochemistry
Utah State University, Logan, Utah 84322 U.S.A.

SUMMARY

Studies are reported examining whether electron transfer-driven energy coupling
in the methanogenic bacteria occurs by Electron Transfer Phosphorylation (ETP)
or Substrate Level Phosphorylation (SLP). The experiments are based on the
requirement of all known ETP systems for a membrane-bound electron transfer
component(s) and for uncoupler sensitivity.

As judged by differential centrifugation and gel exclusion chromatography,
none of the measurable electron transfer reactions appeared to be membrane-bound.
In addition, methanogenesis-driven ATP synthesis in whole cells was unaffected
by uncoupler addition, under conditions where it could be demonstrated that these
compounds were capable of catalyzing proton movement.

It is concluded that methanogenic bacteria may employ a novel mechanism for
coupling electron transfer to ATP synthesis. A possible scheme of SLP in methanogens
is proposed.

1. INTRODUCTION

Undoubtedly the single most important physiological function of metals in
biology (at least quantitatively) is in cellular energy transduction by electron
transfer. An important consequence of this is that metalloprotein-catalyzed
electron transfer in such systems will be obligately coupled to another event,
most commonly ion translocation across a membrane. A fundamental question, therefore,
is how do proteins achieve this obligate coupling?

Energy coupling to all nonphotosynthetic electron transfer occurs by two fundamentally different mechanisms. Electron Transfer Phosphorylation (ETP) involves, in all known cases, the coupling of protein-catalyzed electron transfer to the formation of a transmembrane ion gradient which is subsequently utilized by a membrane-bound ATPase for the synthesis of ATP. In Substrate Level Phosphorylation (SLP), oxidation-reduction of carbon substrate is directly coupled to ATP synthesis, involving the formation of a "high energy intermediate" of the compound undergoing oxidation, usually by direct phosphorylation followed by transfer of the phosphate group to ADP.

The methanogenic bacteria are the sole biological source of methane, and most species are capable of energy conservation by coupling ATP synthesis to the eight-electron reduction of CO_2 by H_2. SLP is argued against by several lines of evidence (1,2), including the demonstration by mass spectrometry that true electron transfer takes place, i.e., electrons and protons in H_2 are separated prior to the reduction of CO_2 (3). It has generally been assumed, therefore, that energy conservation occurs by ETP (2).

We report here the results of studies designed to differentiate SLP from ETP in methanogens. Our approach is based on two absolute requirements for ETP, namely the existence of a tightly membrane-bound electron transfer reaction and sensitivity to uncouplers of ATP synthesis driven by electron transfer.

2. RESULTS

2.1. Is Methanogenic Electron Transfer Membrane-Bound?

There are conflicting reports in the literature as to whether methane-forming activity is associated with membranes (4,5). We have employed two techniques for the separation of membranes from "soluble" protein, differential centrifugation and gel exclusion chromatography. The former technique possesses the advantage of the ability to maintain all fractions oxygen-free (an absolute requirement for methanogenesis), while the latter provides better separation of membranes from large, soluble protein components. We have assayed for membrane localization by labeling of cells with ^{14}C-mevalonic acid (which is a precursor to lipid synthesis in these organisms (6)) and for electron transfer by hydrogenase, methanogenesis, and factor F_{430} (which is a nickel-containing tetrapyrrole cofactor involved in methane formation (7)).

In 1980, we reported the presence in the particulate fraction of M. bryantii of several EPR-detectable centers, including the first observation of Ni(III) in a biological system (8). These findings were interpreted as evidence for the existence of a membrane-bound electron transfer complex. If this were the case, it might be expected that such components would be universally present in all methanogens. Table 1 shows that the complex signals observed in the particulate fraction of M. bryantii are not observed in all species, and in at least one case (M. voltae) only a g = 2.02 oxidized species is observed (which is quite possibly due to nonphysiological oxidation by oxygen exposure). This

result does not support the idea of a membrane-bound electron transfer chain
present in all methanogens.

Table I
Species survey of EPR-visible particulate centers in methanogens

Columns: Methanogen | g=2.02 (ox) | Ni(III) | Radical | g=1.94 (red)

Rows:
M. bryantii | + | + | + | +
M. thermoauto. | + | + | + | +
M. barkeri (acetate) | + | + | + | +
M. barkeri (H2-CO2) | + | + | — | +
M. ruminantium | + | — | + | —
M. hugatei | + | — | + | —
M. voltae (H2-CO2) | + | — | — | —
M. voltae (formate) | + | — | — | —

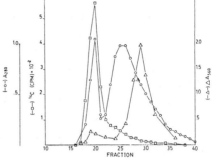

Table I

Species survey of EPR-visible particulate centers in methanogens

Methanogen	g = 2.02 (ox)	Ni(III)	Radical	g = 1.94 (red)
M. bryantii	+	+	+	+
M. thermoauto.	+	+	+	+
M. barkeri (acetate)	+	+	+	+
M. barkeri (H$_2$-CO$_2$)	+	+	—	+
M. ruminantium	+	—	+	—
M. hugateii	+	—	+	—
M. voltae (H$_2$-CO$_2$)	+	—	—	—
M. voltae (formate)	+	—	—	—

Fig. 1.   Resolution of hydrogenase (▲)
and membranes (▫) in the crude
particulate fraction by sepharose
6B chromatography.

We have subsequently performed a
more detailed examination of the subcellular
location of electron transfer components
in M. thermoautotrophicum. Extensive ultracentrifugation (180,000 xg for 2
1/2 hr.) of cell-free extracts sediments 85% of the factor F$_{420}$-reducing hydrogenase as well as most membranes (not shown). However, when this fraction (called
here the "crude particulate") is subjected to further resolution by gel exclusion
chromatography clear separation of hydrogenase from membranes is achieved (Fig. 1),
indicating that this activity is not
tightly membrane-bound (but capable
of sedimentation by an extensive
ultracentrifugation).

Due primarily to the difficulty
of anaerobic column chromatography,
it was not possible to assay fractions
for methyl reductase activity, which
also is present in the crude particulate
fraction (see below). An indication
of the presence of this activity, however,
would be the location of factor F$_{430}$.
Fig. 2 shows an elution profile of
a crude particulate preparation from
cells labeled with radioactive ^{63}Ni;
the majority of label elutes at the
same fraction (approx.number 30) as
the hydrogenase. In order to show
that the factor F$_{430}$ (in distinction
to another form of nickel) elutes in
the included volume, the void volume
(labeled "A" in fig 2) and included

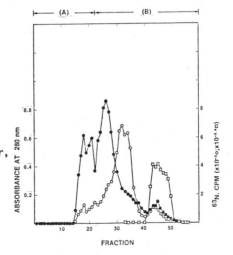

Fig. 2.   Elution profile of ^{63}Ni (○)
and absorbance at 280nm (●) in the
crude particulate fraction by separose
6B. Free factor F$_{430}$ elutes as shown
(▫).

("B") fractions were pooled, concentrated, and subjected to extraction and HPLC for the purification of F_{430} (9). Fig. 3 shows that indeed all of the F_{430} is located in the included fraction, clearly separated from the membrane containing void fraction.

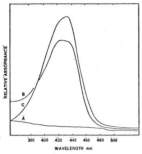

Table II

Separation of hydrogenase and ^{63}Ni from membranes by a 20,000 xg, 1 hr. centrifugation of the crude particulate fraction

Fraction	$\%^{14}C$ (mevalonate)	$\%^{63}Ni$	% Hydrogenase
Crude particulate	100	100	100
Supernatant	23	81	70
Pellet	n.d.	14	14

Fig. 3. Spectrum of purified F_{430} (C) and material treated identically for the detection of F_{430} in the pooled void (A) and included (B) fractions as indicated in fig. 2

Since centrifugation can be performed anaerobically, we developed a protocol for the preparation of various fractions enriched for membranes in order to assay for methane formation (which is irreversibly lost upon exposure to oxygen). Table 2 shows that a 20,000 xg, 1 hr. centrifugation of the resuspended crude particulate fraction results in a pellet enriched for membranes; the majority of hydrogenase and ^{63}Ni, however, remains in the supernatant. Fig. 4 shows that methanogenesis from $H_2:CO_2$ is localized in the crude particulate fraction prepared from cell-free extract (A) but appears to be localized in the supernatant of the low-speed centrifugation (B).

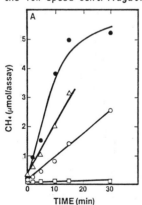

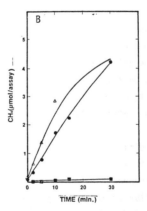

Fig. 4. Methanogenesis from $H_2:CO_2$ in subcellular fractions of M. Therm-oautotrophicum. A: Fractions from a 180,000 xg 2 1/2 hr. centrifugation of cell-free extract; ●, cell-free extract; O, resuspended pellet ("crude particulate"); □, supernatant; △, combined supernatant and pellet. B: Fractions from a 20,000 xg 30 min. centrifugation of crude particulate; ●, before centrifugation; △, supernatant; ■, resuspended pellet.

It thus appears that in <u>M. thermoautotrophicum</u> all electron transfer activities are not tightly membrane-bound, however, are capable of being sedimented by an extensive ultracentrifugation. These results apparently explain conflicting reports of the subcellular location of methanogenic activity (4,5).

Finally, Fig. 5 shows that extensive ultracentrifugation of cell-free extract prepared from <u>M. voltae</u> (180,000 xg, 2 1/2 hr.) results in no appreciable sedimentation of methanogenic activity, consistent with the EPR results in Table 1. Fig. 5 (inset) shows that cell-free extract prepared from this organism exhibits rates of methanogenesis approximately 40% of those in whole cells.

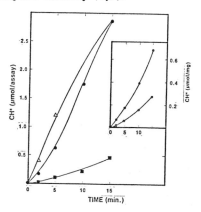

Fig. 5. Methanogenesis from H_2:CO_2 in subcellular fractions of M. voltae. Fractions from a 180,000 xg 2.5 hr. centrifugation of cell-free extract; ●, cell-free extract; △, supernatant; ■, resuspended pellet. Inset: methane formation from cells (●) and cell-free extract (○).

2.2 Is electron transfer-driven ATP synthesis uncoupler sensitive?

Although numerous reports have appeared describing the effects of uncouplers on methanogens (2), in almost all cases the addition of these compounds (which are halogenated hydrocarbons) inhibits electron transfer. It is thus not possible to distinguish uncoupler action from inhibition. We have chosen the extremely potent compound SF6847 for studies reported here, since it is not halogenated and fully uncouples mitochondria at very low (30nM) concentrations (10). In addition, we have utilized cells of <u>Methanococcus voltae</u>, which contains no intracytoplasmic membranes and possesses a fragile, proteinaceous cell wall (11). Effects can thus be interpreted in terms of a single site of action for these compounds, the cytoplasmic membrane.

Fig. 6 shows that addition of the potassium ionophore valinomycin to cells results in ATP synthesis due to the electrogenic efflux of internal K^+ (which has been reported to be approx. 0.7M (12)). This demonstrates the presence of an ion-translocating ATPase in the plasma membrane of this organism. The lack of effect of SF6847

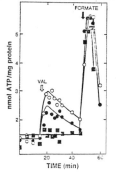

Fig. 6. ATP synthesis in cells of M. Voltae driven by membrane potential and by electron transfer. ○, cells resuspended in buffer lacking potassium; ●, buffer without potassium but containing 5μM SF6847; ■, buffer containing 0.1 M KCl. At t = 18 min. 10μM valinomycin added; at t = 45 min. 58mM formate added.

on this ATP synthesis indicates that the ion moving is not proton(s). In addition, the lack of effect of the combination of valinomycin plus external potassium plus SF6847 on electron transfer-driven ATP synthesis (formate addition at t=50 min.) argues against the obligatory intermediacy of a transmembrane ion gradient in this process. The synthesis of ATP shown in Fig. 6 would presumably be due to two separate mechanisms.

It is important to demonstrate that SF6847 is indeed capable of catalyzing proton movement in this organism; results of experimentation designed to test this are shown in Fig 7. ATP synthesis driven by an electrical potential is again demonstrated, formed by a mechanism identical in principle to that in Fig. 6, except that the driving force is a chemical gradient of protons (instead of potassium) and the ionophore is SF6847 (instead of valinomycin). Thus, cells are preincubated for a short period of time in acid (pH 5) in the presence of uncoupler, and then the pH is rapidly raised to 8 by base addition. Electrogenic proton efflux occurs, catalyzed by SF6847, generating a transmembrane electrical potential, which is utilized for ATP synthesis. It is important to point out that there is no <u>net</u> utilizable driving force for proton movement; the membrane potential is exactly counteracted by a reverse pH gradient. Fig. 7B shows that valinomycin plus potassium

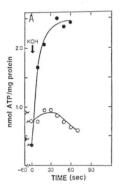 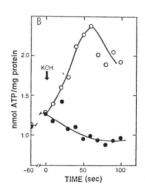

Fig. 7. Uncoupler-induced ATP synthesis. A. Cells preincubated for 3 min. at pH 5; at t = 0 pH was raised to 8 by KOH addition (the buffer contained 0.1 M KCl). ●, with and ○, without 5 M SF6847. B. Same as A, but both vials contained SF6847; ○, without and ●, with 10 μM valinomycin.

eliminates this ATP synthesis, thus demonstrating that the effect is due to the formation of an electrical potential. These results show that (1) SF6847 is competent to catalyze electrogenic proton movement, and (2) the ion(s) translocated by the membrane ATPase is not proton(s).

Finally, Fig. 8 shows that electron transfer-driven ATP synthesis is unaffected by the addition of valinomycin plus external potassium (to eliminate an electrical -potential) plus ammonia (which eliminates transmembrane ΔpH (not shown)), plus SF6847 plus the potent uncoupler S-13.

We conclude from these results that ETP in M. voltae does not appear to involve the obligatory intermediacy of a transmembrane ion gradient, but that cells possess an electrogenic ATPase (not involving potassium or proton(s)), which is possibly involved with maintenance of intracellular ion homeostasis.

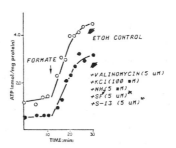

3. Discussion

Data reported here are most consistent with SLP as the mechanism of energy coupling in methanogens. It has been effectively argued, however, that such cannot be the case in methanogens, primarily because (1) methane formation involves the reduction of carbon instead of oxidation, and (2) true electron transfer takes place (see Section 1).

*These compounds are each capable of uncoupling mitochondria at concentrations < 0.02 uM

Fig. 8.   Insensitivity of electron transfer-driven ATP synthesis to ionophores. O , without and ● , with the indicated compounds.

Fig. 9 presents a possible scheme of SLP coupled to methanogenesis. The essential feature is an intramolecular electron transfer between two C_1 units (represented

Fig. 9.   A possible scheme for SLP coupled to methanogenesis.

for simplicity as the free intermediates). According to this mechanism, the energycoupled step involves the oxidation of the formaldehyde to the formate state, with the reduction of the methanol to the methane state; this reaction is coupled to the formation of formyl phosphate (or, possibly more accurately a phosphorylated derivative of formyl tetrahydromethanopterin) and ATP synthesis is accomplished by a subsequent phosphoryl transfer:

$$HCHO + CH_3OH + HO\text{-}P_i \longrightarrow HC\text{-}O\text{-}P_i + CH_4 + H_2O$$

$$HC\text{-}O\text{-}P_i + HO\text{-}ADP \longrightarrow HCOOH + P_i\text{-}O\text{-}ADP$$
$$(ATP)$$

There are several attractive features of such a scheme, including the following:

1. Formyl phosphate has been postulated as an intermediate in other SLP systems (13).

2. The step which results in phosphoanhydride formation is identical in nature to all known SLP reactions, namely the oxidation of carbon to the acid state (1).

3. The coupling involves the two most energetically favorable oxidation-reduction reactions in the methanogenic sequence; indeed, even including the formation of one mole of ATP the reaction would be highly exergonic (-19.6 kcal/mole (1)).

4. Nonstoichiometric coupling of methane to ATP formation could be a consequence of a reduction of the methyl state (presumably methyl-coenzyme M) by H_2. Although energetically unfavorable, such a reaction might be important ecologically, where methane formation results in the removal of acidic equivalents (14).

5. It has recently been demonstrated that reducing equivalents can be transferred intramolecularly from one C_1 intermediate to another at physiologically significant rates in the absence of a soluble electron carrier (15).

6. The intramolecular electron transfer involving two C_1 units (one presumably being methyl-coenzyme M) provides a possible explanation for the stimulation of methanogenesis from CO_2 by methyl-coenzyme M (the "RPG" effect (16)).

7. The four two-electron transfer reactions responsible for entry of reductant (H_2) occur by true electron transfer, separate from the phosphorylation reaction; the scheme is thus consistent with the deuterium labeling experiments described in Section 1.

8. Analogous schemes can be proposed for ATP synthesis coupled to methanogenesis from other substrates.

Supported by a research grant from the Division of Biological Energy Research, U.S. Department of Energy, and the Department of Chemistry and Biochemistry, Utah State University. This work was done during the tenure of an Established Investigatorship of the American Heart Association (to J.R.L.) and with funds contributed in part by the Utah Heart Association.

4. References

(1) R. K. Thauer, K. Jungermann, and K. Decker, Bact. Rev. 41, (1977) 100-180.

(2) L. Daniels, R. Sparling, and G. D. Sprott, Biochim. Biophys. Acta (1984) 113-163.

(3) R. W. Spencer, L. Daniels, G. Fulton, and W. H. Orme-Johnson, Biochemistry 19, (1980) 3678-3683.

(4) R. P. Gunsalus and R. S. Wolfe, J. Bact. 135 (1978) 851-857.

(5) F. D. Sayer, S. Mahadevan, and J. D. Erfle, Biochem. J. 221 (1984) 61-69.

(6) G. D. Sprott, K. M. Shaw, and K. F. Jarrell, J. Biol. Chem. 258 (1983) 4026-4031.

(7) W. L. Ellefson, W. B. Whitman, and R. S. Wolfe, Proc. Natl. Acad. Sci. U.S.A. 79 (1982) 3707-3710.

(8) J. R. Lancaster, Jr., FEBS Lett. 115 (1980) 285-288.

(9) G. Diekert, V. Konheiser, K. Piechulla and R. K. Thauer, J. Bact. 148 (1981) 459-464.

(10) H. Terada and K. Van Dam, Biochim. Biophys. Acta 387 (1975) 507-518.

(11) W. E. Balch, G. E. Fox, L. S. Magrum, C. R. Woese, and R. S. Wolfe, Microb. Rev. 43 (1979) 260-296.

(12) K. F. Jarrell, G. D. Sprott, and A. T. Matheson, Can. J. Microbiol. 30 (1984) 663-668.

(13) D. H. Buttlaire, C. a. Balfe, M. F. Wendland, and R. H. Himes, Biochim. Biophys. Acta 567 (1979) 453-563.

(14) L. Daniels, Trends Biotech. 2 (1984) 91-98.

(15) J. C. Escalante-Semerena and R. S. Wolfe, J. Bact. 158 (1984) 721-726.

(16) R. P. Gunsalus and R. S. Wolfe, Biochem. Biophys. Res. Comm. 76 (1977) 790-795.

Magnetic Circular Dichroism and Electron Paramagnetic Resonance Studies of Nickel-Containing Hydrogenases

Michael K. JOHNSON, Isabel C. ZAMBRANO, Melvin H. CZECHOWSKI, Harry D. PECK, Jr., Daniel V. DERVARTANIAN, Jean LEGALL

Department of Chemistry, Louisiana State University, Baton Rouge, LA 70803, USA (M.K.J. and I.C.Z.) and Department of Biochemistry, University of Georgia, Athens, GA 30602, USA (M.H.C., H.D.P., D.V.D. and J.G.)

SUMMARY

   Nickel-containing hydrogenases from Methanobacterium thermoautotrophicum (Δ H strain) and Desulfovibrio gigas have been investigated by low temperature magnetic circular dichroism (MCD) and electron paramagnetic resonance (EPR) spectroscopy. The results demonstrate that low temperature MCD measurements provide a method for identifying both the optical transitions of paramagnetic nickel and the cluster-type of constituent iron-sulfur centers in hydrogenases. Four distinct types of EPR signal assigned to the nickel center were identified in D. gigas hydrogenase during redox cycling. Evidence is presented for spin interaction involving the nickel center and and a reduced tetranuclear cluster in reduced D. gigas hydrogenase.

1 INTRODUCTION

   MCD spectroscopy performed at temperatures down to 1.5 K with magnetic fields up to 5 tesla provides an optical probe for paramagnetic chromophores. Moreover electronic ground state information, such as spin state, g-values, zero field splitting parameters, can be obtained for individual, paramagnetic chromophores by investigating the magnetic field and temperature dependence of discreet MCD

Abbreviations: MCD, magnetic circular dichroism; EPR, electron paramagnetic resonance; XAS, X-ray absorption spectroscopy; Fd, ferredoxin.

transitions (1-3). The detailed form of the low temperature MCD spectrum, together with magnetization data, has proven effective as a method of determining iron-sulfur cluster-type and characterizing the electronic and magnetic properties of iron-sulfur clusters, even in multicomponent metalloenzymes (2, 4-6).

Nickel has recently been recognized as an integral component of many bacterial hydrogenases including those from several Methanobacterium and Desulfovibrio species (7). All contain at least one iron-sulfur cluster in addition to nickel. The electronic transitions localized on nickel should provide a sensitive monitor of the redox state, coordination number and geometry, and ligand type. However, since the optical transitions attributable to nickel are obscured in the UV-visible absorption spectrum by intense S--->Fe charge transfer bands from iron-sulfur clusters, information concerning redox state and coordination of nickel has thusfar been confined to that obtained via EPR (8-13) and X-ray absorption spectroscopy (XAS) (14,15). In this work, we demonstrate that low temperature MCD spectroscopy is uniquely capable of identifying the optical transitions associated with the Ni(III) center in hydrogenases from Methanobacterium thermoautotrophicum and Desulfovibrio gigas. Furthermore it enables characterization of the type of iron-sulfur clusters in D. gigas hydrogenase.

2. M. THERMOAUTOTROPHICUM HYDROGENASE

The sample of M. thermoautotrophicum (Δ H strain) hydrogenase used for spectroscopic investigations had a specific activity of 712 μmoles H_2 evolved $min^{-1}mg^{-1}$ and was isolated aerobically as described in ref. 16. Gel electrophoresis indicated that the sample was not completely free of contaminating proteins.

2.1 EPR studies - M. thermoautotrophicum hydrogenase, as isolated, exhibits a rhombic EPR signal, g = 2.300, 2.230, 2.014, that is observable up to 120 K (Fig. 1). A similar signal has been observed in almost all samples of purified nickel-containing hydrogenases (7) and, based on studies of enzyme enriched with [61]Ni, it is assigned to a low spin Ni(III) center (10,13). The g-values are consistent with a tetragonally distorted octahedral environment (13). In contrast to D. gigas hydrogenase (see below), M. thermoautotrophicum hydrogenase shows no other EPR signals over the temperature range 5 to 120 K, indicating the absence of any oxidized, paramagnetic iron-sulfur centers, with S = 1/2 ground states, in the enzyme as prepared.

2.2 MCD studies - Room temperature absorption and low temperature MCD spectra of M. thermoautotrophicum hydrogenase, as prepared, are shown in Fig. 2. The broad, featureless absorption spectrum with a shoulder at approximately 400 nm is typical of that exhibited by iron-sulfur proteins containing tetranuclear clusters. Optical transitions from the Ni center are obscured by the broad envelope of S--->Fe charge

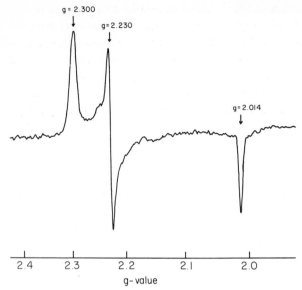

Fig. 1 EPR spectrum of __M. thermoautotrophicum__ hydrogenase, as prepared. Conditions: 70 K; microwave power, 1 mW; frequency, 9.018 GHz; modulation amplitude, 0.63 mT. Sample in 0.15 M Tris/HCl pH 7.5 buffer with 50% (v/v) ethylene glycol.

transfer bands. However, the variable temperature MCD spectra show temperature-dependent transitions in the regions 300-460 nm and 530-670 nm, and magnetization data (not shown) indicate that the paramagnetic chromophore has a $S = 1/2$ ground state. Since the form of the spectrum is quite distinct from that of any known paramagnetic iron-sulfur cluster and no such center is apparent in the EPR data, the

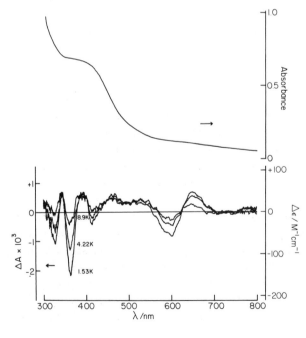

Fig. 2 Room temperature absorption (upper panel) and low temperature MCD spectra (lower panel) of __M. thermo-autotrophicum__ hydrogenase. Sample as in Fig. 1. MCD spectra at 1.53, 4.22 and 8.9 K (intensity decreasing with increasing temperature); magnetic field, 4.5 T; pathlength, 1.67 mm. $\Delta\varepsilon$ scale based on Ni(III) concentration of 120 µM, as assessed by EPR spin quantitation.

temperature dependent MCD bands are assigned to the Ni center. In light of the optical spectra reported for Ni(III) complexes (17) and the recent XAS results (14,15), the transitions in the regions 530-670 nm and 300-460 nm may be assigned to d-d and S--->Ni charge transfer bands respectively. More detailed assignments and the diagnostic use of the MCD spectra to determine Ni coordination environment, must await MCD studies of structurally well characterized Ni(III) complexes. At present, low temperature MCD provides a valuable spectroscopic criteria for assessing the appropriateness of inorganic analog complexes.

3. D. GIGAS HYDROGENASE

The periplasmic hydrogenase from D. gigas was isolated aerobically as previously described (9). Samples used in spectroscopic investigations contained 0.9-1.0 gatm Ni and 11-12 gatm non-heme Fe per 89 KD (62 and 29 KD subunits) and had a specific activity of 432 μmoles H_2 evolved min^{-1} mg^{-1}. As isolated, the enzyme is inactive. Activity ensues, after a variable initial lag period, on reduction with H_2 or with dithionite (18-20).

3.1 EPR studies - D. gigas hydrogenase, as isolated, displays a characteristic Ni(III) EPR signal (Fig. 3a), and spin quantitation accounts for between 80% and 90% of the total Ni content of the enzyme. At temperatures below 30 K an additional isotropic signal is observed, centered around g = 2.02 and accounting for approximately 1 spin/molecule. Preliminary Mössbauer studies (11) indicate that this signal arises from an oxidized [3Fe-xS] center. However, compared to oxidized [3Fe-xS] centers in bacterial ferredoxins (21), this signal is narrower and more isotropic and undergoes slower spin relaxation (saturates at microwave powers > 1 mW at 10 K). On prolonged incubation at room temperature under H_2 or on reduction with dithionite both signals disappear and a new rhombic species is developed, g = 2.19, 2.15, 2.02, (Fig. 3b), which maximally accounts for 40% of the total Ni content of the enzyme. The ´g = 2.19´ signal is a common feature of all reduced Ni-containing hydrogenases investigated thusfar (10,13,22), and its appearance coincides with that of hydrogenase activity (11). While EPR experiments on enzyme enriched with ^{61}Ni show that it is associated with Ni, there is as yet no consensus among researchers as to whether the signal corresponds to monovalent or trivalent Ni (13,22).

The ´g = 2.19´ signal has two unique properties: light sensitivity and unusual temperature dependence behavior (Fig. 4). It is readily photolysed at temperatures below 100 K to give a rhombic EPR signal, g = 2.29, 2.13, 2.05, (Fig. 3c), accounting for the same spin quantitation as the unphotolysed signal. Analogous behavior was first observed by Albrecht and coworkers for the equivalent species in Chromatium vinosum hydrogenase (22), and interpreted in terms of reversible photolytic bond cleavage of an axial H or H^- bound to a Ni(I) center. As shown in Fig. 4, the form of the EPR signal from the ´g = 2.19´ species changes drastically below 10 K. While the

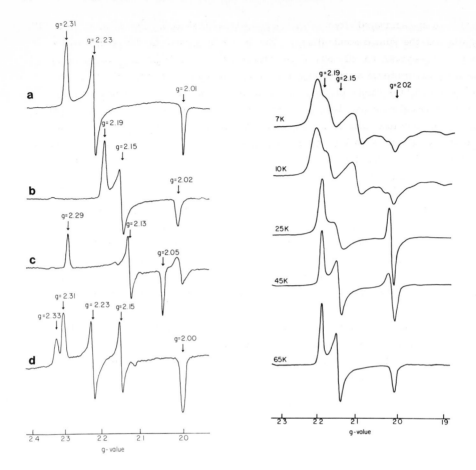

Fig. 3 (left panel) EPR spectra of Ni species in D. gigas hydrogenase. EPR conditions and buffer mixture as in Fig. 1. Enzyme concentration = 140 μM. (a) As isolated. (b) Incubated for 24 hours under H_2 at room temperature. (c) As (b) after photolysis for 1 min at 70 K using a Xenon arc lamp. (d) Re-air-oxidized.

Fig. 4 (right panel) Temperature dependence of the EPR spectrum of H_2-reduced D. gigas hydrogenase. Conditions and sample as in Fig. 3b.

origin of the complex, fast relaxing signal observed below 10 K (Fig. 4) is not fully understood at present, we tentatively assign it to a paramagnetic Ni species spin coupled to a paramagnetic, reduced iron-sulfur cluster, although no EPR signals attributable to the latter were observed   (cf. J.J.G.Moura et al in this book).

A fourth type of Ni EPR signal was apparent in the re-air-oxidized sample of hydrogen-reduced hydrogenase, g = 2.33, 2.15, 2.00, (Fig. 3d), in addition to the original Ni signal of the as isolated enzyme. Since this form of the enzyme undergoes reductive activation faster than the as isolated sample, we attribute this signal to

Ni(III) in an ´activated´ form of the enzyme. The total spin concentration of the Ni signals and the spin concentration of the ´g = 2.02´ signal in the re-air-oxidized sample corresponded to only 60% of the respective values in the as isolated enzyme. A broad signal, centered at g = 12, was observed in the re-air-oxidized sample and during the initial stages of hydrogen reduction of the enzyme. In light of the MCD results reported here (see below) and the recent EPR studies of Thermus thermophilus Fd (23), we conclude that reduced [3Fe-xS] clusters are responsible for this signal. Loss of the ´g = 12´ signal in more reduced samples suggests a conformational change about the reduced [3Fe-xS] center and/or spin-spin interaction involving this cluster and another paramagnetic metal center.

3.2 MCD studies - MCD studies of as isolated D. gigas hydrogenase show temperature-dependent bands throughout the visible region (Fig. 5). Magnetization data (not shown) show that all transitions originate from S = 1/2 ground states, and the form of the spectrum is consistent with overlapping contributions from a Ni(III) chromophore of the type observed in as isolated M. thermoautotrophicum hydrogenase and an oxidized [3Fe-xS] cluster similar to those in bacterial ferredoxins (2,21).

Prolonged incubation under H_2 or reduction with dithionite results in partial bleaching and a featureless absorption spectrum that monotonically increases with increasing energy (Fig. 6). Low temperature MCD spectra of the reduced enzyme (EPR as in Fig. 3b) reveal the complexity of the underlying electronic transitions (Fig. 6) and magnetization plots at 720 nm, 405 nm and 370 nm (not shown) show that the low temperature MCD is dominated by transitions from a reduced [3Fe-xS] cluster. The characteristic S = 2 ground state of reduced, EPR-silent [3Fe-xS] centers affords magnetization data that is unique among known iron-sulfur clusters (2,21). At other

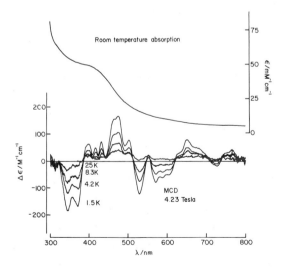

Fig. 5 Room temperature absorption (upper panel) and low temperature MCD spectra (lower panel) of D. gigas hydrogenase, as isolated. Sample as in Fig. 3a. Temperature and magnetic field as indicated, pathlength = 0.164 cm. Intensity of all bands increasing with decreasing temperature.

wavelengths, notably at 575 nm and 640 nm, significant contributions from an S = 1/2 chromophore are evident. Since almost identical MCD spectra were observed for dithionite-reduced samples having negligible amounts of ´g = 2.19´ Ni EPR signal, we conclude that paramagnetic, reduced [4Fe-4S] clusters (S = 1/2 ground state) are present. Mössbauer studies of the as isolated enzyme indicated the existence of two diamagnetic [4Fe-4S]$^{2+}$ clusters in addition to the oxidized [3Fe-xS] center (11). On the basis of the reported low temperature MCD spectra of reduced trinuclear and tetranuclear clusters (2), the spectrum of reduced D. gigas hydrogenase can be rationalized in terms of contributions from one reduced [3Fe-xS] and one or two [4Fe-4S]$^{1+}$ clusters. Furthermore the decrease in visible absorption on reduction (A_{400}(red)/A_{400}(ox) = 0.62), compared with other multicluster iron-sulfur proteins, suggests that all the constituent iron-sulfur clusters are reduced. The absence of observable EPR signals from the [4Fe-4S]$^{1+}$ clusters is attributed to weak spin-spin interaction, either intercluster or involving paramagnetic Ni.

4.CONCLUSIONS AND PROSPECTS

Low temperature MCD spectroscopy furnishes a means of investigating the optical transitions of paramagnetic Ni in hydrogenases, particularly those, such as M. thermoautotrophicum hydrogenase, which do not contain a [3Fe-xS]. In these instances, it promises to become a useful probe of Ni coordination environment and a means of determining the redox state of Ni responsible for the ´g = 2.19´ EPR signal.

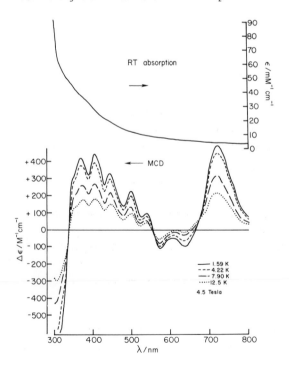

Fig. 6 Room temperature absorption (upper panel) and low temperature MCD spectra (lower panel) of H_2-reduced D. gigas hydrogenase. Sample as in Fig. 3b. MCD spectra recorded at 4.5 T, 1.59 K (———), 4.22 K (- - - -), 7.9 K (— —), 12.5 K (·······), pathlength = 0.155 cm.

Knowledge of the redox state of Ni in the active enzyme is crucial to any mechanistic understanding of hydrogenase activity.

In agreement with the Mössbauer (11) and analytical data, the low temperature MCD studies are consistent with the presence of one [3Fe-xS] and two [4Fe-4S] clusters in D. gigas hydrogenase. Futhermore they demonstrate that, after reductive activation of the enzyme, one or both of the tetranuclear clusters are in the paramagnetic reduced state and the trinuclear cluster has not been converted to a tetranuclear cluster (as is the case in aconitase (24)). The combination of the MCD and EPR results suggest the existence of spin-spin interactions between the metal centers in reduced D. gigas hydrogenase. Since the ´g = 2.19´ EPR signal is observed in Ni-containing hydrogenases that do not contain [3Fe-xS] clusters (13,22), it seems probable that spin interaction between Ni and a $[4Fe-4S]^{1+}$ is responsible for the unusual temperature dependence of this signal and the absence of EPR signals from reduced tetranuclear clusters. Additional intercluster spin interactions between reduced tetranuclear clusters or between one tetranuclear and one trinuclear cluster could also be present.

ACKNOWLEDGEMENTS

This research was supported by grants from the LSU Center for Energy Studies 0106, PRF 14857-G3, NIH GM 33806, and NSF PCM-8305753 (M.K.J.) and NSF DMB-8419632 (J.L., D.V.D. and H.D.P.)

REFERENCES

1. Thomson, A.J. and Johnson, M.K., Biochem. J. 191 (1980), 411-420.
2. Johnson, M.K., Robinson, A.E. and Thomson, A.J. in T.G. Spiro (ed.), Iron-Sulfur Proteins, John Wiley and Sons 1982, New York, pp. 367-406.
3. Browett, W.R., Fulcaloro, A.F., Morgan, T.V. and Stephens, P.J., J. Am. Chem. Soc. 105 (1983), 1868-1872.
4. Johnson, M.K., Thomson, A.J., Robinson, A.E. and Smith, B.E., Biochim. Biophys. Acta 671 (1981), 61-70.
5. Johnson, M.K., Bennett, D.E., Morningstar, J.E., Adams, M.W.W. and Mortenson, L.E., J. Biol. Chem. 260 (1985), 5456-5463.
6. Johnson, M.K., Morningstar, J.E., Bennett, D.E., Ackrell, B.A.C. and Kearney, E.B., J. Biol. Chem. 260 (1985), in press.
7. Moura, J.J.G., Teixeira, M., Moura, I., Xavier, A.V. and LeGall, J., J. Mol. Cat. 23 (1984), 304-314.
8. Lancaster, R., Science 216 (1982), 1324-1325.
9. LeGall, J., Ljungdahl, P.O., Moura, I., Peck, H.D., Jr., Xavier, A.V., Moura, J.J.G., Teixeira, M., Huynh, B.H. and DerVartanian, D.V., Biochem. Biophys. Res.

Commun. 106 (1982), 610-616.

10. Moura, J.J.G., Moura, I., Huynh, B.H., Kruger, H.-J., Teixeira, M., DuVarney, R.C., DerVartanian, D.V., Xavier, A.V., Peck, H.D., Jr. and LeGall, J., Biochem. Biophys. Res. Commun. 108 (1982), 1388-1393.

11. Teixeira, M., Moura, I., Xavier, A.V., DerVartanian, D.V., LeGall, J., Peck, H.D., Jr., Huynh, B.H. and Moura J.J.G., Eur. J. Biochem. 130 (1983), 481-484.

12. Cammack, R., Patil, D., Aguirre, R. and Hatchikian, E.C., FEBS Lett. 142 (1982), 289-292.

13. Kojima, N., Fox, J.A., Hausinger, R.P., Daniels, L., Orme-Johnson, W.H. and Walsh, C.T., Proc. Natl. Acad. Sci. USA 80 (1983), 378-382.

14 Lindahl, P.A., Kojima, N., Hausinger, R.P., Fox, J.A., Teo, B.K., Walsh, C.T. and Orme-Johnson, W.H., J. Am. Chem. Soc. 106 (1984), 3062-3064.

15. Scott, R.A., Wallin, S.A., Czechowski, M.H., DerVartanian, D.V., LeGall, J., Peck, H.D., Jr. and Moura, I., J. Am. Chem. Soc. 106 (1984), 6864-6865.

16. Johnson, M.K., Zambrano, I.C., Czechowski, M.H., Peck, H.D., Jr., DerVartanian, D.V. and LeGall, J., Biochem. Biophys. Res. Commun. 128 (1985), 220-225.

17. Haines, R.I. and McAuley, A., Coord. Chem. Rev. 39 (1981), 77-119.

18. Fernandez, V.M., Aguirre, R. and Hatchikian, E.C., Biochim. Biophys. Acta 790 (1984), 1-7.

19. Lissolo, T., Pulvin, S. and Thomas, D., J. Biol. Chem. 259 (1984), 11725-11729.

20. Berlier, Y.M., Fauque, G., Lespinat, P.A. and LeGall, J., FEBS Lett. 140 (1982), 185-188.

21. Beinert, H. and Thomson, A.J., Arch. Biochem. Biophys. 222 (1983), 333-361.

22. Van der Zwaan, J.W., Albracht, S.P.J., Fontijn, R.D. and Slater, E.C., FEBS Lett. 179 (1985), 271-277.

23. Hagen, W.R., Dunham, W.R., Johnson, M.K. and Fee, J.A., Biochim. Biophys. Acta 828 (1985), 369-374.

24. Kent, T.A., Dreyer, J.-L., Kennedy, M.C., Huynh, B.H., Emptage, M.H., Beinert, H. and Münck, E., Proc. Natl. Acad. Sci. USA 79 (1982), 1096-1100.

Molybdenum-
Biochemistry

Approaches to The Molybdenum Centers of 'Oxo-Typ' Enzymes

John H. Enemark, W. E. Cleland, Jr.

Department of Chemistry, University of Arizona

Tucson, Arizona 85721   USA

David Collison, Frank E. Mabbs

Chemistry Department, University of Manchester

Manchester M13 9PL   ENGLAND

SUMMARY

A large series of monomeric oxomolybdenum(V) complexes possessing the hydrotris(3,5-dimethylpyrazolyl)borate ligand, L, has been prepared and characterized by electrochemical methods and by electron paramagnetic resonance spectroscopy. The pseudo-octahedral oxo-Mo(V) complexes, LMoOXY, exhibit facial stereochemistry. All of the complexes undergo reversible reduction to the Mo(IV) state, and their EPR spectra are markedly dependent on the nature of X and Y.

1 INTRODUCTION

Molybdenum is an essential trace element which is found in enzymes such as xanthine oxidase, sulfite oxidase, and nitrate reductase (1,2). The chemical reactions catalyzed by these enzymes all involve a change in the number of oxygen atoms in the substrate as illustrated in reaction 1, the oxidation of sulfite to sulfate.

$$SO_3^{2-} + H_2O \rightarrow SO_4^{2-} + 2e^- + 2H^+ \qquad\qquad (1)$$

There is strong evidence that these enzymes possess a common molybdenum cofactor
(3). EXAFS studies support a monomeric molybdenum center with at least two -SR
ligands bound to the molybdenum atom (4).

An overall chemical reaction cycle for the oxo-molybdenum centers of such
enzymes involving Mo(IV), Mo(V) and Mo(VI) is shown in Figure 1. Berg and Holm
(5) have developed an elegant chemical model for the oxo-transfer reaction between Mo(IV) and Mo(VI) shown at the bottom of Figure 1. Our interest has been
in sythetic analogs for the EPR active Mo(V) species shown at the top of Figure
1. The EPR signals of these Mo(V) states are observed upon reduction of the
enzyme with substrate or dithionite and are usually present in equilibrium with
both Mo(IV) and Mo(VI) (6). The Mo(V) signal appears within milliseconds after
adding a reducing agent and may change appearance for hours. Kinetics measurements (6) have shown that the Mo(V) states are sufficiently long lived to be
intermediates in the catalytic cycle. Rapid freezing methods (6) have been
important in obtaining frozen samples in the earliest stages of development of
the EPR signal. In the absence of crystal structures of molybdoenzymes,
detailed interpretation of the enzyme EPR specra is difficult and present
descriptions of the coordination environment of the molybdenum centers in enzymes rest upon comparisons of the spectra of the enzymes with those of well-
characterized molybdenum complexes.

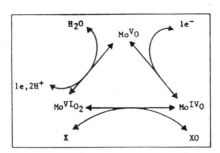

Figure 1. Schematic representation of the reactions of the molybdenum centers
of molybdoenzymes

The isolation and characterization of Mo(V) complexes which may be synthetic analogs of the Mo(V) states in enzymes are difficult because of the propensity of oxo-Mo(V) complexes to dimerize in the presence of trace amounts of water to diamagnetic products. Our approach to this problem has been to create a steric pocket for the molybdenum atom in order to inhibit such dimerization reactions.

A simple pocket shaped ligand is hydrotris(3,5-dimethylpyrazolyl)borate, L. Complexes of this ligand were extensively studied by Trofimenko (7), who first isolated the oxo-Mo(V) complex, LMoOCl$_2$ (8). We have developed an improved synthetic route to LMoOCl$_2$ and to related monomeric oxo Mo(V) complexes, LMoOXY, possessing the stereochemistry shown in Figure 2, including several complexes which contain at least two thiolate ligands coordinated to the molybdenum atom (9).

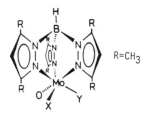

R=CH$_3$

Figure 2.   Stereochemistry of the LMoOXY complexes.

2   SYNTHESIS

2.1   Preparation of LMoOCl$_2$

Reaction of MoCl$_5$ with THF under anaerobic conditions yields MoOCl$_3$(THF)$_2$, presumably via oxygen atom abstraction from solvent. Addition of KL to the reaction mixture and heating to 50°C results in LMoOCl$_2$ in 50–70% yield.

2.2   Preparation of LMoOXY complexes

A series of LMoOXY complexes have been prepared where X, Y are monodentate anionic ligands such as halides, pseudohalide, and $^-$SR, $^-$OR (R=alkyl, aryl) or the bidentate chelates (XCH$_2$CH$_2$Y)$^{2-}$, (X-C$_6$H$_4$-$\underline{o}$-Y)$^{2-}$ where X and Y are O or S (9). These complexes are prepared from the common precursor LMoOCl$_2$, by ligand substitution reactions 2, 3.

$$LMoOCl_2 + 2HX + 2Et_3N \rightarrow LMoOX_2 + Et_3NHCl \qquad (2)$$

$$LMoOCl_2 + 2NaX \rightarrow LMoOX_2 + 2NaCl \qquad (3)$$

The resulting products are purfied by chromatography on silica gel with benzene
as eluent. The LMoOXY complexes are air and water stable.

3 ELECTROCHEMISTRY

The electrochemical behavior of the LMoOXY complexes was examined by cyclic
voltammetry and controlled potential coulometry. Cyclic voltammetry was performed at a Pt button working electrode in acetonitrile and DMF over the potential range +1.5 to -2.0V. All complexes exhibit well-defined quasireversible
one-electron reductions in this potential range as demonstrated by i_{ap}/i_{cp} = 1.
Controlled potential coulometry at a platinum cathode was used to verify the
one-electron nature of the reduction processes indicated by the cyclic voltammetric measurements. Potentials for Mo(V)/Mo(IV) couples of selected complexes
together with several molybdoenzyme potentials are shown in Figure 3.

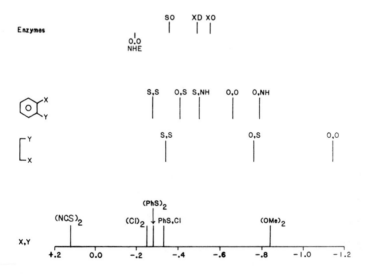

Figure 3. Top line - Mo(V/IV) reduction potentials for sulfite oxidase (SO),
xanthine oxidase (XO), and xanthine dehydrogenase (XD) vs. NHE (from ref. (2)).
Lower lines - Mo(V/IV) potentials for selected LMoOXY complexes vs. Ag/AgCl in
acetonitrile solution.

The reduction potentials of the LMoOXY complexes span a range of over 1.2
volts, depending on the nature of the X and Y ligands. Complexes with sulfur
donor atoms are more easily reduced than complexes with hard donor atoms such as
alkoxide. Although the reduction potentials for the LMoOXY complexes measured

in nonaqeous solvents are not directly comparable to potentials measured for
the analogous enzymic processes, Figure 3 shows that the range of potentials
for the complexes do encompass the Mo(V/IV) reduction potentials of sulfite oxidase, xanthine oxidase and xanthine dehydrogenase (2).

4 ELECTRON PARAMAGNETIC RESONANCE SPECTROSCOPY

The EPR spectra of the LMoOXY complexes have been obtained in toluene at room
temperature and in frozen solution. The EPR spectra of these complexes are
markedly dependent upon the nature of the X and Y ligands coordinated to the
molybdenum atom and show large hyperfine splittings due to ^{95,97}Mo. The results
for selected complexes, molybdoenzymes and the molybdenum cofactor are collected
in Table 1. The results summarized in Table 1 clearly show that when two sulfur
atoms are present in the coordination sphere, one of the principal g values will
be greater than 2.00, as is observed in the enzymes (2,6). The extensive series

Table 1   EPR Data for Molybdoenzymes, the Molybdenum Cofactor and Selected
          LMoOXY Complexes

	g_1	g_2	g_3	$\langle g \rangle$	$\langle A\ ^{95,97}(Mo) \rangle$ (Gauss)	Ref
sulfite oxidase (low pH)	2.003	1.972	1.965	1.980	--	2,6
xanthine oxidase (very rapid)	2.025	1.955	1.949	1.976	34	2,6
molybdenum cofactor 1	2.029	1.978		1.995	--	10
LMoO(SEt)$_2$	2.011	1.952	1.931	1.966	40	a
LMoO(SPh)$_2$	2.004	1.950	1.937	1.967	39.0	a
LMoO(SCH$_2$CH$_2$S)	2.016	1.971	1.942	1.976	38.9	a
LMoO(tdt)	2.004	1.974	1.937	1.972	37.3	a

tdt=   a) this work

of LMoOXY complexes has enabled us to investigate the subtle differences produced in the EPR spectrum by chelating vs. monodentate ligands, by aromatic vs.
saturated ligands and by changing a single donor atom in the coordination
sphere. Figure 4 shows the effect on the EPR spectrum produced by variation of
the type of sulfur donor ligand.

The LMoOXY complexes with X = Y (i.e. LMoOX$_2$) possess C$_S$ symmetry with the oxo group, the molybdenum atom and one of the nitrogen atoms of the pyrazo-lylborate ligand lying in the mirror plane. Thus, the unique direction in these complexes is the vector normal to the mirror plane, (i.e., normal to the MoO bond) not a vector parallel to the MoO bond as occurs in tetragonal oxo Mo(V) complexes. The EPR spectra of several complexes have been simulated, but a

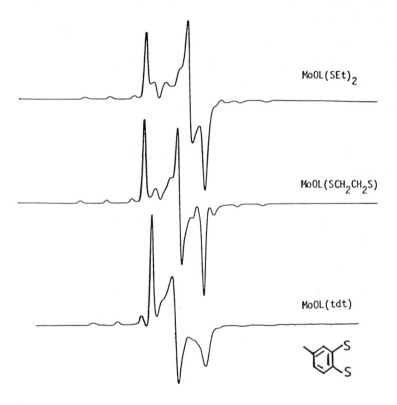

Figure 4. EPR spectra of LMoO(SR)$_2$ complexes showing the effect produced by variation of the type of sulfur donor ligand. Spectra were taken at x-band frequency in frozen toluene solution at 77K.

detailed understanding of the directions of the components of the g and A ten-sors in relation to the molecular coordinate system will require a complete single crystal EPR experiment.

The stable monomeric oxomolybdenum(V) complexes synthesized in this study provide good starting points for structural and spectroscopic models for the inhibited states of the 'oxo-type' molybdenum enzymes.

5 ACKNOWLEDGEMENTS

We acknowledge support by the National Institutes of Environmental Health Sciences and the North Atlantic Treaty Organization.

6 REFERENCES

(1) R. C. Bray in P. D. Boyer (ed.), The Enzymes, Academic Press, New York, 1975, Vol. XII, Part B, Chapter 6.

(2) J. T. Spence, Coord. Chem. Rev. 48 (1983) 59-82.

(3) J. L. Johnson in M. Coughlan (ed.), "Molybdenum and Molybdenum Containing Enzymes," Pergamon Press, New York, 1980, pp. 347-383.

(4) S. P. Cramer, R. Wahl. K. V. Rajagopalan, J. Am. Chem. Soc. 103 (1981) 7721-7727.

   J. Bordas, R. C. Bray, C. D. Garner, S. Gutteridge, S. S. Hasnain, Biochem. J. 199 (1980) 499-508.

(5) J. M. Berg, R. H. Holm, J. Am. Chem. Soc. 106 (1984) 3035-3037.

(6) R. C. Bray, Adv. Enzymol. Relat. Areas Mol. Biol. 51 (1980) 107-165.

(7) S. Trofimenko, Chem. Rev. 72 (1972) 497-509.

(8) S. Trofimenko, Inorg. Chem. 10 (1971) 504-507.

(9) W. E. Cleland, Jr., K. Barnhart, K. Yamanouchi, D. Collison, F. E. Mabbs, R. B. Ortega, J. H. Enemark, to be submitted.

(10) T. R. Hawkes, R. C. Bray, Biochem. J. 222 (1984) 587-600.

Models for The Molybdenum Centers of The Molybdenum Hydroxylases

Jack T. Spence and Carol C. Hinshaw

Department of Chemistry and Biochemistry
Utah State University, Logan, Utah 84322 U.S.A.

John H. Enemark, Shannath L. Merbs and R. B. Ortega

Department of Chemistry
University of Arizona, Tucson, Arizona 85721

SUMMARY

New dioxo-Mo(VI) complexes (MoO_2L) with tetradentate N_2O_2 ligands have been synthesized, and the X-ray crystal structure of one complex obtained. The complexes undergo reversible one-electron reversible electrochemical reduction on both the cyclic voltammetry and coulometry time scales, giving monomeric complexes formulated as dioxo-Mo(V) species, $[MoO_2L]^-$. The EPR spectra of these Mo(V) complexes are highly rhombic, with extremely low g values ($<g> = 1.887$) and high A values ($<A> = 6.1$ mT). Upon protonation, a transient EPR signal is observed which may be attributed to $MoO(OH)L$; substitution with F^- gives $MoO(F)L$ which exhibits ^{19}F coupling of 1.5 mT. The relevance of the results to enzymatic Mo centers is discussed.

INTRODUCTION

Recent EXAFS and EPR results indicate the molybdenum centers of sulfite oxidase and assimilatory nitrate reductase in their oxidized (Mo(VI)) and reduced (Mo(V), Mo(IV)) states have ligand sets as follows (1,2):

$$0 = \underset{\underset{X}{|}}{\overset{\overset{O}{\|}(VI)}{Mo(SR)_{2-3}}} \qquad HO-\underset{\underset{X}{|}}{\overset{\overset{O}{\|}(V, IV)}{Mo(SR)_3}}$$

(SR = thiolate S, X = O, N or thioether S).

The molybdenum centers appear to undergo two-electron reductions or oxidations by substrate, followed by successive one-electron transfers to or from the heme and/or flavin centers; for sulifte oxidase, these reactions are:

$$SO_3^{2-} + Mo(VI) \longrightarrow SO_4^{2-} + Mo(IV)$$

$$Mo(IV) + Fe(II)(heme) \longrightarrow Mo(V) + Fe(III)(heme)$$

$$Mo(V) + Fe(II)(heme) \longrightarrow Mo(VI) + Fe(III)(heme)$$

Because the rates of electron transfer are rapid, the distribution of electrons at any degree of reduction is determined by the relative reduction potentials of the Mo, heme and flavin centers.

Most dioxo-Mo(VI) complexes give oxo-bridged-Mo(V) dimers upon one or two-electron reduction, mainly because equilibrium 3 is strongly in favor of the dimer (3):

$$2MoO_2L + H_2O \xrightarrow{2e^-} Mo_2O_3L_2 + 2OH^- \qquad 1$$

$$MoO_2L + H_2O \xrightarrow{2e^-} MoOL + 2OH^- \qquad 2$$

$$MoOL + MoO_2L \rightleftharpoons Mo_2O_3L_2 \qquad 3$$

Successful models must, therefore, be amenable to reduction without formation of the biologically irrelevant dimer (dimer formation is prevented in the enzymes by restraints imposed by the protein).

Several approaches to the solution of this problem have proved successful. Complexes of type I undergo facile one-electron electrochemical reduction,

I.   X = O, S; R = $(CH_2)_2$, $(CH(Me))_2$, (C_6H_4)

accompanied by deprotonation of the amino groups and loss of H_2O, to give oxo-Mo(V) monomers (4,5). These monomers are stable to H_2O and OH^-, and EPR shows the presence of two equivalent trigonal N ligands, indicating the structure is likely square-pyramidal:

Their stability to dimerization is a result of this structure, which precludes cis-oxo bridge formation. Type I Mo(V) complexes undergo reversible one-electron electrochemical reduction to Mo(IV) complexes, the structures of which have not been determined; the electrochemical reversibility, however, suggests deprotonated N ligands and a square-pyramidal geometry are also present in this state.

   Similarly, complexes of type II undergo irreversible electrochemical one-electron reduction to give stable oxo-Mo(V) complexes with deprotonated N ligands (6):

II. R_1 = t-Bu, R_2 = $(CH_2)_2$, $(CH(Me))_2$, (C_6H_{10})

Without the bulky t-Bu groups in the 3-positions of the aromatic rings, however, oxo-bridged-Mo(V) dimers are obtained upon reduction, indicating a steric factor is important in prevention of dimerization in these cases. Again, EPR indicates the presence of two equivalent trigonal N ligands in the Mo(V) complexes, suggesting square pyramidal geometry. Essentially identical results were obtained with complexes of type III (6):

$$MoO_2(SC(R)_2CH_2NHCH_2CH_2NHCH_2C(R)_2S) \xrightarrow{e^-} [MoO(SC(R)_2NCH_2CH_2NCH_2C(R)_2S)]^- + H_2O$$

III.   R = Me, Et

In some cases with both II and III complexes a second one-electron reduction to the Mo(IV) state is observed (5,6).

RESULTS AND DISCUSSION

   While these results are interesting, they are not entirely satisfactory from the biomimetic viewpoint, since in all cases (I, II, III complexes) the oxo-Mo(V) complexes (and probably the oxo-Mo(IV) complexes) have an open trans position (trans to oxo), while EPR results from the enzymes strongly suggest the OH⁻ group in the reduced states is in a cis position (7). This is a result of the deprotonation of the NH groups upon reduction, giving trigonal (sp^2) amido N, which favors a planar ligand structure and square pyramidal geometry (5,6). Furthermore, reduction results in loss of an oxo group, rather than protonation (protonation and retention of oxo appears to be the case for the enzymes) (7).

To prevent this, we have synthesized a number of similar complexes with alkylated amino groups (type IV) and investigated their reductions:

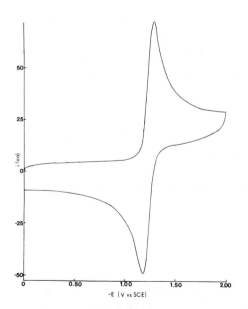

R_1 = H; R_2, R_3 = Me, Et
IV R_1 = H; R_2 = Me; R_3 = H
R_1 = t-Bu; R_2, R_3 = Me

In all cases where both R_2 and R_3 = Me or Et, the Mo(VI) complexes undergo reversible one-electron electrochemical reduction on both the CV (cyclic voltammetry) and coulometric time scales to give stable monomeric oxo-Mo(V) species; one-electron electrochemical oxidation regenerates the original dioxo-Mo(VI) complex (fig. 1, table 1). With one exception, these are the only reported dioxo-Mo(VI) complexes which undergo completely reversible one-electron coulometric reduction (the exception,

Fig. 1. CV of MoO$_2$L (L = IV, R_1 = H; R_2, R_3 = Me). MeCN, 0.10 M [(n-Bu)$_4$N] [BF$_4$]5.00 x 10^{-4} M, scan rate = 0.100 V sec^{-1}, glassy carbon electrode.

Table 1. Electrochemical Parameters of MoO$_2$L^a

E$_{pc}$^{b}	E$_{pa}$^{b}	E^b	n^c
-1.28	-1.18	0.100	1.2±.03

a)   L = IV, R$_1$ = H; R$_2$, R$_3$ = Me

b)   E$_{pc}$ = CV reduction, E$_{pa}$ = CV oxidation peak, V vs. SCE. MeCN, 0.100
     M [(n-Bu)$_4$N][BF$_4$].

c)   electrons/molecule, coulometric reduction.

MoO$_2$(SCH$_2$CH$_2$NMeCH$_2$CH$_2$NMeCH$_2$CH$_2$S), is reversibly reduced by one electron at 0^0;
significantly, it also has N-alkylated amino groups (8)). Identical results
were obtained for complexes with R$_1$ = H or t-Bu, indicating the steric requirement
necessary for prevention of dimerization with type III complexes is unimportant
here. When only one N is alkylated (R$_3$ = H), however, reduction gives an EPR
silent dimer.

The low temperature (77 K) EPR spectra of type IV oxo-Mo(V) complexes (R$_2$,
R$_3$ = Me, Et) are most unusual (fig. 2). The spectra are highly rhombic, with

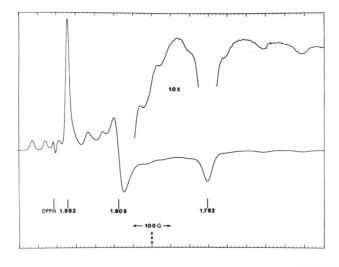

Fig. 2. EPR spectrum of [MoO$_2$L]$^-$ (L = IV; R$_1$ = H; R$_2$, R$_3$ = Me). MeCN, 77K,
5.00 x 10^{-4} M.

g values spanning a range of ~350 Gauss and extremely low <g> (1.89) and large <A> (61 Gauss) values (table 2). No such EPR parameters have been reported for

Table 2. EPR Parameters of One-electron Reduction Product of MoO_2L[a].

				$^{95,97}Mo$ (mT)				^{19}F (mT)	
g_1	g_2	g_3	<g>[b]	A_1	A_2	A_3	<A>[b]	<g>[c]	<A>[c]
1.982	1.905	1.782	1.887	5.0	3.5	10.0	6.1	1.920	1.6

a) L = IV, R_1 = H; R_2, R_3 = Me

b) Room temperature, all other values at 77 K, MeCN, 0.100 M [(n-Bu)$_4$][NBF$_4$], obtained directly from spectra.

c) Room temperature, after addition of five equivalents of [(n-Bu)$_4$N]F and one equivalent of CF_3SO_3H.

any Mo(V) complex (9), suggesting a highly unusual structure not previously observed. The room temperature spectrum is broad (peak to peak width ~36 Gauss) making it difficult to observe at the low concentrations (~5 x 10^{-4} M) used in the electro-chemical cell. Its <g> and <A> values, however, are in good agreement with the low temperature values, and double integration of the signal indicates a spin concentration of 99 $\pm$ 25% of total Mo. Power saturation studies of the low temperature signal indicate a considerably faster relaxation time than for the "normal" Mo(V) complex, $MoOCl(oxine)_2$ (9), in keeping with its high rhombicity. While the $MoOCl(oxine)_2$ signal reaches a maximum and begins to decrease at ~10 mW power, this signal begins to level off only at ~50 mW, and shows no decrease, even at maximum power available.

Consideration of the EPR spectrum and the completely reversible electrochemical behavior of this complex suggests the one electron reduced species is a dioxo-Mo(V) complex:

$$MoO_2L \xrightarrow{e^-} [MoO_2L]^-$$

L = type IV ligands; R_2, R_3 = Me, Et.

Thus, the reduction is electrochemically reversible, because it involves only the addition of an electron, with no oxo loss. The highly unusual EPR spectrum suggests a structure with greatly distorted octahedral geometry, or an unusual ground state; since no other examples are known, however, the origin of this effect is uncertain.

The X-ray crystal structure of MoO_2L (L = type IV ligand, R_1 = H; R_2, R_3 = Me) has been determined (fig 3). There is considerable departure from octahedral geometry but the complex has 2-fold axis and C_2 symmetry (table 3). The N-methyl

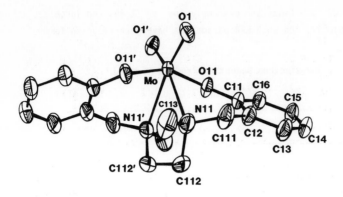

Fig. 3. X-ray structure of MoO_2L (L = IV; R_1 = H; R_2, R_3 = Me). H atoms omitted for clarity.

Table 3. Bond Distances and angles MoO_2L (L = IV, R_1, = H; R_2, R_3 = Me)

Bond Distances (A)

Atom1	Atom2	Distance	Atom1	Atom2	Distance
Mo	O1	1.702(1)	C11	C12	1.395(2)
Mo	O11	1.934(1)	C11	C16	1.396(2)
Mo	N11	2.390(1)	C12	C13	1.399(2)
O11	C11	1.349(1)	C12	C111	1.505(2)
N11	C111	1.491(2)	C13	C14	1.373(2)
N11	C112	1.477(3)	C14	C15	1.379(2)
N11	C113	1.505(2)	C15	C16	1.384(2)
			C112	C112'	1.514(4)

Bond Anges (deg)

Atom1	Atom2	Atom3	Angle	Atom1	Atom2	Atom3	Angle
O1	Mo	O1'	108.25(7)	C111	N11	C113	104.9(2)
O1	Mo	O11	95.66(5)	C112	N11	C113	110.4(2)
O1	Mo	O11'	97.99(5)	O11	C11	C12	122.4(1)
O1	Mo	N11	163.09(6)	O11	C11	C16	117.2(1)
O1	Mo	N11'	88.55(5)	C12	C11	C16	120.4(1)
O11	Mo	O11'	156.59(6)	C11	C12	C13	117.7(1)
O11	Mo	N11	79.68(4)	C11	C12	C111	123.8(1)

Table 3. (continued)

011	Mo	N11'	81.77(4)	C13	C12	C111	118.4(1)
N11	Mo	N11'	74.74(7)	C12	C13	C14	122.0(1)
Mo	011	C11	137.39(8)	C13	C14	C15	119.5(1)
Mo	N11	C111	109.23(9)	C14	C15	C16	120.3(1)
Mo	N11	C112	109.2(1)	C11	C16	C15	120.0(1)
Mo	N11	C113	111.6(1)	N11	C111	C12	115.7(1)
C111	N11	C112	111.4(1)	N11	C112	C112'	111.1(1)

Numbers in parentheses are standard deviations in the last digits.

---

groups may offer some steric hindrance to dimer formation upon reduction, possibly accounting for the stability of the monomer. If the EPR spectrum and the reversible electrochemistry are the results of a dioxo-Mo(V) structure, however, no clue as to the reason for its stability is apparent from the crystal structure of the dioxo-Mo(VI) complex.

Experiments are underway to prepare the ^{17}O labeled dioxo-Mo(VI) complex $(Mo^{17}O_2L)$. If the formulation of the Mo(V) complex as a dioxo-Mo(V) species $([Mo^{17}O_2L]^-)$ is correct, the EPR spectrum should exhibit ^{17}O splitting (^{17}O, $I = 5/2$) if both oxo groups are present, since one will be in the plane of the orbital containing the unpaired electron; such ^{17}O splittings have been observed with Mo enzymes (7). Attempts to protonate the Mo(V) complex have been made, with the possibility of obtaining the biologically relevant MoO(OH)L. Preliminary results indicate the presence of a transient species, with a splitting of the Mo(V) EPR signal of 1.6 mT (fig. 4). Similar splittings, attributed to ^1H,

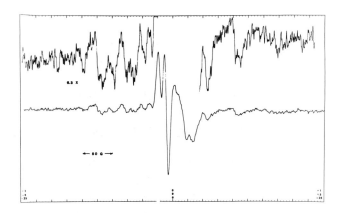

Fig. 4. EPR spectrum of $[MoO_2L]^-$ (L = IV; R_1 = H; R_2, R_3 = Me). MeCN, rt, 5.00 x 10^{-4}M, after addition of 5.00 x 10^{-4}M CF_3SO_3H

have been observed with Mo enzymes (7). This transient species, with a $\langle g \rangle$ value = 1.935, disappears within minutes, giving an EPR signal without splitting and $\langle g \rangle$ = 1.942. Treatment of the protonated species with F^- gives a stable (Mo(V) signal exhibiting ^{19}F ($I = 1/2$) coupling of 1.5mT (fig. 5) and $\langle g \rangle$ = 1.920.

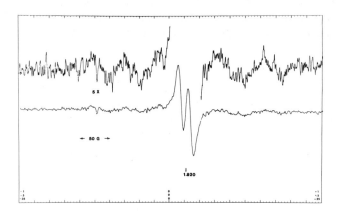

Fig. 5.   EPR spectrum of $[MoO_2L]^-$ ($L = IV$; $R_1 = H$; R_2, $R_3 = Me$).   MeCN, 5.00 x 10^{-4} M, after addition of 5.00 x 10^{-4} M CF_3SO_3H and 2.50 x 10^{-3} M $[(\underline{n}Bu)_4]F$.

These results indicate, because of the magnitude of the coupling, both the OH^- and F^- ligands occupy a cis position in the complex.   The results are summarized:

$$MoO_2L \underset{-e^-}{\overset{e^-}{\rightleftharpoons}} [MoO_2L]^- \xrightarrow{H^+} MoO(OH)L \xrightarrow{F^-} MoO(F)L$$

$$-1.23V \qquad g = 1.887 \qquad\qquad \downarrow g = 1.935 \qquad g = 1.920$$

$$\text{(vs SCE)} \qquad\qquad\qquad [MoOL]^+$$

$$g = 1.942$$

Work to confirm these results, as well as to obtain the sulfur analogues of these complexes, is underway and will be reported later.

Acknowledgement.   Financial support of this work by NIH Grant GM 08347 and NSF Grant CHE-8402136 (JTS) and NIH Grant ES 00966 JHE) is gratefully acknowledged. We thank Dr. R. Ortega for assistance with the X-ray structure determination.

References

1. S. P. Cramer, R. Wahl, K. V. Rajagopalan, J. Am. Chem. Soc. 103 (1981) 7721.

2. S. P. Cramer, L. S. Solomonson, M. W. W. Adams, L. E. Mortenson, J. Am. Chem. Soc. 106, (1984) 1467.

3. G. J.-J. Chen, J. W. Mcdonald, W. E. Newton, Inorg. Chem. 15 (1976) 2612.

4. J. T. Spence, M. Minelli, P. Kroneck, J. Am. Chem. Soc. 102 (1980) 4538.

5. O. A. Rajan, J. T. Spence, C. Leman, M. Minelli, M. Sato, J. H. Enemark, P. M. H. Kroneck, K. Sulger, Inorg. Chem. 22 (1983) 3065.

6. P. Subramanian, J. T. Spence, R. Ortega and J. H. Enemark, Inorg. Chem. 23 (1984) 2564.

7. S. Gutteridge, R. C. Bray, Biochemistry 21 (1982) 5992. R. C. Bray, S. Gutteridge, M. T. Lamy, T. Wilkinson, Biochem. J. 211 (1983) 227. R. C. Bray, S. Gutteridge, M. T. Lamy, T. Wilkinson, Biochem. J. 211 (1983) 227.

8. C. Pickett, S. Kumar, P. A. Vella, J. Zubieta, Inorg. Chem. 21 (1982) 908.

9. M. I. Scullane, R. D. Taylor, M. Minelli, J. T. Spence, K. Yamanouchi, J. H. Enemark, N. D. Chasteen, Inorg. Chem. 18 (1979) 3213. J. T. Spence, Coord. Chem. Reviews, 48 (1983) 59.

Copper-Molybdenum Sulphur Clusters and Relevance to Molybdenum-Induced Copper-Deficiency in Ruminants

C. David Garner, John R. Nicholson, Stuart K. Hagyard, John Charnock

The Chemistry Department, Manchester University, Manchester M13 9PL, England

Colin F. Mills

The Rowett Research Institute, Bucksburn, Aberdeen AB2 9SB, Scotland

SUMMARY

Series of complexes of $[MoOS_n]^{2-}$ (n=2,3, or 4) bound to Cu(I) have been prepared and characterised by structural spectroscopic techniques.

1   INTRODUCTION

Although the tetrathiometallate(VI) ions $[MS_4]^{2-}$ (M=Mo or W) were first isolated in the 1980's, their interesting ability to coordinate metal ions was not recognised until almost a hundred years later, for example when Müller et al. prepared $[Ni(WS_4)_2]^{2-}$ (1). The ions are extremely versatile ligands and have been shown to function as bidentate chelates to a wide variety of metals ion (2).

The first indication of the biological antagonism between Cu and Mo arose from the work of Ferguson et al. (3) who found that the disease could be prevented or cured by feeding the animals with copper sulphate. The antagonistic effects of Mo on Cu metabolism in ruminants are synergised by a variety of dietary sources of sulphur both inorganic and organic (4), which can be metabolized via sulphide (e.g. $[SO_4]^{2-}$ or S-amino acids). The mecahnisms of these interactions are not understood and the quantitative effects of dietary Mo and S sources upon

Scheme   The Synthesis and Interconversion Reactions
of Copper(I)-Thiomolybdate(VI) Complexes

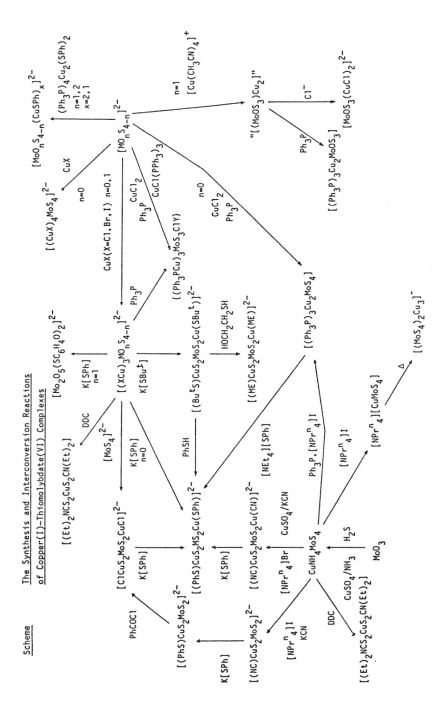

absorption or retention by ruminants are poorly defined. However, the species specificity of the action of Mo as an antagonist of Cu absorption is related to the fact that, in contrast to ruminants, little opportunity exists in the digestive tract of non-ruminants for the generation of sulphide. Mo, given as $[MoO_4]^{2-}$, is remarkably well-tolerated by non-ruminants (5). In contrast, when $[MoS_4]^{2-}$ is given orally to rats, the effct on Cu metabolism closely reflect those found in ruminants after ingestion of molybdenum, i.e. Cu absorption is inhibited and systemic inhibitory effects on Cu metabolism become evident (6). Furthermore, $[MoO_2S_2]^{2-}$ and $[MoOS_3]^{2-}$ are capable of modifying the tissue distribution of absorbed Cu in rats. The presence of $[MoO_4]^{2-}$ has been demonstrated for in vitro incubation of rumen contents or microorganisms with added $[MoO_4]^{2-}$ and $[SO_4]^{2-}$ (7). However, the formation of $[MoO_{4-n}S_n]^{2-}$ ($0 < n < 4$) in vitro in the rumen may be favoured over $[MoS_4]^{2-}$ by the rapid turnover rate of sulphide within this organ and the pH value of 6.5.

Therefore, we have investigated the chemical interactions between Cu and $[MoO_{4-n}S_n]^{2-}$ (n = 2,3, or 4) ions to establish the nature of the species which are formed and their characteristic spectroscopic properties.

2   RESULTS AND DISCUSSION

A summary of the reactions of $[MoO_{4-n}S_n]^{2-}$ ions with copper salts and the interconversions of the resultant complexes is summarised in the Scheme

A number of points of interest arise from the interconversion reactions carried out:

(i) RS^- (R=alkyl, aryl) ligands appear to be the strongest ligands for binding to the copper in these complexes. However, PhCOCl is capable of effecting the substitution of Cl^- for PhS^- and also, in this reaction, the disubstituted copper adduct, $[ClCuS_2MoS_2CuCl]^{2-}$, is formed from the mono-adduct. From spectroscopic studies of the solutions containing $[(PhS)CuS_2MoS_2]^{2-}$, there has been no evidence to suggest that the equilibrium (1) does not lie well to the left.

$$2[(PhS)CuS_2MoS_2]^{2-} \rightleftharpoons [(PhS)CuS_2MoS_2Cu(SPh)]^{2-} + [MoS_4]^{2-} \quad \ldots\ldots(1)$$

The mechanism by which PhCOCl effects thiolate substitution and conversion of a CuS_2MoS_2 moiety into a CuS_2MoS_2Cu moiety, remains unclear.

(ii) The apparent non-existence of complexes having a Cu:Mo ratio of greater than 2:1 when the ligand on copper is RS^- or CN^-; with PPh_3 liganded to copper these are limited to the two neutral complexes $[\{MoS_3Cu_3Cl\}(PPh_3)_3S]$[8] and $[\{MoS_3Cu_3Cl\}(PPh_3)_3O]$[9] having cubane-type structures. Reactions of all of the MoS_4/Cu_x (x=3,4) complexes with thiolate result in the formation of the $[MoS_4(CuSR)_2]^{2-}$ complex. It appears that the weakest ligands for copper(I) in these complexes studied, i.e. Cl, Br, I, allow the formation of 4:1 (Cl, Br) and 3:1, (Cl, Br, I) Cu:Mo complexes, whereas the stronger ligands, SR^-, CN^- restrict this ratio to 2:1.

(iii) There is a tendency for one copper atom to be tetrahedrally coordinated and one to be trigonally coordinated when PPh_3 is liganded to copper in the 2:1 Cu:Mo complexes studied. This is seen in $[(Ph_3P)_3Cu_2MoS_4]$[9] and in $[(Ph_3P)_3Cu_2MoOS_3]$ and is extended to the analogous silver and gold complexes: $[(Ph_3P)_3Ag_2MoS_4]$[10] and $[(Ph_3P)_3Au_2MoOS_3]$. Müller et al.[9] have isolated $[(Ph_3P)_4Ag_2MoS_4]$, in which both silver atoms have approximately tetrahedral coordination geometry, though this is unstable in solution in the absence of an excess of PPh_3. Also, the $[(Ph_3P)_2Au_2MoS_4]$ complex has been characterised, and the series of complexes $MoO_nS_{4-n}M_2'(PPh_3)_x$ (n=0, 1; M'=Cu, Ag, Au; x=2-4) is currently being investigated in this laboratory.

(iv) The inability to structurally characterise a Cu-Mo-S complex in which a bidentate ligand is bound to copper. Although copper has been found in an approximately tetrahedral coordination geometry in the complexes containing PPh_3 ligands just described and also in $[MoS_4(CuBr)_4]^{2-}$, reactions involving bidentate S-donor ligands have not led to the isolation of a crystalline product containing the $\{S_2CuS_2Mo\}$ moiety. Studies with the o-xylene-α,α'-dithiolate ligand appeared to be promising but are at present, inconclusive

The structures of key compounds have been determined by X-ray crystallography[11-14] and the salient features are apparent from, for example, $[(PhS)CuS_2MoS_2]^{2-}$.[11] MoS_4 coordinates as a bidentate ligand to copper, the sulphur atoms involved in ligation have longer Mo-S bonds (2.221(9)Å) and subtend a smaller angle (106.7(1)°) at molybdenum than their terminal counterparts (2.162(6)Å and 111.2(1)°, respectively). The Cu---Mo distance of 2.636(1)Å allows for a direct metal-metal interaction.

The Cu-Mo-S complexes have been characterised by i.r., Raman, uv/vis., EXAFS, and ^{95}Mo NMR spectroscopy, not only to define their basic properties but also identify those techniques which would be useful to probe the possible formation of these aggregates in vivo. Presently, ^{95}Mo NMR spectroscopy[15] would appear to have attractive possibilities and these and other investigations are continuing.

3   ACKNOWLEDGEMENTS

We thank the S.E.R.C. for financial support.

4. REFERENCES

(1) A Müller and E. Diemann, J. Chem. Soc., Chem. Commun., 65(1971).

(2) A. Müller, E. Diemann, R. Jostes, and H. Bögge, Angew. Chem. Int. Ed. Engl., 20, 934 (1981), and references therein.

(3) W.S. Ferguson, A.L. Lewis, and S.J. Watson, J. Agric. Sci., 33, 44 (1943).

(4) N.F. Suttle, in W.G. Hoekstra, J.W. Suttle, H.E. Ganther, W. Mertz (eds.), "Trace Element Metabolism in Animals", University Park Press, Baltimore, Maryland, p. 612.

(5) C.F. Mills, in "Biological Roles of Copper", Ciba Foundation 79, Published November 1980 by Excerpta Medica, pp. 49-69.

(6) I. Bremner and C.F. Mills, Phil. Trans. R. Soc. Lond., B294, 75 (1981), and references therein.

(7) T.T. El-Gallad, C.F. Mills, I. Bremner, and R. Summers, J. Inorg. Biochem., 18, 323 (1983).

(8) A. Müller, H. Bögge, and U. Schimanski, J. Chem. Soc., Chem. Commun., 91 (1980).

(9) A. Müller, H. Bögge, H.-G. Tölle, R. Jostes, U. Schimanski, and M. Dartmann, Angew. Chem., Int. Ed. Eng., 19 654 (1980).

(10) A. Müller, H. Bögge, and U. Schimanski, Inorg. Chim. Acta, 69, 5 (1983).

(11) S.R. Acott, C.D. Garner, J.R. Nicholson and W. Clegg, J. Chem. Soc., Dalton Trans., 713 (1983).

(12) W. Clegg, C.D. Garner, and J.R. Nicholson, Acta Cryst., C39, 552 (1983).

(13) W. Clegg, C.D. Garner, J.R. Nicholson, and P. Raithby, Acta Cryst., C39, 1007 (1983).

(14) J.R. Nicholson, A.C. Flood, C.D. Garner, and W. Clegg, J. Chem. Soc., Chem. Commun., 1179 (1983).

(15) M. Minelli, J.H. Enemark, J.R. Nicholson, and C.D. Garner, Inorg. Chem., 23, 4384 (1984).

Nucleic Acid Metal Ion Interactions

Metal Ion Binding to Nucleosides and Nucleotides

R. Bruce Martin

Chemistry Department, University of Virginia
Charlottesville, Virginia 22901   USA

SUMMARY

The N1 versus N7 dichotomy for binding of first-transition-row metal ions to
purine nucleosides has been resolved by recourse to linear stability constant
logarithm versus pK_a plots for a variety of related ligands. Stability constant
logarithms for Ni^{2+}, Cu^{2+}, and Zn^{2+} binding at pyridine or purine N1 type nitrogens
and imidazole or purine N7 type nitrogens display a linear relationship with pK_a
for each metal ion and nitrogen type. The slopes of all lines vary only from 0.3
to 0.5. For all three aqueous metal ions and $(dien)Pd^{2+}$, at the same pK_a, the
stability constant for N7 binding is 0.8 to 1.2 log units stronger than for N1
binding. For neutral adenosine the N1 site is intrinsically 320 times more basic
than the N7 site. However, for the above three aqueous metal ions the ratio of N1
to N7 bound adenosine complexes is projected to be 3, 2.5, and 1, respectively.
Thus solutions of neutral adenosine and these aqueous metal ions contain comparable
amounts of N1 metalated and N7 metalated complexes. N7 coordination in purine
bases predominates at low pH and gives way to favored N1 coordination for $(dien)Pd^{2+}$,
Cu^{2+}, and Zn^{2+} between pH 1.5 to 2.7 for adenosine, pH 6.1 to 6.7 for inosine, and
pH 6.9 to 7.5 for guanosine. Thus for all three purine nucleosides metal ion
binding at both N1 and N7 sites is important in neutral solutions.

INTRODUCTION

In neutral solutions alkali and alkaline earth metal ions bind significantly to
the phosphate group of nucleotides but only weakly to nucleosides. For transition

metal ions the nucleotide phosphate and nitrogen base sites offer potentially competitive binding loci. Some transition metal ions such as Pd(II) and Pt(II) coordinate at the nucleic base nitrogens of nucleotides while first transition row metal ions interact more strongly but not exclusively at the phosphate group. Only in strongly basic solutions does metal ion induced hydroxy group deprotonation enable the ribose sugar to become competitive with phosphate and nucleic base binding sites. In RNA and DNA polymers the phosphate group is now only weakly basic and becomes a much weaker metal ion binding site than in nucleotides. Therefore, nucleosides provide suitable models for specific metal ion binding to extended nucleic acid polymers, when the negative charge at the phosphate for each polymer nucleotide residue is compensated by a background cation. Helical forms of the polymers restrict accessibility of all nucleic base metal ion binding sites except N7 of purine bases (1).

In pyrimidine bases metal ion binding occurs predominantly at N3. For uracil and thymine metal ion binding is inhibited by the proton at N3 and the binding is often pH dependent in neutral solutions. Unless deprotonated in quite basic solutions exocyclic amino groups are not metal ion binding sites (1).

Purine nucleosides display a dichotomy between binding at N1 or N7. The proton greatly favors N1. The presence of the 6-amino group in adenosine results in $pK_a \simeq 4$ at N1, while in the two 6-oxopurines, inosine, and guanosine, $pK_a \simeq 9$ at N1. Thus in slightly acidic and neutral solutions both N1 and N7 remain unprotonated in adenosine while in the 6-oxopurines only N7 is unprotonated and metal ions must compete with the proton for binding at N1. As a result on these relative basicity grounds, in acidic solutions a metal ion N1/N7 binding ratio will be greater in adenosine than in the 6-oxopurines, where N7 metal ion binding is favored. In neutral and basic solutions when the pH becomes high enough, depending upon the metal ion, the metal ion displaces the proton at N1. Under these conditions the 10^3-fold greater ratio of intrinsic N1 to N7 basicities in the 6-oxopurine nucleosides than in adenosine suggests a greater likelihood of metal ion coordination at N1 in the former than in adenosine.

The remainder of this article shows that the purine base N1/N7 binding ratio is much greater for protons than for metal ions. Relative to the proton, metal ions strongly favor binding at N7. In no case, however, does a metal ion strongly prefer to bind at N7 rather than at N1. A conclusion of this research is that Zn^{2+} distributes equally between the N1 and N7 sites of adenosine. Zn^{2+} is present in nucleic acid polymerases.

Crystal structure determinations (2) have given an exaggerated impression of the extent of metal ion binding to N7 in purine nucleosides and nucleotides. For two reasons, one advertent and one inadvertent, crystals have been collected from acid solutions which protonate N1 and favor metal ion binding at N7. To avoid precipitation of metal ion hydroxides, solutions are often acidic when made up. In concentrated unbuffered solutions, protons displaced from N1 on only a fraction of the

ligands will render the solution more acidic, forcing the majority of remaining
metal ions to coordinate at N7.

2 PALLADIUM(II) COMPLEXES

Resolution of the N7 vs. N1 dichotomy in purine nucleosides and their phosphates
begins in studies of the complex (diethylenetriamine)palladium(II) (dienPd^{2+}). For
our purpose this complex exhibits three important features. First, because the
complex is diamagnetic, pronounced broadening and shifting of NMR peaks to not
occur. Second, since the complex exchanges slowly between the N7 and N1 sites,
the relative populations of all species in solution may be deduced from ^{1}H NMR
spectra. Finally, as the tridentate ligand diethylenetriamine occupies three sites
about the strongly square-planar Pd(II), only the fourth site remains free to undergo substitution at N1 or N7 (3-5). With a pair of cis sites that may undergo substitution, enPd^{2+} chelation reactions become more complex than dienPd^{2+} coordination
and are not discussed further here (6-8).

An extensive evaluation of chemical shifts and peak intensities in proton NMR
spectra conducted over a wide pH range permitted identification and quantification
of all species present in solutions containing dienPd^{2+} and adenosine, AMP, inosine,
IMP, and GMP (3,4). From the derived equilibrium constants among the species
important generalizations emerged (4,9). Five straight lines appear in a log
stability constant vs. pK_a plot. All five straight lines display virtually identical slopes of 0.67 ± 0.02. The lowest straight line passes through points for 6
pyrimidine N3 nitrogens cytidine, uridine, thymidine, and their 5'-monophosphates
and for 10 purine N1 nitrogens adenosine, inosine, AMP, IMP, GMP, and the corresponding species of each of the 5 ligands with a dienPd^{2+} bound at N7. The 16
points spanning 8 pK_a units fit well on a single line. Thus points for N3 of
pyrimidine nucleosides and their monophosphates fall on the same straight line as
points for N1 of purine nucleosides and their monophosphates. The same straight
line accomodates both the points for nucleosides and for their
5'-monophosphates. It also does not matter whether a dienPd^{2+} is already coordinated at N7. Thus for dienPd^{2+} binding at the pyridine-like nitrogens, N3 of
pyrimidine nucleosides and nucleotides and N1 of purine nucleosides and nucleotides,
the stability constants correlate with the basicity of the binding site (4,9).

In contrast to the simple dependence on basicity of dienPd^{2+} binding to pyridine-
like N1-type nitrogens, its binding to the imidazole-like N7 nitrogens of purines
indicates that additional factors may augment the stability. The second lowest line
passes through points for adenosine with and without a proton at N1, benzimidazole,
and 1-methylimidazole. This line representing the base line for N7 binding includes
two points for adenosine. Points for 5'-AMP lie 0.5-0.6 log unit above the N7 base
line. Points for inosine lie 1.6 log units above the N7 base line. Points for
5'-IMP and 5'-GMP lie 0.7 log unit above the inosine line; about the same difference

is observed between 5'-AMP and adenosine. Thus presence of a 6-oxo group on a purine base enhances dienPd^{2+} binding at N7 (but not N1) by 1.6 log units. Independently, presence of a 5'-monophosphate group augments binding at N7 (but not N1) by 0.5-0.7 log units. What structural features are responsible for the dienPd^{2+}-N7 binding enhancements of 1.6 log units due to a 6-oxo group and 0.5-0.7 log unit due to a 5'-monophosphate?

The origins of the two enhancements are clarified by investigations of nucleoside and 5'-mononucleotide binding to (1,1,4,7,7-pentamethyldiethylenetriamine)-palladium(II) (pmdienPd(II)) where five methyl groups substitute for all nitrogen-bound hydrogens in coordinated dien (4). Presumably due to steric hindrance, stability constants for pmdienPd^{II} are 0.7-1.9 log units weaker than those for dienPd^{II}. Binding of pmdien^{2+} to pyrimidine N3 and purine N1 sites yields a straight line of slope 0.80, slightly steeper than the 0.67 slope with dienPd^{2+}. Binding of pmdienPd^{2+} to adenosine, benzimidazole, and 1-methylimidazole, representative of N7 binding to purines, yields a slope of 0.79 displaced 1.2 log unit to stronger binding than the pmdienPd^{2+}-purine N1 line.

For the pmdienPd^{2+} complexes of inosine, IMP, and GMP, the stability constants fall 2.3, 2.0, and 1.9 log units, respectively, above pmdienPd^{2+}-N7 base line. Thus in constrast to the dienPd^{2+} results, there is no additional enhancement between a N7-bound purine nucleoside and its 5'-mononucleotide with pmdienPd^{2+}. Additionally the point for AMP-pmdienPd^{2+} N7 binding falls on the N7 base line, which contains the point for adenosine. These results are consistent with a 0.4-0.5 log unit promotion of the phosphate deprotonation upon dienPd^{2+} binding to N7 of AMP, IMP, and GMP and the lack of promotion upon binding of pmdienPd^{2+} (3,4).

Due to the terminal methyl groups, rotation of pyrimidines, benzimidazole, and purines is restricted in pmdienPd^{2+} complexes, and two rotamers are evident in proton magnetic resonance spectra. With benzimidazole and purine nucleosides and 5'-nucleotides there is an approximately 2:1 mole ratio of the two rotamers. Nuclear Overhauser effect experiments and chemical shift analysis permit identification of all peaks for pmdien methyl groups and aromatic ring protons (4).

In summary, plots of stability constant logarithms vs. pK_a for dienPd^{2+} binding to a variety of nitrogen heterocycles yield straight lines, all of 0.67 slope. Points for binding at pyridine like purine N1 and pyrimidine N3 nitrogens in nucleosides and 5'-mononucleotides fall on a single straight line. The base line for binding at imidazole like purine N7 nitrogens is 0.8 log unit stronger than for N1 binding. N7 binding to purine bases with a 6-oxo group is enhanced by 1.6 log units above the N7 base line. The presence of a 5'-phosphate group enhances N7 binding (but not N1 binding) by 0.5-0.7 log unit. Weaker binding occurs wtih pmdienPd^{2+} and the straight line slopes are 0.79. The N7 base line rises 1.2 log units above the N1 line. Presence of the 6-oxo group enhances pmdien binding by 2.3 units. There is no enhancement of pmdienPd^{2+} binding to N7 due to the 5'-phosphate of nucleotides(4).

The lack of enhancement due to a 5'-phosphate for pmdienPd^{2+} in contrast to a
consistent 0.5-0.7 log unit enhancement for AMP, IMP, and GMP complexes of dienPd^{2+}
strongly suggests intramolecular hydrogen bonding from a coordinated dien nitrogen
to the phosphate group in a macrochelate. This conclusion is supported by the 0.4-
0.5 log unit acidification of the phosphate deprotonation with dienPd^{2+} but not with
pmdienPd^{2+}.

Perhaps surprisingly the high enhancement of inosine N7 binding is actually
greater for pmdienPd^{2+} at 2.3 log units than for dienPd^{2+} at 1.6 log units. This
comparison rules out hydrogen bonding from nitrogen-bound hydrogens on chelated
dien to the 6-oxo group as the cause of enhancement with dienPd^{2+}. To be reviewed
below, the aqueous metal ions Ni^{2+}, Cu^{2+}, and Zn^{2+} exhibit no binding enhancement at
N7 of 6-oxopurines.

Investigations of Pd(II) complexes have proven extremely useful for establishing
a thermodynamic base line for the much more slowly reacting Pt(II) complexes, including antitumor Pt(II) complexes (5, 10, 11-13). A similar enhanced binding for
antitumor cis-(amine)PtCl$_2$ complexes to N7 of guanosine, to that found for dienPd^{2+}
to 6-oxopurines, accounts for the observed favored Pt binding at guanosine N7 from
among the naturally occurring nucleoside sites. The order of bindings sites shows
preference of guanosine N7 over other sites (1, 3, 5, 13). It is not necessary to
postulate N7-O6 chelation by the cis-(amine)platinum(II) complexes, nor is it
likely to occur (1, 6, 8, 14). Kinetic factors also favor binding of Pt(II) at N7
in 6-oxopurines. Once bound at N7 the relatively inert Pt sticks and migration to
protonated N1 is difficult (5).

3 FIRST-TRANSITION-ROW METAL IONS

Unlike Pd(II), alkali- and alkaline-earth-metal ions and metal ions of the first-
transition row favor interaction with the phosphate rather than the nucleic base of
nucleotides (1). Therefore, to favor binding to the nucleic base, we now limit our
discussion to nucleosides.

With its diamagnetic and slow-exchange properties, Pd(II) allows direct determination of its distribution among ligand sites from peak intensities in ^{1}H NMR
spectra. These advantages are lost when investigating the first-transition-row
metal ions because they exchange rapidly among ligand sites and in most cases are
paramagnetic as well. Selective broadening and changes in other relaxation parameters are not reliable indicators of paramagnetic metal ion binding sites in the
nucleic bases (1, 15-17). However, what we have learned from Pd(II) about the
excellent correlations between stability constants and basicity may be applied
effectively to first-transition-row metal ions.

Plots of log K_1 vs. pK_a for Cu^{2+} binding to 15 3- and 4-substituted pyridines
and for Ni^{2+} to 8 of the same ligands each yield good straight lines of slope 0.46
and 0.27, respectively (9). Points for Cu^{2+} binding to cytidine and 7-methylinosine

fit on the Cu^{2+} line. The latter result supports the view that the purine N1 nitrogen acts as a pyridine type nitrogen. Similar plots of ligands with N7 type nitrogens for Ni^{2+}, Cu^{2+}, and Zn^{2+} yield good straight lines over a span of nine pK_a units (9,10).

Stability constant logarithms for Ni^{2+}, Cu^{2+}, and Zn^{2+} binding at pyridine or purine N1 type nitrogens and imidazole or purine N7 type nitrogens display a linear relationship with pK_a for each metal ion and nitrogen type. The slopes of all lines vary only from 0.3 to 0.5. For all three aqueous metal ions and $dienPd^{2+}$, at the same pK_a, the stability constant for N7 binding is 0.8-1.2 log units stronger than for N1 binding (9,10).

In contrast to the results for $dienPd^{2+}$ where points for inosine fall 1.6 log units above the N7 base line, all N7 points for first-transition-row metal ions fall on a single line for each aqueous metal ion. Evidently there is little if any increase in stability due to hydrogen bond formation from coordinated water to O6 of inosine and guanosine.

The excellent log K vs. pK_a correlations provide part of the basis for estimation of N1/N7 metal ion binding ratios. All that remains is to estimate the intrinsic pk_a for proton binding at the nucleic base nitrogens. All the common nucleic bases protonate first predominantly at N1 then at N7. We also need to know the pk_{17} value for deprotonation from the N7 site when the N1 site is not protonated. We set up the standard microconstant scheme for two acidic groups with four microconstants (10). For the decisive additional item of required information, we use 7-methylinosine with $pk_1 = 6.57$ and 7-methylguanosine with $pk_1 = 7.2$ as models for deprotonation from N1 in an N7 protonated species. From the properties of a cyclic system we obtain pk_{17} as 3.2 and 4.1 for deprotonation at N7 in inosine and guanosine, respectively, when N1 is not protonated (10).

From these results we find the intrinsic tendency to bind a proton at N1 over N7 as $10^{5.6}$ and $10^{5.1}$ for inosine and guanosine, respectively. Thus for the two 6-oxo-purines, the N1 site possesses intrinsically more than 10^5 times greater basicity than the N7 site. At any pH, the ratio of molar concentrations of N1 to N7 mono-protonated species is about 10^5. Note that the above difference is not the same as the difference between the two successive acidity macroconstant logs, $pK_{a2}-pK_{a1}$, because pK_{a1} refers to further protonation of a species already bearing a proton at N1.

A similar but slightly more involved argument leads to $pk_{17} = 1.1$ for adeno-sine (10). The intrinsic tendency for adenosine to bind a proton at N1 over N7 becomes $10^{2.5}$. Thus the intrinsic basicity ratio of N1 over N7 is about 10^3 times greater in the 6-oxopurines than in adenosine.

A summary of stability constants for binding of several metal ions to the N1 and N7 sites of adenosine appears in Table 1 (10). The last column of the table gives the molar ratio of N1 to N7 protonated and metalated complexes. Except for the proton the ratio ranges from 0.5 to 4 with values centering near unity. Thus we conclude that the N1 and N7 sites of neutral adenosine bind metal ions with com-

TABLE 1.

Neutral Adenosine Stability Constants

	log K_1	log K_7	$[BM_1]/[M_7B]$
H^+	3.6	1.1	320
Ni^{2+}	1.4	0.9	3
Cu^{2+}	1.7	1.3	2.5
Zn^{2+}	0.2	0.2	1
dienPd(II)	4.5	3.9	4
dienPd(II)[a]	4.87	4.51	2.3
dienPt(II)[a]			0.5

a. Observed values for 5'-AMP at pH 5.

parable strength. Solutions composed of neutral adenosine and metal ions contain both N1-metalated and N7-metalated complexes. The 3:1 N1/N7 ratio for adenosine and aqueous Ni^{2+} is consistent with a switch to greater N7 coordination to help account for the 11 times greater stability of $HOP_3O_9Ni^{2-}$ (18). The last two entries in Table 1 for 5'-AMP show that dienPt^{2+} favors N7 relative to N1 4.5 times more than dienPd^{2+} (10).

TABLE 2.

Intrinsic log ($[N1]/[N7]$) Binding Ratios

	adenosine	guanosine	inosine
H^+	2.5	5.1	5.6
CH_3Hg^+	-0.1	2.7	3.3
dienPd^{2+}	0.6		1.5
Ni^{2+}	0.5	0.8	1.0
Cu^{2+}	0.4	1.4	1.6
Zn^{2+}	0.0	1.0	1.2

Intrinsic [N1]/[N7] binding ratios reported as the log of the binding ratio are tabulated in Table 2 for several metal ions and nucleosides (10). The proton and CH_3Hg^+ favor N1 over N7 bonding about 10^3 times more in the 6-oxopurines than in adenosine. dienPd^{2+}, Cu^{2+}, and Zn^{2+} favor N1 over N7 about 10 times more in the 6-oxopurines than in adenosine.

Due to the greater basicity of N1 over N7 in all three purine nucleosides and to the relative metal ion binding strengths at each site, a change in dominant binding site from N7 to N1 occurs as the pH increases. The pH at which the changeover occurs is termed the crossover pH (1). Calculated values for the crossover pH appear in Table 3 (10). The results in Table 3 indicate that for adenosine with

TABLE 3

Crossover pH Values from N7 to N1 Coordination

	adenosine	inosine	guanosine
CH_3Hg^+		4.3	5.6
$dienPd^{2+}$	1.5	6.1	
Ni^{2+}	~ 2.1	7.1	7.8
Cu^{2+}	2.3	6.1	6.9
Zn^{2+}	2.7	6.7	7.5

most metal ions N1 coordination dominates at pH > 3. At pH > 4.5 the [N1]/[N7] adenosine molar ratio is given by the antilog of the values in Table 2.

4   REFERENCES

(1) R.B. Martin, Y.H. Mariam, Met. Ions. Biol. Syst. 8 (1979) 57-124.

(2) R.W. Gellert, R. Bau, Met. Ions. Biol. Syst. 8 (1979) 1-56.

(3) K.H. Scheller, V. Scheller-Krattiger, R.B. Martin, J. Am. Chem. Soc. 103 (1981) 6833-6839.

(4) S.H. Kim, R.B. Martin, Inorg. Chim. Acta 91 (1984) 11-18.

(5) R.B. Martin in "Platinum, Gold, and Other Metal Chemotherapeutic Agents"; Lippard, S.J., Ed., American Chemical Society; Washington, D.C., 1983, ACS Symp. Ser. No. 209, Chapter 11, pp. 231-244.

(6) I. Sovago, R.B. Martin, Inorg. Chem. 19 (1980) 2868-2871.

(7) U.K. Haring, R.B. Martin, Inorg. Chim. Acta 78, (1983) 259-267.

(8) U.K. Haring, R.B. Martin, Inorg. Chim. Acta 80 (1983) 1-5.

(9) R.B. Martin, Accts. Chem. Res. 18 (1985) 32-38.

(10) S.H. Kim, R.B. Martin, Inorg. Chim. Acta 91 (1984) 19-24.

(11) M.C. Lim, R.B. Martin, J. Inorg. Nucl. Chem. 38 (1976) 1911-1914.

(12) M.C. Lim, R.B. Martin, J. Inorg. Nucl. Chem. 38 (1976) 1915-1918.

(13) P.I. Vestues, R.B. Martin, J. Am. Chem. Soc. 103 (1981) 806-809.

(14) D.J. Nelson, P.L. Yeagle, T.L. Miller, R.B. Martin, Bioinorg. Chem. 5 (1976)
      353-358.

(15) W.G. Espersen, R.B. Martin, J. Am. Chem. Soc. 98 (1976) 40-44.

(16) W.G. Espersen, W.C. Hutton, S.T. Chow, R.B. Martin, J. Am. Chem. 96 (1974)
      8111-8112.

(17) W.G. Espersen, R.B. Martin, J. Phys. Chem. 80 (1976) 161-164.

(18) Y.H. Mariam, R.B. Martin, Inorg. Chim. Acta 35 (1979) 23-28.

The Influence of Metal Ion-Nucleic Acid Interactions on Genetic Information Transfer

G.L. Eichhorn, P. Clark, Y.A. Shin, J.J. Butzow, J.M. Rifkind, R.P. Pillai,
P.P. Chuknyiski, D. Waysbort

Laboratory of Cellular & Molecular Biology, Gerontology Research Center,
National Institute on Aging, National Institutes of Health, DHHS, Baltimore,
MD 21224, USA

One of the major concerns of our laboratory for many years has been the interaction
of metal ions with nucleic acids, and the impact of these and other metal interactions on genetic information transfert (GIT). All of the steps of this GIT require metal ions, and there is evidence that the metals may be involved in genetic
regulation. Nevertheless, under certain conditions, these same metals are capable
of introducing error into GIT. It is therefore of great importance to understand
how metals can produce both the beneficial and the deleterious effects.

REACTIONS OF METALS WITH NUCLEIC ACIDS

Since the nucleic acids are the molecules primarily responsible for GIT, an
understanding of the reactions of metals with nucleic acids can be of significance
in unterstanding the effects of metals on GIT. We have found that metal ions can,
in fact, have profound effects on nucleic acids, such as the degradation of RNA,
the mispairing of bases, changes in macromolecular conformation; all of these have
implications for GIT (1).

Different Metals

Not all metals, however, produce all of these effects, and probably no two metals
produce them at the same rate and to the same extent. The recognition of this fact
leads to the realization that different metals can influence the nucleic acids very

differently. And, of course, they do. Some metals stabilize double helices and other ordered structures, while other metals destabilize them. Some metal-nucleic acid complexes are in fast exchange with their products of dissociation, while others require much time for formation as well as dissociation. There are, of course, similarities among these complexes - e.g., N-7 of purines is an important binding site for many metals (though not all). Yet the differences are very important.

Comparisons with Pt-DNA Reaction

The differences must be remembered in relating some of the above reactions to the chemistry of platinum-DNA complexes. These complexes have aroused great interest, as this symposium amply demonstrates, and justifiably so, because of the antitumor activity of "cisplatin". As a result, a great deal is now known about the Pt-DNA interaction, and it is sometimes assumed that this knowledge can be readily extrapolated to other metal-nucleic acid complexes.

RNA SYNTHESIS

GIT includes the synthesis of DNA, RNA and protein. We have focused on RNA synthesis with the E. coli RNA polymerase enzyme. This enzyme contains an intrinsic metal, zinc, at the initiation site, and a required activating metal - e.g., magnesium - at the elongation site. At both sites a nucleoside triphosphate substrate is bound to the metal. The selection of substrate at both sites is guided by a DNA template, one of whose strands is copied through recognition of its bases by complementary substrates.

Structure at the Active Site

The distances from intrinsic metal to substrate at the initiation site and from activating metal to substrate at the elongation site have been previously determined by Chatterji and Wu (2), and by Bean, Koren and Mildvan (3), respectively. We have found that the template does not affect the structure at the elongation site, and Chatterji, Wu, and Wu (4) have shown that the template does affect the structure at the initiation site. These studies and our present ESR studies on the relationship between the metals on the two sites make it possible to propose a map of the active site of the enzyme.

RNA Synthesis and Template Conformation

The conformational changes induced by metal binding to DNA affect RNA synthesis by RNA polymerase. We have followed the conformational change from B to Z DNA under a variety of conditions, and have found that changes in the rate of RNA synthesis precisely correlate with the conformational transition in every instance (5).

RNA Synthesis with Different Metals

A number of metal ions can satisfy the requirement for an activator at the elongation site (6). Both cis and trans- $Pt(NH_3)_2Cl_2$ inhibit RNA synthesis (cis much more than trans), and we have shown that the inhibition is due to reaction with the DNA template (7). The activating metals differ from each other in their ability to cause the enzyme to differentiate between correct and incorrect substrates.

INORGANIC STRUCTURE PROBES

We have shown some time ago that the ability of the enzyme to differentiate between the ribonucleoside and deoxynecleoside structures can be mimicked by the copper acetate dimer. The two oxygen ligands of a bridging acetate are displaced by two hydroxyl groups of the ribose on the ribonucleoside; the reaction cannot occur with a deoxynucleoside with only one hydroxyl. This reagent is therefore a ribonucleoside structure probe. We do not propose this reaction as a serious model for RNA polymerase in that we do not believe that the selection mechanism in the enzyme works in the same manner. Recent attempts to use a rhodium dimer in this way proved unsuccessful, but the rhodium dimer was able to differentiate between adenine and the other nucleotide bases by the formation of a π-bonded complex with the adenine.

REFERENCES

(1) G.L. Eichhorn, Adv. Inorg. Biochem., 3, 1 (1981).

(2) D. Chatterji, F.Y.-H. Wu, Biochemistry, 21, 4657 (1982).

(3) B.L. Bean, R. Koren, A.S. Mildvan, Biochemistry, 16, 3322 (1977).

(4) D. Chatterji, K. Wu, F.Y.-H. Wu, J. Biol. Chem., 259, 284 (1984).

(5) J.J. Butzow, Y.A. Shin, G.L. Eichhorn, Biochemistry, 23, 4837 (1984).

(6) V.W. Armstrong, D. Yee, I. Eckstein, Biochemistry, 18, 4120 (1979).

(7) R.C. Srivastava, J. Froehlich, G.L. Eichhorn, Biochimie, 60, 879 (1978).

(8) N.A. Berger, G.L. Eichhorn, Nature (New Biology), 239, 237 (1972).

Influence of Decreasing Solvent Polarity on The Stability and Structure of Nucleotide-Metal Ion Complexes

Helmut Sigel

Institute of Inorganic Chemistry, University of Basel, Spitalstrasse 51, CH-4056 Basel, Switzerland

SUMMARY

The effect of dioxane on the stability of complexes formed between Cu^{2+} and ATP or UTP is summarized. Evaluation of these results shows that the percentage of the macrochelated isomer of $Cu(ATP)^{2-}$, in which the metal ion is coordinated to the phosphate residue and also to N-7 of the purine moiety, decreases with increasing amounts of dioxane added to an aqueous solution. Similar results are observed for the intramolecular stacking interactions between nucleic base moieties and the aromatic rings of 2,2'-bipyridyl or 1,10-phenanthroline (= Arm) in ternary $Cu(Arm)(NTP)^{2-}$ complexes: a decrease in the extent of stacking in $Cu(Arm)(ATP)^{2-}$ results from addition of dioxane; however, this decrease is much smaller compared with the decrease in stability of the unbridged $(Arm)(NTP)^{4-}$ adducts. Some general conclusions are indicated: it is emphasized that studies in solvents with lower polarity than water are important for understanding the selectivity and reactivity occurring in active-site cavities of enzymes, especially as there is now experimental evidence that the dielectric medium at these sites is reduced, compared to an aqueous solution.

Abbreviations: Arm, aromatic ligand like Bpy or Phen; ATP^{4-}, adenosine 5'-triphosphate; Bpy, 2,2'-bipyridyl; M, metal ion; NTP^{4-}, nucleoside 5'-triphosphate like ATP^{4-} or UTP^{4-}; Phen, 1,10-phenanthroline; UTP, uridine 5'-triphosphate.

1. INTRODUCTION

One of the remarkable features of living organisms is that their life-sustaining chemical reactions occur to a first approximation at atmospheric pressure and close to room temperature. Responsible for this effectiveness are the biological catalysts, the enzymes. The catalyzed reactions occur at so-called active sites, which are usually located in more or less deep cavities formed by high-molecular-weight proteins.

It has been reasoned for a long time that in these active-site cavities the polarity is reduced, compared with the polarity of bulk water. Indeed, for the hemoprotein cytochrome c an *effective* dielectric constant of approximately 50 has been estimated (using redox potentials) for the interaction of the heme iron, buried 7 Å beneath the protein surface, with specific lysine residues on the protein surface (1). Similarly, *equivalent solution* dielectric constants of about 35 and 70 have been estimated (based on stability constants of Zn^{2+}-carboxylate complexes in water-organic solvent mixtures) for the active-site cavities of bovine carbonic anhydrase and carboxypeptidase A, respectively (2).

These examples allow the conclusion that indeed many biological reactions proceed in a medium with a polarity smaller than that of water. Keeping this in mind we studied (3) the influence of increasing amounts of dioxane on the stability and structure of complexes formed by Cu^{2+} and ATP or UTP. These nucleoside 5'-triphosphates (NTP^{4-}) are important substrates for many enzymic reactions, very often being active only in the presence of divalent metal ions (4,5). Cu^{2+} is also of biological importance (6), and there are indications that $Cu(ATP)^{2-}$ itself might be a natural active form of Cu^{2+} (7).

$R = $ —riboyl 5'—O—$\overset{\overset{O}{\|}}{\underset{\underset{O_-}{|}}{P}}_\alpha$—O—$\overset{\overset{O}{\|}}{\underset{\underset{O_-}{|}}{P}}_\beta$—O—$\overset{\overset{O}{\|}}{\underset{\underset{O_-}{|}}{P}}_\gamma$—$O^-$

ATP^{4-} UTP^{4-}

2. SOLVENT INFLUENCE ON COMPLEX STABILITY

The acidity constants of $H_2(NTP)^{2-}$ and the stability constants of the resulting Cu^{2+} complexes were determined by potentiometric pH titrations (3). Some of the results are summarized in Table 1. It is evident that the stability of the UTP complexes increases with increasing amounts of dioxane in the aqueous solvent mixture, while for the ATP complexes the situation is more complicated.

Table 1.   Negative logarithms of the acidity constants for $H_2(NTP)^{2-}$ and logarithms of the stability constants for the corresponding binary $Cu(H \cdot NTP)^-$ and $Cu(NTP)^{2-}$ complexes in water and dioxane-water mixtures $(I = 0.1, NaNO_3; 25^{\circ}C)^a$

Solvent	NTP	$pK^H_{H_2(NTP)}{}^b$	$pK^H_{H(NTP)}{}^b$	$logK^{Cu}_{Cu(H \cdot NTP)}$	$logK^{Cu}_{Cu(NTP)}$
water	ATP	4.01 ± 0.01	6.49 ± 0.01	3.57 ± 0.08	6.32 ± 0.04
	UTP	2.0 ± 0.1	6.46 ± 0.01	~ 2.8	5.81 ± 0.06
30% (v/v) diox.-water	ATP	3.68 ± 0.02	6.82 ± 0.01	3.53 ± 0.06	6.40 ± 0.05
	UTP	2.37 ± 0.06	6.84 ± 0.01	3.31 ± 0.09	6.16 ± 0.05
50% (v/v) diox.-water	ATP	3.59 ± 0.02	6.90 ± 0.02	3.64 ± 0.05	6.34 ± 0.05
	UTP	2.60 ± 0.05	6.92 ± 0.01	3.79 ± 0.07	6.24 ± 0.03

[a] Abstracted from tables 3 and 4 of reference 3. The errors are *three* times the standard error of the mean value or the sum of the probable systematic errors, whichever is larger.   [b] In $H_2(ATP)^{2-}$ one proton is bound to N-1 of the purine system $(pK^H_{H_2(ATP)})$ and the other to the terminal γ-phosphate group. In $H_2(UTP)^{2-}$ both protons are located at the triphosphate chain and one of them is at the terminal γ-phosphate group; to this latter proton corresponds $pK^H_{H(UTP)}$.

In restricting ourselves in this connection to $Cu(NTP)^{2-}$ complexes a more detailed evaluation becomes possible based on Figure 1, where log $K^{Cu}_{Cu(NTP)}$ is plotted versus $pK^H_{H(NTP)}$. The linear relation between log $K^{Cu}_{Cu(NTP)}$ and $pK^H_{H(UTP)}$ implies that UTP^{4-} has the properties of simple O-donor ligands, like formate or acetate (2,3,8). In contrast, the "bell-shaped" curve obtained with Cu^{2+}/ATP emphasizes the more complicated situation and indicates the participation of other donor atoms.

3. SOLVENT INFLUENCE ON THE STRUCTURE OF $Cu(ATP)^{2-}$

The differences in solvent influence on the Cu^{2+} complexes of ATP^{4-} and UTP^{4-} are arising from the wellknown fact that many of the divalent transition metal ions interact in aqueous solution not only with the phosphate residue, but also with N-7 of ATP^{4-} (5,9,10), thus giving rise to the intramolecular equilibrium 1:

$$\underset{M^{2+}}{phosphate-ribose-base} \quad \overset{K_I}{\rightleftharpoons} \quad \underset{base-e}{\overset{phosphate-r}{M^{2+} \underset{b}{\overset{i}{}} \underset{o}{} s}} \qquad (eq. 1)$$

In $Cu(UTP)^{2-}$ a metal ion/base interaction becomes possible only above
the neutral pH range upon deprotonation of N-3 leading thus to the species $Cu(UTP-H)^{3-}$ (9). Hence, $Cu(UTP)^{2-}$ has a stability representative
for the open isomer in equilibrium 1, allowing the calculation of the
dimensionless equilibrium constant K_I according to equation 2,

$$K_I = (K^M_{M(NTP)} / K^M_{M(NTP)_{op}}) - 1 \qquad \text{(eq. 2)}$$

and then also of the percentage for the macrochelated isomer, $Cu(ATP)^{2-}_{cl}$
(for details see ref. 3 /I = 0.1, $NaNO_3$; 25°C):

Solvent	K_I	% $Cu(ATP)^{2-}_{cl}$
water	2.09+0.36	68+4
30% (v/v) dioxane-water	0.82+0.21	45+6
50% (v/v) dioxane-water	0.32+0.15	24+9

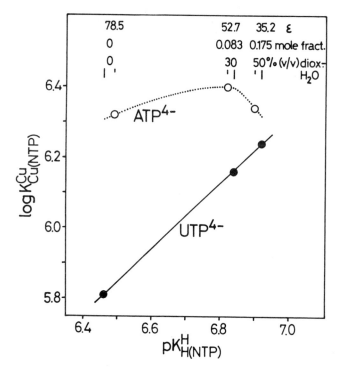

Fig. 1. Relationship
between log $K^{Cu}_{Cu(NTP)}$
and $pK^H_{H(NTP)}$ for the
$Cu(ATP)^{2-}$ (○) and
$Cu(UTP)^{2-}$ (●) complexes (Table 1) resul-
ting from the addition of increasing amounts of dioxane to the solvent
(I = 0.1, $NaNO_3$; 25°C). The percentages of dioxane in the mixed aqueous
solvents, the mole fractions of dioxane and the corresponding dielectric
constants, ε (from ref. 11), are inserted at the top of the figure.

Table 2. Logarithms of the stability constants for the ternary Cu(Arm)(NTP)$^{2-}$ complexes in water and dioxane-water mixtures (I = 0.1, NaNO$_3$; 25°C), together with the corresponding values for $\Delta \log K_{M/Arm/NTP}$ (eq. 4)[a,b]

Solvent	NTP^{4-}	$\log K^{Cu(Bpy)}_{Cu(Bpy)(NTP)}$	$\log K^{Cu(Phen)}_{Cu(Phen)(NTP)}$	$\Delta \log K_{Cu/Bpy/NTP}$	$\Delta \log K_{Cu/Phen/NTP}$
water	ATP	6.65±0.02	6.88±0.07	0.33±0.04	0.56±0.08
	UTP	6.16±0.05	6.17±0.05	0.35±0.08	0.36±0.08
30% (v/v) diox./H$_2$O	ATP	6.26±0.02	6.37±0.02	-0.14±0.05	-0.03±0.05
	UTP	6.08±0.04	6.06±0.05	-0.08±0.06	-0.10±0.07
50% (v/v) diox./H$_2$O	ATP	5.88±0.05	5.93±0.07	-0.46±0.07	-0.41±0.09
	UTP	5.78±0.02	5.81±0.07	-0.46±0.04	-0.43±0.08

[a] See footnote (a) in Table 1.   [b] For the stability of the protonated ternary Cu(Arm)(H·NTP)$^-$ complexes see reference 3.

Similar trends in solvent influence must be expected for ATP^{4-} complexes with other metal ions, like Mn^{2+}, Zn^{2+} or Cd^{2+}, for which the position of equilibrium 1 in aqueous solution has been quantified earlier (9,12-14); moreover, corresponding conclusions apply also to other purine-nucleotide complexes (9,15,16). For Mg(ATP)$^{2-}$ and Ca(ATP)$^{2-}$ the metal ion/base interaction is small or even not existing (5,9,12); hence, solely a solvent influence on complex stability similar to that for Cu(UTP)$^{2-}$ must be expected (Fig. 1), i.e. without large structural changes; this is also true for other metal ion complexes of pyrimidine-nucleotides, including UTP^{4-} (9,15,16).

4. SOLVENT INFLUENCE ON MIXED LIGAND COMPLEXES

2,2'-Bipyridyl and 1,10-phenanthroline (= Arm) facilitate studies of mixed ligand complexes containing transition metal ions due to their large affinity towards these ions, and are therefore often employed (17-19). In addition, their complexes are receiving increasing attention (20) as excellent intercalators for nucleic acids. We have used (3) Bpy and Phen to study mixed ligand complexes with Cu^{2+} and ATP or UTP: addition of dioxane decreases their complex stability somewhat (Table 2). This becomes more clear if a direct comparison between the stabilities of the binary and ternary complexes is made by considering the position of equilibrium 3:

$$M(NTP)^{2-} + M(Arm)^{2+} \rightleftharpoons M(Arm)(NTP)^{2-} + M^{2+} \qquad (eq. 3)$$

The corresponding equilibrium constant $10^{\Delta logK}$ is defined by equation 4:

$$\Delta \log K_{M/Arm/NTP} = \log K_{M(Arm)(NTP)}^{M(Arm)} - \log K_{M(NTP)}^{M}$$
$$\log K_{M(NTP)(Arm)}^{M(NTP)} - \log K_{M(Arm)}^{M} \qquad (eq. 4)$$

Equilibrium 3 is on its right side in water and on its left in 50% dioxane-water (Table 2). Hence, there must be a different solvent influence on the stabilities of the binary and ternary complexes.

The influence of dioxane on the stability and structure of the binary $M(NTP)^{2-}$ complexes has been discussed (Sections 2 & 3). Regarding the mixed $M(Arm)(NTP)^{2-}$ complexes earlier studies (14,18,21-24) showed that intramolecular stacking interactions may occur in aqueous solution between the aromatic rings of Bpy or Phen and the heterocyclic base moieties of UTP or ATP (Figure 2). Such interactions have been described also for mixed ligand complexes containing besides a nucleotide an amino acid with a suitable side-chain residue (18,24-27). Further related examples are known (19, 28-32), and in several instances this type of intramolecular ligand-ligand interaction has also been observed in the solid state (33-35).

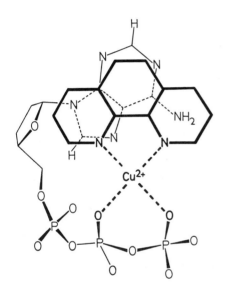

Fig. 2. Possible structure for the intramolecular stack in the ternary $Cu(Phen)(ATP)^{2-}$ complex.

5. COMPARISON OF THE SOLVENT INFLUENCE ON THE STABILITY OF BINARY AND METAL ION-BRIDGED STACKS

The indicated stacking interactions are expected to be influenced by dioxane. Indeed, recent studies (3) on the solvent dependence for the positions of equilibrium 5,

$$Arm + NTP^{4-} \xrightarrow{K_{st}} (Arm)(NTP)^{4-} \qquad (eq. 5)$$

involving binary stacks, and of the intramolecular equilibrium 6

$$\underset{\text{rib—base}}{\underbrace{\hspace{3cm}}} \quad \xrightleftharpoons{K_{I/st}} \quad \underset{\text{base}\diagdown\text{rib}}{\hspace{3cm}} \qquad \text{(eq. 6)}$$

confirm this expectation. Some of the results are summarized in Table 3 (for the detailed reasonings leading to these results see ref. 3).

Obviously, the formation of binary stacks is strongly inhibited by dioxane (Table 3); a result in accord with previous observations (8,36, 37). The formation degree of the metal ion-bridged stacks is also some-what reduced by dioxane, though to a much lesser extent. The following calculations (3), which apply for 10^{-3} M reactant solutions (I = 0.1, $NaNO_3$; ~25°C; pH ~7), demonstrate this clearly:

Solvent	% (Phen) (ATP)$^{4-}$	%Cu (Phen) (ATP)$^{2-}$	Promotion-Factor
water	3.5	90	~25
50% dioxane-water	0.18	46	~250
Inhibition-Factor	~1/20	~1/2	

Table 3. Stability constants, K (M^{-1}), for the binary (Arm) (NTP)$^{4-}$ stacking adducts (eq. 5),^{a} and estimations of the dimensionless equilibrium constants $K_{I/st}$ (eq. 6)^{b} and of the extent of the intramolecular aromatic-ring stacks (Fig. 2) for ternary Cu (Arm) (NTP)$^{4-}$ complexes^{b} in water and dioxane-water mixtures (I = 0.1, $NaNO_3$)$^{a-c}$

Solvent	NTP^{4-}	K_{st} (M^{-1})		Cu (Bpy) (NTP)$^{2-}$		Cu (Phen) (NTP)$^{2-}$	
		(Bpy) (NTP)$^{4-}$	(Phen) (NTP)$^{4-}$	$K_{I/st}$	% stack	$K_{I/st}$	% stack
water	ATP	16 +4	38 +8	5.9	86± 3	11	92± 2
	UTP	~1		~1.2	~55	~1.3	⌄57
30% (v/v) diox./H$_2$O	ATP	3.5+2	4.8+1.1	1.0	50+11	1.6	62± 9
	UTP			~0.32	~24	~0.26	~21
50% (v/v) diox./H$_2$O	ATP	0.4+0.2	1.8+0.7	0.62	38+14	0.95	49+12
	UTP			~0.29	~22	⌄0.48	~32

[a] By ^{1}H NMR shift measurements (27°C) in D$_2$O and dioxane-d$_8$/D$_2$O mixtures.
[b] Based on equilibrium constants determined by potentiometric pH titrations (25°C) in H$_2$O and dioxane/H$_2$O mixtures.   [c] All data from ref. 3.

A metal ion-bridge between the aromatic moieties favors stacking by a factor of about 25 in aqueous solution and of about 250 in 50% dioxane-water. Hence, in both solvents the formation of certain ligand-ligand associations may be favored giving thus rise to selective interactions; however, in the present example this selectivity is considerably more pronounced in the mixed solvent (see also refs 8 & 32).

6. CONCLUSIONS AND OUTLOOK

The described results show that a change in the polarity of the solvent may alter the stability and structure of binary and ternary complexes, and that this change may also affect selectivity. However, as indicated in the 'Introduction', one further aim is to understand the relation between such effects and the reactivity of a system. Clearly, the solvent influence on the stability-structure-reactivity relationship will be difficult to assess, though its knowledge is crucial for understanding the action of enzymes. Therefore, some preliminary results (38), which appear of interest in this connection, are included in Table 4.

Protons and metal ions promote the hydrolysis of nucleoside 5'-triphosphates to orthophosphate and the corresponding nucleoside 5'-diphosphates. Table 4 reveals the effect of dioxane on such a dephosphorylation reaction for "free" ATP and for the Zn^{2+}/ATP 1:1 system. In both cases the reactivity increases significantly by going from water to 50% dioxane-water: For ATP the dephosphorylation rate increases by a factor of about 4, while for Zn^{2+}/ATP the promotion-factor is about 14.

With ATP the increased reactivity may partly be attributed to the higher formation degree of protonated $H(ATP)^{3-}$, which is more reactive

Table 4. Solvent influence on the dephosphorylation rate of ATP (10^{-3} M) and Zn^{2+}/ATP (each 10^{-3} M) at pH 7.5 (I = 0.1, $NaClO_4$; $50^{\circ}C$).[a] The initial rates (v_o = d[PO_4]/dt; Ms^{-1}) are given as $v_o \times 10^8$

Solvent	ATP		Zn^{2+}/ATP (1:1)	
	v_o	% $H(ATP)^{3-}$	v_o	% $Zn(ATP)^{2-}$
water	0.032	9[b]	0.25	90[c]
30% (v/v) dioxane-water	0.073	17[b]	0.77	
50% (v/v) dioxane-water	0.137	20[b]	3.5	

[a] Preliminary results (38).   [b] These formation degrees have been calculated with the values given for $pK^H_{H(ATP)}$ in Table 1.   [c] This value was read from figure 2 in reference 14.

than ATP^{4-} (39). However, this formation degree is only about doubling, i.e. this can be only part of the reason for the increased rate. Furthermore, for the Zn^{2+}/ATP system the formation degree of $Zn(ATP)^{2-}$ is about 90% already in aqueous solution; a change in concentration of this species can therefore not be responsible for the 14-fold promotion.

It is known (39-42) that in the most reactive intermediates two positively charged ions are bound to the triphosphate chain. As the concentration of Na^+ is relatively large under the experimental conditions (Table 4) it seems probable that due to the decrease in the polarity of the solvent the coordination tendency of Na^+ increases enough to allow its participation in the formation of a reactive intermediate; thus the additional factor of two in the "ATP" system could be explained.

However, the possible participation of Na^+ in the dioxane-water mixtures seems hardly able to explain the promotion factor of about 14, observed with Zn^{2+}/ATP. From detailed mechanistic studies (39,41) in aqueous solution it is known that for Zn^{2+}/ATP the reaction proceeds via dimers, hence one must assume that the addition of dioxane influences also the stability and/or structure of these intermediates.

Whatever the final explanation for the facilitated dephosphorylation of these ATP systems in the low-polarity dioxane-water mixtures may be, it is an interesting observation with regard to the transphosphorylation reactions occurring in nature. As emphasized in the 'Introduction', in the active sites of enzymes a lowered polarity must be expected.

Research supported by the Swiss National Science Foundation under project No. 2.022-0.83.

7. <u>REFERENCES</u>

(1) D. C. Rees, *J. Mol. Biol. 141* (1980) 323-326.

(2) H. Sigel, R. B. Martin, R. Tribolet, U. K. Häring & R. Malini-Balakrishnan, *Eur. J. Biochem.* (1985) in press.

(3) R. Tribolet, R. Malini-Balakrishnan & H. Sigel, *JCS Dalton Trans.* (1985) in press.

(4) G. L. Eichhorn & L. G. Marzilli (Eds.), *Advances in Inorganic Biochemistry*, Vol. 3: "Metal Ions in Genetic Information Transfer"; Elsevier: Amsterdam 1981.

(5) H. Sigel (Ed.), *Metal Ions in Biological Systems*, Vol. 8: "Nucleotides and Derivatives: Their Ligating Ambivalency"; Marcel Dekker: New York and Basel 1979.

(6) H. Sigel (Ed.), *Metal Ions in Biological Systems*, (a) Vol. 12: "Properties of Copper", (b) Vol. 13: "Copper Proteins"; Marcel Dekker: New York and Basel 1981.

(7) C. Tallineau, M. Barriere, M. Boulard, P. Boulard-Heitzmann, R. Pontcharraud, D. Reiss & O. Guillard, *Biochim. Biophys. Acta 775* (1984) 51-56.

(8) H. Sigel, R. Malini-Balakrishnan & U. Häring, *J. Am. Chem. Soc.* (1985) in press.

(9) K. H. Scheller, F. Hofstetter, P. R. Mitchell, B. Prijs & H. Sigel, *J. Am. Chem. Soc. 103* (1981) 247-260.

(10) R. B. Martin, *Acc. Chem. Res. 18* (1985) 32-38.

(11) G. Åkerlöf & O. A. Short, *J. Am. Chem. Soc. 58* (1936) 1241-1243, and *J. Am. Chem. Soc. 75* (1953) 6357.

(12) P. Schneider, H. Brintzinger & H. Erlenmeyer, *Helv. Chim. Acta 47* (1964) 992-1002.

(13) Y. H. Mariam & R. B. Martin, *Inorg. Chim. Acta 35* (1979) 23-28.

(14) H. Sigel, K. H. Scheller & R. M. Milburn, *Inorg. Chem. 23* (1984) 1933-1938.

(15) K. H. Scheller & H. Sigel, *J. Am. Chem. Soc. 105* (1983) 5891-5900.

(16) H. Sigel & K. H. Scheller, *Eur. J. Biochem. 138* (1984) 291-299.

(17) H. Sigel, B. E. Fischer & B. Prijs, *J. Am. Chem. Soc. 99* (1977) 4489-4496.

(18) H. Sigel, "Stability, Structure and Reactivity of Mixed Ligand Complexes" in D. Banerjea (Ed.), *Coordination Chemistry-20*, Pergamon Press: Oxford 1980, pp. 27-45.

(19) H. Sigel, *Angew. Chem. Int. Ed. Engl. 21* (1982) 389-400.

(20) J. K. Barton, *Comments Inorg. Chem. 3* (1985) 321-348.

(21) P. Chaudhuri & H. Sigel, *J. Am. Chem. Soc. 99* (1977) 3142-3150.

(22) P. R. Mitchell & H. Sigel, *J. Am. Chem. Soc. 100* (1978) 1564-1570.

(23) Y. Fukuda, P. R. Mitchell & H. Sigel, *Helv. Chim. Acta 61* (1978) 638-647.

(24) P. R. Mitchell, B. Prijs & H. Sigel, *Helv. Chim. Acta 62* (1979) 1723-1735.

(25) H. Sigel & C. F. Naumann, *J. Am. Chem. Soc. 98* (1976) 730-739.

(26) H. Sigel, B. E. Fischer & E. Farkas, *Inorg. Chem. 22* (1983) 925-934.

(27) G. Arena, R. Calì, V. Cucinotta, S. Musumeci, E. Rizzarelli & S. Sammartano, *Thermochimica Acta 74* (1984) 77-86, and *JCS Dalton Trans.* (1984) 1651-1658.

(28) B. E. Fischer & H. Sigel, *J. Am. Chem. Soc. 102* (1980) 2998-3008.

(29) H. Sigel, *Experientia 37* (1981) 789-798.

(30) S.-H. Kim & R. B. Martin, *J. Am. Chem. Soc. 106* (1984) 1707-1712.

(31) O. Yamauchi & A. Odani, *Inorg. Chim. Acta 100* (1985) 165-172.

(32) H. Sigel, R. Tribolet & K. H. Scheller, *Inorg. Chim. Acta 100* (1985) 151-164.

(33) K. Aoki, *J. Am. Chem. Soc. 100* (1978) 7106-7108.

(34) P. Orioli, R. Cini, D. Donati & S. Mangani, *J. Am. Chem. Soc. 103* (1981) 4446-4452.

(35) W. S. Sheldrick, *Z. Naturforsch.; Anorg. Chem., Org. Chem. 37b* (1982) 863-871.

(36) K. A. Connors & S.-r. Sun, *J. Am. Chem. Soc. 93* (1971) 7239-7244.

(37) B. Farzami, Y. H. Mariam & F. Jordan, *Biochemistry 16* (1977) 1105-1110.

(38) H. Sigel & R. Tribolet, results to be published.

(39) H. Sigel, F. Hofstetter, R. B. Martin, R. M. Milburn, V. Scheller-Krattiger & K. H. Scheller, *J. Am. Chem. Soc. 106* (1984) 7935-7946.

(40) H. Sigel & F. Hofstetter, *Eur. J. Biochem. 132* (1983) 569-577.

(41) H. Sigel & P. E. Amsler, *J. Am. Chem. Soc. 98* (1976) 7390-7400.

(42) R. M. Milburn, M. Gautam-Basak, R. Tribolet & H. Sigel, *J. Am. Chem. Soc. 107* (1985) 3315-3321.

Uptake, Essentiality and Toxicity of the Chemical Elements

Amavadine, an Oxovanadium(IV) Compex of N-Hydroxy-Imino-α,α'-Dipropionic Acid

G. Bemsky

Centro Brasileiro de Pesquisas Físicas, Rio de Janeiro, Brasil

Judith Felcman

Departamento de Química, Pontifícia Universidade Católica (R.J.), Rio de Janeiro
Brasil.

J.J.R. Fraústo da Silva, I. Moura, J.J.G. Moura, M. Cândida Vaz, L.F. Vilas-Boas

Centro de Química Estrutural, Complexo I, Instituto Superior Técnico, 1000 Lisboa
Portugal

SUMMARY

   N-hydroxy-imino-α,α'-dipropionic acid (HIDPA), the ligand suggested to be present
in Amavadine, an oxovanadium(IV) complex that occurs in the toadstool *Amanita
muscaria*, has been synthesized, as well as two other related compounds, N-hydroxy-
-iminodiacetic and imino-α,α'-dipropionic acids, which could show how the introduction of the N-hydroxyl and of the two methyl groups in the skeleton of iminodiacetic
acid affected its metal complexing properties.

   The N-hydroxyl group lowers the basicity of the nitrogen atom of the ligands to
such an extent that the $(VO)L_2$ complex forms preferentially to VOL at pH ~ 6,
contrarily to what happens with iminodiacetic acid and its more common derivatives.

   The UV, vis and IR spectra of the 1:2 complex formed with HIDPA were analogous to
those previously reported for Amavadine and the EPR spectrum of that complex was
completely superimposable to that obtained from frozen pieces of specimens of
Amanita muscaria, confirming the identity of the natural complex.

   The reason for the selection of this ligand is discussed in terms of the requirements of a prosthetic group of a possible enzyme of the toadstool which may be a
primitive peroxidase.

INTRODUCTION

Although the presence of vanadium in vegetal ashes has been referred to for the first time more than one century ago, it wasn't until 1931 that TER MEULEN reported a definite determination of the contents of this element in a plant, namely in the toadstool *Amanita muscaria* |1|.

Results obtained since then have shown that *Amanita muscaria* is indeed unusual in these respects, concentrating comparatively high amounts of vanadium, up to 120 ppm dry weight.

More recently it has been reported that high vanadium content is not restricted to *Amanita muscaria* and that other *Amanita* species also contain this metal, e.g. *Amanita regalis* (169 ppm) and, particularly *Amanita velatipes* (397 ppm), an American variety of *Amanita pantherina* |2|. Still, the ability to concentrate vanadium seems to be a unique property of just a few probably primitive species of the genus *Amanita*.

In 1972, BAYER and KNEIFEL isolated a vanadium containing compound from a German variety of *Amanita muscaria* (Black Forest and Schonbuch) which they named "amavadine" |3|. About 40 mg of the compound were obtained per kg of the fresh mushrooms by an elaborate procedure which included extraction with methanol of a thawed mixture of frozen mushrooms, followed by isolation through a series of chromatographic processes using celulose, sephadex and cation exchange resins.

Table 1 summarizes the properties of amavadine, as reported by Bayer and Kneifel.

Following hydrolysis by 6N HCl, which gives mainly alanine, or by 1N NaOH, which affords sodium pyruvate and acetaldehyde as well as alanine, and after reduction by zinc and acetic acid which yields $\alpha\alpha'$-iminodipropionic acid, a first model of amavadine as 2:1 complex of this last ligand was assumed. Additional information came from EPR spectroscopic detection of a nitroxyl radical on oxidation of amavadine in alkaline media. Finally, a dimethylester $C_8H_{15}NO_5$ was isolated after methanolysis of amavadine in methanol/H_2SO_4; this was identified as dimethyl *N*-hydroxy-imino-$\alpha\alpha'$--dipropionate and the corresponding acid was postulated as the natural ligand in the complex |4|.

The structure proposed by these authors for amavadine, taking into account the various data obtained, is represented below, as (I):

I

Structure proposed for Amavadine

Table 1: Some properties of Amavadine

Colour	pale blue
Melting point	no melting point; colour disappears at 170°C, turns to yellow at 185°C and to brown at 220°C
UV. vis. spectra	bands at 775 nm ($\epsilon = 19.3$), 715 nm ($\epsilon = 18.9$), 565 nm ($\epsilon = 23.5$), 270 nm (sh., $\epsilon = 6800$), 235 nm
(ϵ/mol^{-1} l cm^{-1})	(sh., $\epsilon = 12300$), 218 nm(sh., $\epsilon = 12600$)
IR	strong CO band at 1600-1650 cm^{-1} and a V = O band at 985 cm^{-1}
EPR	indicative of VO^{2+}
M.W. (osmometry)	415
Composition (analysis)	$C_{12}H_{22}N_2VO_{12}$ (with two free acid groups)

To confirm this structure Kneifel and Bayer refer the preparation of the ligand N-hydroxy-imino-$\alpha\alpha'$-dipropionic acid from hydroxoammonium chloride and α-bromo-propionic acid and state, without details, that a 2:1 complex with VO^{2+} is identical with natural amavadine in chromatographic behaviour, EPR, electronic spectra and IR absorption, differing only on chirality from the natural complex whose two optically active carbon atoms exist in the L-configuration. They also refer that it could not be excluded that in the fungal mycelium of the toadstool, the amavadine may be fixed as a metal cofactor to a macromolecular component by a loose bond destroyed during the process of isolation |4|.

No further papers have been published by these or other authors since these preliminary findings to which all reviews on biological vanadium are referred to, but, recently, GILLARD and LANCASHIRE compared the EPR spectra of segments of frozen mushrooms to vanadyl complexes of various amino-acids, as models for amavadine, and discussed the results in a short note |5|. According to these authors the 2:1 complexes of simple aminoacids are not good models, the type of spectrum observed for amavadine being closer to that found for the 2:1 complexes of L-cysteine or L-serine |5|. Since the original observations of Bayer and Kneifel had not been confirmed and N-hydroxy-imino-$\alpha\alpha'$-dipropionic acid seemed a rather unusual selection for a biological ligand, we have decided to synthesize this and other related compounds to see how the introduction of the N-hydroxyl and the two methyl groups in the more common iminodiacetic acid skeleton affected its metal complexation properties.

The study of the VO^{2+} complexes of these ligands would also allow a more direct comparison with the amavadine also present in specimens of *Amanita muscaria* collected in Portugal (Melides).

RESULTS AND DISCUSSION

The synthesis of N-hydroxy-imino-$\alpha\alpha'$-dipropionic acid (HIDPA) is not easy due to the high solubility of the ligand in water and alcohol; this may be the reason for the absence of definite or further studies since the work of Bayer and Kneifel and failures to synthesize it have indeed been reported |6|.

After various attempts we managed to obtain pure samples of NaHL.LH$_2$ and of NaHL (L being the completely ionised ligand), confirmed by elemental analysis, titration and NMR spectra. The related ligands imino-$\alpha\alpha'$-dipropionic acid (IDPA) and the closely similar N-hydroxyiminodiacetic acid (HIDA) were easier to synthesize |7|.

The most striking effect observed was the pronounced lowering of the basicity of the imino nitrogen of HIDA and HIDPA compared with that of IDPA or of iminodiacetic

Table 2: Proton ionization constants (pKa$_1$ and pKa$_2$), stability constants of VO^{2+} complexes (log K$_{ML}$ and log K$_{ML_2}$) and proton ionization constants of VO^{2+} aqua-aminopolycarboxylates, T = 25.0 ± 0.1 °C, μ = 0.10 M (KNO$_3$)

Ligand (acid)	H·		VO²·			
	pKa$_1$	pKa$_2$	log K$_{ML}$	log K$_{ML_2}$	− log K$_1$	− log β_{22}
Iminodiacetic	2.61 ± 0.02	9.34 ± 0.01	9.00 ± 0.02		5.8 ± 0.1	9.1 ± 0.1
Imino-αα'-dipropionic	2.43 ± 0.01	9.38 ± 0.01	9.54 ± 0.01		6.1 ± 0.1	9.2 ± 0.1
N-hydroxyiminodiacetic	2.82 ± 0.01	5.48 ± 0.03	7.16 ± 0.03	6.10 ± 0.05	5.0 ± 0.1	6.4 ± 0.1
N-hydroxyimino-αα'-dipropionic	2.74 ± 0.02	5.77 ± 0.02	7.34 ± 0.02	5.51 ± 0.05	5.0 ± 0.1	6.6 ± 0.1

$$K_1 = [VO(OH)L]\ [H^·] / [VO(H_2O)L];\ \beta_{22} = [(VO)_2(OH)_2 L_2]\ [H^·]^2 / [VO(H_2O)L]^2$$

Table 3: Spectral parameters for VO^{2+} complexes of IDPA, HIDA and HIDPA (concentration of the complexes for UV = 1.82 × 10^{-4} M; for vis. 4.54 × 10^{-3} M). T = 25 °C

VO(IDPA) (pH = 4.6)		VO(HIDA)$_2$ (pH = 6.3)		VO(HIDPA)$_2$ (pH = 5.8)	
λ/nm	ϵ/mol^{-1} l cm^{-1}	λ/nm	ϵ/mol^{-1} l cm^{-1}	λ/nm	ϵ/mol^{-1} l cm^{-1}
260	990	214 (sh)	12400	220 (sh)	13900
580	10.6	232	11870	236	14800
776	20.5	270 (sh)	5500	272 (sh)	7750
		565	24.4	560	29.0
		706	19.6	700	23.1
		790	20.0	790	23.8

acid (IDA); the practical consequence of this fact is that formation of ML$_2$ complexes of VO^{2+} with HIDPA is possible, whereas with IDPA and the normal IDA derivatives the introduction of the second molecule of the ligand occurs at a pH in which the hydroxide ion competes more favourably for VOL, yielding not VOL$_2$ but VOL.OH and the dimer (VO)$_2$L$_2$(OH)$_2$.

Table 2 and Figs. 1 and 2 illustrate the results obtained |7|.

The hypothesis of Bayer and Kneifel is therefore supported by our results but the availability of the ligands allowed more direct confirmations.

In Fig. 3 and 4 the UV and visible electronic spectra of the vanadyl complexes of IDPA, HIDA and HIDPA are presented and the data are summarized in Table 3.

Comparing these results with those obtained by Bayer and Kneifel for amavadine, the vanadyl complex extracted from the toadstool, the close similarity between this complex and VO^{2+}(HIDPA)$_2$ is apparent. The absorption peaks are practically identical and the differences in molar absorptivities indicate just that the extracted amavadine is more dissociated at the ligand to metal ratio 2:1.

The EPR spectra of the 2:1 VO^{2+} complexes of the three novel ligands and that of frozen pieces of specimens of *Amanita muscaria* were also recorded and the g and A parameters obtained by superimposing these with spectra simulated with an adequate computer program |8| are shown in Table 4, together with the corresponding data obtained

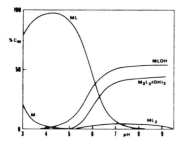

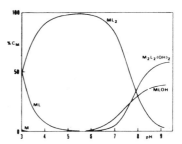

Fig. 1: Distribution of the species as function of pH for VO^{2+} complexes with IDPA, in the ligand to metal ratio 5:1.
Total vanadium concentration = 7.69 $\times 10^{-4}$ M.
T = 25 $^\circ$C; μ = 0.10 M KNO$_3$. A K$_{ML_2}$ constant of the order of that found for the VO^{2+} complex of glycine was tentatively adopted (K$_{ML_2}$ = 5.4 $\times 10^4$)

Fig. 2: Distribution of the species of as function of pH for VO^{2+} complexes with HIDPA, in the ligand to metal ratio 5:1.
Total vanadium concentration = 7.69 $\times 10^{-4}$ M;
T = 25 $^\circ$C; μ = 0.10 M KNO$_3$

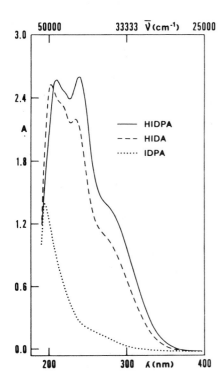

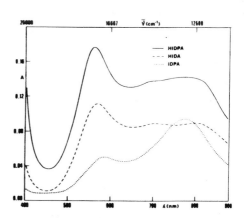

Fig. 3: UV electronic spectra of VO^{2+} complexes of HIDPA, HIDA and IDPA in the ligand to metal ratio 5:1.
Total vanadium concentration = 1.82 $\times 10^{-4}$ M

Fig. 4: Visible spectra of VO^{2+} complexes of HIDPA, HIDA and IDPA in the ligand to metal ratio 5:1.
Total vanadium concentration = 4.54 $\times 10^{-3}$ M

by Gillard and Lancashire for 2:1 VO^{2+} complexes of some amino-acids and by PILBROW *et al.* for 1:1 complexes of polyamino-carboxylic acids |9|.

In Figs. 5 and 6 the EPR spectra obtained from pieces of *Amanita muscaria* and for the 2:1 complex of VO^{2+} with *N*-hydroxy-imino-$\alpha\alpha'$-dipropionic acid are presented together with the simulated spectra.

The data presented in Table 4 again show the striking similarity of amavadine and $VO(HIDPA)_2$ giving further and definite support to the structure proposed by Bayer and Kneifel for the product isolated from *Amanita muscaria*.

Further support comes from the study of solid $VO(HIDPA)_2$, isolated from a methanol solution by evaporation, which has melting behaviour analogous to that described for amavadine; its IR spectrum exhibits a broad CO band centered at 1610 cm^{-1} and a VO^{2+} band at 970 cm^{-1}.

N-hydroxyiminodiacetic acid behaves in very much the same manner as *N*-hydroxy-imino-$\alpha\alpha'$-dipropionic acid but its VO^{2+} complexes are not so closely similar to amavadine.

It can be shown that $g_{||}$ and $A_{||}$ are approximate functions of the last ionization constants of the ligands (different for 2:1 and 1:1 complexes) and that $A_\perp$ is on the range 45–46 for 2:1 complexes and 60–63 for 1:1 complexes.

The values of $A_{||}$ and $g_{||}$ are linearly related for the VO^{2+} complexes of aminoacids and polyaminocarboxylic acids – Fig. 7 – but $VO(HIDPA)_2$, $VO(HIDA)_2$ and amavadine behave differently. The reason for this fact is still not clear; it may be related

Table 4: EPR parameters for "amavadine" and for various oxovanadium(IV) complexes of amino acids [5] and aminopolycarboxylic acids (T = 77 K)

	Conditions	$g_{||}$	$g_\perp$	$10^4 A_{||}/cm^{-1}$	$10^4 A_\perp/cm^{-1}$
A. *muscaria* (England)	direct in the mushroom	1.920	1.982	153	45
A. *muscaria* (Portugal)	"	1.919	1.982	157	46
$VO(L\text{-}ala)_2$	pH 6.6	1.943	1.976	163	55
$VO(serine)_2$	pH 11.0	1.955	1.976	150	45
$VO(cysteine)_2$	pH 7.8	1.962	1.976	143	45
VO(EDTA)	pH 5.8	1.943	1.980	168	60
VO(EGTA)	pH 5.5	1.941	1.975	173	63
VO(DTPA)	pH 5.5	1.943	1.980	167	63
VO(TTHA)	pH 5.5	1.943	1.980	168	60
VO(EDDA)	pH 7.0	1.944	1.977	169	57
VO(NTA)	pH 6.9	1.936	1.975	175	65
VO(IDPA)	pH 5.3	1.939	1.980	170	60
$VO(HIDA)_2$	pH 5.4	1.913	1.983	157	45
$VO(HIDPA)_2$	pH 5.4	1.919	1.982	157	46

to differences in coordination of the nitrogens (*cis* or *trans*-coordination) or to the type of group bound (or not) in the axial position *trans* to the oxo group, but the data available is insufficient to support a definite answer to the problem.

Another question for which no answer has been found is why is a VOL_2 complex necessary for the toadstool and which function does it perform.

A speculative suggestion is offered |7|, taking into account the characteristics that make VO^{2+} unique among the common metal ions.

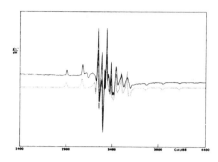

Fig. 5
EPR spectrum of "amavadine".
Experimental conditions: temperature 20 K, microwave power
2 mW, modulation amplitude 0.5 mT, microwave frequency
9.451 GHz, scan time 500 s. The superimposed dotted spectrum was simulated using the spectrum parameters of Table 4

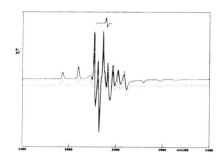

Fig. 6
EPR spectrum of 2:1 VO^{2+} complex of HIDPA.
Experimental conditions: temperature 77 K, microwave power
2 mW, modulation amplitude 0.5 mT, microwave frequency
9.261 GHz, scan time 500 s. The superimposed dotted spectrum was simulated using the spectrum parameters of Table 4

Firstly, VO^{2+} behaves as a transition metal ion forming complexes as stable as
those of nickel(II) |10| with the donor atoms occupying the remaining octahedral
sites around the V(IV) ion, i.e., complexes with a square pyramidal structure
relative to VO^{2+}. However, unlike all common metal ions, these coordination sites
are not all equivalent: the apical site *trans* to the oxo ligand on vanadium (IV) is
far more labile toward substitution reactions than the *cis* equatorial sites |11| -
typical rate constants are k > 10^7 s^{-1} for the first case and k ≈ $10^{-1}s^{-1}$ for the
second. Furthermore, oxovanadium(IV) complexes are oxidised by outer sphere oxidants
provided that an aqua-ligand is present in an equatorial site, but the conjugate base,
the hydroxo complex, is oxidised much more rapidly to give *cis*-oxo species |11|.
Other metal ions of sub-groups IV, V and VI of the Periodic Table also form oxo-
cations, e.g. Ti, Cr and Mo, but solubility reasons exclude titanium complexes, redox
properties and inertness of Cr(III) exclude chromium, and molybdenum(V) complexes
with common ligands are frequently binuclear with $Mo_2O_4^{2+}$ cores.

Hence a VO^{2+} complex is particularly advantageous if a reaction center ensuring
high substitution rates is necessary, provided that the equatorial coordination positions are blocked to avoid the formation of hydroxocomplexes or their dimers and to
prevent oxidation; such a complex must expose the apical site *trans* to the oxo ligand
to the reaction medium. The selection of a ligand such as *N*-hydroxy-imino-αα'-di-
propionic acid satisfies the required conditions: a 2:1 square pyramidal complex of
VO^{2+} can be formed, avoiding the formation of hydroxocomplexes and their dimers,
which might prevent coordination to the apical sites besides being easily oxidisable.

The choice of a tridentate ligand may also be of some significance; note that in
the VO^{2+} complexes of tetradentate nitrilotriacetic acid or pyridinemethylimino-
-diacetic acid the apical site *trans* to oxygen is blocked by the nitrogen atom of the
iminodiacetic moiety and substitution rates of reaction are much smaller |11|. In
these conditions it is likely that "amavadine" is indeed "unique" for its function,
but it is still not clear what kind of function it performs.

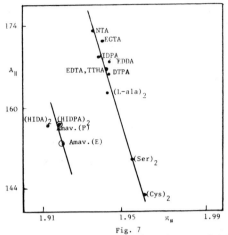

Fig. 7

Correlation of values of $A_\parallel$ with $g_\parallel$ for several 1:1
and 2:1 complexes of polyaminocarboxylate and
aminocarboxylate complexes of VO^{2+}, according to
the data obtained in the present work (NTA, EDDA,
IDPA, HIDA and amavadine) and by various other
authors (|5|, |9|).

Recently, it was found that a vanadium enzyme is present in at least a species of brown algae – Ascophyllum nodosum – and that this enzyme has a bromoperoxidase activity |12|. In the active form, vanadium is present as V(V) but it is not unlikely that amavadine in the *Amanita* toadstool is also a cofactor of an enzyme with a protective oxidase or peroxidase function and the idea that some rather primitive species used this metal for functions that were later taken over by more effective iron-enzymes is worth exploring. Our studies are continuing in these lines.

ACKNOWLEDGEMENTS

    The authors thank Prof. F.M. Catarino from the Faculty of Sciences of Lisbon and his collaborators for providing us with specimens of *Amanita muscaria*.

    Financial assistance is acknowledged from CNPq (Brasil) and I.N.I.C. (Portugal).

REFERENCES

|1| H. TER MEULEN, Rec. Trav. Chim. Pays-Bas, <u>50</u> (1931) 491-504.

|2| H.-U. MEISH, W. REINLE, J.A. SCHIMITT, Naturwiss., <u>66</u> (1979) 620-621.

|3| E. BAYER, H. KNEIFEL, Z. Naturforsch., <u>27b</u> (1972) 207.

|4| H. KNEIFEL, E. BAYER, Angew. Chem. Intern. Ed., <u>12</u> (1973) 508.

|5| R.D. GILLARD, R.J. LANCASHIRE, Phytochemistry, 23 (1983) 179-180.

|6| M.A. NAWI, T.L. RIECHEL, Inorg. Chim. Acta, 93 (1984) 131-140.

|7| J. FELCMAN, J.J.R. FRAÚSTO DA SILVA, M. CÂNDIDA VAZ, Inorg. Chim. Acta, 93
     (1984) 101-108.

|8| J.R. PILBROW, M.E. WINFIELD, Mol. Phys., 25 (1973) 1073 and references therein.

|9| T.D. SMITH, J.F. BOAS, J.R. PILBROW, Aust. J. Chem., 27. (1974) 2535-2545.

|10| J. FELCMAN, J.J.R. FRAÚSTO DA SILVA, Talanta, 30 (1983) 565-570.

|11| K. SAITO, in D. BANERJEE (ed) "Coordination Chemistry - XXth ICCC",
     Pergamon Press, Oxford 1980 173-180.

|12| R. WEVER. H. PLAT and E. DE BOER, Rev. Port. Química, 27 (1985) 169-170

Metal Ions and Plants

Margaret E. Farago

Chemistry Department, The Bourne Laboratory,
Royal Holloway and Bedford New College, (University of London),
Egham, Surrey TW20 OEX, U.K.

SUMMARY

   A brief introduction is given to the processes involved in the uptake of metal
ions by higher plants. Of the essential elements required by plants to sustain
healthy growth, only three are absorbed by the aerial parts: carbon, oxygen and
hydrogen, other elements are absorbed and transported by a complex mechanism which
begins at the root. Mechanisms of mineral uptake are described briefly. Some plants
grow on soils where the concentrations of metals are normally toxic, such metal
tolerant species have been used as indicators of particular environmental conditions.
Some studies of metal tolerant plants are described.

1 INTRODUCTION

1.1 Inorganic composition of plants

   Fresh plant material is 80–90% water, and of the remainder over 90% consists of C,
O and H. Organic material is removed from the dried plant samples by ashing, and the
remaining 1.5% of the plant's fresh weight represents its mineral content. Table 1
shows the typical composition of corn.

   It has long been known that plants require at least ten elements for healthy
growth: N, S, P, K, Ca, Mg, Fe, C, H, O. These elements, with the exception of iron,
are called macronutrients, since they are needed in relatively large amounts. Small
quantities of iron are sufficient, and a number of other elements are required in even
smaller amounts: these are the micronutrients.

Table 1. Elemental composition of the corn plant <u>Zea mays</u>, cited in ref. (1).

Element	% of dry weight	Element	% of dry weight
O	44.43	P	0.20
C	43.57	Mg	0.18
H	6.24	S	0.17
N	1.46	Cl	0.14
Si	1.17	Al	0.11
K	0.92	Fe	0.08
Ca	0.23	Mn	0.04

1.2 Criteria of essentiality

Not all elements detected in plant tissues are deemed to be essential. Criteria of essentiality have been proposed by Epstien (1) in 1965. An element is essential (a) if, without it, the plant cannot complete its life cycle, and (b) if it is part of the molecule of an essential plant constituent or metabolite. The experimental evidence for essentiality comes from solution culture (hydroponic) methods. As the experimental techniques and the quality of the water used in the experiments have improved, the number of essential micronutrients has tended to increase. Other elements are known to be beneficial, and some of these may be essential for some species (Table 2).

Table 2. Status of elements in plant nutrition (after Hewitt and Smith (2))

<u>Essential</u> <u>macronutrients</u>	K Ca Mg C H O P N S
<u>Essential</u> <u>micronutrients</u>	Fe Cu Mn Zn Mo Co V Na Rb B Si Cl I Se
<u>Beneficial or of</u> <u>restricted essentiality</u>	Ni Al Sr Sn Cr Br F

2 <u>THE UPTAKE OF MINERALS BY PLANTS</u>

The root is the plant organ by which inorganic nutrients are taken into the plant.

Bowling (3) has discussed in detail the theories of mineral uptake by plant roots; he suggests that there are four links in the uptake chain: movement of ions or complexes in the soil to the roots; uptake into the root; transport across the root to the vascular system; and transport to the shoot.

2.1 Movement of metal ions in soil

Organic and humic materials in soils act as ligands and the resulting complexes can be important in the movement of metal ions (4). Both diffusion and mass flow (5) of the soil solution are important in the movement of ions to roots. Both occur simultaneously, and mathematical treatments including both factors have been developed by Passioura (6) and by Nye and Marriott (7). Both chelation and surface adsorption (e.g. on clays and hydrous oxides) are pH dependent, and this in turn affects the availabilty of nutrients and toxic elements. Acid soil conditions result in low availability of macronutrients, but increased availability, sometimes producing toxic effects, of Mn Fe and Al.

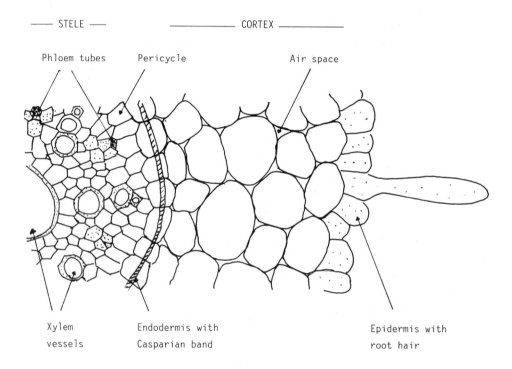

Fig. 1. Transverse section of a typical root.

2.2 The root as an absorbing organ

Theories concerning the complex mechanisms of uptake by plant roots have been discussed by Bowling (3) and Epstein (1). The outer layer of the root, the epidermis, is provided with extensions, the root hairs, with a pectic coating which allows them to adhere to soil particles. The hairs also greatly enhance the area of contact with the soil. A transverse section of a typical root is shown in Fig. 1. The majority of the root consists of relatively large and loosely arranged parenchyma cells, with air spaces, known collectively as the cortex. The central portion of the root, the stele, contains the vascular system which is responsible for the transport of food, water and minerals throughout the plant. These tissues contain the xylem, which conducts water and nutrients up to the aerial parts, and the phloem, which functions as a conductor of organic material from the leaves to the roots. The stelar portion of the root is surrounded by a distinct layer of cells, the endodermis, which separates the stele from the cortex. The chief feature of the endodermis is the appearance of a ribbon-like strip surrounding the walls of each cell. This is the Casparian strip or band, which is composed of suberised (waxy) material, which forms an impermeable barrier to water and ionic solutes. In order to reach the xylem, water and dissolved salts must pass through the living portions of the cells by passing through a membrane, the plasmalemma, (Fig. 2), which probably provides the control for the entry of water and dissolved salts into the plant.

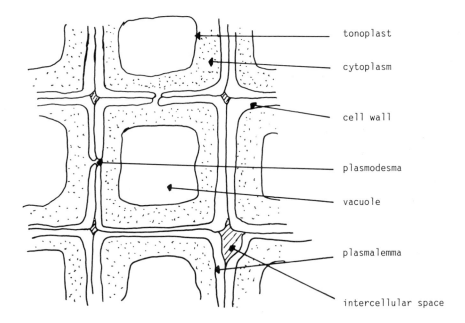

Fig. 2. Diagram of typical plant cells (after Hewitt and Smith (2))

Early experimenters found that metal ions were able to diffuse passively in and out of the root, up to the Casparian strip. The ions occupy the porous cell wall spaces of the epidermis and cortex. The volume occupied by such metal ions is known as the "outer" space of the root, and can be calculated (8) :

$$\text{"Outer space" in cm}^3 \text{ g}^{-1} = \frac{[\text{Diffusible ions}] \text{ in } \mu \text{ mol g}^{-1} \text{ fresh wt}}{[\text{External concentration}] \text{ in } \mu \text{ mol cm}^{-3}}$$

Some of the metal ions which diffuse into the root cannot diffuse out because they are held by negatively charged sites on the cell walls, which result from dissociated carboxyl groups. The volume occupied by these ions in known as the Donnan Free Space (D.F.S.) (9). Together the two components, the "outer" and the D.F.S. are known as the Apparent Free Space (A.F.S.).

It is generally agreed that ions on their way to the vascular system must cross at least one membrane by a process that requires energy. This process, "active transport", probably requires the action of specific ionophores, the nature of which has not yet been elucidated. There is evidence for transport accross the root by two general pathways:

(i) Cell wall pathway: ions cross the cortex by means of the cell walls;

(ii) Symplasm pathway: ions cross the cortex by means of cytoplasmic drift through the small common areas between the cells (the plasmodesmata). The continuum of cytoplasm which extends from cell to cell through the plasmodesmata is known as the symplasm.

2.3 Uptake kinetics

The rate of absorption of an ion (v) can be monitored and plotted as a function of the external concentration, it is found to obey Michaelis—Menten kinetics given by:

$$v = \frac{V_{max} \cdot [S]}{K_m + [S]}$$

where, V_{max} = maximum velocity of uptake at which the carrier is saturated
K_m = Michaelis constant (concentration of ion giving half maximum rate of absorption
[S] = ionic concentration.

There have been many reports of ion uptake which follow Michaelis-Menten kinetics involving various plant species and metal ions (e.g. Mn^{2+}, Zn^{2+}, Cu^{2+}).

The Michaelis-Menten equation can undergo linear transformation, for example by taking reciprocals on both sides of the equation (Lineweaver and Burke plot, Fig. 3):

$$\frac{1}{v} = \frac{K_m}{V_{max}[S]} + \frac{1}{V_{max}}$$

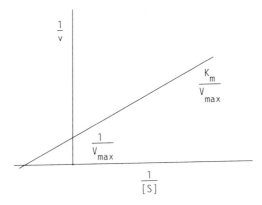

Fig. 3. Lineweaver and Burke plot.

At low ionic concentrations (< 1 m mol dm^{-3}) where simple Michaelis-Menten kinetics are followed, the mechanism is highly specific for a particular cation. When the ionic concentratiom $[S_{max}]$ corresponding to V_{max} is reached, all carrier sites for the cation are assumed to be occupied; the carrier system is saturated. When the external ion concentration exceeds $[S_{max}]$, then another uptake hyperbolic phase is found. Epstein (10) studied the uptake of labelled K^+ by excised barley roots over a wide range of KCl concentrations. $[S_{max}]$ for the first phase (system 1) was about 0.2 m mol dm^{-3}, the second phase (system 2) is multiphase, showing a complex of hyperbolic isotherms. There are other differences between the two systems:

System 1:   High affinity for K^+
K^+ uptake not affected by Na^+
Anions have little effect on K^+ uptake
Ca^{2+} stimulating

System 2:   Low affinity for K^+
K^+ uptake competitively inhibited by Na^+
K^+ uptake affected by anions
Ca^{2+} inhibiting

There has been some argument as to whether both mechanisms occur in the same membrane, or system 1 is at the plasmalemma, and system 2 at the tonoplast (Fig. 2). While it is generally agreed that system 1 occurs at the plasmelemma, most controversy has concerned the location of system 2. Epstein et al. (11-13) suggest that system 2 operates in parallel with system 1 in the plasmalemma, whereas Laties (14,15) has taken the view that system 2 is at the tonoplast. If this is true, then when $[S_{max}]$ is exceeded, the tonoplast and not the plasmalemma must be rate limiting for ion uptake. This means that at high concentrations, where system 2 operates, the plasmalemma must become more permeable to ions so that they enter the cytoplasm by diffusion at rates greater than V_{max} for system 1. Only if this assumption is made does the tonoplast become rate limiting. Bowling (16) has pointed out that the assumption that there is no cytoplasmic control over salt uptake is unwarranted, in fact there is a high degree of control by the outer membrane, even at high external concentrations.

3 TOXICITY AND TOLERANCE

3.1 Toxicity

Metals are important for healthy plant life, but excesses or deficiencies have profound effects on the growth and morphology of plants. Excessive concentrations of some metals in soils, which produce toxic symptoms, may come about in a variety of ways: the presence of naturally occurring ore bodies; exploitation of mineral resources; agricultural practices; and waste disposal.

Bowen (17) has classified toxic elements into three groups.

1. Very toxic: those elements such as Be, Cu, Hg, Ag, Sn, which are toxic at concentrationa of less than 1 ppm in the soil.
2. Moderately toxic: toxic symptoms become apparent at concentrations ranging from 1 - 100 ppm. These include most of the d-block elements and most of those from Groups III, IV, V and VI of the Periodic Table.
3. Scarcely toxic: this group includes most of the s-block elements and the halogens in addition to the macronutrients.

Metal toxicity in plants often results in changes in morphology such as dwarfism, abnormally shaped fruits, necrosis of the leaves and stunting of root growth. The physiology of metal toxicity in plants has been reviewed (18). The most common toxic effect is chlorosis. In an early study (19) the effects of some metal cations were monitored and the severity of the chlorosis was observed to be in the order:

$$Co^{2+} > Cu^{2+} > Zn^{2+} > Ni^{2+} > Cr^{3+} > Mn^{2+} > Pb^{2+}$$

However, other toxic symptoms were evident, principally dwarfing and necrosis, which were distinct from the induced chlorosis. On this basis a second order was established:

$$Ni^{2+} > Co^{2+} \gg Zn^{2+} > Cu^{2+} \gg Cr^{3+} \ = \ Mn^{2+}, \ Pb^{2+}$$

That the induced chlorosis was due to interference with iron metabolism was shown by painting the leaf surfaces with $FeSO_4$ solution, which restored chlorophyll production. The mechanism by which chlorosis is induced is not fully understood.

3.2 Indicator plants

Plants which are diagnostic of particular environmental conditions are known as indicator plants. The qualitative term metal indicator species can be used to describe species which grow over, and thus indicate, soils containing high concentrations of metals. Plants which grow on soils with metal concentrations which are normally toxic are metal tolerant, or metallophytes. Some of these plants exclude the toxic metals from their tissues, others assimilate the metals present to such a degree that thay are termed accumulators. An accumulator is defined (20) as having a metal concentration in the tissues greater than that in the soil.

The history of the use of plants as indicators of mineralisation is long, and geobotanical prospecting is now well established (21,22).

3.3 Metal tolerence

Various mechanisms of tolerance have been proposed to explain how some plants cope with toxic conditions, and how some species have developed tolerant ecotypes (23–25). Mechanisms are usually divided into external and internal types. The former covers those few situations where the metal is unavailable to the root (26). Internal mechanisms can be grouped loosely under four headings (26).

1. Metal is available to root but is not taken up
   e.g. alteration of cell wall membrane resulting in decreased permeability to toxic metal ion
2. Metal is taken up but is rendered harmless within the plant
   e.g. deposition in cell walls or vacuole
3. Metal is taken up but excreted
   e.g. by guttation, leaching or leaf fall
4. Metal is taken up but metabolism is altered to accomodate increased concentration of toxic metal
   e.g. increase of enzymes inhibited by metal.

Baker (27) has discussed three ways in which the response of plants to increasing
soil levels may be reflected in the metal concentrations in the aerial plant parts.
These are: accumulators, where metals are concentrated in plant tissues from high or
low background levels; indicators, where the metal in the plant parts is proportional
to that in the soil; and excluders, where the concentration of metal in the tops of
the plant is low and constant, over a wide range of soil concentrations. This last
type of response results from differential uptake and transport between root and
shoot.

4 STUDIES OF METAL TOLERANT PLANTS

4.1 Copper tolerant Armeria maritima

The sea pink or thrift, Armeria maritima, has long been recognised as a metal
indicator. In 1857 it was reported (28) as indicating the presence of copper in North
Wales. Anomalous plant communities of Armeria maritima and Minuartia verna occur over
the Coed-y-Brenin porphyry deposit (29-31). The largest anomaly is in the copper
impregnated Dolfrwynog Bog. Drainage from surrounding hills has lead to very high
concentrations of copper (20,000-30,000 ppm) (31), so that in the 19th century the
peat was worked as a copper deposit. The distributions of Armeria maritima and
Minuartia verna are clearly related to high copper levels in the soils.

A. maritima from the Bog was shown to be copper tolerant, by a standard root
elongation method (32). In contrast, plants from a maritime, non-copper site were not
tolerant to copper and their growth was seriously affected. Copper is found to
accumulate in the roots and is transported to the tops. 85% of the copper in the
roots remains in the outer portion. The roots of copper tolerant A. maritima contain
high levels of the amino acid proline (33), which is present not only in plants
growing in the bog, but also in plants grown from seeds collected from the bog, and
grown with or without added copper. The high proline concentrations were not found in
the roots of plants from the maritime, non-copper site. Nor were they found in the
roots of plants grown, with or without copper, from seed from the non-copper site
(34).

Thus the high proline content does not seem to be a response to toxic levels of
Cu, but rather an inherited characteristic. This is somewhat surprising since the
function of the proline might be as a constituent part of a metallothionein-type
protein, in that case it might be expected to result as a response to toxic levels of
Cu. Selection however, seems to occur fairly rapidly. For example, in a study of the
Californian monkey flower, Mimulus guttatus, it was found (35) that the roots of
non-tolerant plants were damaged, leading to a selection for copper tolerance on
copper soil at the germination and seedling stage. Copper tolerance appears to be
linked to specific copper binding proteins in yeast (36) and in a green alga (37).

4.2 The nickel accumulator, Hybanthus floribundus

Hybanthus floribundus grows over outcropping serpentenite in the Eastern
Goldfields area of Western Australia. It accumulates very high concentrations of
nickel in its tissues, up to 1.35% on a dry mass basis (38-41). Nickel is
concentrated in the leaves, and the majority of this nickel is water soluble.
Complexes of dibasic acids have been found in the aqueous extracts of H. floribundus
and other nickel accumulating plants (42-44). For a number of Ni accumulators, Ni
levels are correlated with concentrations of such acids, particularly of citric or
malic acid (44,45). Still and Williams (46) have discussed the selective accumulation
of Ni by plants, and have concluded that the selectivity occurs in the uptake by the
root. They point out that citrate or malate complexes cannot alone constitute the
selectivity mechanism. The difference in the thermodynamic stability of nickel and
cobalt complexes is only a factor of three, but for many Ni-accumulators, selectivity
for Ni over Co is more than two orders of magnitude, although the normal Ni:Co ratio
in serpentenite soils is about 7. Table 3 shows some data for the metal content of
soil and organs of Hybanthus floribundus collected from the same areas.

Table 3. Comparison of data for metal content of Hybanthus floribundus.

	Ni	Ni	Cu	Co	Zn
Metal conc (μg/g dry weight)					
Soil	770[a]	7000[b]	1000[b]	100[b]	50[b]
Root	316[a]	2925	19	53	600
Leaf	6542[a]	13250	15	46	32
Ratios of metal concentrations					
leaf:root	20.6	4.5	0.8	0.9	0.05
leaf:soil	8.4	1.9	0.015	0.5	0.6
Root:soil	0.42	0.42	0.02	0.5	13.2

[a] Results from ref. (47), root concentration averaged; [b] averaged rounded results
from ref. (39).

The data in Table 3 is limited and comes from a number of sources, nevertheless some tentative conclusions can be made.

(i)   The ratios of metal concentrations in the leaves to metal concentrations in the soil are: Ni, 4.5; Co, 0.9; Cu, 0.8; Zn, 0.5. Co and Cu appear thus to move freely in the plant. Ni accumulates in the leaves and Zn in the roots.

(ii)   Ni:Co ratios in the root are in the same range as those on the soil. Thus the "selectivity" for Ni, in that Ni is transported to, and accumulates in the leaves does not reside in the roots. As far as Co is concerned Hybanthus floribundus acts as an indicator in Baker's sense (27).

(iii) There appears to be a maximum loading of the storage sites in the leaves. The ratio of nickel in roots to that in soil for our sample (41) and Severne's sample (42) are identical (0.42). However, the ratio of Ni in leaves to Ni in soil is much higher (20.6) for Severne's sample than for ours (4.5). Our sample, collected from Widgiemooltha, where soil Ni is very high, probably has reached the maximum Ni loading in the leaf sites.

Histological examination has shown (41) that large epidermal cells in the leaves and main stems of the plant contain remarkable concentrations of Ni. More than half the Ni in the green parts of the plant is water soluble, and is probably associated with carbohydrates. During rainfall, leaching of the nickel could be a mechanism by which the plant rids itself of part of the Ni burden. In the Eastern Godfields area, the rain occurs in the cool winter period, the summers being hot and dry (39). Thus such leaching would occur in the non-growth period and would remove much of the Ni accumulated in the previous growing season.

4.3 The water hyacinth, Eichhornia crassipes

The water hyacinth, Eichhornia crassipes, is a free floating water plant which is found in many tropical and sub-tropical areas. It has a highly prolific vegetative reproduction system and has spread through many regions, clogging rivers, lakes and streams, competing for space with other aquatic weeds. These plants have been shown to be generally tolerant to a large number of metals and to organic compounds. They have been shown to remove substantial amounts of Ag, Co and Sr from solution. Other studies have ranged from Cu, Mn and Zn, to the more toxic elememts Cd, Pb, Hg and Ni (48-57).

One of the principal aims of our studies on the uptake of metals by the water hyacinth, is to investigate the uptake as a function of the chemical species. i.e. the ligands and the oxidation state of the metal. A series of experiments has been carried out using various complexes of the platinum group metals (58-60). We have shown that Pt, Pd, Ru, Rh, Ir and Os are taken into the plant tissues when added to nutrient media. Toxicities of the metal species vary and decrease in the following order:

Pt(II) ~ Pd(II) > Os(IV) ~ Ru(III) > Ir(III) ~ Pt(IV) > Rh(III)

——→

decreasing order of toxicity for metals applied in nutrient solution at 10 ppm

With the water hyacinth Pt(II) is much more toxic than is Rh(III) which appears to have a tonic effect, and becomes phytotoxic at concentrations of greater than 30 ppm. When treated with 10 ppm of Rh(III) the biomass of the water hyacinth increased some 7% more than control plants grown under the same conditions, but without Rh.

Toxic effects, as well as growth restriction, were noticed on the leaves of plants treated with cis[Pt(NH$_3$)$_2$Cl$_2$], these were mainly longitudinal brown streaks, which were particularly noticeable on the newer leaves and leaves of the vegetative daughter plants. These effects were also observed when water hyacinths were treated with Pt in other complex compounds. Distinct colour differences were noticed in the colour of roots of the daughters of rhodium treated plants: the red colour may be due to the presence of rhodium complex or to the enhanced production of a natural pigment.

Table 4 shows the amount of platinum taken up into the plant organs on treatment with the various complexes. In general the applied metals accumulate in the roots, howevever, after treatment with the cationic Pt complex [Pt(NH$_3$)$_4$]Cl$_2$ and the rhodium complex, the metals are more evenly distributed throughout the whole plant. The effects of platinum metal treatment on the concentrations of Ca, Cu, Fe, Mn and Zn are very small. Water hyacinths have variable mineral composition and morphology (57,61–65). Our control plants, all grown from the same stock, have a largely constant composition showing the same trends. Both Ca and Mn have higher concentrations in the the leaves than in the roots. Cu, Fe and Zn are in higher concentrations in the roots than in the tops. The results show a remarkable consistency between the metal content of the control plants and those treated with platinum and rhodium (61). The toxicity of platinum does not appear to be involved with the uptake of these elements.

The results of sequential extraction of the dried plant material from the treatment of water hyacinths with cis [Pt(NH$_3$)$_2$Cl$_2$], show that in the leaves and floats almost half the platinum present (48%) is insoluble and is associated with cellulose and lignin. Lesser amounts are associated with soluble pectate (29%) and 16% is removed by the enzyme pronase, and thus can be considered as associated with proteins and/or amino acids. In the roots of the treated plants the values were 35%, 9.5%and 14% respectively. More platinum in the roots appeared in the fraction containing water soluble low molecular weight materials. Thus in the water hyacinth, the cell wall acts as an ion exchange medium, the combined percentage of total Pt in the cell wall material together with water soluble pectates accounts for 49% in the roots. This figure rises to 69% in the leaves.

Very little is known or understood concerning the extent to which platinum metal complexes can alter the growth patterns of plants. It seems certain, however that if such complexes reach plant roots in a soluble form, they can be taken up into plant tissues.

Table 4. Platinum and rhodium uptake by water hyacinth grown in nutrient solution with added complexes (complex concentration = 0.5 μg cm^{-3}(ppm)). (Data from ref. (61)).

complex	Plant part	No.	Biomass dry/g	Pt/Rh conc μg g^{-1} (ppm)	Total Pt μg
Control	leaves	22L	1.24	–	–
	floats	22F	1.01	–	–
	roots	22R	0.42	–	–
$K_2[PtCl_4]$	leaves	19L	0.87	62	54
	floats	19F	0.66	112	74
	roots	19R	0.39	1694	661
$PtCl_4$	leaves	20L	1.02	100	102
	floats	20F	0.83	175	145
	roots	20R	0.39	1588	619
$[Pt(NH_3)_4]Cl_2$	leaves	21L	1.21	102	123
	floats	21F	1.14	123	140
	roots	21R	0.50	242	121
cis $[Pt(NH_3)_2Cl_2]$	leaves	15L	–	43	–
	floats	15F	–	109	–
	roots	15R	–	537	–
$Na_3[RhCl_6]$	leaves	16L	3.02	183	525
	floats	16F	2.85	59	168
	roots	16R	1.53	118	181

4 REFERENCES

(1)   E. Epstein, Mineral Nutrition in Plants, Wiley, London 1972.

(2)   E. J. Hewitt, T .A. Smith, Plant Mineral Nutrition, English University Press, London 1975.

(3)   D. J. F. Bowling, Uptake of Ions by Plant Roots, Chapman and Hall, London 1976.

(4)   W. L. Lindsay in E. W. Carson (Ed.) The Plant Root and its Environment, Charlotsville University Press, Virginia 1974, p. 509.

(5)   M. C. Drew, P. H. Nye, Plant and Soil, 31 (1969) 407-424.

(6)   J. B. Passioura, Plant and Soil, 18 (1963) 225-238.

(7)   P. H. Nye, F. H. C. Marriott, Trans. 9th Cong. Int. Soil Sci. Soc., 1 (1968) 127-134.

(8)   E. Epstein, Plant Physiol., 30 (1955) 529-535.

(9)   G. E. Briggs, A. B. Hope, M. G. Pitman, J. Exper. Bot., 9 (1958) 128-141.

(10)   E. Epstein, Nature (Lond.), 212 (1966) 1324-1327.

(11)   R. M. Welch, E. Epstein, Proc. Nat. Acad. Sci. (USA), 61 (1968) 447-453.

(12)   R. M. Welch, E. Epstein, Plant Physiol., 44 (1969) 301-304.

(13)   E. Epstein, New Phytol., 71 (1972) 873-874.

(14)   K. Torii, G. G. Laties, Plant Physiol., 41 (1966) 863-870.

(15)   U. Luttge, G. G. Laties, Planta (Berlin), 74 (1967) 173-187.

(16)   Reference 3, Chapter 5.

(17)   H. J. M. Bowen, Trace Elements in Biochemistry, Macmillan, London 1966.

(18)   C. D. Foy, R. L. Chaney. M. C. White, Ann. Rev. Plant Physiol., 29 (1978) 511-566.

(19) E. J. Hewitt, _Nature (Lond.)_, 161 (1948) 498–490.

(20) P. J. Peterson, Int. Symp. Uptake Util. Metals by Plants, Phytochem. Soc. Hull (1981).

(21) H. L. Cannon, _Science (NY)_, 132 (1960) 591–598.

(22) R. R. Brooks, Geobotany and Biogeochemistry in Mineral Exploration, Harper and Row, New York 1972.

(23) J. Antonovics, J. D. Bradshaw, R. G. Turner, _Adv. Ecol. Res._, 7 (1971) 1–85.

(24) S. Wainwright, H. W. Woolhouse in M. J. Chadwick, G.T. Goodman (Eds.), Ecology and Resource Degredation and Renewal, Blackwell, Oxford 1975.

(25) H. W. Woolhouse, _Chem. Brit._, 16 (1980) 72–76.

(26) M. E. Farago, _Coord. Chem. Revs._, 36 (1981) 155–182.

(27) A. J. M. Baker, _J. Plant Nutrit._, 3 (1981) 643–654.

(28) W. J. Henwood, _Edin. New Phil. J._, 5 (1857) 61–13.

(29) R. Rice, G. J. Sharp, _Trans. Inst. Min. Metall._ (Sect. B: Applied Earth Sci.), 85 (1976) 1–13.

(30) M. M. Cole, _Trans. Inst. Min. Metal._ (Sect B.: Applied Earth Sci.), 89 (1980) 73–91.

(31) M. E. Farago, W. A. Mullen, M. M. Cole, R. F. Smith, _Environ. Pollut._, (Series A), 21 (1980) 225–244.

(32) T. McNeilly, A. D. Bradshaw, _Evolution (Lancaster, PA)_, 22 (1968) 108–116.

(33) M. E. Farago, W. A. Mullen, _Inorg. Chim. Acta_, 32 (1979) L93–94.

(34) M. E. Farago, W. A. Mullen, _Inorg. nucl. Chem. Lett._, 17 (1981) 275–277.

(35) A. D. Allen, P. M. Sheppard, _Proc. Roy. Soc. Lond. B_, 177 (1971) 177–196.

(36) S. Naiki, S. Yamagata, _Plant Cell Physiol._, 17 (1976) 1281–1295.

(37) B. A. Silverberg, P. M. Stokes, L. B. Ferstenberg, J. Cell Biol., 69 (1976) 210-114.

(38) B. C. Serverne, R. R. Brooks, Planta (Berlin), 103 (1972) 91-94.

(39) M. M. Cole, J. appl. Ecol., 10 (1972) 269-320.

(40) M. E. Farago, A. J. Clark, M. J. Pitt, Inorg. Chim. Acta, 24 (1977) 53-56.

(41) M. E. Farago, I. E. D. A. W. Mahmoud, Min. and Environ., 5 (1984) 113-121.

(42) P. Pelosi, R. Fiorentini, C. Gallopini, Agr. Biol. Chem., 40 (1976) 1641-1642.

(43) J. Lee, R. D. Reeves, R. R. Brooks, T. Jaffre, Phytochem., 17 (1978) 1033-1035.

(44) W. J. Kersten, R. R. Brooks, R. D. Reeves, T. Jaffre, Phytochem., 19 (1980) 1963-1965.

(45) T. Jaffre, W. J. Kersten, R. R. Brooks, R. D. Reeves, Proc. Roy. Soc. Lond. B, 205 (1979) 385-394.

(46) E. R. Still, R. J. P. Williams, J. Inorg. Biochem., 13 (1980) 35-40.

(47) B. C. Serverne, Nature (Lond.), 248 (1974) 807-808.

(48) C. E. Boyd, Econ. Bot.,24 (1970) 95-103.

(49) C. E. Boyd, E. Scarsbrook, Aquat. Bot., 1 (1975) 253-261.

(50) B. C. Wolverton, R. C. McDonald, New Scientist, 71 (1976)318-320.

(51) B. C. Wolverton, R. C. McDonald. Ambio, 8 (1979) 2-9.

(52) B. C. Wolverton, R. C. McDonald, NASA ReportTM-X72727 (1975).

(53) C. R. Johnson, T. J. Sheehand, Proc. FL State Hort. Soc., 90 (1977) 118-119.

(54) K. Tatsuyama, H. Egawa, H. Yamamoto, M. Nakamura, Zasso Kenkyu, 24 (1979) 260-264.

(55) K. Tatsuyama, H. Egawa, T. Yamagishi, Zasso Kenkyu, 22 (1977) 151-156.

(56) L. Widyanto, M. Clark, L. Thompson, F. Shore, Practical Applications of Biochemistry in Developing Countries, Proc. 1st. FAOB Symp. (1978) p 189.

(57) C. E. Boyd, D. H. Vickers, Hydrobiologia, 38 (1971) 409-404.

(58) M. E. Farago, P. J. Parsons, in S. J. Lippard (Ed.), Platinum. Gold and other Chemotherapeutic Agents: Chemistry and Biochemistry. ACS symposium Sries No. 209 (1983) 297-311.

(59) M. E. Farago, P. J. Parsons, Inorg. Chim. Acta, (Bioinorg.) 79 (1983) 233-234.

(60) M. E. Farago, P. J. Parsons, Environ. Technol. Lett., 6 (1985) 165-174.

(61) M. E. Farago, P. J. Parsons, in D. Hemphill (Ed.), Proc. 19th Ann. Conf. on Trace Elements in Environ. Health, (1985), in the press.

(62) T. N. Cooley, D. F. Martin, J. Inorg. nucl. Chem., 39 (1977) 1893-1896.

(63) T. N. Cooley, D. F. Martin, W. C. Durden, B. D. Perkins, Water Res., (1979) 343-348.

(64) T. N. Cooley, D. F. Martin, J. Inorg. nucl. Chem., 43 (1980) 151-153.

(65) K. J. Thomas, in G. Thyagarajam (Ed.), Proc. Int. Conf. on Water Hyacinth, United Nations Environment Programme, Nairobi (1984) pp 161-164.

The Participation of Hemoglobin and Myoglobin in The Reduction of Fe(III) and Cu(II)

Paul Saltman, Lois Eguchi, and Kaspar Hegetschweiler

Department of Biology, University of California, San Diego,
La Jolla, California, 92093, U.S.A.

SUMMARY

The proposal that hemoglobin (Hb), myoglobin (Mb) and other heme proteins may participate directly in the reduction of Fe(III) has been confirmed by _in vitro_ studies which characterize the kinetics and mechanisms of the reaction. Further, it has been demonstrated that Cu(II) can also be reduced by Hb and Mb. The mechanism for the reaction involves an outer-sphere electron transfer. One of the binding sites on sperm whale Mb has been identified as histidines 113 and 116. Both chelated and ionic Cu(II) and chelated Fe(III) perturbs these histidines as characterized by NMR spectroscopy. Superoxide does not participate in the reduction. The nature of the chelating agent presenting the metals to the heme protein profoundly influences the rate of the reaction. Not only are the stability constants of the chelates important, but their redox potentials also play a fundamental role. ATP is the most effective endogenous Fe(III) chelator. It is as effective as nitrilotriacetate (NTA) in the reaction. Zn(II) and Ni(II) bind at the same site and inhibit the reduction of Fe(III). In the presence of Cu(II), there is an enhancement of the rate of Fe(III) reduction. This phenomenon may explain the iron/copper interaction observed in animals and humans. Hb and Mb, heretofore considered primarily oxygen binding and transport proteins, thus play a fundamental role in the redox reactions of trace elements in the cell.

1. INTRODUCTION

There are eight fundamental metabolic and chemical parameters which
govern the metabolism of trace elements by all bacterial, plant and
animal systems. These include: availability, solubility, permeability,
ligand exchange, transport, assimilation, storage and excretion (1).
Our laborabory has primarily been concerned with the chemistry, biochemistry, physiology, and nutrition of iron. Quite clearly, each of the
parameters enumerated above profoundly affect iron metabolism of an
organism. As with several of the trace elements, iron serves four basic
functions in all living cells. It is responsible for the redox reactions of heme and non-heme iron enzymes. It is responsible for O_2 transport and storage primarily as Hb and Mb. It is involved in the catalytic
centers of several enzymes including an acid phosphatase and aconitase.
Iron is also an important structural unit in storage and transport
proteins.

Under aerobic conditions, iron exists primarily in the ferric form
(2). The mechanisms by which Fe(III) is reduced to Fe(II) have been of
long-standing interest to biochemists. Under anaerobic conditions, it
is possible to reduce Fe(III) using either $FMNH_2$ or $FADH_2$ (3). Relatively high non-physiological concentrations of these reduced flavins
are needed. Under aerobic conditions, superoxide, thiols, ascorbate
and other strong reducing agents have been demonstrated in vitro to
participate in Fe(III) reduction. It is clear that such reduction is
necessary prior to the incorporation of Fe(II) into heme and non-heme
iron proteins. It is not clear whether such a reduction process is required for the mobilization of Fe(III) into and out of the iron storage
protein, ferritin.

Early studies by Egyed et al. (4) indicated that Hb could serve as a
reducing agent in the removal of Fe(III) from transferrin to form Fe(II)-
bipyridine$_3$(bipy). Subsequently, we showed that rabbit erythrocytes
treated with a specific divalent ionophore, A23187, were able to mobilize intracellular radioactive Fe(II) out of the cell in the presence of
extracellular chelating agents such as EDTA (Fig. 1) (5). The strength
of Fe(III) binding by the external chelator governed the extent of efflux.
These experiments proved either that the intracellular environment maintains Fe(II), or that the intracellular equilibrium between Fe(III) and
Fe(II) provides Fe(II) to the ionophore at a rate which exceeds external
oxidation and subsequent chelation. When Hb was oxidized with nitrite
or blocked with CO, the efflux of Fe(II) was inhibited (Fig. 2). This
result provided strong evidence that Hb itself might be the direct

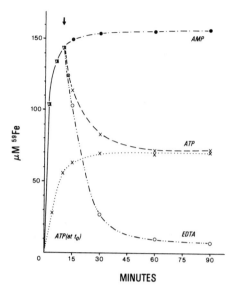

Fig. 1.   Effect of different chelators on ^{59}Fe(II) uptake and efflux
by erythrocytes in presence of A23187.   (From Ref. 5)

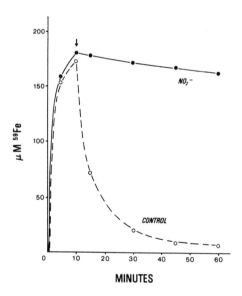

Fig. 2.   Effect of NaNO$_2$ on ^{59}Fe(II) uptake and efflux by erythrocytes
in the presence of A23187.   (From Ref. 5)

reductant of intracellular Fe(III). Subsequent experiments showed that both Hb and Mb were able to facilitate, _in vitro_, the reduction of Fe(III) (6).

There is an extensive literature regarding the ability of Hb and Mb to reduce both Fe(III) and Cu(II) (7). The standard assay for Hb, the Drabkin reaction, relies on the rapid oxidation of Hb by $Fe(CN)_6^{3-}$ to metHb and subsequently, cyanometHb. Early experiments by Antonini, Brunori and others (8) studied the reaction of Hb as a reducing agent. They made no mention of its potential physiological and biological importance. Rifkin and his collaborators have studied the Cu(II) reaction with Hb and demonstrated that only two of the four heme groups participate in the reduction of ionic Cu(II) (9). Further, a mechanism was proposed involving either an inner-sphere electron transfer to the heme iron or an outer-sphere transfer to the edge of the porphyrin ring (10).

The research reported here addresses four basic issues: the mechanism of the redox reaction, the effect of chelating agents on the rate of reduction, the nature of the binding site(s) on the heme protein, and the interaction between metals.

2.   THE MECHANISM OF THE REACTION

The rate of Fe(III)-NTA reduction by Hb was followed using two simultaneous means of assay. The formation of metHb was followed by measuring its absorbance at 630 nm. The reaction in the presence of bipy produced a chromogenic Fe(II) complex which was measured at 520 nm. Fig. 3 shows a time course of metHb and $Fe(II)-(bipy)_3$ concentrations and indicates identical rates of formation.

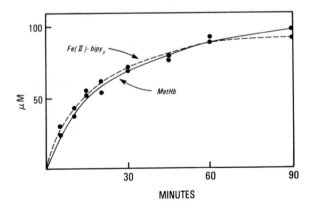

Fig. 3   Time course of methemoglobin and Fe(II)-(bipy)$_3$ formation.
(From Ref. 6)

The possibility that superoxide, generated by the reaction of O_2
with heme iron, mediates the reduction of Fe(III)-NTA was tested by
carrying out the reaction anaerobically.   Fig. 4 demonstrates that the
reaction proceeds more rapidly in the absence of O_2 than in its presence.

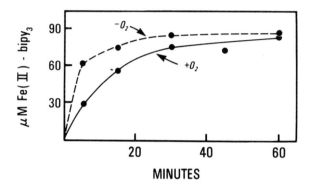

Fig. 4.   Effect of O_2 on hemoglobin reduction of Fe(III)-NTA.
(From Ref. 6)

Further evidence that superoxide is not involved was demonstrated by
the inability of superoxide dismutase to inhibit the redox reaction.
Superoxide generated from xanthine oxidase is able to reduce Fe(III)-
NTA.   However, unlike Hb, superoxide dismutase greatly affects the
reduction.

The overall reaction scheme for the reduction of Fe(III) is:

$$O_2\text{-Fe(II)-Hb} \rightleftharpoons \text{Fe(II)-Hb} + O_2$$
$$\text{Fe(II)-Hb} + \text{Fe(III)-chelator} \rightleftharpoons \text{Fe(III)-Hb} + \text{Fe(II)-chelator}$$

A similar mechanism was proposed by Cassatt et al. (11).

Consideration of the molecular structure of the various Fe(III) chelates makes it unlikely that the metal could form an inner-sphere coordination with the heme iron.   Thus, as a first approximation, the
metal complex must bind at some other coordinating site favoring an
outer-sphere electron transfer mechanism.   More will be said of this
later.

3. THE ROLE OF CHELATORS IN THE REACTION MECHANISM

A variety of synthetic and natural chelating agents were assayed for their ability to present Fe(III) to Hb for subsequent reduction, Table 1.

Table 1. Effect of chelators on Fe(III) reduction

Chelator (Fe:chelator)	Fe(II)-(bipy)$_3$/h
	μM
NTA (1:1)	108
ATP (1:10)	105
EDTA (1:1)	37
Citrate (1:20)	21
Citrate (1:1)	27
Citrate (1:1) + 50 mM ATP	105

Of particular interest is the hexacyanide complex of Fe(III) (not shown in table) which is reduced within seconds. It is the most rapid complexing agent assayed. Both low-molecular weight complexes of citrate either as the mononuclear form (1:20) or as the polynuclear configuration (1:1) are relatively unreactive. Of most interest to us is the reactivity of the ATP complex. Not only can ATP present Fe(III) effectively to Hb, but it can also mobilize Fe(III) from polynuclear Fe(III)-citrate for reduction.

4. NATURE OF THE BINDING SITES

With the cooperation of Dr. Peter Wright of the Scripps Clinic and Research Foundation, we have used proton NMR techniques to study the interaction between small inorganic complexes and metalloproteins. The instrument used was a 500 MHz FT NMR spectrometer with which we were able to identify significant interaction between the metals, Fe(III) and Cu(II), and histidines 113 and 116 on Mb. At present we are unable to clearly delineate the binding sites on Hb. The kinetics and reaction mechanism of Mb are similar to those previously observed for Hb with respect to the reduction of Fe(III).

Corresponding experiments were carried out on the effect of increasing concentrations of Fe(III)-NTA on the rate of reduction by Hb, Fig. 5. It was found by kinetic analysis that the K_m is 2.0 mM which is in reasonable agreement with the results for Mb using the NMR technique.

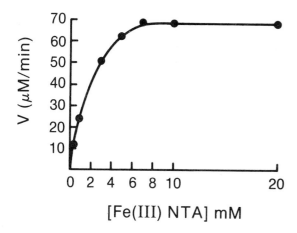

Fig. 5.   Effect of increasing concentrations of Fe(III)-NTA on initial
          rate of reduction by hemoglobin.

5.   INTERACTION OF HEMOGLOBIN AND MYOGLOBIN WITH OTHER METAL IONS

The rate of reduction of ionic or chelated Cu(II) is very rapid by
both proteins. We confirmed the observations of Rifkind et al. (9)
that when ionic Cu(II) is presented to Hb, only two of the hemes are
oxidized. However, Cu(II)-bathocuproine is able to oxidize all four
of the hemes. When Cu(II) is the presenting chelate at concentrations
greater than 1 Cu:1 heme, Hb precipitates and the reaction is blocked.

One of the most interesting observations to emerge from our studies
is the interaction between iron and copper. Cu(II) enhances the rate
of Fe(III)-NTA reduction and the oxidation of Hb, Fig. 6. Kinetic analysis of this phenomenon reveals that there is an alteration in the
K_m of hemoglobin for Fe(III)-NTA. It has long been known that copper
affects the metabolism of iron. Indeed, copper deficiency produces a
well characterized anemia. It has been proposed that Cu influences
Fe(II) oxidation by ceruloplasmin. An alternative proposal for the
mechanism by which the   copper   deficiency manifests anemia is to
decrease the rate of Fe(III) reduction. Thus, copper may manifest a
profound consequence on Fe(III) mobilization from depot tissues within
the cell for subsequent incorporation into heme and non-heme iron proteins. The rate of Fe(III) reduction is strongly inhibited by the presence of Zn(II) and Ni(II). It is quite possible that interactions of
these metal ions with iron observed in nutritional experiments could be
caused at the level of Fe(III) reduction.

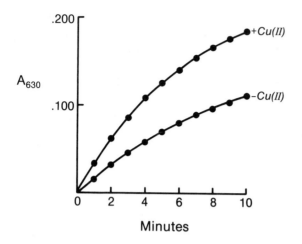

Fig. 6.   Effect of $CuSO_4$ on the initial rate of reduction of Fe(III)-
NTA by hemoglobin.

6. CONCLUSIONS

Our observations correlate well with the work of Dr. Harry Gray and
his collaborators who have also studied the ability of Mb, Hb and other
heme proteins to participate in outer-sphere electron transfer reactions
(12). The mechanism is not completely understood. It would appear that
electrons are able to reversibly flow from the reduced heme iron to the
amino acid residues of the protein backbone and there, by an outer-
sphere transfer, be accepted by either Fe(III) or Cu(II). The binding
site on Mb is defined as histidines 113 and 116. It remains to be seen
whether there are other secondary sites on Mb. The nature of the binding sites on Hb is not clear. Nor is there a chemical understanding of
the precipitation of Hb with concentrations greater than 1 Cu per heme.

Although it is clear that Hb does participate in the transport, assimilation and mobilization of iron in red cells, it is not clear what
heme proteins, if any, function in liver and spleen which are the primary sites of iron metabolism in the intact animal. Perhaps cytochromes
P_{450} or b_5 are the cellular electron donors in such systems where Mb
and Hb are low or nonexistent.

Chelating agents play a fundamental role in the reaction mechanism.
The ability of ATP to function as an endogenous Fe(III) chelate is indicated. Other endogenous low-molecular weight complexing agents involved in the mobilization and transport of iron remain to be identified.

Hb and Mb, heretofore considered primarily as O_2 transport proteins, are potent reducing agents for Fe(III) and Cu(II) within biological systems. The mechanism involves an outer-sphere electron transfer in which an electron moves along a relatively long distance, approximately 21 Å, from the heme iron to the site of metal reduction. Specific metal binding sites on the protein surface are involved for optimal reduction. Physical and chemical parameters, redox potentials, binding as a function of metal chelation and site specificity remain to be determined.

ACKNOWLEDGMENTS

This work was supported by Research Grant AM-12386 from the United States Public Health Service. L. Eguchi was a recipient of a Predoctoral Award 5T32 AM-07233 from the United States Public Health Service.

REFERENCES

1.   P. Saltman, J. Hegenauer and L. Strause in O. M. Rennert and W. Y. Chen (Eds.), Metabolism of Trace Elements, Vol. I, CRC Press, Florida 1984, p. 1-16.

2.   T. Spiro and P. Saltman in A. Jacobs and W. Worwood (Eds.), Iron in Biochemistry and Medicine, Academic Press, London 1974, pp. 1-28.

3.   R. R. Crichton, Trends Biochem. Sci. 9 (1984) 283-286.

4.   A. Egyed, A. May and S. Jacobs, Biochim. Biophys. Acta. 629 (1980) 391-398.

5.   A. Egyed and P. Saltman, Biol. Trace Element Res. 6 (1984) 357-364.

6.   L. Eguchi and P. Saltman, J. Biol. Chem. 259 (1984) 14337-14338.

7.   E. Antonini, M. Brunori and J. Wyman, Biochemistry 4 (1965) 545-551.

8.   E. Antonini and M. Brunori. Hemoglobin and Myoglobin in their Reaction with Ligands, American Elsevier, New York 1971.

9.   J. M. Rifkind, L. D. Lauer, S. H. Chiang and N. C. Li, Biochemistry 15 (1976) 5337-5343.

10.   M. A. Agustin and J. K. Yandell, Inorganica Chim. Acta, $\underline{37}$ (1979) 11-18.

11.   J. C. Cassatt, C. P. Marini and J. W. Bender, Biochemistry $\underline{14}$ (1975) 5470-5475.

12.   R. Margalit, I. Recht and H. B. Gray, J. Am. Chem. Soc., $\underline{105}$ (1983) 301-302.

Vanadium Metabolism. Vanadyl(IV) Electron Paramagnetic Resonance Spectroscopy of Selected Tissues in The Rat

N. Dennis Chasteen[*], Ellen M. Lord[*] and Henry J. Thompson[#]

Departments of [*]Chemistry and [#]Animal and Nutritional Sciences,
University of New Hampshire, Durham, N.H. 03824, USA

SUMMARY

   Electron paramagnetic resonance spectra of the stomach, duodenum, liver, spleen, kidney, lung, feces, and urine of female Sprague-Dawley rats maintained on an AIN-76 diet supplemented with 25 ppm vanadium show well-defined signals due to the VO^{2+} ion. The EPR spectra and other data from our laboratories are discussed in terms of the metabolism of this biologically active element.

1 INTRODUCTION

   The trace element vanadium has attracted considerable attention in recent years owing to its physiological and biochemical activity (1,2). Vanadium is a potent inhibitor of numerous phosphate metabolizing enzymes including most ATPases, phosphotransferases, nucleases, and phosphatases (1,2). In addition, this element has been shown in test animals to inhibit cholesterol biosynthesis, act as a diuretic, influence cardiac muscle contraction, and behave as an insulin mimetic agent, among other effects (1,2).

   We have had a long standing interest in the biochemistry vanadium, especially in the characterization of vanadium complexes with various proteins and in the use of VO^{2+} as an EPR spin probe of such complexes (3). Because of its broad range of physiological activity, we have recently initiated studies of vanadium as a possible cancer preventative agent. Our preliminary findings suggest that dietary vanadyl(IV) sulfate is an effective inhibitor of N-methyl-N-nitrosourea induced mammary gland carcinogenesis in the female rat (4). Accordingly, we have undertaken an investi-

gation of vanadium metabolism with the long range goal of understanding the inhibition of chemically induced carcinogenesis.

Here we report representative EPR spectra obtained with tissues of rats maintained on diets supplemented with 25 ppm vanadium and discuss our findings in relationship to the known metabolism of this element. The metabolism of vanadium in the
rat has been extensively studied by Sabbioni and co-workers (e.g. 5-8). Our studies
confirm their results and provide new insight into the chemical form of vanadium
in-vivo.

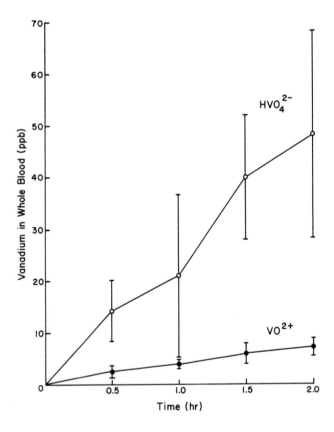

Fig. 1.   Concentration of vanadium in blood as a function of time following gastric
           intubation of solutions of vanadyl(IV) and vanadate(V) salts. Most points
           are an average value for four animals (two male, two female).

2 MATERIALS AND METHODS

Twenty-five virgin female Sprague-Dawley rats at 50 days of age were maintained on a casein based American Institute of Nutrition diet (AIN-76) supplemented with 15 ppm V as high purity vanadyl(IV) sulfate (Aldrich) and given water ad libitum. After 28 days, the supplementation was increased to 25 ppm. Urine and fecal samples were collected for five day periods from animals housed in metabolism cages. After 180 days, the experiment was terminated and the animals sacrificed.

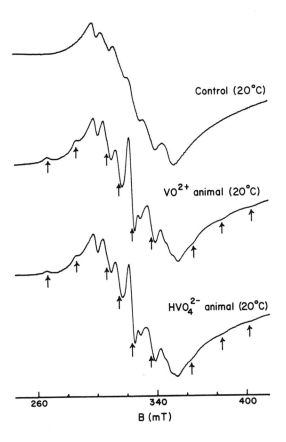

Fig. 2.   EPR spectra of fecal pellets. Arrows denote some of the vanadium lines.

To avoid oxidation of vanadium(IV) to vanadium(V), animals were dissected in a nitrogen filled glove bag. The excised tissues were immediately frozen in liquid nitrogen in a nitrogen atmosphere and stored in a sealed jar over dry ice until used. X-band electron paramagnetic resonance spectra were obtained at room temperature in a

quartz flat cell or tissue cell or at -165°C in quartz tubes (3mm i.d., 4mm o.d.) on
Varian E-4 or E-9 spectrometers interfaced to a MINC-23 (Digital Equipment Corporation)
laboratory computer for signal averaging. Typical instrument parameters employed
were: field set = 3300 G; scan range = 2000 G; time constant = 3.0 s; scan time =
16 min; modulation amplitude = 10 G; microwave power = 4 mW for -165°C spectra or
200 mW for room-Temperature spectra; and gain = 1 X 10^3 to 1 X 10^4.

Gastric intubation experiments were performed on male and female rats by administering 25 µg V per 250 g body weight as $VOSO_4$ or NH_4VO_3 radio-labeled with [48]V in
a 5% glucose solution at approximately pH 2 and 8, respectively. The $VOSO_4$ solution
also contained 1 mM ascorbic acid to ensure that the vanadium remained in the reduced VO^{2+} form. Approximately 1 ml per animal of the 25 ppm V solution was intubated.
Animals were fasted for 24 hr prior to intubation. Drinking water was provided <u>ad</u>
<u>libitum</u>. Whole blood and the cellular and serum fractions were gamma counted for
[48]V.

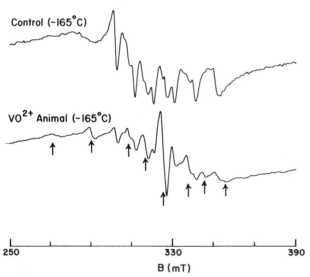

Fig. 3.   EPR spectra of duodenum plus contents. The prominent VO^{2+} lines are
indicated by arrows. Mn^{2+} lines are present in both samples.

3 RESULTS AND DISCUSSION

Figure 1 shows the vanadium concentration in blood following gastric intubation of
vanadyl(IV) sulfate or ammonium metavanadate. 91 ± 9% (9 animals) of the vanadium
was found associated with the plasma fraction. Similar results have been reported
after direct injection of vanadium into the blood stream (6,7). Chromatography and
electrophoresis of plasma in our laboratories and elsewhere (6,8) indicates that 40 -
50% of vanadium is associated with the iron transport protein transferrin. Recovery

from the Sephadex columns is incomplete so these values should be considered lower
limits. Vanadium is known to bind to the specific sites of transferrin <u>in-vitro</u> as
either vanadium(IV) or vanadium(V)(9,10). The metal probably exists in both oxidation
states in blood as a result of the oxygen tension and the presence of reducing agents
such as ascorbate and catecholamines. There is evidence that interconversion between
vanadium oxidation states may occur in blood <u>in-vivo</u> (11).

The preliminary results in Figure 1 suggest selective uptake of vanadium(V) relative to vanadium(IV), a result in accord with the feeding studies of others (12).
Preferential absorption of iron as Fe(II) relative to Fe(III) is a well known phenomenon. Selectivity for vanadium by oxidation state is perhaps not surprising in
view of the fact that VO^{2+} and Fe^{3+} have similar coordination chemistries, both
forming very stable complexes with oxygen donor ligands and readily hydrolyzing in
the absence of such complexing agents (2,3). The opposite is true of V(V) and Fe(II).

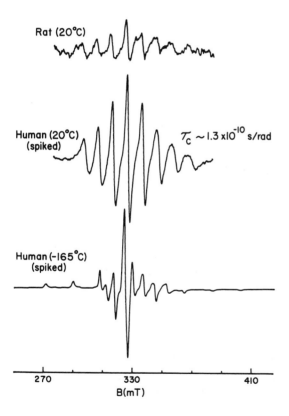

Fig. 4.   EPR spectra of rat and human urine samples.

The low concentration of vanadium in the circulation when either salt is employed (Fig. 1) suggests that only a few percent of the intubated vanadium is systemically absorbed. A significant fraction of vanadium is known to clear slowly from the circulation following injection (6) so the blood levels are an approximate indication of uptake. The toxicology literature indicates relatively inefficient uptake of orally administered vanadium (1,2,12,13).

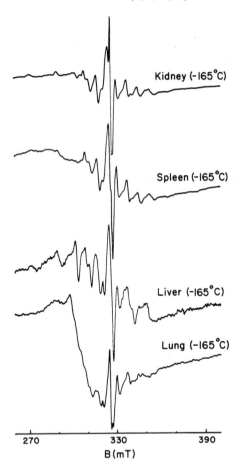

Fig. 5.   EPR spectra of organ tissues containing vanadium in the 1-10 ppm range. The spectra of kidney and spleen are essentially that of a VO^{2+}-ferritin complex.

Low systemic absorption is further indicated by EPR spectra of fecal pellets of animals on AIN-76 diets supplemented with either $VOSO_4$ or NH_4VO_3 (Fig. 2). In addition to the six-line pattern attributable to Mn^{2+} shown for the control, the feces of animals maintained on either vanadium salt also show strong VO^{2+} lines denoted by arrows. (The analysis of VO^{2+} EPR spectra is discussed in reference 3). Evidently most or all of the vanadium(V) from dietary NH_4VO_3 undergoes a one electron reduction to form VO^{2+} in the gastrointestinal tract. The contents of the stomach and duodenum of animals on either salt show EPR lines from VO^{2+} (Fig. 3). Consistent with this finding is the observation by EPR that vanadate(V) is quantitatively reduced to VO^{2+} when NH_4VO_3 is mixed with the AIN-76 diet at pH 1.5, the approximate pH of the stomach. Thus components of the diet can readily reduce vanadium(V) to vanadium(IV). The above results are in accord with the fact that vanadate(V) is a rather strong oxidant at pH 7 and below.

The vanadium(IV) in fecal pellets appears to be associated with dietary fiber or other insoluble components. The VO^{2+} EPR spectrum (Fig. 2) is unaltered in intensity or lineshape when pellets are extracted with water. The low bioavailability of Fe^{3+} is in part due to its strong association with dietary fiber (e.g. 14). The same may be true of VO^{2+}.

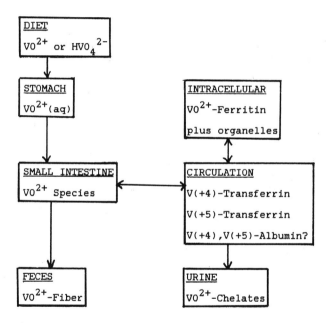

Fig. 6.   Schematic outline of vanadium metabolism in the rat.

It is known that only a small fraction of systemically absorbed vanadium is excreted in the bile, the urine being the major route of vanadium elimination (5,6). Vanadium appears in the urine within a few hours of addition of either $VOSO_4$ or NH_4VO_3 to the diet as shown by EPR spectroscopy (Fig. 4, upper spectrum). The same spectrum is obtained when either vanadium(IV) or vanadium(V) is added directly to human urine (Fig. 4, middle spectrum) indicating that reduction of HVO_4^{2-} to VO^{2+} occurs. The short rotational correlation time of 0.13 ns calculated from the 20°C spectrum of the formed complex suggests a molecular weight in the 300-500 range. Minor species are also presented as evidenced by small peaks in the wings of frozen solution spectra (Fig. 4, bottom). Both high and low molecular weight vanadium complexes have been observed when urine is chromatographed (6).

The EPR spectra of kidney, spleen, liver, and lung at -165°C are shown in Figure 5. These organs are known to accumulate vanadium (1,2,6,7) and are also rich in iron. VO^{2+} lines are observed for all tissues in addition to those of Mn^{2+}, and possibly of Cu^{2+} and Fe^{3+} as well. The VO^{2+} lines are most clearly seen in the spectra of kidney and spleen and to a lesser extent in liver; they correspond to the spectrum of a previously reported VO^{2+}-ferritin complex (15). Sabbioni and co-workers (8) have shown that a substantial amount of vanadium is associated with the ferritin fraction of homogenates of liver from animals injected with vanadium-48. Our data indicate that a specific VO^{2+} complex is formed with this protein in-vivo.

A schematic diagram summarizing current knowledge of the metabolism of vanadium is shown in Figure 6. Parallels between iron and vanadium metabolism are evident (8). Ingested vanadium(V) forms VO^{2+} in the acidic milieu of the stomach. It appears to remain largely as VO^{2+} in the gastrointestinal tract and is excreted in the feces as such. Upon absorption through the intestinal mucosal cells, the majority of the vanadium is found in the plasma where at least 50% of the element is associated with transferrin. Transferrin is known to bind a wide variety of metal ions in addition to iron (16) and may also play a role in their transport. It is also possible that some vanadium is bound to albumin in plasma, but dissociates during the chromatographic and electrophoretic steps. During long term feeding of vanadium, the majority of the element is excreted in the urine as an unidentified low molecular weight VO^{2+} complex (this work).

Intracellularly, significant amounts of EPR active vanadium is bound as VO^{2+} to ferritin, the iron storage protein. Vanadium has also been shown to associate with a variety of organelles including the nucleus (7) where it may influence neoplastic transformations. While the origin of the cancer preventative effect of vanadium is unclear, it is likely that transferrin mediates the uptake of vanadium by iron requiring tissues and by neoplastic tissues as well. Cancer cells have a high iron requirement and many transferrin receptors on their cell surfaces (17-19). Vanadium delivery to cells by transferrin could be the first step in the mechanism of antineoplastic activity of this element. Once inside the cell, any of a number of mechanisms could be operating to block carcinogenesis.

4 ACKNOWLEDGEMENT

This research was supported by Grants GM 20194 and CA 38265 from the National Institutes of Health.

5 REFERENCES

(1) B.R. Nechay, Ann. Rev. Pharmacol. Toxicol. 24 (1984) 501-521.

(2) N.D. Chasteen, Structure and Bonding 53 (1983) 107-138.

(3) N.D. Chasteen in L. Berliner and J. Reuben (Eds.), Biological Magnetic Resonance,
     Vol. 3, Plenum Publishing Co. New York 1981, pp. 53-117.

(4) H.J. Thompson, N.D. Chasteen, L.D. Meeker, Carcinogenesis 5 (1984) 849-850.

(5) E. Sabbioni, E. Marafante, J. Rade, C. Gregotti, A. Di Nucci, L. Manzo, Toxicol.
     Eur. Res. 3 (1981) 93-98.

(6) E. Sabbioni, E. Marafante, Bioinorg. Chem. 9 (1978) 389-407.

(7) E. Sabbioni, E. Marafante, L. Amantini, L. Ubertalli, C. Birattari, Bioinorg.
     Chem. 8 (1978) 503-515.

(8) E. Sabbioni, E. Marafante, J. Toxicol. Environ. Health 8 (1981) 419-429.

(9) N.D. Chasteen, L.K. White, R.F. Campbell, Biochemistry 16 (1977) 363-368.

(10) W.R. Harris, C.J. Carrano, J. Inorg. Biochem. 22 (1984) 201-218.

(11) W.R. Harris, S.B. Friedman, D. Siberman, J. Inorg. Biochem. 20 (1984) 157-169.

(12) R.D.R. Parker, R.P. Sharma, J. Environ. Path. Toxicol. 2 (1978) 235-245.

(13) J.D. Bogden, H. Higashino, M.A. Lavenhar, J.W. Bauman, Jr., F.W. Kemp, A. Aviv,
     J. Nutr. 112 (1982) 2279-2285.

(14) M.J. Leigh, D.D. Miller, Am. J. Clin. Nutr. 38 (1983) 202-213.

(15) N.D. Chasteen, E.C. Theil, J. Biol. Chem. 257 (1982) 7672-7677.

(16) N.D. Chasteen, Coord. Chem. Rev. 11 (1977) 1-36.

(17) E.H. Morgan, Mol. Aspects Med. 4 (1981) 1-123.

(18) E.D. Weinberg, Physiol. Rev. 64 (1984) 65-101.

(19) M.G. Baines, F.L. LaFluer, B.E. Holbein, Immun. Lett. 7 (1983) 51-55.

Concepts in Nickel Carcinogenesis

E. Nieboer, R.I. Maxwell, F.E. Rossetto, A.R. Stafford, and P.I. Stetsko

Department of Biochemistry and Occupational Health Program, McMaster University, 1200 Main Street West, Hamilton, Ontario, Canada L8N 3Z5.

SUMMARY

Experimental evidence is presented of the relevance to nickel carcinogenesis of surface properties of solid nickel compounds, of the bioavailability and intra-cellular compartmentalization of Ni^{2+}, of the intrinsic non-specificity of molecular interactions of Ni^{2+}, and of the ability of nickel compounds to participate in dioxygen radical reactions.

1 INTRODUCTION

Excess nasal and lung cancers are known to be associated with the refining of nickel (1). Epidemiological data support the notion that the cancer risk is most significant for exposures to solid nickel compounds that are intermediates in pyro-metallurgical refining processes (e.g., nickel subsulphide, Ni_3S_2) (1). Animal studies have confirmed that crystalline nickel compounds of limited water solubility

---

Abbreviations: A, absorbance; CD, circular dichroism; DDC, sodium diethyldithio-carbamate; DDW, doubly deionized distilled water; EDTA, ethylenediaminetetraacetic acid; GGH, glycylglycyl-L-histidine; HEPES, N-2-hydroxyethyl-piperazine-N'-2-ethanesulphonic acid; HSA, human serum albumin; PIPES, piperazine-N,N'-bis(2-ethane-sulphonic acid); PMNs, polymorphonuclear leukocytes; SOD, superoxide dismutase; TPA, 12-0-tetradecanoylphorbol-13-acetate; TRIS, N-tris(hydroxymethyl)aminomethane; VBS, veronal-buffered saline; XRD, X-ray diffraction spectrometry.

tend to be carcinogenic, while amorphous nickel compounds and water-soluble salts are weakly or non-carcinogenic (2-4). It may be visualized that in target organs (namely lung and nasal mucosa in man) extracellular and intracellular pools of particulate nickel compounds provide a continuous intracellular flux of Ni^{2+}. Cell culture studies have indeed shown that crystalline nickel sulphides are phagocytized and promote nuclear enrichment of Ni^{2+} more effectively than water-soluble nickel salts (5,6). However, in man and animals intracellular compartmentalization of Ni^{2+} must necessarily be balanced by extracellular transport and excretion. Once accumulated in the nucleus, Ni^{2+} is believed to be the ultimate carcinogen from the point of view of the somatic mutation model of cancer. A number of molecular mechanisms may be postulated for metal-ion induction of somatic mutations. These include: DNA conformational changes (e.g., B-DNA→Z-DNA), DNA damage (e.g., strand breaks and cross-links), non-isomorphous replacement of endogenous metal ions critical to replication and repair (e.g., Mg^{2+} and Zn^{2+}), and alterations of chromatin structure (3).

In this brief article, we review some of our experimental evidence for the inclusion of the following concepts into a model of nickel carcinogenesis: (i) surface reactivity of solid nickel compounds; (ii) bioavailability of Ni^{2+}; (iii) intracellular compartmentalization of Ni^{2+}; (iv) the intrinsic lack of specificity of interactions of Ni^{2+} with DNA; and (v) participation of the Ni(III)/Ni(II) redox couple in dioxygen radical biochemistry.

2 EXPERIMENTAL PROCEDURES

2.1 Reactivity of Solid Compounds

Source of compounds. Nickel powder and α-NiS were purchased from Alfa Products and NiO from Aldrich Chemical Co., while samples of α-Ni_3S_2, β-NiS and α-NiS were donated by INCO Canada Ltd. These compounds were characterized by XRD. Amorphous NiS was prepared by H_2S precipitation from 0.01 M $NiCl_2$ in 0.1 M NH_4NO_3, and colloidal $Ni(OH)_2$ by neutralizing 0.1 M $NiCl_2$ to pH 8 with 2.0 M NaOH. Aliquots of suspensions of these two compounds in appropriate buffers were employed in experiments. Dried $Ni(OH)_2$ was obtained by air drying colloidal $Ni(OH)_2$, the crystallinity of which was confirmed by XRD (also see (7)).

Haemolysis. Samples of the nickel compounds or their suspensions were preincubated with gentle agitation for 1 h in VBS (4 mM, 0.15 M NaCl, pH 7.2, 23°C). Subsequently, a 2-ml suspension of freshly isolated erythrocytes (10^7 cells ml^{-1} in VBS) were added and the incubation was continued for another 2 h. On centrifugation, 2 ml of the supernatant were analyzed spectrometrically for haemoglobin after ferricyanide treatment. Results are expressed relative to haemolysis induced by 0.1% v/v Triton X-100.

Protein Adsorption. Samples were preincubated with gentle agitation for 1 h in 1 ml of TRIS-buffered saline (40 mM, 0.15 M NaCl, pH 7.4, 23°C) and incubated for 1 h with HSA (carrier plus ^{125}I-labelled HSA, prepared as described previously (8)). After centrifugation, an aliquot of the supernatant was counted for residual ^{125}I-gamma activity.

2.2 Cellular Uptake and Release of $^{63}Ni^{2+}$

Cultured B-lymphoblasts of human origin were incubated for 2 h at 37°C in VBS buffer (5 mM, 0.19 M NaCl, pH 7.4) with $^{63}NiCl_2$ (2×10^6 cells ml^{-1}). After suitable washing with VBS, the cell pellet was resuspended and incubated for 30 min in VBS containing ligands at concentrations $10^{-7} - 10^{-3}$ M. After washing, the cell-associated ^{63}Ni was assessed by liquid scintillation spectrometry (9).

2.3 Metal-Ion Induced Conformational Transitions of Poly d(G-C)·Poly d(G-C)

Aliquots containing 13 nmoles (in 10 mM HEPES, pH 7.6) of poly d(G-C)·poly d(G-C) and serial volumes of metal salt (from stock solutions of the nitrate, chloride or acetate salt at pH < 2.0) were diluted to 0.5 - 0.75 ml with HEPES buffer (10 mM, pH 7.6). (Phosphate buffer replaced HEPES in a few instances.) The mixture was incubated for 2.5 h at 37°C, and subsequently the absorbance ratio A(295 nm)/A(260 nm) was measured. Appropriate corrections for background absorbance by the metal ion were made. Selective CD spectra were also recorded.

2.4 Nickel Redox Properties and Active Oxygen Studies

Stock solutions (10^{-3} M) of NiGGH were prepared by adding GGH to 0.1 M $NiCl_2 \cdot 6H_2O$ in DDW and diluting to volume with the appropriate buffer (0.1 M phosphate, pH 7.4; 0.1 M HEPES, pH 7.4; or 0.1 M PIPES, pH 7.0). These preparations are unstable and are readily oxidized in air. The effect (followed by VIS absorption spectrometry) of O_2, KO_2, H_2O_2 and $Na_2IrCl_6 \cdot 6H_2O$ on Ni(II)GGH and/or its oxidized products were examined. The influence of catalase and SOD (both from bovine liver) were also tested in some of these systems. Further, the effect of the NiGGH complexes were examined in two systems known to generate the superoxide anion, O_2^-. One assay involved the enzyme system xanthine/xanthine oxidase (10) and the other human PMNs stimulated by TPA (11). In both cases, the reduction of ferricytochrome c was taken as diagnostic of O_2^- production. This can be monitored by measuring the increase in absorbance at 550 nm (10,11). PMNs were isolated from human blood by a standard Ficoll-Hypaque procedure (11,12), and their concentration in the assay mixture was 10^6 to 10^7 cells ml^{-1}.

3   RESULTS AND DISCUSSION

3.1 Bioavailability of Ni^{2+}

The protein adsorption data provide direct evidence that physical properties of solid nickel compounds might determine their biological activity. The protein adsorption capacities for the non-crystalline, amorphous NiS and colloidal $Ni(OH)_2$ are significantly higher than those for the crystalline nickel compounds (including metallic powders). Slopes of protein adsorption curves yielded the sequence (in µg mg^{-1}):colloidal $Ni(OH)_2$ (570 ± 10) > amorphous NiS (300) >>> NiO (8.0 ± 0.5) > Ni powder (4.3 ± 0.4) > α-NiS and β-NiS (3.4 ± 0.2) > dried $Ni(OH)_2$ (2.9 ± 0.1) > α-Ni_3S_2 (2.2 ± 0.4). Ranking by haemolytic ability roughly parallels this order. The non-crystalline compounds are the least carcinogenic in animals (colloidal $Ni(OH)_2$ is non-carcinogenic and amorphous NiS weakly so (4,7)). For rats, Sunderman (4) established the carcinogenicity sequence: α-Ni_3S_2, β-NiS > NiO >> Ni powder >>> amorphous NiS (material of median particle size of < 2 µm was injected intramuscularly). Dried, crystalline $Ni(OH)_2$ is known to be carcinogenic (7).

The Ni powder employed in our study, like NiO, had a rough surface and appeared aggregated when examined by scanning electron microscopy. All of the other compounds exhibited a smooth surface morphology. In a detailed comparison of colloidal and dried $Ni(OH)_2$, we have shown that the colloidal material adsorbs Zn^{2+} more extensively, is more cytotoxic, and reduces phagocytosis of latex spheres by rabbit alveolar macrophages (13,14).

As depicted in Fig. 1, the coating of colloidal $Ni(OH)_2$ by protein virtually eliminates its haemolytic ability, but does not affect that of dried $Ni(OH)_2$. It appears that crystalline solids are less susceptible to inactivation and clearance and thereby enhance the availability of Ni^{2+} to tissues. Cell culture studies have confirmed that crystalline nickel sulphides are phagocytized and promote high intracellular levels of Ni^{2+} (5,6,15). Amorphous, non-crystalline nickel sulphide is much less effective. After uptake, particulates have been observed in endocytic vacuoles and seem to aggregate in the perinuclear region (5). Such intracellular particulates have a reduced dissolution half-life. Whole-body autoradiography with radiolabelled crystalline α-Ni_3S_2 in mice provides evidence of a gradual release of Ni^{2+} after intramuscular injection. Considerable intracellular location of particulate α-Ni_3S_2 within fibroblasts and macrophages occurs in tissues at the site of injection (for review see (2)).

It is concluded that surface passivity of solids (i.e., smooth exterior, crystallinity, low surface charge, low surface activity with respect to protein adsorption and cell lysis, and moderate solubility) appears to be predisposing to carcinogenicity. Presumably, extracellular and intracellular pools of such relatively passive particulates provide a continuous inward cellular flux of Ni^{2+}.

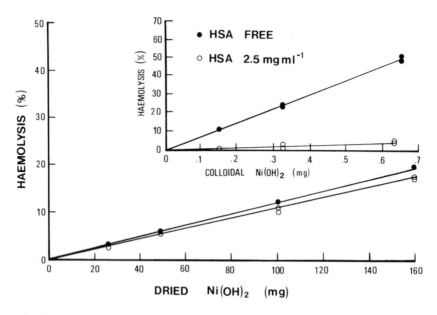

Fig. 1. The effect on erythrocyte haemolysis of preincubating dried and colloidal Ni(OH)$_2$ with human serum albumin (2.5 mg ml^{-1}); single points denote negligible deviation between duplicates.

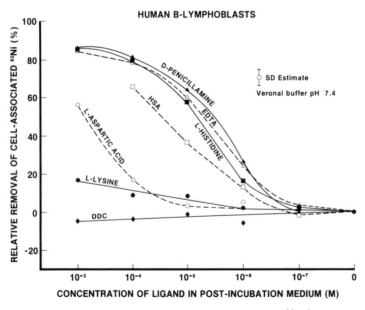

Fig. 2. The ability of chelating agents to remove ^{63}Ni^{2+} from pre-loaded human B-lymphoblast cells.

3.2 Intracellular Compartmentalization of Ni^{2+}

Compartmentalization of Ni^{2+} within cells is likely regulated by the relative concentrations and affinities for Ni^{2+} of intracellular and extracellular ligands. This is illustrated by the data in Fig. 2 for B-lymphoblasts (60% of the cell-associated Ni^{2+} is associated with the cell pellet after lysis and 40% with the lysate (16)). Ligands with known affinity for Ni^{2+} can remove substantial quantities from the cell. Conversely, the same ligands prevent uptake (16). Physiologic concentrations of HSA ($\sim 6 \times 10^{-4}$ M in serum) and L-histidine ($\sim 7 \times 10^{-5}$ M in serum) removed about 80% of cell-associated Ni^{2+}. In plasma, a total of 75% of Ni^{2+} is bound to protein (mostly HSA) and the remainder to ligands of low relative molecular mass (likely L-histidine) (17; Sanford and Nieboer, unpublished data). The latter form is excreted by the kidney. It may be visualized that intracellular compartmentalization of Ni^{2+} such as in the nucleus, must be balanced by transport out of cells and subsequent excretion. Exposures to water-soluble salts of nickel are characterized by rapid excretion ($t_{1/2} \sim 1$ day) as opposed to exposure to solid refining intermediates (nickel oxides and sulphides; $t_{1/2}$ estimated at ~ 3 y) (18,19). Consequently, the probability of intracellular accumulation of Ni^{2+} in individuals exposed to water-soluble salts is lowered, as is presumably the opportunity to express fully its carcinogenic potential.

3.3 Molecular Aspects Related to Nickel Carcinogenesis

Metal-Ion Induced Conformational Transitions of Poly d(G-C)·Poly d(G-C). Recently, reports have appeared that certain metal ions are able to induce conformational transitions in oligodeoxynucleotides from the normal right-handed B-helix to the left-handed Z-helix (e.g. 20). Ni^{2+} is one of the metal ions (21; Fig. 3). It has been speculated that this conformational transition may play some role in the carcinogenic process (21,22). For example, metal-ion induced conformational changes may cause the expression of genome segments such as an oncogene that normally are repressed (3). The data in Fig. 3 indicate that non-carcinogenic metals also have the ability to convert B-DNA to Z-DNA. In fact, we have shown that the B→Z transition for poly d(G-C)·poly d(G-C) is correlated with the ability of metal ions to participate in complex formation (Rossetto and Nieboer, unpublished data). For class B or 'soft' metal ions (nitrogen/sulphur seeking (23,24)), the metal ion/poly-deoxynucleotide mole ratio for mid-phase (half) conversion was small (e.g., 0.3 for Ag^+) compared to class A or 'hard' ions (oxygen seeking) for which much larger ratios were required (e.g., 100 for Al^{3+}). The following correlation was obtained: $y = -1.01 \log x + 3.26$ (correlation coefficient = 0.95, n = 20); with $y = X_m^2 r$, an index to covalent interactions or affinity for nitrogen/sulphur donor atoms in which X_m is the Pauling electronegativity and r the ionic radius (23); x = transition-midpoint metal ion/polydeoxynucleotide mole ratio; and n, the number of metal ions tested. It is concluded that since B→Z conversion of DNA is an intrinsic property

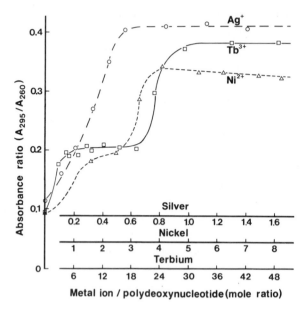

Fig. 3. Metal-ion induced B→Z transitions of poly d(G-C)·poly d(G-C). Note that the class B or 'soft' ion Ag^+ exhibits a monophasic transition, while those for the borderline ion Ni^{2+} and the class A or 'hard' ion Tb^{3+} are biphasic. For Ni^{2+} and Tb^{3+}, the second phase corresponds to the B→Z transition. (The Ag^+ and Ni^{2+} data are for nitrate salts, while the Tb^{3+} curve is for the chloride; all measurements were in 10 mM HEPES, pH 7.6.)

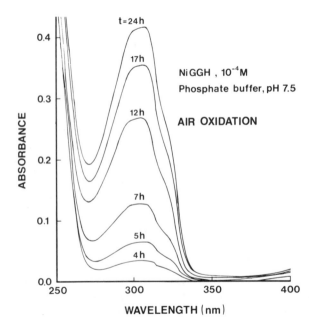

Fig. 4. Air oxidation of the nickel complex of glycyl-glycyl-L-histidine (NiGGH).

of most metal ions, unusual intranuclear compartmentalization of Ni^{2+} must prevail
if this phenomenon is relevant to nickel carcinogenesis. Generally, transitions
induced by class B ions were monophasic, by class A ions biphasic, and by borderline
ions of either type.

Nickel Redox Properties and Active Oxygen Studies. The Ni(III)/Ni(II) redox
couple has been implicated in a number of hydrogenases (A.V. Xavier, this volume).
It has also been known for some time that peptide complexes of Ni^{2+} are susceptible
to air oxidation yielding ESR-confirmed Ni^{3+} species (25,26). Since chemical
promoters of cancer appear to have the capacity to stimulate phagocytic cells to
produce dioxygen radicals (27) and metal ions catalyze processes involving molecular
oxygen (20), we have investigated the ability of nickel peptide complexes to
participate in dioxygen radical reactions.

Table 1. Reactivity of Ni(GGH) Toward Dioxygen

Reagent	Reaction	Buffer[a]	Result[b]		
			1	2	3
O_2	oxidation	1,2,3	+	++	+++
O_2^-	oxidation	2,3	nd	+	++
	reduction	2,3	nd	++	+
H_2O_2	oxidation	1,2,3	-	+	-
	reduction	1,2,3	[c] +++	+++	+++
$IrCl_6^{2-}$	oxidation	1,2	+++	+++	nd

(a) Buffers: 1, 0.1 M HEPES, pH 7.4; 2, 0.1 M
    PIPES, pH 7.0; 3, 0.1 M Phosphate, pH 7.4.
(b) nd, not determined; the number of plus
    signs denotes relative reactivity.
(c) Catalyzed by the enzyme catalase and
    inhibited by SOD.

At pH 7.5, Ni(II)GGH is air-oxidized relatively rapidly as illustrated in Fig. 4. The only other oxidizing agent found to be effective was $IrCl_6^{2-}$ (Table 1). Hydrogen peroxide is a good reducing agent for the oxidized product. The enzyme catalase catalyzes this reaction, while SOD inhibits it (Table 1). The latter suggests that O_2^- is involved in the process. By contrast, O_2^- alone acts in an ambivalent manner depending on the buffer employed.

The enzyme xanthine/xanthine oxidase is a known source of O_2^- and hydroxyl radicals
(·OH) (28). Addition of Ni(II)GGH or its partially oxidized product reduces the O_2^-
measured by ferricytochrome c reduction to background levels. During the reaction
(< 2 min), the Ni(II)GGH undergoes partial oxidation. The ferricytochrome c
reduction curves depicted in Fig. 5 show that Ni(II)GGH or its oxidized product
also reduce the flux of O_2^- generated by PMNs stimulated by TPA. It has not been
established for these two systems whether the diminished levels of O_2^- denote a
conversion to ·OH.

These preliminary results for the reaction of Ni(II)GGH with dioxygen illustrate
that Ni(II)-complexes can participate in dioxygen radical biochemistry. Recruitment
of phagocytizing cells (including PMNs and macrophages) is known to occur in response

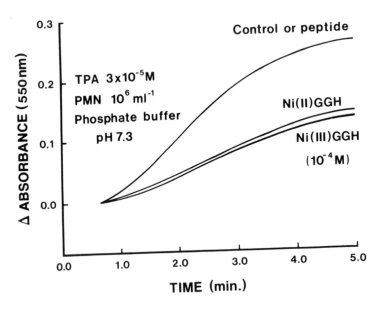

Fig. 5.   Inhibition by unoxidized and oxidized NiGGH of TPA-induced superoxide anion generation by human PMNs. Δ absorbance denotes the change in absorbance accompanying the reduction of ferricytochrome c (see text).

to deposition of particles in the respiratory tract (29). Such an event is accompanied by the oxygen burst which is characterized by the production of oxygen radicals, which in excess can damage tissues. In vitro, dioxygen radical generation by enzyme systems (e.g., xanthine/xanthine oxidase) or intact cells (e.g., human PMNs) result in damage of exogenous and endogenous DNA respectively (30,31). As already indicated, such consequences have implication for cancer. It is obvious that the detailed characterization of the interplay between nickel complexes and dioxygen is a promising avenue of research. Preliminary studies with Ni(II)-complexes of other peptides and HSA show trends similar to those reported for Ni(GGH). The potential toxicological consequence of the Ni(III)/Ni(II) redox couple is evident from a recent report which illustrates that a Ni(II)-macrocyclic polyamine catalyzes the hydroxylation of non-activated aromatic compounds (e.g., benzene (32)).

3.4 Concluding Comments

It is clear that in nickel carcinogenesis consideration must be given to the surface properties of solids, the cellular availability of Ni^{2+}, and the ability of nickel complexes to participate in dioxygen radical biochemistry. Since interactions of Ni^{2+} with DNA are non-specific, specificity must be gained in another manner such as through preferential intranuclear compartmentalization.

4 REFERENCES

1. F.W. Sunderman, Jr. (Ed.-in-Chief), Nickel in the Human Environment, IARC
   Scientific Pub. No. 53, Oxford University Press, Oxford, 1984, 1-124.
2. F.W. Sunderman, Jr., Environ. Health Perspect. 40 (1981) 131-41.
3. F.W. Sunderman, Jr., Ann. Clin. Lab. Sci. 14 (1984) 93-122.
4. F.W. Sunderman, Jr., in (2), pp. 127-42.
5. M. Costa, Biol. Trace Element Res. 5 (1983) 285-95.
6. P. Sen and M. Costa, Cancer Res. 45 (1985) 2320-5.
7. K.S. Kasprzak, P. Gabryel and K. Jarczewska, Carcinogenesis 4 (1983) 275-9.
8. E. Nieboer, S.L. Evans and J. Dolovich, Br. J. Ind. Med. 41 (1984) 56-63.
9. K.S. Kasprzak and F.W. Sunderman, Jr., Pure Appl. Chem. 51 (1979) 1375-89.
10. J.M. McCord and I. Fridovich, J. Biol. Chem. 244 (1969) 6049-55.
11. M. Markert, P.C. Andrews and B.M. Babior, Methods in Enzymol. 105 (1984) 358-65.
12. P. Davis, C.L. Miller and A.S. Russell, J. Rheumatol. (Suppl. 8) 9 (1982) 18-24.
13. E. Nieboer, R.I. Maxwell and A.R. Stafford, in (2), pp. 439-58.
14. R.I. Maxwell and E. Nieboer, Ann. Clin. Lab. Sci. 14 (1984) 403.
15. K. Hansen and R.M. Stern, Environ. Health Perspect. 51 (1983) 223-6.
16. E. Nieboer, A.R. Stafford, S.L. Evans and J. Dolovich, in (2), pp. 321-31.
17. M. Lucasson and B. Sarkar, J. Toxicol. Environ. Health 5 (1979) 897-905.
18. A. Tossavainen, M. Nurminen, P. Mutanen and S. Tola, Br. J. Ind. Med. 37 (1980)
    285-91.
19. W. Torjussen and I. Andersen, Ann. Clin. Lab. Sci. 4 (1979) 289-98.
20. J.H. Van de Sande, L.P. McIntosh and T.M. Jovin, EMBO J. 1 (1982) 777-82.
21. P. Bourtayre, L. Pizzorni, J. Liquier, J. Taboury, E. Taillandier and J.-F.
    Labarre, in (2) pp. 227-34.
22. A. Rich, A. Nordheim and A.H.J. Wang, Ann. Rev. Biochem. 53 (1984) 791-846.
23. E. Nieboer and D.H.S. Richardson, Environ. Pollut. (Ser. B) 1 (1980) 3-26.
24. E. Nieboer and W.E. Sanford, Rev. Biochem. Toxicol. (1985) in press.
25. F.P. Bossu and D.W. Margerum, Inorg. Chem. 16 (1977) 1210-4.
26. F.P. Bossu, E.B. Paniago, D.W. Margerum, S.T. Kirksey, Jr. and J.L. Kurtz,
    Inorg. Chem. 17 (1978) 1034-42.
27. J.L. Marx, Science 219 (1983) 158-9.
28. B. Halliwell and J.M.C. Gutteridge, Biochem. J. 219 (1984) 1-14.
29. B.A. Katsnelson and L.I. Privalova, Environ. Health Perspect. 55 (1984) 313-25.
30. H.C. Birnboim, Science 215 (1982) 1247-9.
31. K. Brown and I. Fridovich, Acta. Physiol. Scand. Suppl. 492 (1980) 9-18.
32. E. Kimura and R. Machida, J. Chem. Soc. Chem. Comm. (1984) 499-500.

ACKNOWLEDGEMENTS

    Financial support from the Natural Science and Engineering Research Council of
Canada is gratefully acknowledged.

Selenium Metabolism in Man and Animals

Raymond J. Shamberger

Department of Biochemistry, The Cleveland Clinic Foundation, 9500 Euclid Avenue, Cleveland, Ohio (USA) 44106

SUMMARY

Deficiencies of selenium and vitamin E can cause several different animal diseases and large economic losses in domestic animal production. Some of the deficiencies include liver necrosis, muscular dystrophy, exudative diathesis, pancreatic degeneration, mulberry heart disease, retardation of growth, reproductive problems, and peridontal disease. In man, selenium deficiency has been linked to both cancer and heart disease. The above diseases processes may be linked to glutathione peroxidase and a cellular defense mechanism against free radical attack.

1 INTRODUCTION

After Berzelius first discovered selenium in 1818, selenium became known as one of the most toxic elements. However, selenium was later recognized to be an essential trace element. Deficiencies of selenium leading to animal disease and large economic losses in domestic animal production were first observed. Later, selenium deficiency was related to human cancer and heart disease. The objective of this study is to review the relationship between selenium and both animal and human disease and to relate these observations to known biochemical reactions of selenium.

2 SELENIUM AND ANIMAL DISEASE

2.1 Liver Necrosis

Liver necrosis, which was first described in 1935, is a rapidly developing condition which can cause an apparently healthy rat to become ill and die within a day or two. Upon necropsy, massive hepatic necrosis is found. The liver necrosis, however, could be prevented by an ingredient present in crude casein, kidney and liver powder called Factor 3. Factor 3 was at first thought to be a vitamin but was later found to be organically bound selenium (1).

When the liver necrosis occurs in pigs, it is called hepatosis dietetica. Lesions of hepatosis dietetica are frequently found in pigs which have died of mulberry heart disease. Hepatosis dietetica is less common than mulberry disease, but when present, usually involves a very high proportion of pigs in a herd and many mortalities. This disease occurs most often in young pigs up to three months of age. Clinical signs are not readily apparent, with pigs suddenly collapsing and dying. Occasionally before death, pigs will show dyspepsia, vomiting, and diarrhea and may be lethargic, and icturic areas of massive necrosis over the capsular and cut surfaces of the liver are frequently observed. In addition to rats and pigs, hepatic necrosis can also occur in monkeys. After nine months on a selenium deficient diet, monkeys develop alopecia, lose body weight, and are listless. Upon necropsy, several lesions were observed, including hepatic necrosis, skeletal muscle degeneration, myocardial degeneration, and nephrosis. Some of the animals and the clinical disorders associated with selenium or vitamin E deficiency are listed in Table 1.

Table 1. Clinical disorders associated with selenium-vitamin E deficiency in animals

Species	Condition
Cattle (calf)	Skeletal and cardiac myopathy, slowed growth, unthriftiness
Cattle (adult)	Skeletal myopathy (paralytic myoglobinuria), placental retention, unthriftiness, embryonic death
Chicken (young)	Exudative diathesis, skeletal myopathy, encephalomalacia, pancreatic necrosis, slowed growth
Chicken (adult)	Skeletal myopathy, decreased egg production and hatchability
Horse (adult)	Skeletal myopathy; poor racing performance
Horse (foal)	Skeletal and cardiac myopathy and steatitis
Monkeys	Lack of growth, lack of hair growth, testicular degeneration, liver necrosis
Rabbits	Erythrocyte hemolysis, skeletal myopathy, testicular degeneration
Rats	Skeletal myopathy, liver necrosis, lack of growth, lack of hair growth, testicular degeneration, fetal death resorption, incisor depigmentation
Sheep (lamb)	Skeletal and cardiac myopathy, slowed growth, unthriftiness
Sheep (adult)	Infertility in ewes (embryonic death), periodontal disease, unthriftiness
Swine (growing pig)	Hepatosis dietetica, skeletal myopathy, "mulberry heart disease," gastric ulceration
Turkey and duck (young)	Skeletal, cardiac, gizzard and intestinal myopathy, lack of feather growth

2.2 Nutritional Musclar Dystrophy

One of the most widely recognized of the selenium-vitamin E responsive disorders in calves and lambs is nutritional muscular dystrophy (NMD). NMD is a degenerative disease of the skeletal and cardiac muscles occurring most often in sheep and cattle but also occurs in several other animal species. NMD occurs most commonly in suckling lambs and beef calves at 1-3 months of age but rarely occurs in mature animals. NMD appears after the dams and offspring have been released to pasture and the NMD is worsened by exercise. A congenital form may also be found in animals at birth and in fetuses which have been aborted. The clinical signs of NMD are variable and depend on the tissues affected and the severity of the deficiency. Lambs and calves with severely degenerated muscles may not be able to suckle and as a result, die of inanition.   The usual signs of NMD are stiffness (stiff lamb disease), weakness, trembling, and frequent respiratory problems with elevated temperatures which may be related to infections such as pneumonia. The skeletal muscles commonly affected are the most active, e.g., diaphragm, intercostal, myocardium, and the pelvic and hind-leg muscles. Microscopically the lesions range from hyaline degeneration to a coagulation necrosis of the muscle fibers. A moderate fibrous proliferation replaces the muscle fibers and macrophages and lymphocytes also appear. Abnormally elevated levels of serum glutamic oxalacetic transaminase, as well as lactic acid dehydrogenase and creatinine have also been observed with NMD. Experimental NMD has been shown to respond to either selenium or vitamin E administration.

2.3 Exudative Diathesis

Exudative diathesis in chickens and turkeys is characterized by accumulations of large amounts of fluid under the skin of the abdomen and breast of chicks between three and six weeks of age. The chicks become dejected, lose condition, show leg weakness, and some become prostrate and die. Once animals develop this condition, they will usually die within a few days. By adding as little as 0.1 ppm of selenium as selenite to a vitamin E-deficient diet, exudative diathesis can be prevented in chicks.

2.4 Pancreatic Degeneration

Chicks fed a severely selenium-deficient diet but supplemented with vitamin E and bile salts, develop a severe atrophy of the pancreas. If selenium is not added to the deficient diet, the animals will die of pancreatic insufficiency. The amount of selenium required to prevent pancreatic degeneration was found to be related to the amount of vitamin E in the diet.

2.5 Mulberry Heart Disease

Mulberry heart disease often occurs together with hepatosis dietetica in pigs, but sometimes itself will cause death. The clinical patterns are usually those of a rapidly growing healthy pig suddenly developing heart failure and dying within hours. The disease has been called "mulberry heart disease" because the affected animals frequently have such an extensive cardiac hemorrhage that the heart has a reddish-purple gross appearance, which resembles that of a mulberry. Administration of selenium increases tissue selenium levels and prevents the disease.

2.6 Growth

Growth impairment of selenium deficient rats has been observed. However, in the offspring of selenium-deficient mothers, additional signs of selenium deficiency have been observed. The rats tended to grow poorly and had sparse or absent hair. Several adult squirrel monkeys have been fed a low-selenium semipurified diet with adequate vitamin E. Body weight loss, alopecia, and listlessness developed in the monkeys after they were on the diet for nine months.

2.7 Reproductive Problems

In some selenium-deficient areas, 30% of the ewes that were mated failed to produce lambs. The infertility in ewes is due to early embryonic death and may be prevented by giving selenium before mating. In addition, losses of premature calves can be prevented by administering selenium and vitamin E to pregnant cows two months before mating. Several investigators have suggested that prepartal nutrition may affect the incidence of retained placenta of parturient dairy cows.

In rats fed selenium-deficient diets, sperm motility and morphology appeared to be normal at four months, but 50% of the animals in the 11-12 month interval produced sperm with decreased motility and a characteristic midpiece breakage (2). Although active spermatogenesis was observed in some of the seminiferous tubules of selenium-deficient rats born to females on a selenium-deficient diet, poor motility of spermatozoa from these males was observed with most of the sperm showing breakage of the fibrils in the axial filaments. Autoradiographs showed that ^{75}Se was concentrated in the midpiece of the sperm. Subcellular fractionation showed that the mitochondria of the testes contained the greatest amount of selenium. This suggests that there may be a specific need for selenum in the mitochondria which is exclusively located in the sperm midpiece.

2.8 Peridontal Disease

Peridontal disease has been observed in New Zealand ewes three to five years of age and causes a loss of physical condition resulting from difficulty in mastication. Peridontal disease is characterized by loosening and shedding of permanent premolars and molars, and sometimes also the incisors. The loosening of teeth is also associated with gingival hyperplasia, gingival alveolar infection, and resorption. Selenium administration will greatly reduce the incidence, but other factors may also be involved.

3 SELENIUM AND CANCER

3.1 Breast and Colon Cancer

   Dietary selenium seems to have its greatest protective effect against animal, breast, or colon cancers which are known to be fat responsive tumors. Selenium, at greater than nutritional levels, has been shown to inhibit both viral and chemically induced breast cancer. Schrauzer and Ishmael (3) have added 2 ppm of sodium selenite to the drinking water of mice and found that the incidence of spontaneous mammary tumors induced by the Bittner milk virus was reduced from 82% to 10%. Medina and Shephard (4) have found that the SeO_2 added to the drinking water inhibited 7,12-dimethylbenzanthracene DMBA-induced mammary carcinogenesis in BALB/c, C3H/StWi, and BD2F mice. Thompson and Tagliaferro (5) and Ip and Sinha (6) have reported that dietary selenium decreased the incidence of rat mammary tumors induced by 7,12-dimethylbenzanthracene. Anticarcinogenic activity was dependent on the amount of selenium that was ingested. In addition, vitamin E was found to have a synergistic effect on selenium in the chemoprevention of mammary carcinogenesis in rats (7). Rats fed an adequate amount of selenium but fed an increasing amount of unsaturated fat such as corn oil, showed an increased tumor incidence (8). When the amount of dietary selenium was increased, the tumor yields were correspondingly increased (9). The enhancement of carcinogenesis by dietary fat and its decrease by selenium may indicate that some type of peroxidation or peroxides are involved in either the initiation or promotion phase of carcinogenesis.

   Jacobs et al. (10) have reported that selenium added to the drinking water reduced the total number of colon tumors induced by 1,2-dimethylhydrazine (DMH) or methylazoxymethanol acetate. Selenium decreased the incidence of DMH-induced colon tumors by more than 50%. Even though the percentage of MAM-induced tumors was about the same as the positive controls, the number of tumors per animal were reduced in both the DMH and the MAM groups. Soulier et al. (11) have added selenium to the drinking water and observed a decreased incidence of azoxymethane-induced cancer in rats fed a 30% beef fat diet. Birt et al. (12) have found that there was a decrease in colon cancer induced by bis(2-oxopropyl nitrosamine) in rats fed dietary selenium.

3.2 Liver, Skin, and Pancreatic Cancer

   Dietary selenium at 5 ppm (13) and selenium added to the drinking water (14) have reduced the incidence of liver tumors induced by dimethylaminobenzene (DAB). Because the rats on the 5 ppm selenium diet showed a slower weight gain and decreased food intake, the anti-tumor effect at 5 ppm may have been due to selenium toxicity. Balanski and Hadsiolov (15) have fed diethylnitrosamine (DEN) to rats also receiving selenium diets containing 1, 5, or 10 ppm of sodium selenite. Even though there was not a significant difference between the number of animals with tumors, there was a decrease in the total number of tumors in the selenium fed rats. However, Dzhioev (16) has also added selenium to rat diets and found that the percentage of rats with tumors was reduced from 100% to 27%. LeBoeuf et al. (17) and Baldwin et al. (18) have observed that dietary selenium has significantly reduced the development of gamma-glutamyltranspeptidase-positive liver foci (GGTP foci) induced by DEN or aflatoxin in rats. Dietary selenium significantly inhibited the number of mice and skin lesions induced by DMBA-croton oil and benzopyrene (19). The number of cancers formed later in the benzopyrene experiments was also decreased in the mice fed 1.0 ppm of sodium selenite. Dietary selenium has reduced the incidence of azaserine induced preneoplastic abnormal acinar cell nodules in rat pancreas (20).

3.3 Epidemiological Relationships

   Two epidemiological studies using different populations showed an inverse relationship between environmental selenium and the incidence of cancer. One showed an inverse relationship of cancer mortality to selenium bioavailability in United

States forage crops (21), and the other related the level of selenium in blood from different countries to cancer mortality (22). Salonen et al. (23) in Finland and Willett et al. (24) in the United States have studied the relationship of the pre-diagnostic serum selenium and the cancer incidence for several years in several thousand people. Salonen et al. (23, 24) observed in two studies that a serum selenium of less than 45 ug/liter was associated with a relative increased risk of 3.1 and 5.8. When selenium and vitamin E were combined, the relative cancer risk increases to 11.4 (24). Willett et al. (24) reported that the risk of cancer for subjects in the lowest quintile of serum selenium was twice that of subjects in the highest. The association between low selenium level and cancer was strongest for gastrointestinal and prostatic cancers. In addition, low blood selenium has been related to lung cancer mortality in Chinese mine workers (26). Certainly in all of these prospective studies, other factors could be involved.

Even though there are almost 50 studies showing that selenium levels greater than nutritional levels reduce cancer in animals and epidemiological and prospective studies show a relationship to selenium, a large clinical trial is needed to definitely establish the efficacy of selenium.

4 SELENIUM AND HEART DISEASE

4.1 Animals

Electrocardiograms of rats (27) and lambs (28) maintained on selenium-deficient diets show an increased T wave followed by an elevated S-T segment, a pattern which resembles that of myocardial infarction in man. In some cases, there is a fall of blood pressure and circulatory failure. In addition to the changes seen in rats and sheep, severe myopathy of the heart can occur in many other animal species such as pigs (mulberry heart disease), calves, chickens, and ducks. The change in electro-cardiograms could be related directly to the eventual circulatory collapse caused by selenium deficiency.

4.2 Humans

Keshan disease is an endemic cardiomyopathy which has been related to an extremely low intake of selenium (>20 ug) in parts of China. The main pathological lesion is a multiple focal myocardial necrosis scattered throughout the heart muscle with various degrees of cell infiltration and different stages of fibrosis. Mortality from Keshan disease is usually high from congestive heart failure in children less than 15 years of age. The Keshan Disease Research Group of the Chinese Academy of Medical Sciences has treated 36,603 children with 1.0 mg of sodium selenite per week. Only 21 cases occurred during the four years of investigation. However, there were 107 cases in 9,642 children in the control group who were not treated with sodium selenite (29). Many of the latter control cases were reversed when the children were given selenite. In some cases, however, irreversible cardiac damage occurred and was not reversed by selenite. Two cases of cardiomyopathy due to selenium deficiency have been identified in two hospital patients and may be similar to Keshan disease. Shamberger et al. (30) have compared the selenium content of certain forage crops in the United States to male and female age specific death rates for coronary heart disease and found significantly lower death rates in the high selenium areas. The severe cardiomyopathy observed in Keshan disease may be related to mulberry disease observed in selenium deficient animals. Large clinical trials are really needed to establish a relationship between selenium and atherosclerosis and myocardial infarction.

5 SELENIUM BIOCHEMISTRY

5.1 Selenium as a Component of Glutathione Peroxidase

Mills (31) reported that cattle erythrocytes contained catalase as well as yet another enzyme active against H_2O_2 and in the presence of reduced glutathione could prevent the oxidative denaturation of hemoglobin and red cell hemolysis induced in vitro by H_2O_2 or ascorbic acid. Mills (32,33) showed that this enzyme, glutathione peroxidase[2] (GSH-Px; EC 1.11.1.9) was also present in other organs such as the liver, lungs and kidney, and partially purified it from erythrocytes. Later work showed that GSHpx utilized reducing equivalents from GSH in the reduction of H_2O_2, lipid hydroperoxides, or sterol hydroperoxides by the following general reaction:

$$ROOH + 2GSH \xrightarrow{GSHpx} ROH + H_2O + GSSG$$

Rotruck et al. (34, 35) have studied the effects of dietary selenium on oxidative damage to rat erythrocytes and discovered erythrocyte GSHpx, a selenium-dependent enzyme, which contains selenium as an essential component. GSH-Px had a molecular weight of about 80,000 which consists of four apparently identical subunits. Both ovine and bovine erythrocytes were found to contain four g-atoms of selenium per mole GSHPx or one selenium per subunit. The four selenium atoms in the tetramer are located on its surface in the form of selenocysteine. A separation of 21 A between adjacent selenium atoms suggests that only one selenium atom is present per active site. The region around the active site forms a flat depression on the surface of the subunit, which makes the active site accessible to substrates. Animals fed selenium-deficient diets showed rapid reductions in GSH-Px activity that are well-correlated with the onset of selenium deficiency symptoms, and selenium-deficient animals show rapid increases in tissue GSH-Px activity when supplemented with selenium. It is likely much of the animal disease and some of the human disease related to selenium deficiency is caused directly or indirectly by a decreased glutathione peroxidase levels.

5.2 Effect of Selenium on the Protection of Biological Membranes

Organisms, which live under aerobic conditions or which gain their energy from the reduction of molecular oxygen to water, may form superoxides or peroxides, which are highly reactive intermediates of oxygen reduction. H_2O_2 is known to be produced by several enzymes, not only within the peroxisomes, but also in the microsomal, mitochondrial and soluble fractions of the cell (36). Up to 5% of oxygen is utilized in rat liver to produce hydrogen peroxide. Much of this hydrogen peroxide results from the dismutation of superoxide anions which suggests that H_2O_2 and O_2- may be present at the same time in biological material. When present together, a highly reactive oxygen species such as ·OH and also singlet oxygen may be formed. These oxygen species may react with a variety of organic compounds and biological structures susceptible to oxidative damage.

Phospholipid constituents of biological membranes may be oxidized leading to structural damage and possible disruption of cell integrity. Lability to lipid peroxidation in membranes is dependent upon the polyunsaturated fatty acid content of the constituent phospholipids. Membranes which contain high levels of polyunsaturated fatty acids in their phospholipids are especially labile to lipid peroxidation. Membranes which contain high levels of polyunsaturated fatty acids include the erythrocyte plasma membrane and various subcellular membranes of mitochondria, and the microsomal fraction of the cell. Peroxidation in mitochondria is associated with both swelling and lysis. Peroxidation of microsomal membrane lipids is associated with structural alterations of these membranes when examined by electron microscopy. Peroxidative damage of lysosomal membranes may lead to the release of many types of hydrolytic enzymes which disrupt normal cell function. However, lysosomal membranes contain less lipid than either mitochondria or microsomes and are, therefore, less labile to lipid peroxidation than are mitochondria and microsomes.

5.3 Cellular Defense Mechanism

GSH-Px, catalase, superoxide dismutase, glutathione transferase and vitamin E form an important part of the cellular defense against a free radical attack on biological structures. Vitamin E combines with free radicals and, thereby, prevents undesirable peroxidations of polyunsaturated fatty acids in tissues. GSH-Px plays a major role in detoxifying lipid peroxides of unsaturated fat by reducing them to non-toxic hydroxy fatty acids. This reduction prevents the decomposition into free radicals that can reinitiate peroxidation. Peroxide is also unable to react with superoxide radicals to form ·OH ion. Therefore, dietary selenium (as part of GSH-Px) and vitamin E may act together in a synergistic fashion to protect tissues from oxidative damage. The alterations in cellular biochemistry because of the breakdown of the cellular oxidant defense mechanism, may lead to some of the animal and human diseases described in this chapter.

6 REFERENCES

(1) K. Schwarz, C.M. Foltz, J. Am. Chem. Soc. 79 (1957) 3292-3293.

(2) S.H. Wu, J.E. Oldfield, P.D. Whanger, and P.H. Weswig, Nutr. Rep. Int. 13 (1976) 159-173.

(3) G.N. Schrauzer, D. Ishmael, Ann. Clin. Lab. Sci. 4 (1974) 411-417.

(4) D. Medina, F. Shephard, Carcinogenesis 2 (1981) 451-455.

(5) H.J. Thompson, A.R. Tagliaferro, Fed. Proc. 39 (1980) 1117.

(6) C. Ip, D.K. Sinha, Cancer Res. 41 (1981) 31-34.

(7) P.M. Horvath, C. Ip, Cancer Res. 43 (1983) 5335-5341.

(8) C. Ip, Nutr. Cancer 2 (1981) 136-142.

(9) C. Ip, Cancer Res. 41 (1981) 4386-4390.

(10) M.M. Jacobs, B. Jansson, A.C. Griffin, Cancer Lett. 2 (1977) 133-138.

(11) B.K. Soulier, P.S. Wilson, N.D. Nigro, Cancer Lett. 12 (1981) 343-348.

(12) D.F. Birt, T.A. Lawson, A.D. Julius, C.E. Kunice, S. Salamsi, Cancer Res. 42 (1982) 4456-4459.

(13) C.C. Clayton, C.A. Baumann, Cancer Res. 9 (1949) 575-582.

(14) A.C. Griffin, M.M. Jacobs, Cancer Lett. 3 (1977) 177-181.

(15) R.M. Balanski, D.H. Hadsiolov, Comptes Rendus de l' Academie Bulgare Des Sciences 32 (1979) 697-698.

(16) F.D. Dzhioev, Desitvie, Obraz, Opred, Mater Simp, 3rd Ed., G.O. Looga (Ed.) Tallinn, USSR (1978) 51-53.

(17) R.a. LoBoeuf, B.A. Laishes, W.C. Hoekstra, Fed. Proc. 42 (1983) 669.

(18) S. Baldwin, R.S. Parker, N. Misselbeck, Fed. Proc. 42 (1983) 1312.

(19) D.F. Birt, T.A. Lawson, A.D. Julius, C.E. Kunice, S. Salamsi, Cancer Res. 42 (1982) 4456-4459.

(20) T.O. O'Conner, L.D. Youngman, T.C. Campbell, Fed. Proc. 42 (1983) 670.

(21) R.J. Shamberger, C.E. Willis, CRC Crit. Rev. Clin. Lab. Sci. 2 (1971) 211-221.

(22) G.N. Schrauzer, D.A. White, C.J. Schneider, Bioinorg. Chem. 7 (1977) 23-24.

(23) J.T. Salonen, G. Alfthan, J.K. Huttun, P. Puska, Amer. J. Epidem. 120 (1984) 342-349.

(24) J.T. Salonen, R. Salonen, R. Lappetelainen, P.H. Maenpa, G. Alfthan, P. Puska, Brit. Med. J. 290 (1985) 417-421.

(25) W.C. Willett, J.S. Morris, S. Pressel, J.O. Taylor, B.F. Polk, M.J. Stampfer, B. Rosner, K. Schneider, and C.G. Hames, Lancet 2 (1983) 130-134.

(26) Y. Chu, Q. Liu, C. Hou, S. Yu, Biol. Tr. Elem. 6 (1984) 133-137.

(27) K.O. Godwin, Q.J. Exp. Physiol. 50 (1965) 282-288.

(28) K.O. Godwin, F.J. Fraser, Q.J. Exp. Physiol. 51 (1966) 94-102.

(29) X. Chen, G. Yang, J. Chen, X. Chen, Z. Wen, K. Ge, Biol. Tr. Elem. Res. 2 (1980) 91-107.

(30) R.J. Shamberger, S.A. Tytko, C.S. Willis, Tr. Sub. Envir. Hlth. D.D. Hemphill (Ed.) University of Missouri Press, Columbia, Missouri 9 (1975) 15-22.

(31) G.C. Mills, J. Biol. Chem. 229 (1957) 189-197.

(32) G.C. Mills, J. Biol. Chem. 234 (1959) 502-511.

(33) G.C. Mills, Arch. Biochem. 86 (1960) 1-10.

(34) J.T. Rotruck, A.L. Pope, H.E. Ganther, W.G. Hoekstra, J. Nutr. 102 (1972) 689-696.

(35) J.T. Rotruck, A.L. Pope, H.E. Ganther, D.G. Hofeman, W.G. Hoekstra, Science 179 (1973) 588-590.

(36) A. Boveris, N. Oshino, B. Chance, Biochem. J. 128 (1972) 617-630.

Models of Metal-Ion Binding Sites in Biology

Discriminatory Binding of Carbon Monoxide Versus Dioxygen Within Heme Proteins and Model Hemes

Shantha David, David Dolphin, Brian R. James

Department of Chemistry, University of British Columbia, 2036 Main Mall, Vancouver, B.C., Canada V6T 1Y6

SUMMARY

The reversible binding of O_2 and CO to heme proteins occurs at the iron atom. However, the steric and electronic controls provided by the protein play major roles in the nature and extent of coordination of these gases. Both proximal and distal effects are known in the complex protein environments. In order to separately understand these effects, model iron porphyrins have been prepared and their ligand binding examined. We compare here the observations made with model systems containing a "cap" on one face of the porphyrin when the polarity in the vicinity of the iron-ligand binding site is changed.

1. INTRODUCTION

There remains intense current interest in the roles played by proteins in regulating the reversible binding of small ligands, particularly O_2 and CO, at heme centres (1-4). One approach to this research is to synthesize model (i.e. protein-free) iron(II) porphyrins, study the rates and equilibria of their reversible interaction with O_2 and CO, and make comparisons with corresponding data for the protein systems Mb (5) and Hb. A particularly intriguing problem is whether the heme cavity within a protein sterically discriminates between O_2 and CO. Within oxygenated heme proteins, the O_2 unit is coordinated 'end-on' and is bent, while within carbonylated heme proteins the CO unit is bent and/or tilted from the perpendicular of the porphyrin plane because of interactions with the distal residues; within model hemes, the FeCO unit, as in all simple metal carbonyls, is linear whereas the O_2 is again bound in a bent fashion. Somewhat of a controversy has developed as to whether the heme protein binding site structure disfavours CO binding relative to O_2 because of steric reasons; such a factor could play a key role in preventing poisoning of O_2-carrying heme proteins by endogenously and exogenously produced CO.

Such steric interferences to ligation are referred to as distal-side steric effects to distinguish them from other steric effects, for example, that may be manifested on the proximal-side. Thus, within model systems, substitution of N-MeIm by 1,2-Me_2Im or 2-MeIm leads to reduction in CO and O_2 binding at the trans position (6). The steric strain, that prevents movement of the iron into the porphyrin plane, has been used to model the lower affinity tense (T)-state of Hb; coordinated N-MeIm and 1,5-Cy_2Im do not prevent such movement on binding of the sixth ligand, and are used to mimic the relaxed (R)-state (1, 4, 6-10). Other factors effecting O_2/CO binding within heme proteins or models include local polarity and bulk solvent effects, hydrogen-bonding to the coordinated gas or proximal base (with resulting change in its basicity), and porphyrin substituent effects.

The relative importance of the factors influencing O_2/CO binding has been estimated from data on a wide range of model systems synthesized by several groups, and it has been difficult to judge whether in the protein there is a genuine distal steric effect that discriminates against the thermodynamically preferred linear Fe-C-O versus the bent Fe-$O_{\diagdown O}$. Data on binding of isocyanides (RNC) have provided a foundation on which to judge the existence of distal-side steric effects (10-12). The models shown in **1**, developed by Traylor's

Chelated mesoheme, R^1 = CH_2CH_3, R^2 = $CH_2CH_2CO_2CH_3$

Chelated protoheme, R^1 = CH =CH_2, R^2 = $CH_2CH_2CO_2CH_3$

Chelated diacetyldeuteroheme, R^1 = $COCH_3$, R^2 = $CH_2CH_2CO_2CH_3$

Chelated pyrroheme, R^1 = CH_2CH_3, R^2 = H

1

group (13), present a useful reference by which to estimate factors affecting binding at the sixth site; the covalent attachment of the imidazole base to the porphyrin side-chain obviates the necessity of external added base which, with 'bare' four-coordinate hemes, tends to give six-coordinate, low-spin hemes and not the required five-coordinate, high-spin geometry characteristic of Mb and Hb (14).

Olson et al. (11) have carried out detailed studies on isocyanide binding to Mb, Hb, and model systems (Table 1). The usual linear mode of coordination of isocyanides is similar in nature to that of CO, but the isocyanides are more sterically demanding and involve

Table 1. Isocyanide binding in aqueous micelles at 20°C (11)

	Chelated protoheme (1)	Hb, α-subunit
k^{MeNC}	1.0×10^7	3.9×10^5
k^{-MeNC}	0.9	3.9
k^{i-PrNC}	6.9×10^7	1.2×10^4
$k^{-i-PrNC}$	1.5	0.1
k^{t-BuNC}	1.4×10^8	1.2×10^3
$k^{-t-BuNC}$	1.8	0.06

three or more atoms in a vertical orientation relative to the porphyrin plane. The reduction in affinity at Hb compared to the protoheme model with increasing steric bulk (R = Me < i-Pr < t-Bu) is reflected largely in decreased association rates with relatively little change in dissociation rate even for the bulkiest isocyanide. Such a conclusion has been drawn also for binding of CO and O_2 (1, 4, 12, 15), and it is now generally accepted that a distal-side steric interaction between any ligand and environment external to a complex is expressed predominantly in changes in association rate at constant dissociation rates within given systems. This has been interpreted in terms of the $\Delta G^{\ddagger}$ required to disrupt the protein residue in order to establish the correct orientation of the gas molecule prior to coordination. The steric interaction will give rise to lower affinities in heme proteins relative to open model systems (e.g. Table 1).

2. MODEL DESIGN

Synthetic heme models optimally incorporate a porphinato-iron(II) moiety axially bonded by a single imidazole ligand. Problems associated with such modelling are the tendency to give six-coordinate complexes (see above), and the autoxidation of the Fe(II) centre to give finally a μ-oxo-derivative, rather than the requisite reversible O_2-binding (14). One mechanism for autoxidation involves a bimolecular ("dimerization") reaction between initially formed $Fe^{II}O_2$ and residual Fe(II) (16), and this has been prevented by the use of low temperatures or by attachment of the Fe(II) complex to a rigid polymeric surface (17).

Reversible O_2-binding at ambient temperatures, and a crystallographic study of an iron(II)-dioxygen complex, were first achieved using the "picket-fence" porphyrins, 2, a model design incorporating steric bulk on one face only of the porphyrin (18); axial base binding on the open face allows for O_2-binding at the sixth site, with

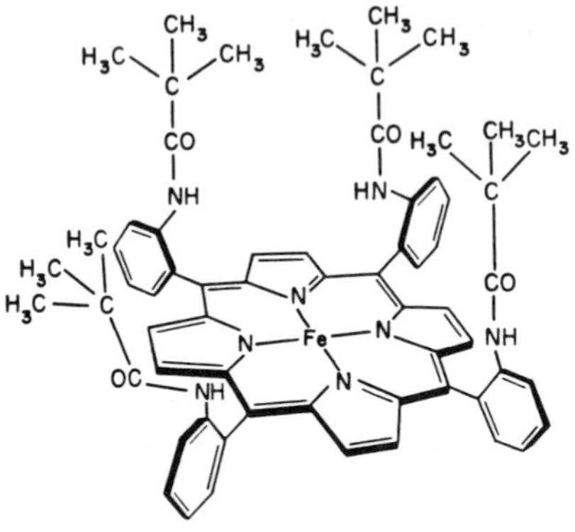

2a Fe(TpivPP)

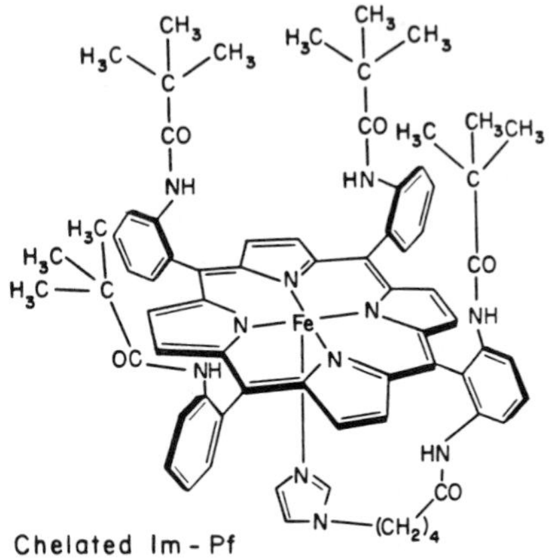

2b Chelated Im‑Pf

"dimerization" prevented sterically.   Variations on a theme have led to pocket porphyrin 3 (4), capped porphyrins 4 (2), and cyclophane hemes 5, 6 (1, 12).   In addition, model systems with steric hindrances on

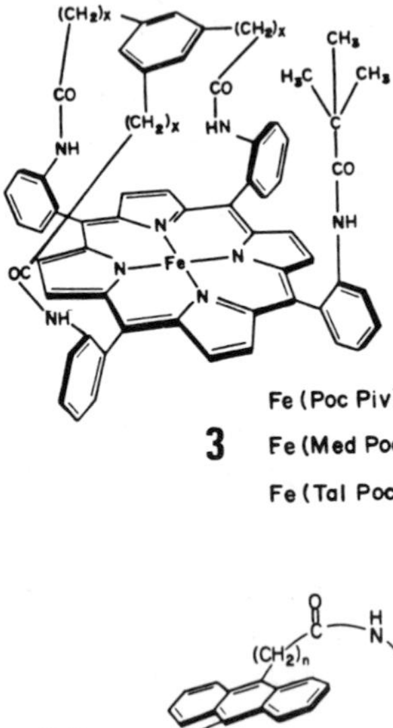

Fe (Poc Piv), x = 1

3   Fe (Med Poc), x = 2

Fe (Tal Poc), x = 3

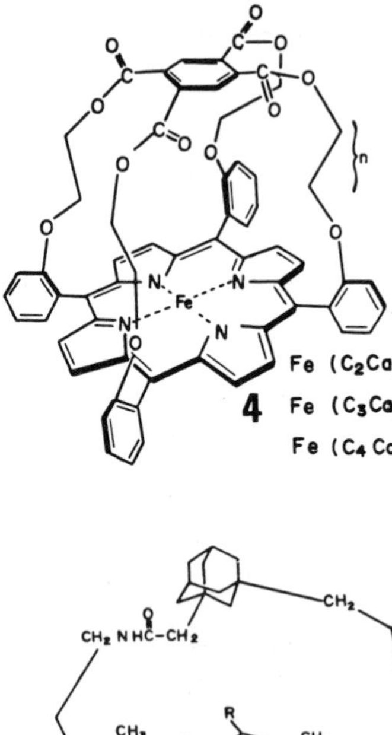

Fe (C₂Cap), n = 2

4 Fe (C₃Cap), n = 3

Fe (C₄Cap), n = 4

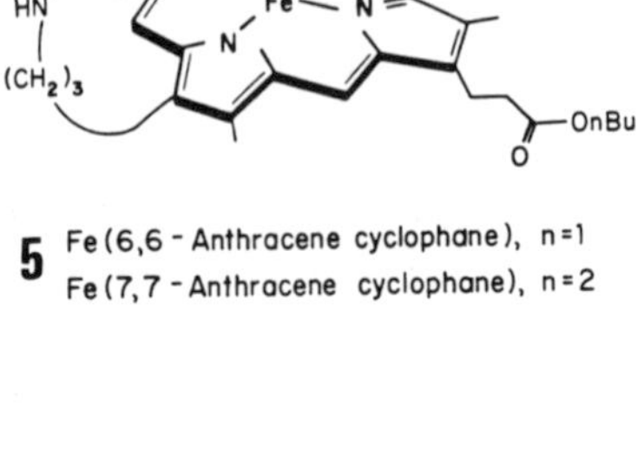

5 Fe (6,6 ‑ Anthracene cyclophane), n = 1
Fe (7,7 ‑ Anthracene cyclophane), n = 2

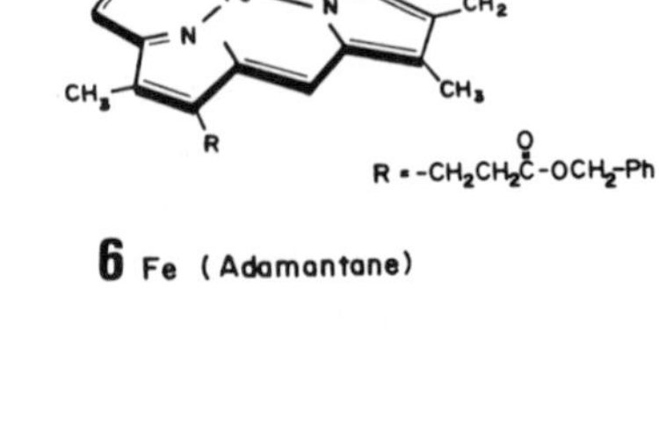

6 Fe (Adamantane)

R = ‑CH₂CH₂C‑OCH₂‑Ph

both porphyrin faces (e.g. the 'basket-handle' porphyrins (19)), as
well as some with protective structures on one face and an appended
nitrogen donor ligand on the other (e.g. **7**, **8**) have been prepared (4,

7 Fe(C$_2$cap-C$_4$strap), n=4
      Fe(C$_2$cap-C$_5$strap), n=5

8

Chelated TPP(Im) B=-NH-(CH$_2$)$_3$-N⌐
Chelated TPP(Py) B=-O-(CH$_2$)$_3$

20). The size of the 'cap' or 'strap' within porphyrins such as **3-7**
can be conveniently varied by changing the number of methylene groups.
The bulky 1,5-Cy$_2$Im base has proved particularly useful for _in situ_
formation of five-coordinate capped hemes because it is not readily
accommodated under the cap (1, 2, 10, 12).

Two fundamentally different approaches have been adopted for the
synthesis of hindered porphyrins. The first is an extension of the
single-step coupling of benzaldehyde and pyrrole to produce TPP (21).
Aromatic aldehydes with ortho amino-substituents are condensed with
pyrrole, and the protective structures are linked to the amino groups
via amide linkages using appropriate acyl chlorides (4, 18);
alternatively, the protective structures are first linked to the
aldehydes at their ortho positions via ester or ether functions, prior
to the coupling with pyrrole (8, 19, 20, 22). The second, more widely
used approach, is to condense, via ester or amide links, a diagonally
β-substituted preformed porphyrin with a terminally bifunctional
molecule carrying appropriate functional groups (1, 15, 23, 24).
Porphyrins produced by such methods are limited in the size of the
cavity produced; in addition, truly hydrophobic cavities cannot be
formed because of the presence of the polar amide, ester or ether
linkages. An early attempt to synthesize such a hydrophobic system
using rigid dipyrromethene precursors resulted in very low yields
during the cyclization step (25). However, based on a synthetic route
used to construct permanently deformed porphyrins (26, 27), we have now
developed an effective method for the synthesis of the durene-capped
porphyrins shown in **9** (28).

The crystal structure of the chloroiron(III) complex with durene-4,4 is shown in **10** (28). Despite the distorted porphyrin core, the square pyramidal geometry at the Fe is typical of other high-spin Fe(III) porphyrins that do not contain a strap (29). The Fe-Cl distance, 2.232(1) Å, is close to that found in Fe(PpIX)Cl, 2.218(6) Å (30), and the distance from Fe to the centre of the phenyl ring of 5.613 Å shows no interaction between the metal and the strap. The Fe is 0.485 Å above the centroid of the porphyrin N atoms; the angle between the best planes of pyrrole rings 1 and 3 is 43.0°, while the corresponding angles between rings 2 and 4 is 17.2°. The bond distances and angles of the porphinato skeleton are nevertheless remarkably similar to those found in 'undistorted' non-strapped complexes such as Fe(TPP) (31) and Fe(PpIX)(SPhNO$_2$) (32).

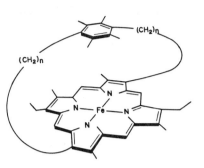

Fe (Durene -4,4), n = 4
9 Fe (Durene -5,5), n = 5
Fe (Durene -7,7), n = 7

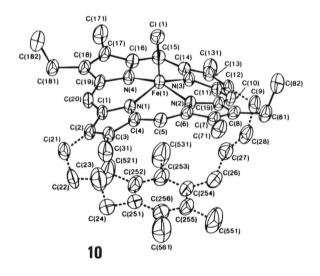

10

Four coordinate Fe^{II}(porp) species were generated <u>in situ</u> in toluene by reduction of the hemin chlorides with 18-crown-6 complexed sodium dithionite (12). Binding of imidazoles to the hemes, and interaction of solutions containing five-coordinate species with isonitriles, CO and O$_2$, were studied by standard spectrophotometric titratiron techniques (8, 12, 14). The O$_2$- binding was readily reversible at 20°C, and decomposition of the O$_2$-adducts to oxo products was relatively slow in the presence of 1.0 M N-base (t$_{1/2}$ > 40 min).

As mentioned above in Section 1, kinetic data for both the on- and off-rates are important criteria for evaluating distal-side effects. At this time, we have only equilibria data to report for the durene systems, but, taken together with literature data, some interesting findings have emerged.

3.   FACTORS AFFECTING BINDING OF ISOCYANIDES CO AND O_2

3.1   Isocyanides

Traylor et al. (10, 12) have used t-BuNC and TMIC as probes for defining central (**11**) and peripheral (**12**) distal steric effects,

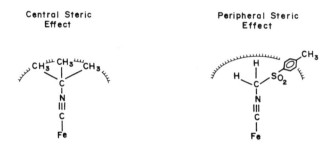

Central Steric Effect	Peripheral Steric Effect
11 t- Butylisocyanide	**12** Tosylmethylisocyanide

respectively, and have shown, for example, using both binding and structural data that the adamantane cap (**6**) provides side hindrance (peripheral), while the anthracene cyclophanes (**5**) provide a roof (central effect). Large ligands can be specifically differentiated by steric effects on the basis of both their size and shape. Table 2 lists some data for binding of isocyanides to five-coordinate hemes.

Table 2. Isocyanide binding to 5-coordinate hemes[a]

System	K^{TMIC}	Peripheral reduction	K^{t-BuNC}	Central reduction	K^{CO}/K^{t-BuNC}
(1) Chelated protoheme	7.0×10^9	1	1.7×10^8	1	2.3
Mb	2.5×10^4	2.8×10^5	8×10^2	2.0×10^5	3.8×10^4
(5) 6,6-Anthracene	7×10^5	10^4	1.5×10^2	1.1×10^6	4×10^3
(6) Adamantane	2×10^5	3.5×10^4	3.0×10^4	6×10^3	6
(9) 7,7-Durene	$>10^5$	-	2×10^5	9×10^2	2×10^2
(9) 5,5-Durene	$>10^5$	-	2×10^3	8.5×10^4	2×10^4
(9) 4,4-Durene	small	$>10^8$	small	$>10^7$	$\sim 10^6$

[a]For the models, axial base = N-MeIm or 1,5-Cy_2Im; benzene or toluene at 20°C. Refs. 1, 10, 12; for durenes (this work).

Compared to the open chelated protoheme, the protein 'cap' of Mb leads to central and peripheral reduction factors of 2.0×10^5 and 2.8×10^5,

respectively, and also effective steric discrimination between CO and
t-BuNC (K^{CO}/K^{t-BuNC} values). The durene series show the expected
trend, the tighter cap giving increased steric hindrance to binding of
both isonitriles. Indeed, for the 4,4-system (**9**), the binding is
negligible at [RNC] = 0.1 M, although n-BuNC was found to bind weakly
under the cap ($K \sim 50$ M^{-1}).

3.2   CO and O_2

As mentioned in Section 1, proximal base effects are important
and are reflected in relaxed/tense (R/T) ratios for CO and O_2 binding
within model hemes utilizing imidazoles either unsubstituted (R) or
substituted (T) in the 2-position. Some data are given in Table 3, and

Table 3.   Proximal base effects; relaxed (R) : tense (T) ratios
for CO and O_2 binding[a]

	System	CO	O_2	Ref.
(cf. 1)	Mesoheme, B:B'[b]	180	-	7
(8)	Chelated TPP(Im): TPP(B")	150	-	4
(2b) (2a)	Chelated Im-Pf: Fe(TpivPP)B"	400	66	4
(3)	Poc Piv, B:B"	40	35	4
(3)	Med Poc, B:B"	40	35	4
(5)	Anthracenes, B:B"[b]	48	48	1
(4)	C_3 Cap, B:B"	34	-	8
(4)	C_2 Cap, B:B"	27	-	8

[a]In toluene at 25°C, unless stated otherwise; B = N-MeIm,
B' = 2-MeIm, B" = 1,2-Me$_2$Im. [b]Aqueous suspension at 20°C.

may be compared to ratios of about 650 (CO) and 300 (O_2) within normal
Hb α-chains (11). For the flat open mesoheme and TPP derivatives the
reduction in CO affinity is 180-150 fold; more encumbered systems give
affinity reduction values of 50-30 for both CO and O_2. The picket-
fence systems, however, seem to be somewhat anomalous among model hemes
(see below in Section 4). Of importance, the proximal effect in T-
state model hemes is reflected about equally in a decrease in k_{on} and
an increase in k_{off}. This is shown for CO binding in Table 4, but is
more difficult to establish for reversible O_2-binding, because of
contributions from electronic effects (4, 10); see below. The same
conclusions can be drawn for R- and T-state normal Hb's (11): the 650

Table 4. Kinetic analysis for R/T model systems (4, 6, 7, 10)[a,b]

System		k^{CO}	Reduction factor	k^{-CO}	Enhancement factor
(cf. 1) Mesoheme (B)[b]		5.8×10^6		0.008	
	(B')	4.8×10^5	12	0.12	15
(cf. 1) Deuteroheme (Im)[c]		1.2×10^7		0.028	
	(B')	1.0×10^6	12	0.45	16
(3) Poc Piv	(B)	5.8×10^5		0.0086	
	(B")	9.8×10^4	6	0.055	6
(3) Med Poc	(B)	1.5×10^6		0.0094	
	(B")	2.1×10^5	7	0.053	6

[a,b]Footnotes as for Table 3. [c]Benzene at 20°C.

factor for CO-binding is reflected in a decrease of k_{on} by a factor of
~65, and an increase in k_{off} of ~10; the 300 factor for O_2-binding
results from k_{on} (x 1/20) and k_{off} (x15). Traylor et al. (1) have
discussed such proximal effects in terms of porphyrin doming in five-
coordinate T-state systems. Doming of the porphyrin has been invoked
also to account for the significantly lower affinity toward O_2 of the
pyridine-strapped C_2-capped models (7) compared to the five-coordinate
$Fe^{II}(C_2cap)py$ (4) analogue with externally added base (20).

Base-elimination pathways have been demonstrated for CO binding
to models with an appended chelate axial base, and result in increased
CO-association and -dissociation rates to and from the four-coordinate
heme (33). Such a mechanism has been invoked to account for increased
k_{on}^{CO} and k_{off}^{CO} values for legume Hb, and chironomous Hb,
and an increased k_{on}^{CO} value for Hb Zurich(β), compared to normal
β-chains of R-state Hb (10, 34). However, the legume Hb and Hb Zurich
possess more open binding pockets and increased association rates for
these systems could result from lack of a distal steric effect
(Sections 1, 4). In heme proteins the base-elimination mechanism may
arise via protonation of the proximal imidazole (34).

The influence of basicity of the proximal ligand on O_2 and CO
binding has been well-documented. Variation within a range of
substituted pyridines is small, while substitution of pyridine by the
better π-donating imidazole gives greatly enhanced O_2 affinity (14, 35-
38), and this is reflected in decreased k^{-O_2} values (Table 5). The
effects are usually much less for CO binding (36-38), but again the

Table 5.   Binding of O_2 and CO to some model hemes: effect of proximal ligand and cap polarity (36-38)[a]

System		k^{O_2}	k^{-O_2}	k^{CO}	k^{-CO}
(2b)	Chelated Im-Pf	2.6×10^8	3.9×10^3	2.9×10^7	0.014
	Chelated py-Pf	3.0×10^8	1.9×10^5	4.8×10^7	0.33
(1)	Chelated Im-meso[b]	2.2×10^7	23	1.1×10^7	0.02
	Chelated py-meso	1.7×10^7	380	1.2×10^7	0.035
(13a)	Amide-py	3.6×10^8	5×10^3	3.5×10^7	0.03
	Amide-Im[c]	3.1×10^8	6.2×10^2	4×10^7	0.0067
(13b)	Ether-py	3×10^8	4×10^4	6.8×10^7	0.069

[a]In benzene or toluene at $25°C$.   [b]Aqueous suspension.   [c]Py of **11a** replaced by Im.

same trends are apparent (Table 5).   The role of the degree of H-bonding between a leu F4 residue and the proximal Im, that in the extreme leads to an axial imidazolate (Im^-), has been studied using Im vs. Im^- systems (39, 40).   The anion system gives considerably decreased CO affinity, but this results from decreased k^{CO} values and was attributed to stabilization of the five-coordinate anionic ground state relative to the transition state (40).   A comparative study with O_2 has not been reported.

      Stabilization of the bound dioxygen via hydrogen-bonding with the distal His E7 residue has now been demonstrated in MbO_2 and α- and β-subunits of human HbO_2 (41, 42), while there is no such H-bonding to the oxygen atom within HbCO (43), data that are consistent with the electronically different nature of the $(Fe^{II}O_2 \leftrightarrow Fe^{III}O_2^-)$ and $Fe^{II}CO$ adducts.   Data on models **13a** and **13b** that differ solely in the

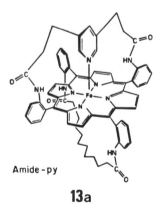

Amide-py

13a

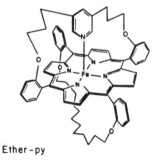

Ether-py

13b

electronic nature of their distal environment (amide vs. the less polar ether link) show that the CO affinity, as measured by on- and off-rates, is essentially the same for both; the O_2 affinity is 10-fold greater for the amide-heme complex, the difference being manifested by a <u>decreased</u> <u>dissociation</u> <u>rate</u> (38, Table 5). Proton nmr studies indicate that the amide proton points toward the centre in the free base porphyrin of **13a**, and is considered to significantly increase the stability of the bound O_2 (44). Five-coordinate hemes having amide linkages within the distal bulk (**5**, **6**, **13a**, **14**) consistently have higher O_2 affinities relative to those with less polar (**4**, **13b**) or open cavities (**1**), and the variation in affinity generally results from decreased dissociation rates (Tables 5, 6). Within hemoproteins, the lack of a distal His E7 in Mb (aplysia) compared to Mb (horse) results in a 6-fold increase in k^{-O_2} (70 vs. 11), while k^{O_2} is 1.5×10^7 for both systems; the data are again consistent with stabilization of bound O_2 via H-bonding in Mb (horse) (45).

Fe SP-15, n = 7

Fe SP-14, n = 6

Fe SP-13, n = 5

R = n-pentyl

14

Table 6. Binding of O_2 and CO to some model hemes of the pyrrole-substituted type[a,b] (1, 12, 15)

	System	k^{O_2}	k^{-O_2}	k^{CO}	k^{-CO}	k^{O_2}/k^{CO}
(1)	Chelated protoheme	6.2×10^7	4000	1.1×10^7	0.025	5.6[c]
(1)	Chelated mesoheme	5.3×10^7	1700	8×10^6	0.03	6.6
(5)	7,7-Anthracene	6×10^7	1000	6×10^6	0.05	10[d]
(5)	6,6-Anthracene	1×10^5	800	3×10^4	0.05	3[e]
(6)	Adamantane	1.5×10^5	690	9.2×10^3	0.05	16[f]
(14)	FeSP-15	1.7×10^6	250	9.1×10^4	0.04	19
(14)	FeSP-14	3×10^5	-	8×10^3	0.04	38
(14)	FeSP-13	-	-	6×10^2	0.07	-
(15)	Fe-Cu-5	1.8×10^6	91	9×10^4	0.02	20
(15)	Fe-Cu-4	5.2×10^5	160	2×10^4	0.02	26

[a]In benzene or toluene at 20°C or 25°C. [b]Chelated hemes have Im base; models have N-MeIm, $1,5Cy_2Im$ or analogue. [c]M value, K^{CO}/K^{O_2} = 2200. [d]M = 1500. [e]M = 4100. [f]M = 530.

Consistent with the $Fe^{\delta+}-O_2^{\delta-}$ (superoxide) formulation is increased O_2-affinity in more polar media (typically by a factor of up to 30 between toluene ($\varepsilon = 2.4$) and, for example, aqueous media ($\varepsilon = 80$)), and this is attributed to stabilization of the charge separation (8, 46). A relatively small effect (3-fold) noted for an $Fe(C_2cap)$ system (4) between DMF ($\varepsilon = 36.7$) and toluene was interpreted in terms of the tight distal pocket restricting the required orientation of solvent molecules for effective solvation of the FeO_2 moiety (8). More polar media can lead to either enhanced (4) or diminished (47) CO binding; however, the variation is slight and is consistent with the more covalent nature of the Fe-CO unit.

Solvation of the five-coordinate heme itself is also considered to effect affinity for binding CO and O_2 (3, 4). With increasing protection, going from TPP to picket-fence (2) systems, solvent stabilization in the ground state is reduced, and affinity for binding the gas is increased; the higher CO-affinites for the more "protected" TMesP and TTPPP systems (vs. TPP) support this suggestion. The data (Table 7) show that the dissociation rates from both open and protected

Table 7.   Binding of CO in TPP and picket-fence systems (3, 4)[a]

System	k^{CO}	k^{-CO}	$P_{1/2}(CO)$
T-state[b]			
Fe(TPP)B	1.6×10^5	0.24	0.15
(2a) Fe(TpivPP)B	1.4×10^6	0.14	0.0089
Fe(TMesP)B	-	-	0.008
Fe(TTPPP)B	-	-	0.009
R-state			
(8) Chelated TPP(Im)	-	-	0.001
(2b) Chelated Im-Pf	3.6×10^7	0.0078	2.2×10^{-5}

[a] In aromatic hydrocarbon solvents, 20-27°C.   [b] B = $1,2\text{-Me}_2\text{Im}$.

hemes are similar, implying that the extent of solvation in the transition state is probably similar for both types. Of significance, the exeptionally high CO (and O_2 affinity) appears to be intrinsic to the TPP-derived systems, and is not apparent in the pyrrole-substituted model hemes (cf. Tables 5, 6).

Finally, porphyrin peripheral effects in the form of simple substituents at the pyrrole positions (cf. 1) can modify CO/O_2 binding, but the electronic effects in hemoproteins are complicated because of steric interactions between the substituent side-chains and the surrounding globin. Within models, increasingly basic groups (ethyl > vinyl > acetyl) give enhanced O_2-binding which results from decreasing $k^{-O}{}_2$ values; CO binding is relatively insensitive to side-chain electronic effects (48).

4. DISCRIMINATORY BINDING OF LINEAR CO RELATIVE TO BENT O_2--EVIDENCE FOR AND AGAINST

Having noted in Sections 1 and 3 the many factors that effect binding of CO and O_2, we will now briefly survey some evidence for and against discriminatory binding, remembering that any such genuine distal steric effect is considered to be reflected largely in differences in on-rates. Thus Hb(Zurich), which has a more open binding pocket than normal Hb, shows an increased k^{CO} (2.2×10^7 vs. 4.5×10^6) with little change in $k^O{}_2$ (6.5×10^7 vs. 5×10^7), the data supporting discriminatory binding in normal Hb (4, 10, 34). In contrast, the CO affinity of R-state normal Hb ($P_{1/2} = 0.001$) is much the same as that of the open chelated protoheme 1 in aqueous suspension ($P_{1/2} = 0.002$) (10, 12, 49). In Mb, however, which shows a reduced CO affinity ($P_{1/2} = 0.024$) relative to R-state Hb, distal steric interactions may play a role in axial ligand binding (12, 49). It should be recalled that normal Hb and Mb both show crystallographically off-axis tilt of the Fe-C-O moiety (1, 49). The relative binding affinities of O_2, NO (bent geometry) and CO in Mb (horse) vs. the protoheme (N-MeIm) complex (cf. 1) are reduced by factors of 1.6, 1.9 and 15.0 for the gases, respectively, and are consistent with depressed CO binding in the protein (50); however, without kinetic data, caution should be exercised in interpretation!

Data for the pocket porphyrin series (3), on comparison with those for the more open chelated picket-fence system (2b) (Table 8),

Table 8. Binding of O_2 and CO to chelated picket-fence and pocket hemes (4)[a,b]

System	k^{CO}	k^{-CO}	$P_{1/2}(CO)$	k^{O_2}	k^{-O_2}	$P_{1/2}(O_2)$
(2b) Chelated Im-Pf	3.6×10^7	0.0078	2.2×10^{-5}	4.3×10^8	2900	0.58
(3) Med Poc (B)	1.5×10^6	0.0094	6.5×10^{-4}	1.7×10^7	71	0.36
(3) Poc Piv (B)	5.8×10^5	0.0086	1.5×10^{-3}	2.2×10^6	9	0.36

[a]In toluene at 25°C. [b]B = N-MeIm.

have been interpreted to give support for discriminatory binding. While O_2 affinities are similar throughout, the CO-affinity is dramatically reduced in the smallest binding pocket (Poc Piv) and this is reflected in the required decreasing k^{CO} values at essentially constant dissociation rates. However, the 'constant' O_2-binding results from decreasing $k^{-O}{}_2$ values as well as the decreasing $k^O{}_2$ values, and an explanation based on special structural requirements for the O_2 was invoked to rationalize the data.

Equilibrium data for the capped porphyrins (4) relative to those for a TPP system (Table 9) have been generally interpreted in terms of

Table 9. Binding of CO, O_2, and NO in TPP and capped hemes, 4 (2, 8)[a]

System	$P_{1/2}(CO)$	$P_{1/2}(O_2)$	$P_{1/2}(NO)$
Fe(TPP)B	0.14	5.3	1.1×10^{-7}
Fe(C_2-cap)B	0.20	27	2.0×10^{-6}
Fe(C_3-cap)B	0.14	6000[b]	3.3×10^{-6}

[a] In toluene, B = $1,2\text{-Me}_2\text{Im}$; CO and NO data at $25°C$; O_2 data at $-45°C$.
[b] Possible interference from B_2 species.

discrimination via a peripheral steric effect against the bent molecules O_2 and NO relative to essentially constant binding for linear CO.

Table 6 gives some data for the anthracene (5) and adamantane hemes (6); on comparison with the chelated meso- or protohemes (1), both CO and O_2 seem to suffer steric hindrance to binding, as evidenced by the reduced association rates. The $k^O{}_2/k^{CO}$ ratios, which seem to offer the best parameter to judge the discriminatory effect, vary by a factor of only 3, and so discrimination against CO is small. Neither the anthracene cap, which was demonstrated to display a central steric effect toward isocyanide, nor the adamantane cap, which displayed a peripheral steric effect toward isocyanide (Table 2), thus shows significant steric differentiation between CO and O_2 binding. Furthermore, even with the extremely hindered strapped hemes (14), the cofacial diporphyrins (15), and a recently described (51) 5,5-pyridine-cyclophane (16), for which CO and O_2 association rates are reduced by

Fe (5,5-Pyridine cyclophane)

Fe–Cu–4, n = 1
Fe–Cu–5, n = 2

15   R=n-pentyl

16   R = $-CH_2CH_2C-OCH_2-Ph$

as much as 10^4 compared to the chelated open-hemes, only relatively small discriminatory effects are seen (Table 6).

In summary, within pyrrole-substituted hemes, the more sterically hindered systems (6, 14, 15) do show slight discrimination between CO and O_2 (Table 6), but the CO on-rates for these models are much less than seen for a heme protein such as Mb, 10^5-10^6 (1, 4, 12); however, models that have CO on-rates of this magnitude show no discrimination at all (Table 6). Within the TPP-derived porphyrin series, k_{on} values for both CO and O_2 (that are comparable to values for heme proteins) decrease to similar extents as the pocket-size reduces, and the primary difference lies in k_{off} for O_2 (Table 8); it is clear, however, that this could result from changes is polarity and H-bonding interactions between the O_2 and the side-chains of the bridge.

The durene-capped series (9) provide ideal reference systems for obtaining data and conclusions that are not clouded by the complications of polarity within the cap. Although available kinetic data are preliminary and limited, several comments can be made. Firstly, the K^{O_2} values are largely insensitive to cap-size, which is entirely consistent with the lack of polar functionality (Table 10).

Table 10. Binding of CO and O_2 to durene and other models[a]

	System	K^{CO}	K^{O_2}	K^{CO}/K^{O_2}(M)
	Mb	2.5×10^7	1.3×10^6	20
(1)	Chelated protoheme	4×10^8	1.5×10^4	2.7×10^4
(9)	7,7-Durene	6.6×10^7	1.3×10^3	5×10^4
(9)	5,5-Durene	8.6×10^7	1.3×10^3	6.5×10^4
(9)	4,4-Durene	4.3×10^6	4.8×10^2	8.6×10^3
(16)	5,5-py-cyclophane	2.7×10^3	1.6×10^2	17

[a]For the models, benzene or toluene at 20°C; axial base for durenes and py-cyclophane is 1,5-Cy_2Im; data for Mb and chelated protoheme from Ref. 12; data for a 5,5-py-cyclophane from Ref. 51.

The association rates for the 7,7-durene system reveal $\sim$10-fold reductions for both gases ($k^{CO} \sim 1 \times 10^6$, $k^{O_2} \sim 6 \times 10^6$) relative to chelated open-hemes (Table 6), with no significant change in M value, K^{CO}/K^{O_2} (52); a similar M value is observed for the 5,5-durene system (Table 10). Secondly, the relative M values within the durene systems (Table 10) might be taken to indicate about a 7-fold discrimination against CO for the 4,4-system but, without on- and off-rate constants, no definite conclusion can be drawn. Finally, data for the 5,5-system, taken together with those for the closely related 5,5-pyridine-cyclophane system (**16**, 51) show a genuinely remarkable effect (Table 10). Both 5,5-systems, which probably have similar pocket sizes, appear not to sterically differentiate between the association of CO and O_2 to any significant extent; furthermore, the hemes show very similar k^{-CO} values of ~0.2 s^{-1} (51, and present work). The overall M value, however, drops from 6.5×10^4 in the durene system to 17 in the pyridine-cyclophane. Significantly, the main difference in the nature of the two systems is expected to be within the electronic properties of the distal environment--hydrophobic links in the durene systems and polar amide/py functions in the pyridine-cyclophane. The major contribution to CO/O_2 differentiation exemplified in the pyridine-heme, relative to open-hemes and the 5,5-durene system, must therefore arise from an increased binding of O_2 relative to CO, within the polar distal pocket of this system. These findings further substantiate a dominance of polarity effects in differentiating CO and O_2 binding in model hemes, and presumably heme proteins.

ACKNOWLEDGMENT.

    This work was supported by the Canadian Natural Sciences and Engineering Research Council and the U.S. National Institutes of Health (AM 17989).

5.   REFERENCES

(1)   T.G. Traylor, S. Tsuchiya, D. Campbell, M. Mitchell, D. Stynes, and N. Koga, J. Am. Chem. Soc. 107 (1985) 604-614, and references therein.

(2)   M. Shimizu, F. Basolo, M.N. Vallejo, and J.E. Baldwin, Inorg. Chim. Acta, 91 (1984) 247-250; 251-255, and references therein.

(3)   K.S. Suslick, M.M. Fox, and T.J. Reinert, J. Am. Chem. Soc., 106 (1984) 4522-4525, and references therein.

(4)   J.P. Collman, J.I. Brauman, B.L. Iverson, J.L. Sessler, R.M. Morris and Q.H. Gibson, J. Am. Chem. Soc., 105 (1983) 3052-3064, and references therein.

(5)   Abbreviations: Mb = myoglobin; Hb = hemoglobin; TPP, TMesP, TTPPP are the dianions of meso-tetraphenyl-, -tetramesityl- and -tetrakis(2,4,6triphenyl-phenyl)porphyrins, respectively; PpIX is the protoporphyrin IX dianion; Pf = the picket-fence porphyrin dianion (**2**); py = pyridine, MeIm = methylimidazole, Cy_2Im =

dicyclohexylimidazole, TMIC = tosylmethylisocyanide; k^A and k^{-A} represent association and dissociation rate constants for gas A, respectively, and have units of $M^{-1}s^{-1}$ and s^{-1}, respectively; $P_{1/2}$ = pressure in torr for 50% formation of gas adduct in solution, and is the inverse of the equilibrium binding constant K^A, which is expressed, however, in units of M^{-1}.

(6)   J.P. Collman, J.I. Brauman, M.D. Kenneth, T.R. Halpert, and K.S. Suslick, Proc. Natl. Acad. Sci. U.S.A., 75 (1978) 564-568.

(7)   D.K. White, J.B. Cannon, and T.G. Traylor, J. Am. Chem. Soc., 101 (1979) 2443-2453.

(8)   T. Hashimoto, R.L. Dyer, M.J. Crossley, J.E. Baldwin and F. Basolo, J. Am. Chem. Soc., 104 (1982) 2101-2109.

(9)   G.B. Jameson, W.T. Robinson, and J.A. Ibers, in "Hemoglobin and Oxygen Binding," ed. Chien Ho, Elsevier, Amsterdam, 1982, p. 25-35.

(10)   T.G. Traylor, D.H. Campbell, S. Tsuchiya, D.V. Stynes, and M.J. Mitchell, in "Hemoglobin and Oxygen Binding," ed. Chien Ho, Elsevier, Amsterdam, 1982, 425-433.

(11)   M.P. Mims, A.G. Porras, J.S. Olson, R.W. Noble, and J.A. Peterson, J. Biol. Chem., 258 (1983) 14219-14232.

(12)   T.G. Traylor, N. Koga, L.A. Deardruff, P.N. Swepston, and J.A. Ibers, J. Am. Chem. Soc., 106 (1984) 5132-5143, and references therein.

(13)   T.G. Traylor, C.K. Chang, J. Geibel, A. Berzinis, T. Mincey, and J. Cannon, J. Am. Chem. Soc., 101 (1979) 6716-6731.

(14)   B.R. James, in "The Porphyrins," ed. D. Dolphin, Academic Press, Vol. V, New York, 1978, p. 205-302.

(15)   B. Ward, C. Wang, and C.K. Chang, J. Am. Chem. Soc., 103 (1981) 5236-5238.

(16)   A.L. Balch, Y-W. Chan, R-J. Cheng, G.N. LaMar, L. Latos-Grazynski, and M.W. Renner, J. Am. Chem. Soc., 106 (1984) 7779-7785, and references therein.

(17)   R.D. Jones, D.A. Summerville, and F.Basolo, Chem. Rev., 79 (1979) 139-179.

180   David, Dolphin, James

(18)   G.B. Jameson, G.A. Rodley, W.T. Robinson, R.R. Gagné, C.A. Reed,
       and J.P. Collman, Inorg. Chem., 17 (1978) 850-857, and references
       therein.

(19)   M. Momenteau, J. Mispelter, B. Loock, and E. Bisagni, J. Chem.
       Soc. Perkin Trans. I, (1983) 189-196.

(20)   J.E. Baldwin, J.H. Cameron, M.J. Crossley, I.J. Dagley, S.R.
       Hall, and T. Klose, J. Chem. Soc. Dalton Trans., (1984) 1739-
       1746.

(21)   A.D. Adler, F.R. Longo, J.D. Finarelli, J. Goldmatcher, J. Assow,
       and L. Korsakoff, J. Org. Chem., 32 (1967) 476.

(22)   M. Momenteau, B. Loock, D. Lavalette, C. Tétreau, and J.
       Mispelter, J. Chem. Soc. Chem. Commun., (1983) 962-964.

(23)   A.R. Battersby, A.J. Bartholomew, and T. Nitta, J. Chem. Soc.
       Chem. Commun., (1983) 1291-1293.

(24)   H. Ogoshi, H. Sigimoto, and Z. Yoshida, Tet. Letters, (1976)
       4477-4480.

(25)   H. Diekmann, C.K. Chang, and T.G. Traylor, J. Am. Chem. Soc., 93
       (1971) 4068-4070.

(26)   T.P. Wijesekera, J.B. Paine, III, and D. Dolphin, J. Org. Chem.,
       in press.

(27)   T.P. Wijesekera, J.B. Paine, III, D. Dolphin, F.W.B. Einstein,
       and T. Jones, J. Am. Chem. Soc., 105 (1983) 6747-6749.

(28)   S. David, D. Dolphin, B.R. James, J.B. Paine, III, T.P.
       Wijesekera, F.W.B. Einstein, and T. Jones, Can. J. Chem.,
       submitted.

(29)   W.R. Scheidt and C.A. Reed, Chem. Rev., 81 (1981) 543-555.

(30)   D.F. Koenig, Acta Cryst., 18 (1965) 663-673.

(31)   K. Anzai, K. Hatano, Y.T. Lee, and W.R. Scheidt, Inorg. Chem., 20
       (1981) 2337-2339.

(32)   S.C. Tang, S. Koch, G.C. Papaefthymiou, S. Foner, R.B. Frankel,
       J.A. Ibers, and R.H. Holm, J. Am. Chem. Soc., 98 (1976) 2414-
       2434.

(33) J. Geibel, J. Cannon, D. Campbell, and T.G. Traylor, J. Am. Chem.
      Soc., 100 (1978) 3575-3585.

(34) G.M. Giacometti, T.G. Traylor, P. Ascenzi, M. Brunori, and E.
      Antonini, J. Biol. Chem., 252 (1977) 7447-7448.

(35) J.E. Linard, P.E. Ellis, J.R. Budge, R.D. Jones, and F. Basolo,
      J. Am. Chem. Soc., 102 (1980) 1896-1904.

(36) J.P. Collman, J.I. Brauman, K.M. Doxsee, J.L. Sessler, R.M.
      Morris, and Q.H. Gibson, Inorg. Chem., 22 (1983) 1427-1432.

(37) T.G. Traylor, D. Dampbell, V. Sharma, and J. Geibel, J. Am. Chem.
      Soc., 101 (1979) 5376-5383.

(38) M. Momenteau and D. Lavalette, J. Chem. Soc. Chem. Commun.,
      (1982) 341-343.

(39) T. Mincey and T.G. Traylor, J. Am. Chem. Soc., 101 (1979) 765-
      766.

(40) M.A. Standford, J.C. Swartz, T.E. Phillips, and B.M. Hoffman, J.
      Am. Chem. Soc., 102 (1980) 4492-4499.

(41) B. Shaanan, J. Mol. Biol., 171 (1983) 31-59; Nature, 296 (1983)
      683-684.

(42) S.E.V. Phillips, J. Mol.Biol., 142 (1980) 531-554.

(43) J.M. Baldwin, J. Mol. Biol., 136 (1980) 103-128, and references
      therein.

(44) J. Mispelter, M. Momenteau, D. Lavalette, and J-M. Lhoste, J. Am.
      Chem. Soc., 105 (1983) 5165-5166.

(45) E.E. Di Iorio, U.T. Meier, J.D.G. Smit, and K.H. Winterhalter, J.
      Biol. Chem., 260 (1985) 2160-2164.

(46)   J.P. Collman, J.I. Brauman, K. Doxsee, T.R. Halbert, and K.S.
      Suslick, Proc. Natl. Acad. Sci. U.S.A., 76 (1979) 6035-6039.

(47) T.G. Traylor, D. Campbell, and S. Tsuchiya, J. Am. Chem. Soc.,
      101 (1979) 4748-4749.

(48) T.G. Traylor, D.K. White, D.H. Campbell, and A.P. Berzinis, J.

Am. Chem. Soc., 103 (1981) 4932-4936.

(49) T.G. Traylor and A.P. Berzinis, Proc. Natl. Acad. Sci. U.S.A., 77 (1980) 3171-3175.

(50) R.W. Romberg and R.J. Kassner, Biochem., 18 (1979) 5387-5392.

(51) T.G. Traylor, N. Koga, and L.A. Deardurff, private communication.

(52) G.B. Jameson and J.A. Ibers, Comments Inorg. Chem., 2 (1983) 97-126.

The Effect of Hydrogen-Bonding of Amides on The Stability of Axial Ligand Compexes of Metalloporphyrins

F. Ann Walker,* Virginia L. Balke, and Joyce T. West

Department of Chemistry, San Francisco State University, San Francisco, CA 94132

SUMMARY

In this study it is shown that amide substituents on the phenyl rings of tetraphenylporphyrins, TPPs, can engage in hydrogen-bond donation to anions displaced by the presence of neutrally-charged axial ligands (as for Fe(III) porphyrins) or to polar, coordinated ligands (as for dioxygen bound to Co(II) porphyrins).

1 INTRODUCTION

For some time we have been interested in two aspects of the physical and chemical properties of heme groups, those caused by the electronic effects of substituents on the porphyrin ring and those caused by the electronic properties of axial ligands. We could call these _cis_ effects and _trans_ effects. We initially began studying symmetrically-substituted tetraphenylporphyrins for two main reasons: First, the meso-tetraphenyl groups provide a relatively simple way of preparing a large number of porphyrins in which electronic and steric effects may be systematically varied, and second, we felt that the four-fold symmetry of tetraphenylporphyrins would simplify the interpretation of physical properties in terms of molecular orbital theory. More recently we have become interested in the properties of unsymmetrically substituted tetraphenylporphyrins and their metal complexes, since such model compounds allow us to vary the distribution of electron density around the porphyrin ring in a controlled manner and thus determine quantitatively the effect of this electron density distribution on the magnetic, spectroscopic, electrochemical and axial ligation properties of these metalloporphyrins. Some interesting general principles have emerged, which will be summarized below. However, in most of the published work which we will describe, the physical properties of porphyrins having amide substituents, ortho, meta, or para-NHCOR, were anomalous. The purpose of this paper is to reiterate the cases in which amide-substituted tetraphenylporphyrins were previously found to behave anomalously, and to report the extensions of our investigation of these substituents, which now allow us to explain the reason for the anomalies.

We have previously reported the nmr spectra of free base and zinc, and of low-spin Fe(III) bis-N-methylimidazole complexes of tetraphenylporphyrins (1,2). We found that when substituents of very different electronic properties were mixed, the resulting unsymmetrically substituted free base and ZnTPP derivatives showed average pyrrole proton nmr shifts which were proportional to the average electronic properties of the phenyl substituents, but that individual pyrrole proton shifts were related to the location of that pyrrole proton with respect to the phenyl rings containing electron-donating substituents: Those pyrrole protons closest to such groups were shifted downfield relative to those close to electron-withdrawing groups, indicating more electron density in the porphyrin σ system near the electron-rich groups. Since the difference in Hammett σ constants (3) of H and p-NHCOCH$_3$ (-0.01) or m-NHCOCH$_3$ (+0.21) are smaller than those utilized in reference (1), we were not surprised that we observed no splitting of the pyrrole proton resonance for the mono-o-, m-, and p-NHCOCH$_3$ derivatives of TPPH$_2$ and TPPZn, and hence did not report their nmr spectra. Likewise, the electronic absorption spectra of the amide-substituted TPP free bases and their Zn(II) complexes were completely normal and indistinguishable from those of TPPH$_2$ and TPPZn, respectively. However, while the electronic absorption spectra of the Fe(III) complexes, both in the high-spin chloroiron and low-spin bis-N-methylimidazole iron(III) forms, were essentially indistinguishable from those of TPPFeCl and TPP(N-MeIm)$_2^+$Cl$^-$, respectively, the nmr spectra of the low-spin complexes were unique and inexplicable at the time the work was published: All other unsymmetrically substituted $(X)_1(Y)_3$TPPFe(N-MeIm)$_2^+$Cl$^-$ complexes in CDCl$_3$ showed splitting of their contact-shifted pyrrole proton resonance into a 1:1:2 pattern if the single phenyl's substituent was more electron-withdrawing than the other three, and a 2:1:1 pattern if the single phenyl substituent was more electron-donating than the other three; the spread of the pyrrole resonances was found to correlate with the difference in Hammett σ constants, $\sigma_X - \sigma_Y$ (2). The only two exceptions to this correlation were the meta- and para-acetamide substituted TPPFe(N-MeIm)$_2^+$Cl$^-$ complexes (ortho-substituted derivatives were not included in this correlation). In each of the acetamides the anomalous pyrrole-proton pattern appeared to suggest that the apparent σ-constants of these two substituents were extremely negative, or in other words, that the amide groups appeared to be very strongly electron donating (2). Derived values of σ_p = -0.4 and σ_m = -1.3 could be assigned, based on Figure 4 of reference 2.

Similar anomalous behavior of the amides was observed during electrochemical studies of Fe(III)/(II) redox of a large series of symmetrical and unsymmetrical TPPFe(N-MeIm)$_2^+$Cl$^-$ complexes in CH$_2$Cl$_2$ (Figure 3 of reference 5), where the redox potential shifts in the positive direction (i.e., to favor Fe(II)) as the sum of the electronic effects of the substituents becomes more positive (electron-withdrawing), whether the porphyrins were symmetrically or unsymmetrically substituted, except for the amides. Again, the meta- and para-NHCOCH$_3$ substituents appear to be strongly electron-donating. However, ortho-amides, o-NHCOR, appear to be electron-with-drawing, but to a varying degree, depending on the nature of the R group. At the time this work was published, we were unable to explain why amides were anomalous.

In our epr studies of low-spin Fe(III) porphyrins (5,6), we found no evidence for anomalous g-values or signal shapes of amide-substituted TPPFe(N-MeIm)$_2^+$Cl$^-$ complexes. Furthermore, no difference in the epr signal was noted when iodide was substituted for chloride as the counterion (6). Hence, anomalies noted in nmr and electrochemical studies were not revealed in the epr investigations.

More recently we have studied the thermodynamics of axial ligand addition to unsymmetrically substituted TPPFe(III) derivatives (4). The reaction is that described by equation 1, where the product contains a formal positive charge at the iron center and the chloride is part of the tight ion pair:

$$\qquad\qquad\qquad\qquad\qquad\qquad\qquad\qquad\qquad (1)$$

This tight ion pair describes the state of the product of reaction 1 in CHCl$_3$ and CH$_2$Cl$_2$, as we have previously shown (7). However, in more polar solvents such as DMF and DMSO, the ions are separated (7).

In our recent studies of reaction 1 we found that Fe(III) exhibits a complex behavior, with symmetrically para-substituted TPP derivatives being much more sensitive to the electronic effects of substituents than symmetrically meta-substituted or unsymmetrically para-substituted TPP derivatives. We explained the unique behavior of symmetrically para-substituted TPPs in terms of the involvement of one of the para-phenyl substituents in direct resonance with the iron center to relieve the positive charge on iron (4). In extending this work to the acetamide-substituted TPPs, we were surprised to see the extent of the anomalous behavior exhibited by these compounds with respect to reaction 1. These results, to be discussed below, provided the key to the cause of the previously-observed anomalies, and led us to several other lines of investigation, including a return to the study of the epr spectra of cobalt porphyrin-dioxygen complexes.

2 EXPERIMENTAL

Specialty chemicals (pyrrole, benzaldehyde, the nitrobenzaldehydes, N-methyl-imidazole, benzimidazole, deuterochloroform) were obtained from Aldrich Chemical Company. Solvents (propionic acid, methylene chloride, chloroform, dimethyl-formamide, dimethylsulfoxide, toluene, benzene) were obtained from Spectrum Chemical Company. For spectroscopic measurements of equilibrium constants, spectroscopic grade chloroform (MCB) was utilized.

The acetamide-substituted tetraphenylporphyrins were prepared by first synthesizing the appropriate mixture of nitrophenylporphyrins by our previously published adaptation of the Adler synthesis (1,2). The mono-ortho-, meta- or para-nitro $TPPH_2$ isomer was separated by gravity chromatography on silica gel (Baker chromatographic grade) utilizing 70:30 benzene:petroleum ether (30-60^0 boiling fraction). The nitro groups were then reduced to amino by means of the $SnCl_2$/HCl method (8), followed by chromatography of the product mono-amino-$TPPH_2$. This purified product was then reacted, with stirring, with a two-fold excess of acetyl chloride or other acid chloride in dry benzene solution containing enough dry pyridine to maintain the porphyrin in its free base (purple) form. After a half-hour reaction time, the reaction mixture was washed at least five times with dilute sodium hydroxide, followed by water, dried over sodium sulfate, and chromatographed on silica gel with benzene to remove any unreacted aminoporphyrin, then eluted with methylene chloride, and the product was evaporated to dryness. Other mono-substituted $TPPH_2$ derivatives were prepared as described previously (1,2). Iron insertion and purification of the TPPFeCl derivatives were effected by the same methods as described previously (4-6).

The $(m-NHCOCH_3)_1$TPPFeCl sample was methylated by the Hakomori method (9): To 75 mL dimethylsulfoxide was added sufficient sodium hydride dispersed in mineral oil to create a 0.1 M solution of the dimsyl anion. This solution was then added to a 20 mg sample of $(m-NHCOCH_3)_1$TPPFeCl, followed by 15 mL methyl iodide. The solution was heated with stirring to 80 ^{0}C for two hours and then stirred at room temperature for two days. Methylene chloride (100 mL) was then added, followed by 10 mL distilled water to quench the remaining dimsyl base. The resulting solution was washed repeatedly with water to remove DMSO, dried over $MgSO_4$ and chromatographed on silica gel, first with CH_2Cl_2 to remove hydrocarbon and free base porphyrin impurities, and then with 5% methanol to elute the iron-containing product. The solution was evaporated to dryness, re-dissolved in dry benzene, and HCl gas bubbled through, followed by re-evaporation to dryness.

Equilibrium constants were measured by spectrophotometric methods as described previously (4,7). A Cary 17 spectrophotometer, equipped with circulating constant temperature bath and jacketed cell holder was utilized in these measurements. The temperature was maintained at 25.0 ± 0.1 °C. Epr studies were carried out on a Varian E-12 equipped with flowing nitrogen temperature controller. The field sweep was calibrated utilizing an nmr gaussmeter, and field-frequency calibration was achieved utilizing a sample of DPPH (g = 2.0036). Temperature calibration was carried out utilizing a small-gauge copper-constantan thermocouple referenced to distilled ice-water. Nmr measurements of ligand exchange rates were carried out by the methods outlined by Satterlee, LaMar, and Bold (10) utilizing the Nicolet NT-360 nmr spectrometer at the University of California, Davis, which was equipped with flowing nitrogen temperature controller. Approximately 1000 transients were collected at each temperature and transformed utilizing an exponential multiplication apodization factor of no more than 5 Hz. The Nicolet software routine NTCCAP, for curve analysis and deconvolution was utilized to obtain the positions, intensities, widths and relative areas of the single (para-substituted) or two partially overlapping (meta and ortho-substituted TPPFe(III)) methyl peaks of coordinated N-methylimidazole.

3 RESULTS AND DISCUSSION

Figure 1 summarizes the results of the measurement of β_2 for reaction 1 for the ortho-, meta- and para-acetamide-substituted TPPFe(III) complexes, in comparison to other symmetrically and unsymmetrically-substituted analogs reported in reference 4. Note that the m-NHCOCH$_3$ derivative has a value of β_2 more than two orders of magnitude larger than expected (log β_2 = 5.36) based upon its Hammett σ-constant (3), and larger even than the value of β_2 measured for the most strongly electron-donating TPP derivative investigated, (p-NEt$_2$)$_4$TPPFeCl (log β_2 = 4.11).

Figure 1. Plot of the values of log β_2 for reaction 1 vs. the sum of the Hammett σ constants of the amide substituents on the phenyl rings of TPPFe(III). The constant used for the ortho-amide is that obtained from the Fe(III)/(II) redox potential (5). The lines represent the data reported in reference (4) for symmetrically- and unsymmetrically-substituted TPPFe(III) complexes.

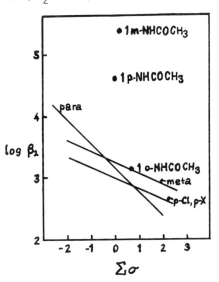

In seeking an explanation of these results we recalled the results of earlier studies of the effect of axial base on the size of β_2 reported from this laboratory

(7): N-H imidazoles were found to have β_2 values about three orders of magnitude larger than N-R imidazoles. This result had been explained on the basis of H-bonding between an imidazole N-H and the displaced Cl^- which is part of the tight ion pair of the product of equation 1 in $CHCl_3$ solution. In fact, the crystal and molecular structure of $TPPFe(HIm)_2^+Cl-$ reported by Hoard and coworkers shows clearly that Cl^- is hydrogen-bonded to an imidazole N-H (11). Thus we postulated that the reason for the anomalously large values of log β_2 for the mono-m- and p-$NHCOCH_3$ derivatives of TPPFeCl was due to H-bond donation from the amide N-H to the displaced Cl^-. According to the predictions of space-filling models (CPK), the meta-amide should hold the Cl^- in about the same position as would a N-H imidazole, while the para-amide would hold Cl^- much further from the Fe(III) center, producing a less stable ion pair. The ortho-amide is more difficult to explain quantitatively because it is pressed so tightly against the porphyrin ring in the region where the axial ligand binds that H-bonding should be disfavored on steric grounds, but favored on ion pair stabilization grounds. Thus, we hypothesized, the resulting β_2 is a balance of these two competing factors. Such H-bond donation of the amide substituents would not only increase β_2 by stabilizing the ion paired product in $CHCl_3$ solution, but also, to the extent that H-bond donation occurred, the amide should become a more electron-donating substituent, which would further stabilize the ion paired product.

Although the above explanation seems plausible, we wished to test this hypothesis by as many means as possible. Below are summarized the results of four tests, all of which are consistent with there being an important role for H-bonding of amides present on the phenyl ring of tetraphenylporphyrins.

Test 1: H-bond competition between an N-H imidazole ligand and a covalently attached amide. Since N-H imidazoles have been shown to hydrogen-bond to displaced Cl^- in $CHCl_3$ solution, we used benzimidazole (log β_2 = 3.33 (7), similar to that for N-methylimidazole binding to TPPFeCl, log β_2 = 3.18 (7)) to see if the possible competition between H-bond donors would decrease the enhancement of β_2 due to the amide's ability to H-bond. Indeed, the value of log β_2 for addition of benzimidazole to $(m-NHCOCH_3)_1$TPPFeCl is 4.15, or only a factor of 7 enhancement of β_2 over that for TPPFeCl, as compared to the factor of 160 enhancement found for addition of N-MeIm to the meta-amide derivative (Figure 1).

Test 2: Removal of H-bonding capability by methylation of the amide. The mono-meta-N-methylacetamide-substituted TPPFeCl derivative, prepared by the Hakomori method (9) (see experimental section) was utilized in this test of our hydrogen-bonding hypothesis. The value of log β_2 for reaction 1 was found to be 3.65 for $(m-N(CH_3)COCH_3)_1$TPPFeCl, as compared to 5.36 for $(m-NHCOCH_3)_1$TPPFeCl, or a decrease of nearly two log units upon methylation of the amide. However, this value of 3.65 for log β_2 is somewhat larger than expected (3.20, Fig. 1) for a single meta-amide substituent where H-bonding is not involved, based upon the expected Hammett σconstant of +0.21 (3). In any case, it is clear that methylation of the amide destroys the anomalously strong tendency for the complex to bind N-methylimidazole.

 Test 3: Axial ligand kinetics. The N-methyl resonance of coordinated N-methylimidazole of TPPFe(N-MeIm)$_2^+$Cl$^-$ derivatives occurs at 18-19 ppm downfield from TMS at 25 $^{\circ}$C in deuterochloroform solution, depending on the phenyl substituents of the TPP. It is well separated from the other resonances of these paramagnetic complexes and hence ideal for use in measuring the rates of axial ligand exchange in the slow-exchange regime of the nmr time scale. Previous studies (10) have shown that electron-donating substituents on the phenyl rings of TPPFe(III) labilize the axial ligands of symmetrically-substituted complexes (Table 1). In the previous studies, only one ligand exchange rate could be measured because of the high symmetry of the porphyrins studied (10). However, in the present case of mono-substituted TPPFe(III) derivatives, two N-methyl peaks are observed if the substituent is present in the meta- or ortho-phenyl position.

 The rate constants for ligand exchange, calculated from the excess linewidths, are listed in Table 1. As is clear from these results, the presence of a para-acetamide actually slows the rate of ligand exchange slightly. If we take the value measured for the para-acetamide as our standard, we see that for the meta-acetamide derivative, where we can measure the rate of exchange of both ligands, one of the two ligand exchange rates is very similar to that of the para-acetamide, while the other is much faster. Moving the amide substituent to the ortho position further enhances the rate of exchange of one ligand, while slightly decreasing the rate of exchange of the other. The ratio of the two rate constants increases from 2.9 to 8.0 on going from meta- to ortho-amide, even though a more bulky amide substituent is present in the ortho case. The effects of ortho-substitution are complex. However, hydrogen-bonding is certainly an important contribution, as can be seen by

TABLE 1. Axial Ligand Exchange Rate Data for Phenyl-Substituted Derivatives of TPPFe(N-MeIm)$_2^+$Cl$^-$ at 25 $^{\circ}$C in CDCl$_3$

Substituents		k, sec^{-1}	k', sec^{-1}	k/k'	Ref.
4 p-OCH$_3$	-1.072	102 8	-	-	10
4 p-CH$_3$	-0.680	81 6	-	-	10
4 p-H	0.000	66 5	-	-	10
4 p-Cl	0.908	35 3	-	-	10
1 p-NHCOCH$_3$	-0.01	46 5	-	-	This work
1 m-NHCOCH$_3$	0.21	40 5	114 10	2.9	This work
1 o-NHCOCH$_2$C$_6$H$_5$	-	31 4	249 20	8.0	This work
1 o-OH	-	15 2	170 14	11.3	This work
1 o-OCH$_2$C$_6$H$_5$	-	19 3	48 5	2.5	This work

considering the o-OH and o-OR substituents: For o-OH, which should be a considerably
stronger H-bond donor than o-NHCOR, the ratio of rate constants for exchange of the
axial ligands is 11.3, as compared to 2.5 for the ortho-ether. Further investigation
of ligand exchange kinetics for additional unsymmetrically substituted TPPFe(III)
derivatives is in progress.

Test 4: H-bonding of ortho-amides to bound dioxygen. Many years ago we and
others investigated the epr spectra of monomeric $Co-O_2$ complexes (12) and the
thermodynamics of reversible dioxygen addition to five-coordinate cobalt porphyrins
(13,14). Recent analyses of thermodynamic parameters for small ligand binding to
various metalloporphyrin model compounds have emphasized the importance of the
polarity of the oxygen-binding pocket (15). The question of H-bonding to bound
dioxygen in model compounds and hemoglobin or myoglobin has been raised by many
workers. Hence we reasoned that if amides are H-bond donors, the ortho-amides should
stabilize the $Co-O_2$ complex. The equilibrium constants for O_2 binding to a series of
five-coordinate cobalt porphyrins were measured from the integrated intensities of
the epr signals of the 5-coordinate starting materials and six-coordinate O_2 adducts,
as described previously (13).

The results are summarized in Table 2. As is evident, the ortho-acetamide
stabilizes the dioxygen complex by about a factor of five as compared to the meta-
and para-acetamides which cannot hydrogen-bond to bound O_2. The ortho-pivalamide
substituent also stabilizes the O_2 adduct somewhat at the low temperature (-57 $^\circ$C) of
the measurements utilizing pyridine as the axial base, but this stabilization effect
disappears at the higher temperature (-19 $^\circ$C) utilized for the N-methylimidazole as
axial base measurements. Thus it appears that the ortho-pivalamido substituent
(which has been utilized extensively in creating the O_2-protecting pockets of the
picket fence and related porphyrins (8,16)) is bulky enough that thermal energy
prevents H-bond stabilization of dioxygen binding at ambient temperatures.

TABLE 2. Equilibrium Constants for Addition of O_2 to 5-Coordinate CoTPP Derivatives
in Toluene Solution.

Substituent		L = Pyridine, T = -57 $^\circ$C $K(O_2)$, M^{-1}	L = N-Methylimidazole, T = -19 $^\circ$C $K(O_2)$, M^{-1}
4 p-H	0.00	166	140
1 p-NHCOCH$_3$	-0.01	124	180
1 m-NHCOCH$_3$	0.21	184	-
1 o-NHCOCH$_3$	-	580	1000
1 o-NHCOC(CH$_3$)$_3$	-	270	210

The additional important information concerning H-bonding of amides to bound dioxygen provided by our epr investigations is that involving motional averaging of the epr signals of the O_2 adducts as a function of temperature. While the epr spectrum of frozen, glassy solutions of the dioxygen adduct of $(o\text{-NHCOCH}_3)_1\text{TPPCoL}$ are identical to those of all other TPPCoL complexes reported to date, the fluid solution spectrum is quite unique.

Figure 2 compares the epr spectra of $(p\text{-NHCOCH}_3)_1\text{TPPCo(N-MeIm)}O_2$ and $(o\text{-NHCOCH}_3)_1\text{TPPCo(N-MeIm)}O_2$ at -71 ^{o}C, where it can be clearly seen that the spectrum of the latter remains glassy-like at this temperature, while that of the corresponding para-acetamide, which cannot H-bond to bound O_2, appears "fluid-like" or "isotropic". The latter spectrum is the type previously observed for Co-O_2 complexes above the freezing point of toluene. Toluene is highly viscous at -71 ^{o}C, and the rotational correlation times of all TPPCo(L)O_2 complexes are not short enough to allow averaging of the x, y, and z components of the g- and A-tensors to produce an isotropic spectrum (17). Furthermore, the average of the glassy epr parameters (g- and A-values) is not the same as those measured from the spectrum of Figure 2a at -71 ^{o}C. Hence, all Co-O_2 complexes reported previously have shown deceptively simple epr spectra in fluid solution due to an internal motion which results in a non-isotropic averaging of the glassy epr parameters. This internal motion must be rotation of the bent O_2 moiety about the Co-O bond, a process which clearly does not occur for the ortho-amide complex, due to H-bonding between the amide N-H and the terminal oxygen. EPR evidence for H-bonding between the acetamide N-H and O_2 can be

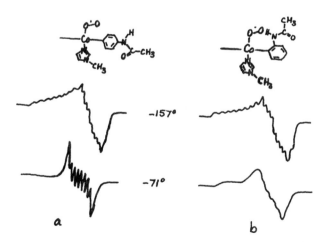

a   b

Figure 2. EPR spectra of Co-O_2 complexes in frozen toluene glasses (-157 ^{o}C and in toluene solution at -71 ^{o}C. a) $(p\text{-NHCOCH3})_1\text{TPPCo(N-MeIm)}O_2$; b) $(o\text{-NHCOCH}_3)_1\text{TPP-Co(N-MeIm)}O_2$.

obtained up to room temperature, and further details of the epr spectra and of the chemical physics of the averaging process which gives rise to the deceptively simple spectra observed previously (Figure 2a at -71 $^{\circ}$C) will be published separately. Suffice it to say that epr spectroscopy gives unequivocal evidence of the involvement of an ortho-amide in H-bonding to coordinated dioxygen.

In addition to the work reported here, Momenteau and coworkers have recently reported a number of elegant studies which present strong evidence that amide-linked "basket-handle" iron(II) porphyrins bind dioxygen much more readily than their ether-linked relatives (18,19), whereas CO binding is not affected by the nature of the basket-handle link to the TPP framework (18), that amide linkages stabilize the coordination of OH$^-$ to Fe(II) (20), and that amide linkages modify the redox chemistry of metalloporphyrins to produce one simultaneous two-electron oxidation rather than two one-electron oxidations of the porphyrin pi system (21).

In conclusion, we have demonstrated that amides are excellent H-bond donors to displaced anions (Cl$^-$ in TPPFeL$_2^+$Cl$^-$) and to coordinated ligands (Co-O$_2$). These demonstrations have important implications to our interpretations of the results of physical measurements on model heme complexes and suggest necessary control experiments which must be done and cautions which must be exercised in extrapolating results from models containing amide substituents to explain data involving heme proteins. Certainly, these proteins often contain similar potential H-bond donors near the heme center which could play similar roles to those discovered in this study. It is hoped that the present study will help focus attention on the potential effects of H-bond donation on the properties of both heme models and proteins.

ACKNOWLEDGEMENTS: The financial support of NIH (AM31038) is gratefully acknowledged. The authors would also like to thank Professor Russell Howe of the University of Auckland for probing questions concerning the nature of the Co-O$_2$ epr spectral averaging process which led us to further investigate this aspect.

REFERENCES:

1. F. A. Walker, V. L. Balke, G. A. McDermott, Inorg. Chem. 21 (1982), 3342-3348.

2. F. A. Walker, V. L. Balke, G. A. McDermott, J. Am. Chem. Soc. 104 (1982), 1569-1574.

3. C. G. Swain, E. C. Lupton, J. Am. Chem. Soc. 90 (1968), 4328-4337.

4. V. L. Balke, F. A. Walker, J. T. West, J. Am. Chem. Soc. 107 (1985) 1226-1233.

5. F. A. Walker, J. A. Barry, V. L. Balke, G. A. McDermott, M. Z. Wu, P. F. Linde, Adv. Chem. Ser. 201 (1982), 377-416.

6. F. A. Walker, D. Reis, V. L. Balke, J. Am. Chem. Soc. 106 (1984), 6888-6898.

7. F. A. Walker, M.-W. Lo, M. T. Ree, J. Am. Chem. Soc. 98 (1976) 7275-7282.

8. J. P. Collman, R. R. Gagne, C. A. Reed, T. R. Halbert, G. Lang, W. T. Robinson, J. Am. Chem. Soc. 97 (1975) 1427-1439.

9. S-I. Hakomori, J. Biochem. (Tokyo) 55 (1964), 205-208.

10. J. D. Satterlee, G. N. LaMar, T. J. Bold, J. Am. Chem. Soc. 99 (1977), 1088-1093.

11. D. M. Collins, R. Countryman, J. L. Hoard, J. Am. Chem. Soc. 94 (1972), 2066-2072.

12. F. A. Walker, J. Am. Chem. Soc. 92 (1970), 4235-4244.

13. F. A. Walker, J. Am. Chem. Soc. 95 (1973), 1154-1159.

14. D. V. Stynes, H. C. Stynes, B. R. James, J. A. Ibers, J. Am. Chem. Soc. 95 (1973), 1796-1800.

15. K. S. Suslik, M. M. Fox, T. J. Reinert, J. Am. Chem. Soc. 106 (1984) 4522-4525.

16. J. P. Collman, J. I. Brauman, T. J. Collins, B. L. Iverson, G. Lang, R. B. Pettman, J. L. Sessler, M. A. Walters, J. Am. Chem. Soc. 105 (1983) 3038-3052.

17. R. Wilson, D. Kivelson, J. Chem. Phys. 44 (1966) 154-168.

18. D. Lavalette, C. Tetreau, J. Mispelter, M. Momenteau, J.-M. Lhoste, Eur. J. Biochem. 145 (1984), 555-565.

19. M. Momenteau, J. Mispelter, B. Loock, J.-M. Lhoste, J. Chem. Soc. Perkin Trans. I (1985), 221-231.

20. D. Lexa, M. Momenteau, J.-M. Saveant, F. Xu, Inorg. Chem. 24 (1985), 122-127.

21. D. Lexa, M. Momenteau, P. Rentien, G. Rytz, J.-M. Saveant, F. Xu, J. Am. Chem. Soc. 106 (1984), 4755-4765.

Structures of Glycinato Compexes of Biochemically Important Divalent Transition-Metal Ions in Solution

Hitoshi Ohtaki

Department of Electronic Chemistry, Tokyo Institute of Technology at Nagatsuta, 4259 Nagatsuta-cho, Midori-ku, Yokohama, 227 Japan

SUMMARY

The structure of mono-, bis- and tris(glycinato) complexes of nickel(II), copper(II) and zinc(II) ions was investigated by the X-ray diffraction and EXAFS methods in solution at 25 °C. The structure of the bis(glycinato)copper(II) complex was not determinable even by the EXAFS method because of its low solubility in water. Thermodynamic quantities for the formation of the complexes which had been determined by potentiometry and calorimetry and kinetic data which were quoted from the literature were discussed on the basis of the structural information thus obtained. The structure of the glycinato complexes of zinc(II) ion determined in solution was compared with that of zinc(II) complexes with other amino acids and some biologically interesting ligands and of enzymes such as carboxypeptidase, carbonic anhydrase and thermolysin in the crystalline state.

1 INTRODUCTION

A number of structural investigations have been examined for biologically interesting substances by the X-ray diffraction method for single crystals. However, it may be expected that a compound has sometimes different structures in solution and in the crystalline state. Nevertheless, structures of complexes and especially biologically interesting compounds have scarcely been determined in solution. Although a remarkable improvement in X-ray and neutron diffraction techniques in these decades allows us to use them for structural investigations of these substances in solution (1), studies so far carried out are rather limited in this field. In recent years the EXAFS method has been applied to studies on local structures of biologically important compounds in solution and in powder, but accumulation of the knowledge is still not sufficient.

In the present paper we show some structural results for glycinato complexes of biologically important divalent transition-metal ions such as nickel(II), copper(II) and zinc(II) ions, which were obtained by the X-ray diffraction and EXAFS measurements for solution samples. The structural information was employed for discussing thermodynamic and kinetic data of the complexes in order to elucidate factors controlling reactivities of the glycinato complexes from the structural point of view. The structural data of the glycinato complexes were compared with those of other amino carboxylato complexes and some enzymes in the crystalline state.

2 METHOD OF MEASUREMENT

Details of the X-ray diffraction and EXAFS methods employed in this study are described elsewhere (2-5). Formation constants of glycinato complexes of nickel(II) ion were determined by potentiometry in 3 mol dm^{-3} LiClO$_4$ aqueous solution at 25 °C (6). Enthalpies of formation of the complexes were determined by calorimetry under the same condition (6). Formation constants, enthalpies and entropies of formation of the glycinato complexes of copper(II) and zinc(II) ions were quoted from the literature (7,8). Rate constants of formation of the complexes were also taken from the literature (9-11).

3 STRUCTURE OF GLYCINATO COMPLEXES IN SOLUTION

The structure of glycinato complexes of nickel(II), copper(II) and zinc(II) ions determined by the X-ray diffraction and EXAFS methods is summarized in Table 1. Since the structure of the bis(glycinato)nickel-(II) complex in a single crystal has been determined by the X-ray diffraction method (12), the data are also shown in the table for comparison. The structure of the bis(glycinato)copper(II) complex was not determinable even by the EXAFS method because of its low solubility in water.

All the complexes investigated are octahedral. For most cases the length of an M^{2+}-OH$_2$ bond increases with the introduction of glycinate ions in the coordination sphere of the M^{2+} ion, as we have seen in the case of ethylenediamine complexes of metal ions (13-16). Thus, water molecules coordinated to a metal ion become more labile and more easily replaceable with an entering ligand at the formation of a higher complex than a lower one.

In the mono(glycinato)copper(II) complex (3), the axial Cu-OH$_2$(ax) distance is longer than the equatorial Cu-OH$_2$(eq), Cu-O(eq) and Cu-N(eq) distances (O and N denote carboxylato oxygen and amino nitrogen atoms, respectively, within a chelating glycinate ion), and therefore, the mono-(glycinato)copper(II) complex has a distorted octahedral structure. On the other hand, the tris(glycinato)cuprate(II) complex Cu(gly)$_3^-$ is regular octahedral. The length of the Cu-O and Cu-N bonds within the tris-(glycinato)cuprate(II) ion is an intermediate value between a long Cu-X(ax) and a short Cu-Y(eq) (X and Y stand for ligand atoms of either O or N) bonds within the aquacopper(II) and mono(glycinato)copper(II) ions.

All the zinc(II) complexes with glycinate ions are regular octahedral and the Zn-O and Zn-N distances practically remain unchanged with varying numbers of glycinate ions in the coordination sphere of zinc(II) ion (4). On the contrary, the nickel(II) glycinato complexes, except for the mono-(glycinato)nickel(II) complex which is regular octahedral, have Ni-O bonds shorter than Ni-N bonds, and the difference between the Ni-O and Ni-N distances is most emphasized in the tris(glycinato)nickelate(II) complex (2).

Table 1. M-OH$_2$, M-O and M-N Bond Lengths (pm) in $[M(gly)_n(OH_2)_m]^{(2-n)+}$ Complexes in Aqueous Solutions at 25 °C.

Complex	Ni^{2+}	Cu^{2+}	Zn^{2+}
M(OH$_2$)$_6^{2+}$	Ni-OH$_2$:204	Cu-OH$_2$(eq):194 Cu-OH$_2$(ax):243	Zn-OH$_2$:208
M(gly)(OH$_2$)$_m^+$	Ni-OH$_2$:208 Ni-O :209 Ni-N :209 m = 4	Cu-OH$_2$(eq):198 Cu-OH$_2$(ax):227 Cu-O :199 Cu-N :199 m = 4	Zn-OH$_2$:212 Zn-O :212 Zn-N :212 m = 4
M(gly)$_2$(OH$_2$)$_m$	(EXAFS) Ni-OH$_2$ Ni-O }:206 *1 Ni-N m = 2	(crystal *2) Ni-OH$_2$:210 Ni-O :206 Ni-N :208 m = 2	–	(EXAFS) Zn-OH$_2$ Zn-O }:208 *1 Zn-N m = 2
M(gly)$_3^-$	Ni-O:203 Ni-N:214	(EXAFS) Ni-O:203 Ni-N:212	Cu-O:202 Cu-N:202	Zn-O:212 (EXAFS) Zn-N:212 Zn-O:214 Zn-N:214

*1 Not separable into each distance. *2 X-ray crystallographic method; *trans*-form.

4 THERMODYNAMIC QUANTITIES AND RATE CONSTANTS OF FORMATION OF GLYCINATO COMPLEXES

Stepwise formation constants, Gibbs energies, enthalpies and entropies

of formation of the glycinato complexes of nickel(II), copper(II) and
zinc(II) ions are summarized in Table 2. Rate constants of formation of
the complexes are also shown in the table.

Table 2. Thermodynamic Quantities and Kinetic Data of Formation of Glycinato Complexes of Nickel(II), Copper(II) and Zinc(II) Ions in Aqueous Solution at 25 °C.

(A) Nickel(II)

Complex	$\dfrac{r}{pm}$	$\log\left(\dfrac{K_n}{M^{-1}}\right)$	$\dfrac{\Delta G^\circ_n}{kJ\,mol^{-1}}$	$\dfrac{\Delta H^\circ_n}{kJ\,mol^{-1}}$	$\dfrac{\Delta S^\circ_n}{J\,K^{-1}\,mol^{-1}}$	$\log\left(\dfrac{k_f{}^{*1}}{M^{-1}\,s^{-1}}\right)$
$Ni(OH_2)_6^{2+}$	204(Ni-OH$_2$)	-	-	-	-	4.4^{*2}
$Ni(gly)(OH_2)_4^+$	$\begin{cases}208(Ni\text{-}OH_2)\\209(Ni\text{-}O)^2\\209(Ni\text{-}N)\end{cases}$	5.74	-32.8	-27.2	18	4.18
$Ni(gly)_2(OH_2)_2$	$\begin{cases}210(Ni\text{-}OH_2)\\206(Ni\text{-}O)^2\\208(Ni\text{-}N)\end{cases}$	4.96	-28.3	-32.2	-13	4.78
$Ni(gly)_3^-$	$\begin{cases}203(Ni\text{-}O)\\214(Ni\text{-}N)\end{cases}$	3.74	-21.3	-35.4	-48	4.62

(B) Copper(II)

Complex	$\dfrac{r}{pm}$	$\log\left(\dfrac{K_n}{M^{-1}}\right)$	$\dfrac{\Delta G^\circ_n}{kJ\,mol^{-1}}$	$\dfrac{\Delta H^\circ_n}{kJ\,mol^{-1}}$	$\dfrac{\Delta S^\circ_n}{J\,K^{-1}\,mol^{-1}}$	$\log\left(\dfrac{k_f{}^{*1}}{M^{-1}\,s^{-1}}\right)$
$Cu(OH_2)_6^{2+}$	$\begin{cases}194(Cu\text{-}OH_2)\\243(Cu\text{-}OH_2')\end{cases}$	-	-	-	-	~9^{*2}
$Cu(gly)(OH_2)_4^+$	$\begin{cases}198(Cu\text{-}OH_2)\\227(Cu\text{-}OH_2')\\199(Cu\text{-}O)^2\\199(Cu\text{-}N)\end{cases}$	8.27	-47.2	-28.3	69.5	9.6
$Cu(gly)_2(OH_2)_2$	-	6.92	-39.5	-28.8	36.4	8.6
$Cu(gly)_3^-$	$\begin{cases}202(Cu\text{-}O)\\202(Cu\text{-}N)\end{cases}$	-	-	-	-	-

(C) Zinc(II)

Complex	$\dfrac{r}{pm}$	$\log\left(\dfrac{K_n}{M^{-1}}\right)$	$\dfrac{\Delta G^\circ_n}{kJ\,mol^{-1}}$	$\dfrac{\Delta H^\circ_n}{kJ\,mol^{-1}}$	$\dfrac{\Delta S^\circ_n}{J\,K^{-1}\,mol^{-1}}$	$\log\left(\dfrac{k_f{}^{*1}}{M^{-1}\,s^{-1}}\right)$
$Zn(OH_2)_6^{2+}$	208(Zn-OH$_2$)	-	-	-	-	7.5^{*2}
$Zn(gly)(OH_2)_4^+$	$\begin{cases}212(Zn\text{-}OH_2)\\212(Zn\text{-}O)^2\\212(Zn\text{-}N)\end{cases}$	4.96	-28.3	-11	58	8.18
$Zn(gly)_2(OH_2)_2$	$\begin{cases}208(Zn\text{-}OH_2)\\208(Zn\text{-}O)^2\\208(Zn\text{-}N)\end{cases}$	4.23	-24.1	-13	34	-
$Zn(gly)_3^-$	$\begin{cases}212(Zn\text{-}O)\\212(Zn\text{-}N)\end{cases}$	2.4	-14	~-10	~-13	-

*1 Ionic medium varied.   *2 Rate constant for water-exchange reaction; s^{-1} unit.

Stepwise formation constants of the glycinato complexes decreased with the number of glycinate ions within the complexes. However, the stepwise formation reactions for the nickel(II) complexes are more exothermic at a higher complex than a lower one. A more negative value in ΔH_n° at a higher complex of nickel(II) ion may be explained in terms of weakened Ni-OH$_2$ bonds within the complex, i.e., a less energy may be needed for removing the water molecules from nickel(II) ion at a higher successive formation reaction of the glycinato complexes. The strength of the Ni-O and Ni-N bonds may also be changed by the introduction of another glycinate ion to the coordination sphere of the nickel(II) ion. However, estimation of the change in the strength of the metal-ligand bonds of the complexes is difficult because the Ni-O bond may be strengthened (i.e., shortened), while the Ni-N bond may be weakened (i.e., elongated). Raman frequencies of the bonds were not observed in this study due to its intensive color.

The decreasing values in K_n (or increasing values in ΔG_n°) are caused by the decrease in the entropies of formation of the complex.

The ΔH_n° values in the copper(II) glycinato complexes are practically independent of n, although the stepwise formation constants of the copper-(II) glycinato complexes decrease with the number of glycinate ions in the coordination sphere. Distortion of the octahedral structure of the copper(II) complexes from the regular form is less pronounced in the mono(glycinato) complex than in the aqua complex, and finally the tris-(glycinato)cuprate(II) ion becomes to be regular octahedral. Therefore, contribution of the Jahn-Teller stabilization of the complexes to the values of ΔG_n° and ΔH_n° may decrease with the number of glycinate ions in the complexes.

In the zinc(II) glycinato complexes the lengths of the Zn-OH$_2$, Zn-O and Zn-N bonds are practically kept constant with changing numbers of glycinate ions, which may reflect approximately constant values of ΔH_n°. However, uncertainties in the ΔH_n° values appearing in the literature (8) are so large that it may be difficult to discuss the variation of ΔH_n° in connection with the change in the bond length.

The rate constant k_f for the reaction

$$ML_{n-1} + L \underset{}{\overset{k_f}{\rightleftharpoons}} ML_n \text{ (charges are omitted)} \qquad (1)$$

may be described in terms of the constants of the following successive reactions:

$$ML_{n-1} + L \underset{}{\overset{K_{os}}{\rightleftharpoons}} ML_{n-1} \cdot L \text{ (outer-sphere complex) } (2)$$

and

$$ML_{n-1} \cdot L \underset{k_{-n}}{\overset{k_n}{\rightleftharpoons}} ML_n \tag{3}$$

where K_{os} denotes the formation constant of the outer-sphere complex and k_n represents the rate constant of the exchange of water molecules bound to the complex $ML_{n-1} \cdot L$ with L. Since the aqua ions of Ni^{2+}, Cu^{2+} and Zn^{2+} and their complexes have the D or I_d mechanism for the ligand exchange reactions, the following relationship approximately holds:

$$k_f = K_{os} \cdot k_n \tag{4}$$

The formation constant of the outer-sphere complex K_{os} is influenced by charges of ML_{n-1} and L, while the rate constant k_n for the exchange of water molecules with L should be affected by the lability of water molecules which are replaceable with an entering L. In the glycinato complexes charges of the complexes decrease with n, and therefore, the K_{os} value should be largest at the first step of the complex formation reactions, i.e., $M^{2+} + L^- = M^{2+} \cdot L^-$ ($K_{os}(M^{2+} \cdot L^-) > K_{os}(ML^+ \cdot L^-) > K_{os}(ML_2 \cdot L^-)$). On the other hand, the k_n value should be larger in a re- action in which a complex has more labile water molecules. In the case of nickel(II) complexes with glycinate ions, the largest k_n value may be expected at the third step of the reactions, i.e., $Ni(gly)_2(OH_2)_2 + gly^-$ = $Ni(gly)_3^- + 2H_2O$, because the $Ni-OH_2$ bond is longest within the $Ni(gly)_2(OH_2)_2$ complex: $k_1(M^{2+}-OH_2) < k_2(LM^+-OH_2) < k_3(L_2M-OH_2)$. The two effects may be superposed in the course of the formation reactions of the complexes, and thus the largest rate constant may result at the for- mation of the bis(glycinato)nickel(II) complex.

5 STRUCTURE OF AMINO CARBOXYLATO COMPLEXES AND ENZYMES WITH ZINC(II) ION

Structures of zinc(II) complexes with various amino acids have been extensively investigated by the X-ray crystallographic method. Structural data of various amino carboxylato complexes of zinc(II) ion are tabulated in Table 3, together with those of some enzymes containing zinc(II) ions at the active center.

It is rather difficult to draw a definite conclusion from the data for variations of bond-lengths and symmetries of the complexes with varying numbers and types of coordinated ligand atoms, but it is seen that com- plexes with one or two nitrogen atoms within amino groups have a coordi- nation number of five or six, while those having more nitrogen atoms in the coordination sphere are four-coordinated. In water zinc(II) ion can form the tris(glycinato)zincate(II) complex, but it is very unstable compared with the mono- and bis(glycinato)zinc(II) complexes. Zinc(II)

Table 3. The Structure of Amino Carboxylato Complexes and Enzymes with Zinc(II) Ion.

Ligand	Ligand Atom[*1]	Symmetry[*2]	Bond Length (pm)		Ref
Glycine (solution)	$(N)(O^-)(O_w)_4$	Oh	M-N :	212	(4)
			M-O⁻ :	212	
			M-O$_w$:	212	
	$(N)_2(O^-)_2(O_w)_2$	Oh	M-N :	208	(4)
			M-O⁻ :	208	
			M-O$_w$:	208	
	$(N)_3(O^-)_3$	Oh	M-N :	212	(4)
			M-O⁻ :	212	
Glycine (crystal)	$(N)_2(O^-)_2(O)_2$	Oh	-		(18)
Aspartic Acid	$(N)(O^-)_2(O)(O_w)_2$	Oh	M-N :	207.7	(19)
			M-O⁻ :	206.0	
				221.2	
			M-O :	218.0	
			M-O$_w$:	210.6	
				217.3	
Glutamic Acid	$(N)(O^-)_2(O)(O_w)$	C_{4V}	M-N :	210.3	(20)
			M-O⁻ :	203.0	
				203.6	
			M-O :	210.6	
			M-O$_w$:	207.0	
L-Serine	$(N)_2(O^-)_2(O)$	C_{4V}	M-N :	205.7	(21)
				206.4	
			M-O⁻ :	196.3	
				211.2	
			M-O :	215.5	
Triglycine	$(N)(O^-)(O)(O_w)_2$	D_{3h}	M-N :	203.4	(22)
			M-O⁻ :	196.4	
			M-O :	218.6	
			M-O$_w$:	197.9	
				212.6	
Ethylenediamine (solution)	$(N)_4$	Td	M-N :	213.1	(13)
	$(N)_6$	Oh	M-N :	227.6	(13)
Histidine (racemic)	$(N_h)_2(N)_2$	Td	M-N$_h$:	200.0	(23)
			M-N^h:	204.9	
L-Histidine	$(N_h)_2(N)_2$	Td	M-N$_h$:	203.4	(24)
			M-N^h:	202.6	
Imidazole	$(N_h)_4$	Td	M-N$_h$:	199.7	(25)
				200.1	
	$(N_h)_6$	Oh	M-N$_h$:	215.3	(26)
				219.2	
				219.3	
				221.0	
				221.4	
				226.4	

Table 3. (cont.)

Ligand	Ligand Atom[*1]	Symmetry[*2]	Bond Length (pm)	Ref
Carboxypeptidase A	$(N_h)_2(O^-)(O)(O_w)$	-	M-N$_h$: 208 210 M-O$^-$: 223 M-O : 233 M-O$_w$: 196	(27,28)
Carboxy anhydrase B	$(N_h)_3(O_w)$	dis-Td	-	(29)
Carboxy anhydrase C	$(N_h)_3(O_w)$	Td	-	(30)
Thermolysin	$(N_h)_2(O^-)(O_w)$	Td	M-N$_h$: 208 210 M-O$^-$: 208 M-O$_w$: 188	(31)
	$(N_h)_2(O^-)(S_{inh})$	Td	M-N$_h$: 200 210 M-O$^-$: 180 M-S : 190	(32)

*1 (N): Amino nitrogen; (N$_h$): Nitrogen atom within hetero-ring; (O$^-$): Oxygen atom within dissociated carboxylate ion; (O): Carbonyl oxygen atom within carboxylate group; (O$_w$): Oxygen atom within water; (S$_{inh}$): Sulfur atom within inhibitor. *2 Oh: octahedral; Td: tetrahedral; C$_{4v}$: tetragonal pyramid; D$_{3h}$: trigonal bipyramid; dis-Td: distorted tetrahedal.

ion does not form the hexaammine complex. The tris(ethylenediamine)zinc-(II) and hexakis(imidazole)zinc(II) complexes are very unstable and can only form in a solution with an extremely large excess of the ligands.

These results indicate that zinc(II) complexes with more than two nitrogen atoms in the coordination sphere strongly prefer the four-coordination structure and those having one or two nitrogen atoms coordinated like to have an octahedral structure by introducing other ligand atoms such as oxygen atoms within water molecules and carboxylate ions. An exception is seen in thermolysin which has two nitrogen atoms but the Td symmetry, but zinc(II) ion in thermolysin is situated in the hole surrounded by a relatively hydrophobic peptide environment and may be rather strongly regulated in the steric arrangement of ligand atoms which are combined through the peptide chain.

Since thermolysin has a Td symmetric $(N_h)_2(O^-)(O_w)$ structure (although the nitrogen atoms belong to imidazole heterocyclic rings), we may expect that the zinc(II) ion in thermolysin has a higher fractional charge than zinc(II) ions within other (N)$_2$-type octahedral complexes, and therefore, thermolysin may have a larger activity than those.

The bonds within carboxypeptidase of the $(N_h)_2(O^-)(O)(O_w)$ coordination, which has a five-coordination structure, are longer than the corresponding bonds of the bis(glycinato)zinc(II) complex $((N)_2(O^-)_2(O_w)_2$-structure). This result suggests that the zinc(II) ion in carboxypeptidase may be more active than that within the bis(glycinato)zinc(II) complex.

The length of the Zn-O bond is usually shorter than that of the Zn-N bond. The M^{2+}-O bond shorter than the M^{2+}-N bond has been found in the structure of the tris(glycinato)nickelate(II) complex in solution (2). The fac-$[Cr(gly)_3] \cdot H_2O$ complex has also a shorter Cr^{3+}-O bond than a Cr^{3+}-N bond in crystal (17).

ACKNOWLEDGMENT

The author thanks Prof. M. Tanaka (Nagoya University) for his valuable discussion. He also thanks Drs. K. Ozutsumi, T. Yamaguchi (Tokyo Institute of Technology at Nagatsuta) and S. Funahashi (Nagoya University) for their kind help.

6 REFERENCES

(1) H. Ohtaki, Rev. Inorg. Chem., 4 (1982) 103-177.
(2) K. Ozutsumi, H. Ohtaki, Bull. Chem. Soc. Jpn., 56 (1983) 3635-3641.
(3) K. Ozutsumi, H. Ohtaki, Bull. Chem. Soc. Jpn., 57 (1984) 2605-2611.
(4) K. Ozutsumi, H. Ohtaki, Bull. Chem. Soc. Jpn., in press.
(5) T. Yamaguchi, K. Ozutsumi, H. Ohtaki, submitted to Bull. Chem. Soc. Jpn.
(6) S. Ishiguro, T. Pithprecha, H. Ohtaki, to be published.
(7) L. G. Sillén, A. E. Martell (Ed.) Stability Constants of Metal-Ion Complexes. Supplement No. 1, Special Publication No. 25, The Chemical Society, London 1971.
(8) A. E. Martell, R. M. Smith (Ed.) Critical Stability Constants, Vol. 1, Plenum, New York 1974.
(9) G. Davies, K. Kustin, R. F. Pasternack, Inorg. Chem., 8 (1969) 1535-1537.
(10) A. F. Pearlmutter, J. Stuehr, J. Am. Chem. Soc., 90 (1968) 858-862.
(11) J. A. Miceli, J. E. Stuehr, Inorg. Chem., 11 (1972) 2763-2767.
(12) H. C. Freeman, J. M. Guss, Acta Crystallogr., Sect. B, 24 (1968) 1133-1135.
(13) T. Fujita, T. Yamaguchi, H. Ohtaki, Bull. Chem. Soc. Jpn., 52 (1979) 3539-3544.
(14) T. Fujita, H. Ohtaki, Bull. Chem. Soc. Jpn., 53 (1980) 930-935.

(15) T. Fujita, H. Ohtaki, Bull. Chem. Soc. Jpn., 55 (1982) 455-460.

(16) T. Fujita, H. Ohtaki, Bull. Chem. Soc. Jpn., 56 (1983) 3276-3283.

(17) R. F. Bryan, P. T. Greene, P. F. Stokely, E. W. Wilso, Jr., Inorg. Chem., 10 (1971) 1468-1473.

(18) B. W. Low, F. L. Hirshfeld, F. M. Richards, J. Am. Chem. Soc., 81 (1959) 4412-4416.

(19) L. Kryger, S. E. Rasmussen, Acta Chem. Scand., 27 (1973) 2674-2676.

(20) C. M. Gramaccioli, Acta Crystallogr., 21 (1966) 600-605.

(21) D. van der Helm, A. F. Nicholas, C. G. Fisher, Acta Crystallogr., Sect. B, 26 (1970) 1172-1178.

(22) D. van der Helm, H. B. Nicholas, Jr., Acta Crystallogr., Sect. B, 26 (1970) 1858-1866.

(23) M. M. Harding, S. J. Cole, Acta Crystallogr., 16 (1963) 643-650.

(24) T. J. Kistenmacher, Acta Crystallogr., Sect. B, 28 (1972) 1302-1304.

(25) C. A. Bear, K. A. Duggan, H. C. Freeman, Acta Crystallogr., Sect. B, 31 (1975) 2713-2715.

(26) C. Sandmark, C.-I. Bränden, Acta Chem. Scand., 21 (1967) 993-999.

(27) D. C. Rees, M. Lewis, R. B. Honzatko, W. N. Lipscomb, K. D. Hardman, Proc. Natl. Acad. Sci. U.S.A., 78 (1981) 3408-3412.

(28) D. C. Rees, M. Lewis, W. N. Lipscomb, J. Mol. Biol., 168 (1983) 367-387.

(29) K. K. Kannan, B. Notstrand, K. Fridborg, S. Lövgren, A. Ohlsson, M. Petef, Proc. Natl. Acad. Sci. U.S.A., 72 (1975) 51-55.

(30) A. Liljas, K. K. Kannan, P.-C. Bergstén, I. Waara, K. Fridborg, U. Carlbon, L. Järup, S. Lövgren, M. Petef, Nature (London), New Biol., 235 (1972) 131-137.

(31) M. A. Holmes, B. W. Matthews, J. Mol. Biol., 160 (1982) 623-639.

(32) A. F. Monzingo, B. W. Mattews, Biochem., 21 (1982) 3390-3394.

Dioxygen Binding and Activation in Dinuclear Copper Complex Systems

Kenneth D. Karlin, Yilma Gultneh, Richard W. Cruse, Jon C. Hayes,
Michael S. Haka, Jon Zubieta

Department of Chemistry, State University of New York (SUNY) at Albany,
Albany, New York 12222 USA

SUMMARY

Recent coordination chemistry studies involving copper/dioxygen
interactions which may be relevant to the active sites of certain copper
metalloprotein are presented. A dinuclear copper(I) complex of $\underline{I}$ ($\underline{II}$)
reacts with O_2 resulting in the hydroxylation of an aromatic ring
contained in $\underline{I}$ to produce a dinuclear phenoxo- and hydroxo-bridged
Cu(II) compound, $\underline{III}$. This reaction is a good model for the action of
the copper monooxygenases. The reaction of dioxygen with a Cu(I) compound containing a mononuclear analog of $\underline{I}$ does not result in the
hydroxylation of the ligand, but causes the irreversible four-electron
reduction of O_2 to give oxo- or hydroxo- species. The observation that
dinuclear Cu(II) derivatives of $\underline{I}$ react with hydrogen peroxide to give
the hydroxylated product $\underline{III}$ suggests that bridged dinuclear
Cu(II)-peroxo intermediates are important in the reaction, $\underline{II} \longrightarrow \underline{III}$.
Spectral studies at low temperature of intermediates obtained by the
reaction of copper(I) complexes containing analogs of $\underline{I}$ with O_2 also
support this hypothesis. The phenol ($\underline{IV}$) which is produced by the
reaction of $\underline{II} \longleftrightarrow \underline{III}$ can be used to synthesize a novel phenoxo-bridged
dinuclear complex $\underline{IX}$; this reacts reversibly with O_2 at low temperature
to produce a peroxo-bridged dinuclear Cu(II) complex $\underline{X}$.

1 INTRODUCTION

The interest in studies relating to the reactivity of dioxygen with copper ion complexes derives from the fact that copper compounds have been established to be useful catalysts in oxidation and oxygenation reactions both in biological and nonbiological systems. A major focus has been in the development of chemical model systems which mimic the functional properties of the biological oxygenases. Our investigations have centered on biomimetic studes of the copper metalloproteins hemocyanin (Hc) and tyrosinase (Tyr) which contain copper active sites in which the Cu(II) centers are electronically coupled. Hemocyanins (1,2) function as dioxygen carriers in the hemolymph of arthropods and molluscs whereas tyrosinase (1-3) is a monooxygenase utilizing O_2 in the hydroxylation of monophenols (i.e. monophenol to o-diphenol) and furthur acts as a two-electron oxidase (i.e. o-catechol to o-quinone).

Spectroscopic and chemical evidence suggest that, in the deoxy form of Hc, two or three imidazole ligands from histidine coordinate to each cuprous ion. A recent x-ray structural investigation of <u>Panulirus interruptus</u> deoxy-Hc shows that three imidazoles are coordinated to each copper center with a Cu(I)...Cu(I) distance of 3.8 $\pm$ 0.4 A (4). Other spectroscopic studies suggest that the reaction of deoxy-Hc with O_2 results in a dinuclear unit with Cu(II) ions separated by 3.6 A which is bridged by the O_2^{2-} ligand (that is derived from O_2) and an "endogenous" oxygen-containing ligand. There are parallels between the structures and reactivities of the Hc and Tyr active sites suggesting that the binding of dioxygen and O_2 "activation" (leading to facile & selective oxygen atom incorporation into a substrate) are related processes (5).

2 A COPPER MONOOXYGENASE MODEL SYSTEM

2.1 Hydroxylation of an Arene in a Dinuclear Copper Complex System

The general scarcity of information available on copper(I) complexes containing nitrogenous ligands initially prompted us to synthesize a Cu(I) derivative of the ligand <u>I</u>. This resulted in the synthesis and crystallographic characterization of <u>II</u>, a compound mimicking some of the suggested structural and coordination properties of deoxy-Hc (6).

Compound **II** is a dinuclear Cu(I) complex where each cuprous ion is
three-coordinate due to bonding to the amino and two pyridyl nitrogen
donors of the tridentate (PY2) arm of the meta-xylyl ligand **I**.   The
coordination about each Cu(I) ion is nearly planar and T-shaped with
N_{py}-Cu-N_{py} ca. 153°.

Upon reaction of **II** with O_2 in DMF or CH_2Cl_2, hydroxylation of the
m-xylyl connecting unit in **I** occurs, resulting in the formation of the
phenoxo- and hydroxo- doubly bridged dinuclear complex **III**.   The
incorporation of oxygen atoms into **III** during this reaction was shown by
x-ray crystallography; each Cu(II) ion is pentacoordinate and is found
in a nearly square based pyramidal geometry.   The phenoxo- oxygen atom
from the hydroxylated and deprotonated ligand and a hydroxo- oxygen atom
bridge the two Cu(II) ions with Cu...Cu = 3.1 A (6).

The observed oxygen atom insertion into an arene and the
stoichiometry of the reaction **II** + O_2 ⟶ **III** is reminiscent of the
action of the copper monooxygenases.   The stoichiometry has been
established by carrying out manometric measurements of O_2 uptake by **II**
in DMF or CH_2Cl_2 where Cu:O_2 = 2:1.   Mass spectrometric analysis (Field
Desorption) of the product **III** prepared by using isotopically pure $^{18}O_2$
show that both atoms of dioxygen are incorporated into the oxygenated
product.   The aromatic ring connecting the PY2 units in **I** has been
hydroxylated, formally an insertion of an O atom into the aromatic C-H
bond.   The other O atom in the product is part of a hydroxide bridging
ligand, where the formal oxidation state of the oxygen atom is -2. Thus,
the overall net reaction can be described as

$$XYL-H + 2Cu^+ + O_2 \longrightarrow 2Cu^{+2} + OH^- + XYL-O^-$$

where XYL-H is the dinucleating ligand **I** and -H is the site of
hydroxylation.   The Cu(II) ions can be leached out of complex **III** to
produce the free phenol, **IV**, completing the sequence involving the
copper mediated hydroxylation of an arene.   The phenol, **IV**, was shown to
retain the ^{18}O label as furthur proof that the source of oxygen atoms in
the hydroxylated product is O_2 (6).

2.2 Reactivity of a Mononuclear Analog

In an effort to identify the nature of intermediates in the course of "activation" of O_2 in the oxygenation reaction described above, studies on the effects of synthetic ligand modifications and variations are being pursued. One such example is a recent study of the reaction of dioxygen with a copper(I) complex of the ligand **V**, which possesses the same PY2 group as is found in **I**, and forms a three-coordinate Cu(I) complex **VI**. It also contains the potential aromatic substrate as the xylyl group in **I**, which may be in the same proximity to the copper ion. However, reaction of **VI** with O_2 in CH_2Cl_2 at room temperature does not result in the hydroxylation of the benzyl group; instead, an oxo-Cu(II) species, **VII**, forms. This reacts reversibly with water to give the dihydroxo- bridged dinuclear Cu(II) compound **VIII**, which we have characterized by x-ray diffraction (7).

V   VI   2+

$$\left[(\underline{A})\, Cu \overset{O}{\diagdown} Cu\, (\underline{A}) \right]^{2+} \quad \overset{+H_2O}{\underset{H_2O}{\rightleftharpoons}}$$

VII   VIII

The finding that the reaction of O_2 with **VI** does not result in the hydroxylation of the benzyl group in **V** is in contrast with the result of the reaction of O_2 with **II**. However, it is consistent with the notion that two Cu(I) ions in the "appropriate" proximity is a requirement for substrate oxygenation as probably occurs in the transformation **II** $\longrightarrow$ **III**. It seems likely that in this mononuclear system, **VI** + O_2, a kinetic pathway leading to reduction of dioxygen beyond the peroxo- stage and without incorporation into a substrate is preferred. Thus, irreversible four-electron reduction to oxo- (**VII**) or hydroxo- (**VIII**) Cu(II) complexes occurs.

2.3 Peroxo-Cu(II) Dinuclear Intermediates in the Hydroxylation Reaction

Based on the known formation of peroxo- species during dioxygen
binding in Hc action, and the possible similarity and/or relationship to
the monooxygenase Tyr, one can hypothesize that reduction of O_2 by the
dinuclear Cu(I) complex **II** proceeds to the peroxo- oxidation level in
the hydroxylation reaction **II** $\longrightarrow$ **III**. Thus, if $Cu(II)_2(O_2^{2-})$ is an
intermediate in this process, it may be possible that the oxygenation
reaction should proceed by the corresponding reaction of a $Cu(II)_2$
derivative of **I** with hydrogen peroxide. We find that this reaction
indeed results in hydroxylation to give **III**. This finding supports the
notion that a peroxo-Cu(II) species such as $Cu(II)_2(O_2^{2-})$ is a common
intermediate in pathways developing either from $Cu(I)_2-O_2$ or
$Cu(II)_2-H_2O_2$ (8).

Dinuclear Cu(II) complexes of **I** were prepared by the reaction of the
ligand with two equivalents of either $Cu(BF_4)_2$ or $Cu(NO_3)_2$ in aqueous
DMF. These react with hydrogen peroxide to give > 90 % yields of
hydroxylated product, **III**, which is identified by IR and UV-VIS
spectroscopy and TLC of the free phenol (**IV**) obtained from the products.
No hydroxylation is observed in the reaction of free ligand, **I**, with
hydrogen peroxide or when the dinuclear Cu(II) complexes of **II** are first
treated with EDTA, then followed by hydrogen peroxide.

To confirm that two copper ions are required for efficient
hydroxylation, analogous reactions were carried out on a Cu(II)
derivative of ligand **V**, the mononucleating analog of **I**. Here, no
hydroxylation occurs in the reaction of $[Cu(\underline{V})]^{2+}$ with H_2O_2. We conclude
that under these conditions it is not sufficient to just have a peroxo-
species in the presence of one copper ion, but that a peroxo-
intermediate involving two Cu ions must be the precursor to oxygen atom
transfer in the reaction of **II** $\longrightarrow$ **III**. To speculate, it may be that the
substrate juxtaposition with the copper ion(s) at the point of O_2
binding is one critical factor in determining whether hydroxylation

occurs. The mode of peroxo- binding (i.e., μ-1,1-, μ-1,2 bridging, hydroperoxo-, etc) probably will affect the reactivity, thus the role of the copper ions(s) in influencing electronic and coordination properties of a bound "dioxygen" ligand will be very important.

Recently, we have obtained furthur evidence for the existence of peroxo-Cu(II)$_2$ intermediates in this system. We have synthesized new analogs of ligand **I**, m-XYL-F and NnPY2 (n=5) (9). The former is the same as **I** except that a flourine atom substitutes for a hydrogen atom at the position shown, thus rendering it less likely to react and be oxygenated. The ligand N5PY2 possesses an 5-carbon methylene chain between amine nitrogen atoms of the PY2 units, instead of the xylyl group.

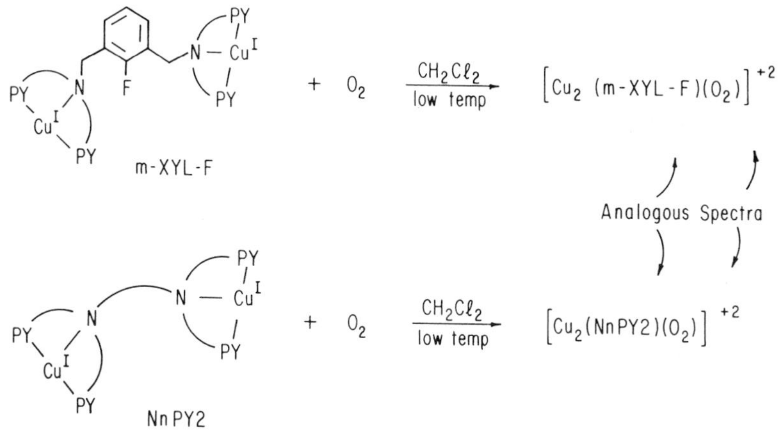

At low temperature, dinuclear Cu(I) complexes of these ligands react with O$_2$ to give metastable species which we have characterized spectroscopically. Striking electronic spectra are observed for both complexes having bands which are typical of charge-transfer transitions. They have absorption maxima: m-XYL-F, 360 nm (18,700), 435 nm (4400), 515 nm (1300); N5PY2, 360 nm (21400), 425 nm (3600), 520 nm (1200). The stoichiometry of dioxygen uptake for the N5PY2 system is Cu:O$_2$=2:1. The combined data suggest that these species are peroxo- Cu(II)$_2$ complexes. Thus, the similarity of these ligands to each other and with **I** provides furthur evidence that the hydroxylation reaction **II** $\longrightarrow$ **III** initially proceeds by the formation of a peroxo-Cu(II)$_2$ species in the reaction of the dinuclear complex **II** with dioxygen.

3 REVERSIBLE BINDING OF DIOXYGEN IN A DINUCLEAR SYSTEM

The occurence of reversible copper-dioxygen binding in natural systems has inspired considerable efforts over the years to mimic this process in synthetic systems (1,10). We have also sought to do this, expecially since we had discovered evidence of peroxo-Cu_2 interemediates in the model monooxygenase system described above. The suggestion of an endogenous bridge in oxy- and met-Hc has resulted in the considerable use of phenol containing dinucleating ligands to model this active site (1). The facile production of **IV** (above) gave us an entry into such a ligand system. Indeed, the phenol **IV** forms a phenoxo-bridged dinuclear Cu(I) complex **IX**, which has been structurally characterized. Compound **IX** reacts with O_2 resulting in the formation of a dinuclear Cu(II)-peroxide complex, **X**, that is stable at low temperature (11).

The structure of **IX** consists of two tetra-coordinate Cu(I) ions bridged by the phenoxo- oxygen atom. The striking feature of this structure is that the Cu...Cu distance is ca. 3.6 A which corresponds to the value found in oxy-Hc. Also, there is an empty "pocket" in the region where a second bridging ligand is known to coordinate in dinuclear Cu(II) complexes of this ligand; this suggested that dioxygen binding to this center would be possible.

When an orange dichloromethane solution of **IX** is exposed to O_2 below -50°C, an intense purple color develops due to the formation of the peroxo-Cu(II)$_2$ complex, **X**. Manometric measurements at -78°C indicate that 1 mol of O_2 is taken up per mole of **IX**. The absorption spectrum of the violet solution exhibits a new strong transition at 505 nm (6300) associated with the formation of **X**. In addition, weaker bands are observed at 385 nm and 610 nm.

Confirming evidence for the formulation of **X** as a peroxo-Cu(II) species comes from resonance Raman spectroscopy. Here, a peak at 803 cm^{-1} is assigned to the O-O stretching vibration of a coordinated peroxo- group. This conclusion is based on (a) the perturbation in the O-O stretch observed upon isotopic substitution of $^{18}O_2$ and (b) a comparison to the O-O stretch values observed for oxyhemocyanins, oxytyrosinase and ionic peroxides (11).

The binding of dioxygen to **IX** to form **X** is reversible, and cycling between oxy- and deoxy- can be followed spectrophotometrically. Rapid warming to room temperature under vacuum removes the bound dioxygen ligand from **X** to regenerate **IX**. Lowering the temperature of the solution followed by bubbling with O_2 produces **X**; several cycles can be carried out in this manner with ca. 10 % decomposition per cycle.

Another line of evidence demonstrating the reversibility of dioxygen binding of **IX** comes from the observation that the same product is obtained in the reaction of either **IX** or **X** with triphenylphosphine or carbon monoxide (L = PPh_3, CO) (9). Compound **IX** reacts with two equivalents of PPh_3 (and CO) to give an adduct **XI** which contains phenoxo-bridged Cu(I) with additional coordination from the amino nitrogen, one of the pyridyl nitrogens of the PY2 units and a PPh_3 ligand (x-ray structure (12)). When the peroxo- complex **X** is reacted with two mole equivalents of L, the same L-Cu(I) adduct, **XI**, is obtained. One mole of dioxygen is liberated as demonstrated by manometric experiments and O_2 identification using alkaline pyrogallol. These results furthur substantiate that the reaction of **IX** with O_2 is an equilibrium process (i.e. reversible); reaction of **X** with L shifts back the equilibrium towards **IX**, liberating O_2 and producing the L-adduct.

4 CONCLUSIONS

We are finding that the dinucleating ligand **I** and its analogs and derivatives produce a variety of interesting Cu(I) and Cu(II) complexes. The chemistry of these compounds show some capability to mimic certain structural and reactivity features observed in the dioxygen carrier hemocyanin and the monooxygenase tyrosinase. While many questions still remain unanswered, the present results demonstrate the validity of the model approach in studying the biochemistry of copper and the field of biomimetic chemistry in general.

5 REFERENCES

(1) K.D. Karlin, J. Zubieta (eds.), Copper Coordination Chemistry: Bio-chemical and Inorganic Perspectives, Adenine Press, Guilderland, New York, 1983.

(2) E.I. Solomon, K.W. Penfield, D.E. Wilcox, Structure & Bonding 53 (1983) 1-57.

(3) E.I. Solomon in T.G. Spiro (ed.), Metal Ions in Biology, Wiley-Interscience, New York (1981) pp. 41-108.

(4) W.P.J. Gaykema, W.G.J. Hol, J.M. Vereijken, N.M. Soeter, H.J. Bak, J.J. Beintema, Nature 309 (1984) 23-29.

(5) M.E. Winkler, K. Lerch, E.I. Solomon, J. Amer. Chem. Soc. 103 (1981)7001-7003.

(6) K.D. Karlin, J.C. Hayes, Y. Gultneh, R.W. Cruse, J.W. McKown, J.P. Hutchinson, J. Zubieta, J. Amer. Chem. Soc. 106 (1984) 2121-2128.

(7) K.D. Karlin, Y. Gultneh, J.C. Hayes, J. Zubieta, Inorg. Chem. 23 (1984) 519-521.

(8) N.J. Blackburn, K.D. Karlin, M. Concannon, J.C. Hayes, Y. Gultneh, J. Zubieta, J.C.S. Chem. Commun. (1984) 939-940.

(9) K.D. Karlin et. al., to be published.

(10) A.D. Zuberbuhler, Met. Ions Biol. Syst. 5 (1976) 325-367.

(11) K.D. Karlin, R.W. Cruse, Y. Gultneh, J.C. Hayes, J. Zubieta, J. Am. Chem. Soc. 106 (1984) 3372-3374, and references therein.

Moessbauer Studies of Synthetic Analogues Simulating Building Blocks of Nitrogenase Reaction Centers

A. Simopoulos[1], A. Kostikas[1], V. Papaefthymiou[1]
D. Coucouvanis[2],[3], M. Kanatzidis[2],[3], E. Simhon[3] and P. Stremple[3]

(1) Nuclear Research Center "Demokritos", 153 10 Aghia Paraskevi Attiki, Greece
(2) University of Michigan, Ann Arbor, Michigan 48109
(3) University of Iowa, Iowa City, Iowa 52242

SUMMARY

This investigation is undertaken to study the electronic and magnetic properties of Fe-Mo-S complexes and 4Fe-4S clusters as a route to understanding the structure and function of the active centers in the nitrogen fixing enzyme nitrogenase. The investigation has been performed by means of Mössbauer Spectroscopy and magnetic susceptibility measurements. Two binuclear (Fe-Mo) and two trinuclear (Fe-Mo-Fe and Mo-Fe-Mo) complexes with sulfur bridges between the metal centers have been studied and compared with the electronic structure and magnetic properties of the Fe-Mo cofactor of nitrogenase. The results imply a high electron affinity of the MoS_4^{2-} and intramolecular spin coupling. A number of 4Fe-4S cubane clusters with mixed terminal ligands have been investigated as possible models for the other major Fe-component of nitrogenase, the "P-clusters". The latter exhibit unique spectral properties which have been attributed to significant differences in the ligation of their Fe_4S_4 cores. Present results indicate that the presumed differences in the ligation of P-clusters could include expansion to five coordination for the three of the four iron atoms of the cluster.

Abbreviations: EXAFS: Extended X-ray Absorption Fine Structure;
Et_2dtc^-: $S_2CN(C_2H_5)_2^-$; Ph: C_6H_5; Et: C_2H_5.

2 INTRODUCTION

The objective of this study is the synthesis and characterization of Fe-Mo-S and
Fe-S complexes with appropriate stoichiometry, electronic structure and electrochemical behaviour to qualify as successful analogs of the Fe clusters in the Fe-Mo protein
of nitrogenase.

Spectroscopic results (Mössbauer, EPR (1) and EXAFS (2))for the Fe-Mo protein led
to a structural model according to which the 30±2 iron atoms of the protein are distributed into two cluster types labelled M and P respectively. The M cluster consists
of two identical centers (cofactor centers) each containing six Fe atoms and one Mo
atom. Four identical P-clusters are proposed each containing four Fe and four S atoms
in a cubane formation.

The native state of the M clusters is EPR active with spin S = 3/2 and can be reduced to the M^R state with S $\geq$ 1 and reversibly oxidized to an EPR silent (S=0) M^{OX}
state. One Mössbauer component in zero field spectra of the Fe-Mo protein is assigned
to the 6 iron atoms of each M cluster. The magnetically perturbed spectra, however,
have been analysed with a model differentiating these atoms through their hyperfine
constant parameters A_i (1). The native state of the P clusters is EPR silent (S=0)
and can be reversibly oxidized to the state P^{OX} with spin S $\geq$ 3/2. Two Mössbauer
components of the Fe-Mo protein spectrum have been assigned to the four iron atoms
of each P cluster in a ratio of 3:1.

The spectroscopic and biochemical studies of the Fe-Mo protein impose the minimum
stoichiometric and structural features that must be present in satisfactory synthetic
analogs. Specifically, for the cofactor component a stoichiometry of Mo:Fe:S $\sim$ 1:6:8
is required with the metal atoms magnetically coupled to give a spin state of S = 3/2.
Quantitative analysis of EXAFS spectra reveals as major structural features 3-4 sulfur
atoms in the first coordination sphere of Mo at a distance of 2.35 Å and 1-3 iron
atoms further out at 2.7 Å. Two possible models consistent with this configuration
have been proposed and are shown schematically below:

Synthetic analogs of both types have been reported, although none satisfies so far
all the stoichiometric, structural and spectroscopic requirements to qualify as bona
fide model of the cofactor center. The complexes studied here belong to the second,

"linear" type and may be considered as building blocks in synthesizing more exact analogs.

For the 4Fe-4S centers (P clusters), if the cubane configuration is accepted as the most plausible structure, the principal requirement is a differentiation of one of the irons, most probably by a different mode of ligation.

In the following we will describe the electronic and magnetic properties of a number of synthetic analogs and we will compare them with those observed for the M and P clusters of the Fe-Mo protein of nitrogenase.

2 SYNTHETIC ANALOGS OF M AND P CLUSTERS

2.1 Material

The following binuclear and trinuclear complexes have been investigated as possible building blocks of the Fe-Mo cofactor of nitrogenase:

A. $[(SPh)_2FeMoS_4](Ph_4P)_2$
B. $(S_5FeMoS_4)(Ph_4P)_2$
C. $(Cl_4Fe_2MoS_4)(Ph_4P)_2$
E. $[Fe(MoS_4)_2](Et_4N)_3$

Their tungsten homologues have been also obtained and studied for comparison reasons.

Mixed ligand cubane clusters of the type $(Fe_4S_4L_xL'_{4-x})(Ph_4P)_2$ have been studied for determination of the role of asymmetric ligation in the P-clusters. Complexes with the following combination of ligands have been examined:

$L_2 = 2SPh^-$, $L'_2 = 2Cl^-$
$L_2 = 2SPh^-$, $L'_2 = 2OPh^-$
$L_2 = 2Cl^-$, $L'_2 = 2OPh^-$
$L_2 = 2SPh^-$, $L'_2 = 2Et_2dtc^-$
$L_2 = 2Cl^-$, $L'_2 = 2Et_2dtc^-$
$L_3 = 3Cl^-$, $L' = Et_2dtc^-$

The molecular structure of typical members for the first and second group of the above complexes are depicted in Figure 1.

2.2 Experimental Apparatus

Mössbauer spectra were obtained in the temperature range 1.4-300 K and in external magnetic fields up to 6T. The source was 100 mCi ^{57}Co(Rh) at room temperature.

Magnetic susceptibility measurements were performed with a vibrating sample magneto-
meter at temperatures between 2 and 300 K and in magnetic fields ranging up to 2T.

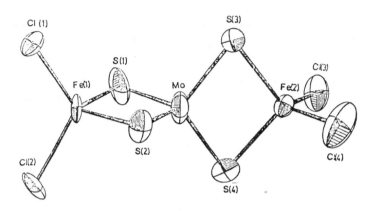

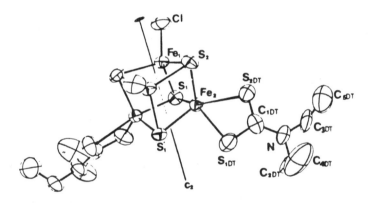

Fig. 1   Structure and labelling of the $(Cl_4Fe_2MoS_4)^{2-}$ (top) and of the
         $[Fe_4S_4Cl_2(Et_2dtc)_2]^{2-}$ (bottom).

2.3 Results and Discussion

2.3.1 Synthetic Analogs for the M-centers

Magnetic susceptibility measurements of the binuclear Fe-Mo complexes and their W
homologues as a function of temperature and magnetic field are in agreement with paramagnetic behaviour for an S=2 spin system. Figure 2 shows such data for complex A.

The data have been fitted according to the following electronic spin Hamiltonian:

$$\mathcal{H}_E = D(S_z^2-2)+E(S_x^2-S_y^2) + \vec{S}\cdot\overset{\approx}{g}\cdot\vec{H}_{ext} \tag{1}$$

where D and E are the axial and rhombic zero field splitting parameters, respectively, and the last term represents the Zeeman interaction arising from an external magnetic field $\vec{H}_{ext}$. The parameters determined in this way are listed in Table I.

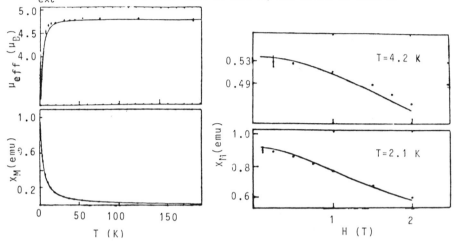

Fig. 2 Magnetic susceptibility data as a function of temperature (left) and magnetic field (right) for the complex $[(PhS)_2FeMoS_4]^{2-}$. The solid lines represent a fit to the data according to the spin Hamiltonian of Eqn. (1) and the parameters listed in Table I.

Mössbauer spectra of the binuclear complex A display a simple quadrupole doublet at temperatures down to 1.4 K. In the presence of an external magnetic field the spectra display magnetic hyperfine interaction (Fig. 3). These data have been fitted according to the following nuclear spin Hamiltonian by using a model similar to that for the evaluation of nitrogenase spectra (1).

$$\mathcal{H}_N = <\vec{S}>\cdot\overset{\approx}{A}\cdot\vec{I} + \frac{e^2qQ}{12}\left[3I_z^2 - \frac{15}{4} + \eta(I_x^2-I_y^2)\right] - g_n\beta_n\vec{H}_{ext}\cdot\vec{I} + I.S. \tag{2}$$

where $<\vec{S}>$ is the expectation value of the electronic spin $\vec{S}$, determined by diagonalization of the Hamiltonian (1), $\overset{\approx}{A}$ is the magnetic hyperfine constant tensor, I the nuclear spin, e^2qQ the quadrupole interaction constant and I.S. the isomer shift. The fine and hyperfine parameters determined in this way are given in Table I. The binuclear complex B displays also simple quadrupole doublet spectra at room and lower temperatures but below 10 K magnetic hyperfine splitting appears (Fig. 3). This behaviour may be attributed to low dimension magnetic ordering. A detailed account of the synthesis, structural characterization and magnetic and electronic properties of the binuclear

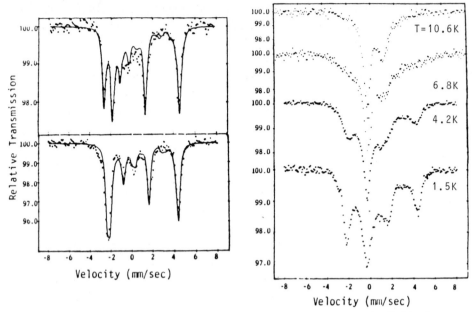

Fig. 3   Mössbauer spectra at low temperatures and external magnetic fields for
$[(PhS)_2FeMoS_4]^{2-}$ (left, top), for $(S_5FeMoS_4)^{2-}$ (left, bottom) and for
$(S_5FeMoS_4)^{2-}$ at zero magnetic field and various temperatures.

complexes is given in Reference (3).

Table I.   Electronic and hyperfine parameters of the binuclear complexes and the
Fe-Mo cofactor as determined by Mössbauer data. Numbers in parenthesis
refer to the electronic parameters determined by magnetic susceptibility
data.

Complex	D °K	E °K	A_z mm/s
$[(SPh)_2FeMoS_4](Ph_4P)_2$	-6.0 (-7.0)	1.8 (2.2)	0.78
$[S_5FeMoS_4](Ph_4P)_2$	-5.0 (-6.0)	1.1 (1.0)	0.73
A_1			0.97
A_2			0.87
Fe-Mo cofactor[a] A_3	+6.0	0.3	0.63
B			-0.53

[a] Data taken from Ref. (1).

The trinuclear complex C displays simple quadrupole doublets in the whole temperature range. Application of an external magnetic field results in a very small magnetic hyperfine splitting even at fields of 6.7 T. This behaviour together with the

magnetic susceptibility data indicates a strong antiferromagnetic coupling within this molecule resulting in a diamagnetic (S=0) spin state. The Mössbauer data of the tri-nuclear complex E on the other hand, display an asymmetric doublet at room temperature which is inverted at temperatures below liquid nitrogen. This inversion has been attributed (4) to electronic spin relaxation of an S=3/2 system with a positive axial field splitting D of ~5 K. A detailed account of the synthesis, structural characte-rization, electrochemistry and magnetic and electronic properties of the trinuclear complexes is given in Reference (5).

Clearly the synthetic models discussed so far cannot be considered as accurate ana-logs for the M clusters of the Fe-Mo cofactor. The stoichiometry requirement (1 Mo:6 Fe atoms) is not fulfilled neither for these models nor for the cubane Fe-Mo clusters proposed by other investigators (6), (7). Comparison however of the characteristic properties of these "precursor" models to those of the reaction centers of nitrogenase may give some insight on the nature of the building blocks of the protein centers. The parameter which is principally related with the electronic charge of the iron site is the isomer shift. It is firmly established that a decrease in the population of d-type orbitals results in a decrease of the isomer shift (8). In Table II we have listed the isomer shifts and quadrupole splittings of the present complexes together with the values of Fe(II) complexes tetrahedrally coordinated either to sulfide or to chloride ligands. The values of the M-center have also been included in the table for comparison. An inspection of this Table shows clearly that a replacement of two sulfur ligands by the MoS_4^{2-} unit results in a decrease of the isomer shift by ~0.2 mm/s. This holds also for the case of the more ionic Cl^- where the replacement of two of them by the MoS_4^{2-} group results in a decrease by ~0.4 mm/s. This correlation indi-cates a strong electron delocalization from the iron towards the MoS_4^{2-} group. A large electron density ($6e^-$ per N_2) is required also at the Fe-Mo cofactor for the reduction of dinitrogen to ammonia in corroboration with its isomer shift value which is within the range of the values observed for the present synthetic analogs. Of particular interest is the complex $[(MoS_4)_2Fe]^{3-}$. The formal oxidation state of Fe in this com-plex is I($3d^7$). Its isomer shift however is much lower than the value expected for a d^7 system, indicating a strong delocalization from the Fe ion to the two MoS_4^{2-} ligands. An extreme case of such a delocalization would result in a valence V (S=1/2) for the two Mo ions and III (S=5/2) for the Fe ion. Antiferromagnetic coupling between these three ions would lead to an S=3/2 spin state of the system, in agreement with the magnetic susceptibility and EPR results (11) for this complex. This spin state has also been detected in the Fe-Mo cofactor.

2.3.2 Synthetic Analogs for the P-clusters

Typical Mössbauer spectra taken at liquid nitrogen temperature are shown in figure 4. We notice that the complexes with Et_2dtc^- ligands display 4 distinct absorption lines while the complexes with monodentate ligands display doublets with a varying degree of asymmetry. The spectra have been fitted with two doublets, each of them

Table II. Isomer shifts (I.S.) and quadrupole splittings (ΔE_Q) of the synthetic analogs, the M-center of the Fe-Mo cofactor and related complexes.

Complex	I.S.[a],[b] (mm/s)	ΔE_Q[a] (mm/s)	Reference
$[(SPh)_2FeMoO_4](Ph_4P)_2$	0.44	1.96	Present work
$(S_5FeMoS_4)(Ph_4P)_2$	0.47	1.45	"
$(Cl_2FeMoS_4)(Ph_4P)_2$	0.59	2.14	"
$(Cl_4Fe_2MoS_4)(Ph_4P)_2$	0.57	1.98	"
$[Fe(MoS_4)_2](Et_4N)_3$	0.42	1.04	"
M-component	0.41	0.81	(1)
$[Fe(SPh)_4](Ph_4P)_2$	0.64	3.24	(9)
$(FeCl_4)^{2-}$	1.01	2.61	(10)

[a] Values at liquid nitrogen temperature

[b] With respect to Fe at room temperature

corresponding to two equivalent iron atoms in the Fe_4S_4 core. There are two ways of
fitting the spectra. The "crossed" combination which is two interpenetrating quadrupole doublets and the "nested" combination where one quadrupole doublet is contained
within the other. A comparison of the spectrum of $[(Fe_4S_4)Cl_2(Etdtc)_2]^{2-}$ to that of
$[(Fe_4S_4)Cl_3(Et_2dtc)]^{2-}$ (Fig. 4) proves in a straightforward way that the "nested"
configuration is the appropriate one for the clusters with the Et_2dtc^- ligands. The
"nested" configuration has been also chosen for clusters with monodentate ligands.
This choice is based on arguments of the temperature variation of the second order
Doppler shift and the comparison of the hyperfine parameters of these clusters to
those of corresponding clusters with symmetric ligands (12). The results of this
analysis, together with results of related complexes and of the P-clusters of nitrogenase are given in Table III.

The 4Fe-4S core with the cubane formation is frequently found in reaction centers
of proteins, a typical example being the class of ferredoxins (14). The formal valence
of the Fe atoms in these reaction centers, as well as their synthetic analogs, is +2
and +3 per each pair of them (oxidized or C-state). Due to the extensive delocalization, however, of the d-electrons within the core, an average valence of +2.5 is
assigned for each Fe atom. This has been clearly demonstrated through the isomer shift
parameter. A notable exception of this general behaviour is observed in the P-clusters
of nitrogenase, supposed also to be in cubane formation (1). The isomer shift and
quadrupole splitting of one of the iron atoms has typical values of Fe^{2+} ions in tetrahedral coordination while the remaining three display hyperfine parameters which do
not match the usual iron valences (Table III). An expansion to five coordination or
replacement of thiolate ligands by other atoms within the protein "backbone" has been

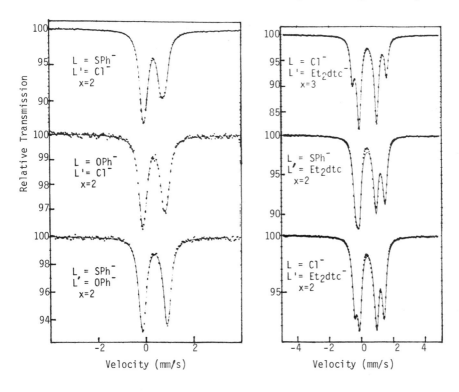

Fig. 4   Mössbauer spectra at 77 K of $(Fe_4S_4L_xL'_{4-x})^{2-}$ complexes with monodentate (left) and mixed mono- and bidentate terminal ligands (right).

suggested for these iron atoms (15).

We notice from Table III that complexes with asymmetric monodentate ligands display a common isomer shift which is intermediate to the isomer shifts of the clusters with the corresponding symmetric ligands. Thus, despite asymmetric ligation, an electron delocalization of the 3d orbitals and an average oxidation state of +2.5 persists for these clusters. The observed variation in the quadrupole splitting reflects the local symmetry of each iron atom. The Mössbauer spectra of the clusters with the bidentate Et_2dtc^- ligands on the other hand display a clear site differentiation. The tetrahedral $LFeS_3$ sites of these complexes show isomer shifts and quadrupole splittings very similar to those found in the symmetric $(Fe_4S_4L_4)^{2-}$ clusters (Table III). A pronounced increase in the I.S. values is found for the five coordinated $Fe-Et_2Dtc$ sites. This value lies between the values reported for the five-coordinate Fe(III) in $ClFe(Et_2Dtc)_2$ (16) (0.49 mm/s at 100 K vs Fe) and the five-coordinate Fe(II) in the $|Fe(Et_2Dtc)_2|_2$ dimer (17) (0.90 mm/s at 100 K vs Fe). Taking into account an expected reduction of the I.S. value in replacing the Cl^- ligand by a S^- ligand in the Fe(III)

Table III.   Isomer shifts[a] (I.S.) and quadrupole splittings of $(Fe_4S_4L_xL'_{4-x})^{2-}$ and of the P-clusters of nitrogenase at 77 K

Complex	L Site I.S.	L Site ΔE_Q	L' Site I.S.	L' Site ΔE_Q
$L_4 = (SPh)_4$	0.43	0.93		
$L_4 = Cl_4$	0.49	0.67		
$L_4 = (OPh)_4$[b]	0.50	1.21		
$L_2 = (SPh)_2$	0.48	0.96		
$L'_2 = Cl_2$			0.46	0.64
$L_2 = (SPh)_2$	0.48	0.91		
$L'_2 = (OPh)_2$			0.47	1.19
$L_2 = Cl_2$	0.46	0.64		
$L'_2 = (OPh)_2$			0.48	0.96
$L_2 = (SPh)_2$	0.47	1.06		
$L'_2 = (Et_2dtc)_2$			0.64	1.84
$L_2 = Cl_2$	0.53	1.06		
$L'_2 = (Et_2dtc)_2$			0.62	1.85
$L_3 = Cl_3$	0.51	1.07		
$L' = (Et_2dtc)$			0.64	2.13
A. vinelandii[c]	0.69	3.02	0.64	0.81
P-clusters	(Fe^{2+})		(D)	
C. pasteurianum	0.64	3.00	0.64	0.70
P - clusters	(Fe^{2+})		(D)	

[a] With respect to Fe at RT
[b] Values at 4.2 K taken for ref. (13)
[c] Values taken from ref. (1)

complex (4) we derive a mean value of ∿0.65 mm/s for these two complexes which is indeed very close to the value observed for the five coordinate Fe-Et$_2$Dtc sites. We may conclude, therefore, that the observed increase of the I.S. value for these sites is primarily a result of a change in the coordination number from four to five and that these sites can also be assigned to a formal oxidation state of +2.5. An extensive description of the synthesis, characterization and electronic properties of the

$[Fe_4S_4L_x(Et_2dtc)_{4-x}]^{2-}$ clusters can be found in reference (18).

3 CONCLUSIONS

The two groups of complexes which were studied in this project were designed to simulate structural and electronic properties of the two major reaction centers of the Fe-Mo protein of nitrogenase: the M- or FeMoco clusters and the P-clusters.

The binuclear and trinuclear Fe-Mo complexes display some interesting properties which may be correlated with the characteristic features of the FeMoco center. They all contain the MoS_4^{2-} moiety which withdraws electronic charge from the Fe(II) ions resulting in their partial oxidation. This ability of the MoS_4^{2-} ligand may well represent a characteristic feature in the Fe-Mo-S aggregates of nitrogenase. Intramolecular antiferromagnetic interaction is present in the trinuclear complexes which in the case of the $Fe(MoS_4)_2^{2-}$ complex results in a S=3/2 ground state. This spin state has also been observed for the native state of the FeMoco clusters.

An extensive charge delocalization prevails in the Fe_4S_4 cores of the cubane clusters with asymmetric ligands resulting in a formal oxidation state of +2.5 for all the Fe atoms. The introduction of bidentate terminal ligands results in a differentiation of the Fe sites (as witnessed by the corresponding spectral components) which is attributed to the change in coordination number of these sites. The P-clusters of nitrogenase on the other hand exhibit a 3:1 distribution of sites D and Fe^{2+} in their spin coupled diamagnetic state. The present results indicate clearly that such a distribution of sites within the Fe_4S_4 core can be achieved with a change in the coordination number without an increase in the charge (core reduction) or charge localization within the core.

REFERENCES

1. B.H. Huynh, M.T. Henzl, J.A. Chrisner, R. Zimmerman, W.H. Orme-Johnson, Biochimica et Biophysica Acta 623 (1980) 124-138.
2. S.P. Cramer, W.O. Gillum, K.O. Hodgson, L.E. Mortenson, E.I. Stiefel, J.R. Chisnell, W.J. Brill, V.K. Shah, J. Am. Chem. Soc. 100 (1978) 3814-19.
3. D. Coucouvanis, P. Stremple, E.D. Simhon, D. Swenson, N.C. Baenziger, M. Draganjac, L.T. Chen, A. Simopoulos, V. Papaefthymiou, A. Kostikas, V. Petrouleas, Inorg. Chem. 22 (1983) 292-308.
4. A. Simopoulos, V. Papaefthymiou, A. Kostikas, V. Petrouleas, D. Coucouvanis, E.D. Simhon, P. Stremple, Chem. Phys. Let. 81 (1981) 261-265.

5.   D. Coucouvanis, E.D. Simhon, P. Stremple, M. Ryan, D. Swenson, N.C. Baenziger, A. Simopoulos, V. Papaefthymiou, A. Kostikas, V. Petrouleas, Inorg. Chem. 23 (1984) 741-749.

6.   G. Christou, C.D. Garner, F.E. Mabbs, M.G.B. Dres, J. Chem. Soc. Chem. Commun. (1979) 91-93.

7.   T.E. Wolff, P.P. Power, R.B. Frankel, R.H. Holm, J. Am. Chem. Soc. 102 (1980) 4694-4703.

8.   L.R. Walker, G.K. Wertheim, Y. Jaccarino, Phys. Rev. Lett. 6,(1961) 98-101.

9.   A. Kostikas, V. Petrouleas, A. Simopoulos, D. Coucouvanis, D.G. Holah, Chem. Phys. Lett. 38 (1976) 582-84.

10. P.R. Edwards, C.E. Johnson, R.J.P. Williams, J. Chem. Phys. 47 (1967) 2074.

11. J.W. McDonald, G.D. Friesen, W.E. Newton, Inorg. Chim. Acta 46 (1980) L79-L80.

12. M.G. Kanatzidis, N.C. Baenziger, D. Coucouvanis, A. Simopoulos, A. Kostikas, J. Am. Chem. Soc. 106 (1984) 4500-4511.

13. W.E. Cleland, D.A. Holtman, M. Sabat, J.A. Ibers, G.C. DeFotis, B.A. Averill, J. Am. Chem. Soc. 105 (1983) 6021-6031.

14. W. Lovenberg (Ed.), Iron-Sulfur Proteins, V. I,II,III, Academic Press, New York (1977).

15. E. Munck, in "Recent Chemical Applications in Mössbauer Spectroscopy", Advances in Chemistry Series, American Chemical Society, Washington, D.C. (1981) p. 305.

16. G.E. Chapps, S.W. McCann, H.H. Wickman, J. Chem. Phys. 60 (1974) 990-997.

17. J.L.K.F. DeVries, C.P. Keijers, E. DeBoer, Inorg. Chem. 11 (1972) 1343-1348.

18. M.G. Kanatzidis, D. Coucouvanis, A. Simopoulos, A. Kostikas, V. Papaefthymiou, J. Amer. Chem. Soc. (in press).

Iron(III) – Catalyzed Cleavage of Catechols

Lawrence Que, Jr., Lloyd S. White, Joseph W. Pyrz

Department of Chemistry, University of Minnesota, Minneapolis, Minnesota 55455, U.S.A.

SUMMARY

Iron(III) catecholate complexes have been synthesized and structurally characterized to test the novel substrate activation mechanism proposed for the intradiol cleaving catechol dioxygenases. In this mechanism, substrate reacts with dioxygen after coordination to the ferric center through only one of the catecholate oxygens. Fe(saloph)catH and Fe(TPP)catH are examples of monodentate catecholate complexes, while [Fe(salen)cat]$^-$ and [Fe(NTA)DBC]$^=$ are chelated catecholate complexes. Of these, only [Fe(NTA)DBC]$^=$ reacts with dioxygen to yield the desired cleavage product in good yield. Our observations suggest that neither the monodentate monoanion nor the chelated dianion of DBC is the species which reacts with dioxygen. The reactivity of [Fe(NTA)DBC]$^=$ towards dioxygen is proposed to result from the rate-determining formation of the monodentate DBC dianion due to the asymmetric chelation of the catecholate in the isolated complex.

Abbreviations: saloph, N,N'-1,2-benzenebis(salicylideneamine); catH$_2$, catechol; TPP, meso-tetraphenylporphyrin; salen, N,N'-ethylenebis-(salicylideneamine); NTA, nitrilotriacetic acid; DBCH$_2$, 3,5-di-tert-butylcatechol; DMSQ, 4,5-dimethoxy-o-benzosemiquinone; PSQ, 9,10-phenanthrenesemiquinone.

1 INTRODUCTION

The oxidative cleavage of catechols to <u>cis,cis</u>-muconic acids is catalyzed by bacterial enzymes with a high-spin ferric center in the active site (1). A variety of spectroscopic approaches have failed to detect the participation of the ferrous oxidation state in the mechanism of these intradiol cleaving catechol dioxygenases (2-6). Because of this, a novel mechanism has been proposed involving substrate activation by the ferric center as a result of its coordination to the iron (7). In order to assess the likelihood of such a mechanism, several iron(III) catecholate complexes have been synthesized and studied for their reactivity towards dioxygen. This paper will summarize the insights derived from these studies.

2 FE(SALEN) COMPLEXES

The demonstrated coordination of tyrosine to the active site ferric center has resulted in the use of the tetradentate salen and saloph ligands as active site analogues (8). Ligand exhange of Fe(salen)OAc or Fe(saloph)OAc in the presence of excess catechol results in the formation of Fe(salen)catH or Fe(saloph)catH, respectively, the first examples of monodentate catecholate coordination to iron(III). Treatment with base removes the remaining catecholate proton and yields the corresponding chelated catecholate complexes. Fe(saloph)catH (9) and K^+[Fe(salen)cat]$^-$ (10) have been characterized crystallographically, confirming the mode of catecholate coordination in the two complexes (Figure 1). Fe(saloph)catH is a

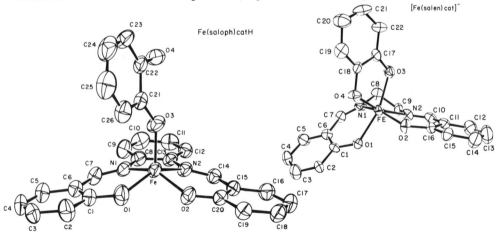

Fig. 1.   ORTEP plots of the structures of Fe(saloph)catH and [Fe(salen)cat]$^-$.

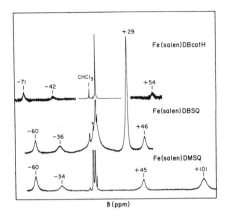

Fig. 2. ^{1}H-NMR Spectra of Iron Complexes in CDCl$_3$.

square pyramidal complex with the catecholate occupying the apical
position, while [Fe(salen)cat]$^-$ is a distorted octahedral complex, one
phenolate of the salen ligand bending out of the plane to accomodate
the bidentate catecholate.

The reactivity studies with dioxygen have used the corresponding
3,5-di-tert-butylcatechol complexes to minimize side products.
Fe(salen)DBC-H reacts immediately with dioxygen in CHCl$_3$ to afford the
one-electron oxidized derivative, Fe(salen)DBSQ, in 80% yield. The
reaction is conveniently monitored by NMR spectroscopy (Figure 2).
Fe(salen)DBC-H exhibits paramagnetically shifted proton resonances
because of the high-spin ferric center (11); at 30°C, the salen resonances are at 71(H-4), -54(H-5), and 42(H-6) ppm and are typical of
five-coordinate Fe(salen)phenolate complexes (12). Upon oxygenation,
these signals are replaced by corresponding signals at 60, -46, and 36
ppm, respectively, and a new intense signal at -29 ppm. This new
resonance has been assigned to the 5-t-butyl protons of the semiquinone complex (11) by comparisons with the spectra of other semiquinone complexes synthesized by the oxidative addition of quinones to
Fe(salen) (13). In Figure 2, comparisons of the spectra of the DBSQ
and DMSQ complexes show that the three resonances assigned to the
salen protons remain in similar positions. The shifts of the resonances assigned to semiquinone protons are proportional to the hyperfine splittings observed for the free semiquinones (14); the 3-t-butyl
resonance of the DBSQ complex remains unshifted from its diamagnetic
position as expected from the near negligible hyperfine splitting

observed for these protons. A crystal structure of Fe(salen)PSQ (10) shows a chelated semiquinone, with a geometry similar to the chelated catecholate complex.

The corresponding chelated catecholate complex, [Fe(salen)DBC]$^-$, however, does not react with dioxygen (11). Indeed, when the expected initial products of the reaction, i.e. Fe(salen)DBSQ and superoxide, are mixed together in THF, the superoxide reduces the DBSQ complex to [Fe(salen)DBC]$^-$ in quantitative yield. This observation is in agreement with the relative redox potentials of the two reactants; cyclic voltammetric studies of the [Fe(salen)DBC]$^-$/Fe(salen)DBSQ couple show the one-electron reduction to occur at -423 mV vs SCE (15), compared to the -700 mV value for O_2/O_2^- couple in aprotic solvents (16). The observed potential indicates that [Fe(salen)DBC]$^-$ is incapable of reducing dioxygen, in contrast to the free DBC$^=$, which is quite reactive with dioxygen. The redox potential of the free DBSQ$^-$/DBC$^=$ is reported to be -1340 mV vs SCE (17). Thus the chelation of the catechol to the Fe(salen) center has stabilized the DBC$^=$ oxidation state by nearly a volt. This is consistent with the known affinity of catecholates for iron(III) (18) and argues against the possibility that chelated catecholate would be the reactive species in the ES complex of the dioxygenases.

3 FE(TPP) COMPLEXES

The flexibility of the salen ligand in accomodating both monodentate and chelated modes of catecholate coordination led us to explore catecholate complexes with the more rigid porphyrin ligand. It was anticipated that the chelation of the catecholate would be less likely to occur in such complexes. Fe(TPP)catH, obtained from the reaction of [Fe(TPP)]$_2$O with an excess of catechol, is a monodentate catecholate complex, as evidenced from its crystal structure (19). That this structure is retained in solution is indicated by its ^{1}H-NMR spectrum. The pyrrole protons are found at 80 ppm, a value typical for other five-coordinate high-spin ferric TPP complexes (20). The catecholate protons exhibit shifts very similar to those of corresponding phenolate complexes. For example, the 4-H resonance of Fe(TPP)DBC-H appears at -110 ppm, as expected for the para proton in a phenolate complex. This also shows that the DBC-H ligand coordinates to the Fe(TPP)$^+$ via the less sterically hindered catechol oxygen. Exposure of this complex to oxygen does not result in a reaction; the complex is air-stable.

The corresponding [Fe(TPP)DBC]$^-$ complex cannot be obtained. Treatment of Fe(TPP)DBC-H with KO-t-Bu results in the partial dis-

placement of the catecholate by the alkoxide; NMR spectra of this
mixture show no changes in shift for the pyrrole and DBC-H 4-H protons
and the appearance of a new resonance at 30 ppm, assigned to the t-
butyl protons of the coordinated t-butoxide.

4 FE(NTA) COMPLEXES

Weller and Weser (21) reported a catechol cleaving system
consisting of the Fe(NTA) complex in an organic solvent-borate buffer
mixture. Over a period of days and in the presence of dioxygen, $DBCH_2$
is catalytically converted to its cleavage product, 3,5-di-tert-butyl-
5-(carboxymethyl)-2-furanone, in 80% yield. Crystals of
$Q_2[Fe(NTA)DBC]$ can be isolated from DMF solutions (15); the complex
reacts in DMF with dioxygen over a period of four days to yield the
cleavage product, i.e.

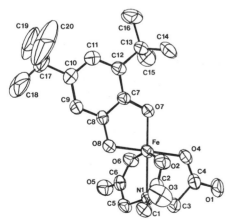

Thus it would appear that $[Fe(NTA)DBC]^=$ is minimally the precursor to
the reactive species.

Cyclic voltammetric studies on $[Fe(NTA)DBC]^=$ show a reversible
wave at -268 mV vs SCE (15), assigned to the DBSQ/DBC couple. This
value is more positive than that found for $[Fe(salen)DBC]^-$ and would
suggest an even smaller tendency for $[Fe(NTA)DBC]^=$ to react with
dioxygen; however, the opposite is apparently true.

The crystal structure of the complex (15) shown in Figure 3 may

Fig. 3.   ORTEP plot of the structure of $[Fe(NTA)DBC]^=$.

suggest an explanation for its reactivity. The complex is a distorted
octahedron with a tetradentate NTA and a bidentate DBC ligand. The
catechol is unsymmetrically chelated to the ferric center, with Fe–O
bonds of 1.89 and 1.98 Å. The asymmetry is attributed to the weakness
of the Fe–N bond (2.22 Å) trans to the shorter Fe–O bond.

   We propose that the reactivity of the [Fe(NTA)DBC]$^=$ complex
results from the breaking of the longer Fe–O bond to yield a
monodentate form of the complex. This monodentate form then reacts
immediately with dioxygen resulting in oxidative cleavage, as
illustrated below.

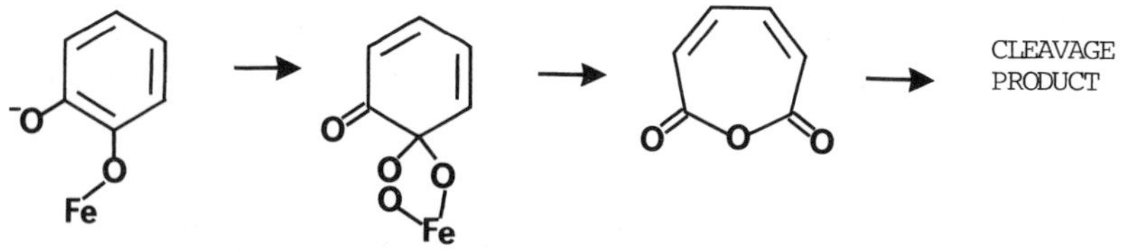

The formation of the monodentate form would be the rate determining
step of this reaction and would be consistent with the observed reactivity of the complex. Because of the affinity of catechol for
iron(III), the breaking of the Fe–O bond would be expected to have a
significant activation barrier. The participation of the anhydride is
indicated by the identity of the product, which must be derived from
the reaction of the proposed anhydride with piperidine. ^{18}O–labeling
experiments are consistent with the mechanism.

   Taken together, the above observations suggest that the reactive
form of the substrate in the catechol dioxygenases must be the dianion
coordinated to the ferric center in a monodentate manner. The
bidentate catecholate dianion is thermodynamically stabilized by
chelation to the iron, as indicated by the redox potentials of the
coordinated ligand. The catecholate monoanion is not strong enough a
reductant to reduce dioxygen in the absence of some other driving
force for the reaction. We believe that the reactivity of
Fe(salen)DBC–H stems from the stability of the chelated semiquinone
complex. In the absence of an available site for semiquinone
chelation, no reaction occurs as in the case of the FeTPP complex.

   The Fe(NTA) complex differs from the Fe(salen) and FeTPP complexes in its ability to effect DBC cleavage. Structurally, NTA is a
tripodal tetradentate ligand while the others are planar tetradentate
ligands. As we have pointed out earlier (15), the tripodal nature of
the ligand may give rise to the asymmetric chelation of the catechol
and thus promote the formation of the reactive monodentate dianion.
Recently, another iron complex with a tripodal ligand, FeLCl$_2$ (L =

2-hydroxy-5-nitrobenzyl-bis(2-picolinyl)amine) has been reported to effect the oxidative cleavage of DBC (22). Our efforts now are directed towards the cleavage properties of iron(III) complexes of tripodal ligands with phenolate functions in order to assess the importance of tyrosines in the enzyme mechanism.

5 REFERENCES

(1) L. Que, Jr., Adv. Inorg. Biochem. 5 (1983) 167-199.

(2) L. Que, Jr., J. D. Lipscomb, R. Zimmermann, E. Munck, N. R. Orme-Johnson, W. H. Orme-Johnson, Biochim. Biophys. Acta. 452 (1976) 320-334.

(3) J. W. Whittaker, J. D. Lipscomb, T. A. Kent, E. Munck, J. Biol. Chem. 259 (1984) 4466-4475.

(4) D. P. Ballou, C. Bull, in W. Caughey, (Ed.), Biochemical and Clinical Aspects of Oxygen, Academic Press, New York 1979, pp. 573-587.

(5) C. Bull, D. P. Ballou, S. Otsuka, J. Biol. Chem. 256 (1981) 12681-12686.

(6) T. A. Walsh, D. P. Ballou, R. Mayer, L. Que, Jr., J. Biol. Chem. 258 (1983) 14422-14427.

(7) L. Que, Jr., J. D. Lipscomb, E. Munck, J. M. Wood, Biochim. Biophys. Acta. 485 (1977) 60-74.

(8) R. H. Heistand, II, R. B. Lauffer, E. Fikrig, L. Que, Jr., J. Am. Chem. Soc. 104 (1982) 2789-2796.

(9) R. H. Heistand, II, A. L. Roe, L. Que, Jr., Inorg. Chem. 21 (1982) 676-681.

(10) R. B. Lauffer, R. H. Heistand, II, L. Que, Jr., Inorg. Chem. 22 (1983) 50-55.

(11) R. B. Lauffer, R. H. Heistand, II, L. Que, Jr., J. Am. Chem. Soc. 103 (1981) 3947-3949.

(12) J. W. Pyrz, A. L. Roe, L. J. Stern, L. Que, Jr., J. Am. Chem. Soc. 107 (1985) 614-620.

(13) C. Floriani, G. Fachinetti, F. Caldorazzo, J. Chem. Soc. Dalton Trans. (1973) 765-769.

(14) C. Trapp, C. A. Tyson, G. Giacometti, J. Am. Chem. Soc. 90 (1968) 1394-1400.

(15) L. S. White, P. V. Nilsson, L. H. Pignolet, L. Que, Jr., J. Am. Chem. Soc. 106 (1984) 8312-8313.

(16) J. Lewis, F. E. Mabbs, A. Richards, J. Chem. Soc. A. (1967) 1014-1018.

(17) E. J. Nanni, Jr., M. D. Stallings, D. T. Sawyer, J. Am. Chem. Soc. 102 (1980) 4481-4485.

(18) K. N. Raymond, S. S. Isied, L. D. Brown, F. R. Fronczek, J. H. Nibert, J. Am. Chem. Soc. 98 (1975) 1767-1774.

(19) M. R. Rogers, L. Que, Jr., unpublished observations.

(20) H. M. Goff in A. B. P. Lever, H. B. Gray (Eds.), Iron Porphyrins, Part I, Addison-Wesley, Reading 1983, pp.237-281.

(21) M. G. Weller, U. Weser, J. Am. Chem. Soc. 104 (1982) 3752-3754.

(22) Y. Nishida, H. Shimo, S. Kida, J. Chem. Soc. Chem. Comm. (1984) 1611-1612.

Structure, Recognition and Transport of Ferric Enterobactin in *E. Coli*

Kenneth N. Raymond, David J. Ecker, Larry D. Loomis, Berthold Matzanke

Department of Chemistry, University of California, Berkeley, California 94720, USA

The transport and uptake of iron by microbes, a process which is essential for their growth, is mediated by low-molecular-weight complexing agents called siderophores (1,2). A siderophore produced by E. coli, enterochelin (3) (here called enterobactin (4)), is the most powerful iron complexing agent known and has been among the most thoroughly studied of the siderophores (5). Ferric enterobactin transport in E. coli has been studied with respect to the specificity of the outer membrane protein receptor and the mechanism of enterobactin-mediated transport of ferric ion across the outer membrane. Transport kinetic and inhibition studies were performed with ferric enterobactin and synthetic structural analogs (Fig. 1) to map the parts of the molecule important for receptor binding. The ferric complex of the synthetic structural analog of enterobactin, 1,3,5-N,N', N''-tris(2,3-dihydroxybenzoyl)-triaminomethylbenzene (MECAM) is transported with the same maximum velocity as ferric enterobactin. A double label transport assay with $^{59}Fe[^{3}H]$-MECAM showed that the ligand and the metal are transported across the outer membrane when a large excess of extracellular complex was added to the cell suspension. At least 60 % of internalized ^{59}Fe enterobactin exchanged with extracellular ^{55}Fe enterobactin (Fig. 2). Internalized $^{59}Fe[^{3}H]MECAM$ was released from the cell as the intact complex when either unlabeled Fe MECAM or Fe enterobactin was added extracellularly. The results suggest a mechanism of active transport of unmodified coordination complex across the outer membrane with possible accumulation in the periplasm. Energy-dependent binding of ^{67}Ga enterobactin was observed, but the rate was substantially lower than the rate of ^{59}Fe enterobactin transport. The results establish important correlations between the coordination chemistry of the metal and the mechanism of receptor-mediated uptake.

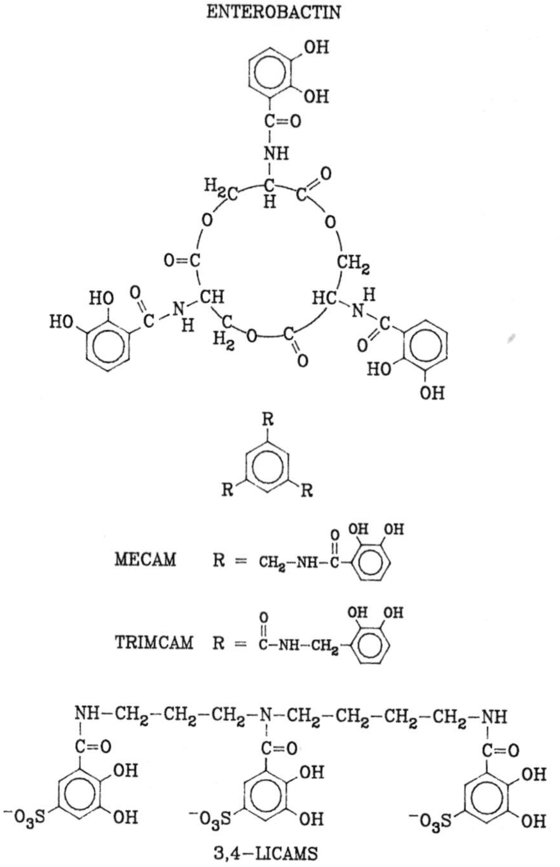

ENTEROBACTIN

MECAM   R = CH₂-NH-C-

TRIMCAM   R = C-NH-CH₂-

3,4-LICAMS

Fig. 1. The strucure of enterobactin and several synthetic enterobactin analogs:
MECAM [1,3,5-N,N',N''-tris(2,3-dihydroxybenzoyl)triaminomethylbenzene]; TRIMCAM
[1,3,5-tris(2,3-dihydroxybenzoylcarbamido)benzene]; and LICAMS [1,5,10-N,N',N''-tris
(5-sulfo-2,3-dihydroxybenzoyl)triazadecane]

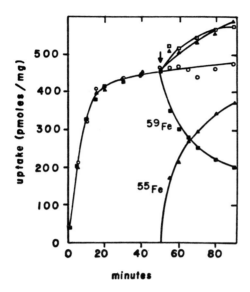

Fig. 2. Exchange of external and cellular ferric enterobactin. The cell concentration was 1.22 mg/mL and the pH was 7.4. In all experiments the initial concentration of ^{59}Fe enterobactin was 2μM; o, ^{59}Fe enterobactin uptake with no additions; Δ,(control) ^{59}Fe enterobactin uptake with the addition (at 51 min, arrow) of the same substrate at 30 μM concentrations; ■, ^{59}Fe enterobactin uptake with addition (at 51 min, arrow) of ^{55}Fe enterobactin at 30 μM concentrations; ▲, ^{55}Fe enterobactin accumulation in the same experiment; □, numerical sum of ^{55}Fe (■) and ^{59}Fe(▲) in the same experiment

REFERENCES

(1) K.N. Raymond, G. Müller, B.F. Matzanke, Topics in Current Chemistry, 123, 49-102 (1984).

(2) J.B. Neilands, Ann. Rev. Nutr., 1, 27-46 (1981).

(3) I.G. O'Brien, F. Gibson, Biochim. Biophys. Acta, 215, 393 (1970).

(4) J.R. Pollack, J.B. Neilands, Biochem. Biophys. Res. Comm., 38, 989 (1970).

(5) G. Müller, Y. Isowa, K.N. Raymond, J. Biol. Chem., (1984), submitted for publication.

Activation of Hydrogen Peroxide by Fe(II) (MeCN)$_4$(ClO$_4$)$_2$ and Fe(III) Cl$_3$ in Acetonitrile: Model Systems for The Active Sites of Peroxidases, Catalase, and Monoxygenase

Donald T. Sawyer, Hiroshi Sugimoto

Department of Chemistry, University of California, Riverside, California 92521, U.S.A.

SUMMARY

Addition of Fe^{II}(MeCN)$_4$(ClO$_4$)$_2$ to solutions of hydrogen peroxide in dry aceto-nitrile catalyzes the rapid disproportionation of H$_2$O$_2$ via initial formation of a Fe^{II}(H$_2$O$_2$)$^{2+}$ adduct, which, in turn, oxidizes a second H$_2$O$_2$ to yield dioxygen. The intermediate of the latter step dioxygenates diphenylisobenzofuran, 9,10-diphenylanthracene, and rubrene, which are traps for singlet-state dioxygen. This intermediate also dioxygenates electron-rich unsaturated carbon-carbon bonds [Ph$_2$C=CPh$_2$ → 2Ph$_2$C(O), PhC≡CPh → PhC(O)C(O)Ph, cis-PhCH=CHPh → 2PhCH(O)]. In the presence of organic substrates such as 1,4-cyclohexadiene, 1,2-diphenyl-hydrazine, catechols, and thiols, the Fe(II)-H$_2$O$_2$/MeCN system yields dehydrogenated products (PhH, PhN=NPh, quinones, and RSSR) with conversion efficiencies that range from 100% to 17%. With substrates such as alcohols, aldehydes, methyl styrene, thioethers, sulfoxides, and phosphines, the Fe^{II}(H$_2$O$_2$)$^{2+}$ adduct promotes their monoxygenation to aldehydes, carboxylic acid, epoxide, sulfoxides, sulfones, and phosphine oxides, respectively.

Solutions of Fe^{III}Cl$_3$ in dry acetonitrile also catalyze the rapid disproportiona-tion of H$_2$O$_2$ to O$_2$ and H$_2$O, but the catalyst remains in the Fe(III) state. In the presence of triphenylphosphine, dimethyl sulfoxide, and olefins the Fe^{III}Cl$_3$-H$_2$O$_2$/MeCN system yields monoxygenated substrates (Ph$_3$PO, Me$_2$SO$_2$, and epoxides). The epoxidation of olefins is especially favored by the Fe^{III}Cl$_3$-H$_2$O$_2$ adduct.

Both of these catalyst systems [Fe^{II}(MeCN)$_4$(ClO$_4$)$_2$ and Fe^{III}Cl$_3$] in dry aceto-nitrile activate hydroperoxides for the dehydrogenation and monoxygenation of organic substrates. Their ability to facilitate these reactions via the oxene chemistry of ferryl (FeO^{2+}) and perferryl (FeCl$_3$O) make them useful reaction mimics for the active sites of <u>peroxidases</u>, <u>catalase</u>, and <u>monoxygenases</u>.

A recent Communication[1] has described the iron(II)-induced activation of hydrogen peroxide in dry acetonitrile for the efficient dehydrogenation and monoxygenation of organic substrates. This chemistry is unique in that the $Fe^{II}(MeCN)_4(ClO_4)_2$ catalyst rapidly disproportionates H_2O_2 in the absence of substrate, but remains in the Fe(II) state (as it does for all of the substrate reactions). Also, the products from the Fe(II)-H_2O_2-substrate reactions in dry MeCN are totally free of those associated with ·OH radical chemistry and the Fenton process.[2-4] Although $Me_2C(O)$ is unreactive, MeCH(O) is monoxygenated; and Me_2SO yields Me_2SO_2 exclusively (with ·OH it yields CH_4, C_2H_6, and MeOH via production of methyl radicals).[4]

IRON(II)-INDUCED ACTIVATION OF H_2O_2

Table 1 summarizes the results from the addition of dry H_2O_2 (98%, dissolved in MeCN) to solutions of various organic substrates in the presence of the Fe(II) catalyst. Three classes of reactions occur on the basis of the substrate: (a) monoxygenations, (b) dehydrogenations and oxidations, and (c) dioxygenations.

The products are in marked contrast to those observed for aqueous Fenton chemistry. However, the presence of 1% H_2O in the MeCN reaction system results in the oxidation of Fe(II) and substrate products that are characteristic of the Fenton process. Fenton chemistry is generally believed to be induced by the ·OH radical that is produced from reduction of H_2O_2 by Fe(II).[5]

$$Fe^{II} + H_2O_2 \longrightarrow Fe^{III}(OH) + ·OH \qquad (1)$$

The unique feature of the anhydrous system for the activation of H_2O_2 is that the acetonitrile matrix for the Fe(II) catalyst causes the Fe(III)/Fe(II) redox potential to be greater than +1.8 V vs NHE, compared to about +0.4 V vs NHE in water at pH 7.[1] This large shift of redox potential precludes the reduction of H_2O_2 by Fe(II). As a result, the Fe(II) catalyst remains in its reduced state for all of the reactions in dry acetonitrile.

At present, little is known about the structure of the activated Fe^{II}-H_2O_2 complexes. The disproportionation reaction for H_2O_2 and the three types of substrate reactions indicate that more than one kind of complex may be present, perhaps in dynamic equilibrium. Scheme 1 presents possible models for the oxidase/monoxygenase function and the disproportionase(catalase)/dioxygenase function.

The addition of H_2O_2 to a solution of $Fe^{II}(MeCN)_4(ClO_4)_2$ that does not contain substrate results in its rapid disproportionation to O_2 and H_2O. A reasonable mechanism involves the side-on configuration (1) for the $Fe^{II}(H_2O_2)^{2+}$ adduct and a concerted transfer of the two hydrogen atoms of the second H_2O_2 (Scheme 1). This dehydrogenation of H_2O_2 is a competitive process with that for the $Fe^{II}(H_2O_2)$-substrate reactions (Table 1). The controlled introduction of dilute H_2O_2 into a Fe(II)/substrate solution limits the concentration of H_2O_2 and ensures that a $Fe^{II}(H_2O_2)^{2+}$-substrate reaction can be competitive with the second-order H_2O_2-disproportionation reaction. Thus, the substrate reaction efficiency is proportional to the relative rates of reaction $(k_{RH}/k_{H_2O_2})$.

Scheme 1

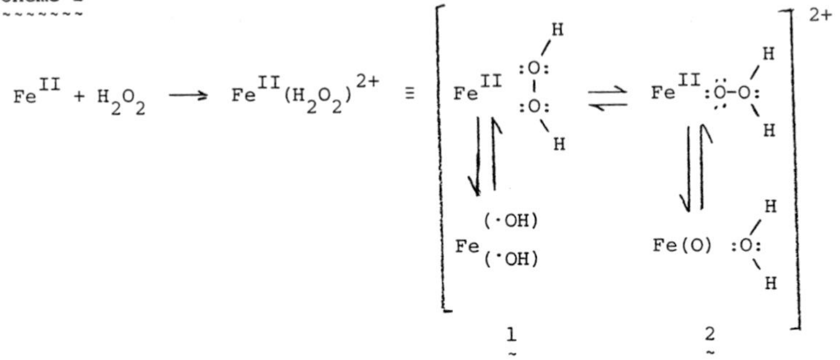

$$Fe^{II} + H_2O_2 \longrightarrow Fe^{II}(H_2O_2)^{2+} \equiv$$

oxidase and monoxygenase model

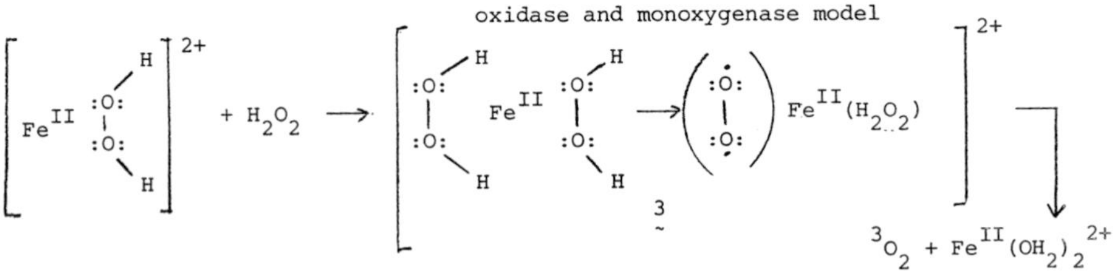

catalase and dioxygenase model

The results of Table 1 confirm that the $Fe^{II}(HOOH)^{2+}$ adducts are effective dehydrogenation agents for substrates such as cyclohexadienes, substituted hydrazines, catechols, and thiols. Because 1,4-cyclohexadiene yields only benzene for the Fe(II)-HOOH adduct, either the bound substrate induces the homolytic scission of the HO-OH bond to give two bound ·OH species (1, Scheme 1) for the concerted removal of two H-atoms from the substrate, or the oxene-like character of the end-on configuration (2, Scheme 1) results in the same concerted removal of two H-atoms. For the 1:1 1,3-cyclohexadiene-$Fe^{II}(HOOH)^{2+}$ adduct a major fraction of the product is the $(\underline{c}-C_6H_7)_2$ dimer, especially for high substrate-Fe(II) ratios. This prompts us to suggest that the dimer results from a bis$(1,3-\underline{c}-C_6H_8)$Fe(II) adduct that is susceptible to the concerted removal of an allylic hydrogen from each (via either configuration 1 or 2)

$$2(1,3-\underline{c}-C_6H_8) + Fe(II) + HOOH \longrightarrow (1,3-\underline{c}-C_6H_7)_2 + Fe^{II}(H_2O)_2^{2+} \qquad (2)$$

Support for such a process is provided by the absence of any $(C_6H_7)_2$ dimer as a product when O_2 is present in the reaction matrix. Thus, with O_2 present the initial formation of $\underline{c}-C_6H_7$· in the reactive complex apparently is followed by a coupling to give $\underline{c}-C_6H_7OO$·, which then dissociates to PhH and HO_2· (eq. 3) [6]

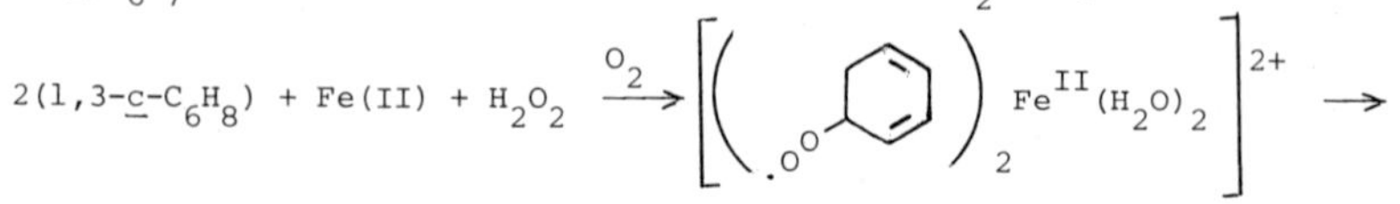

$$2PhH + [2HO_2· \longrightarrow H_2O_2 + O_2] + Fe^{II}(H_2O)_2^{2+} \qquad (3)$$

Table 1. Products from the Iron(II)-induced Monoxygenation, Dehydrogenation, and Dioxygenation of Organic Substrates (RH) by H_2O_2 in Dry Acetonitrile.[a]

Substrate	Reaction Efficiency, 100%[b]	Products
A. Monoxygenation		
blank (H_2O_2)	100	O_2, H_2O, Fe(II)
Ph_3P	100	Ph_3PO
Me_2SO	100	Me_2SO_2
Ph_2SO	100	Ph_2SO_2
EtOH	70	MeCH(O) (90%), MeC(O)OH (10%), O_2
$PhCH_2OH$	100	PhCH(O)
c-$C_6H_{11}OH$	47	$C_6H_{10}(O)$, O_2
MeCH(O)	20	MeC(O)OH, O_2
$Me_2C(O)$	NR	O_2
PhCH(O)	28	PhC(O)OH, O_2
B. Dehydrogenation and Oxidation		
cyclohexane	NR	O_2
$1,4$-c-C_6H_8	59	PhH, O_2
PhNHNHPh	100	PhN=NPh
H_2S	100	H_2SO_4
H_2O (56 mM)	100	Fe(III)
C. Dioxygenation		
	100	
	69	, O_2
	83	, O_2
$Ph_2C=CPh_2$	22	$Ph_2C(O)$, O_2
$PhC\equiv CPh$	42	PhC(O)C(O)Ph, O_2
$PhC\equiv CMe$	26	PhC(O)C(O)Me, O_2
$PhC\equiv CH$	11	PhC(O)CH(O), O_2
c-PhCH=CHPh	52	PhCH(O) (98%), $PhC\equiv CPh$ (2%), O_2
t-PhCH=CHPh	28	PhCH(O), O_2
PhCH=CHMe	32	PhCH(O) + MeCH(O) (85%), PhCHCHOMe (15%), O_2

[a]Ref. 1. Product solution [from the slow addition (~5 min. to give a final 2 mM concentration) of 1 M H_2O_2 (98% H_2O_2 in MeCN) to a solution of 1 mM $[Fe^{II}(MeCN)_4]$ $(ClO_4)_2$ plus 2 mM substrate] analyzed by gas chromatography and assayed for residual Fe(II) by MnO_4^- titration and by colorimetry with 1,10-o-phenanthroline.

[b]100% represents one substrate oxygenation or dehydrogenation per H_2O_2 added. For dioxygenations, 100% represents one substrate converted per two H_2O_2 added.

[c]100%, one H_2S converted to H_2SO_4 per four H_2O_2 added.

This radical-radical coupling by $\cdot O_2 \cdot$ precludes dimerization of the $\underset{\sim}{c}-C_6H_7 \cdot$ radicals and results in benzene as the only product.

Although H_2S is oxygenated to H_2SO_4 by the $Fe^{II}-H_2O_2$ adduct ($4H_2O_2$ per H_2S),[1] thiols (both aromatic and aliphatic) are dehydrogenated by the $Fe^{II}(HOOH)^{2+}$ complex to give disulfides as the only product. The reaction stoichiometry of two RSH molecules per HOOH is the same as for the dimerization of $1,3-\underset{\sim}{c}-C_6H_8$ (eq. 2); a similar bis adduct for the reaction complex probably is formed (eq. 4)

$$2RSH + Fe(II) + HOOH \longrightarrow [(RSH)_2 1]^{2+} \longrightarrow RSSR + Fe^{II}(H_2O)_2^{2+} \quad (4)$$

The results of Table 1 confirm that the $Fe^{II}(HOOH)^{2+}$ adduct oxygenates alcohols (and ethers, activated olefins, thioethers, sulfoxides, and phosphines). The reaction rate for $PhCH_2OH$ is about twice as fast as for $MeCH_2OH$,[7] probably because the C-H bond energy of the methylene group of the former is 10 Kcal lower. A mechanism that is consistent with these observations involves either (a) the homolytic scission of the side-on HO-OH bond (1, Scheme 1) induced by the bound substrate (ROH) and the subsequent abstraction by $HO \cdot$ of a H-atom from the α-carbon, or (b) the direct abstraction by the oxene oxygen of the end-on configuration (2, Scheme 1) of a H-atom from the α-carbon, and the subsequent addition of the resulting $\cdot OH$ group to the carbon radical (eq. 5)

$$PhCH_2OH + Fe(II) + ROOH \longrightarrow \left[(PhC\overset{H}{\underset{\cdot}{\overset{|}{-}}}\overset{H}{\overset{|}{O}}:)Fe(\cdot OH)(ROH) \longrightarrow \right.$$

$$\left. [PhCH(OH)_2 Fe^{II}(ROH)]^{2+} \longrightarrow PhCH(O) + Fe^{II}(H_2O)(ROH)^{2+} \right. \quad (5)$$

The hemiacetal product dissociates to give the aldehyde and H_2O [R'OH when the substrate is an ether (ROR')]. Because ethers are as reactive as alcohols and give the same aldehyde product, the process must be a monoxygenation to the hemiacetal rather than a dehydrogenation (concerted removal of hydrogen atoms from the α-carbon and the OH group). The $Fe^{II}(HOOH)^{2+}$ activated complex also is an effective monoxygenase for aldehydes. The oxene character of the end-on configuration (2, Scheme 1) makes it the dominant reactive complex (eq. 6).

$$PhCH(O) + Fe(II) + HOOH \longrightarrow \left[[PhCH(O)]2 \longrightarrow \right.$$

$$\left. [PhC(O)]Fe(\cdot OH)(OH_2) \right]^{2+} \longrightarrow PhC(O)OH + Fe^{II}(OH_2)^{2+} \quad (6)$$

The dramatic enhancement by molecular oxygen of the rate and extent of the $Fe^{II}(H_2O_2)^{2+}$-$PhCH(O)$ reaction (over 300 turnovers) is indicative of an autoxidation process. Thus, the formation of the reactive intermediate complex provides a bi-radical center than can couple with triplet oxygen ($\cdot O_2 \cdot$) to give $PhC(O)OO \cdot$ in an initiation step (eq. 7a)

Initiation:

$$PhCH(O) + Fe(II) + H_2O_2 \longrightarrow \left[[PhCH(O)]Fe^{II}(H_2O_2) \longrightarrow \right.$$

$$\left. [PhC(O)]Fe(\cdot OH)(H_2O) \right]^{2+} \xrightarrow{\cdot O_2 \cdot} PhC(O)OO \cdot + Fe^{III}(OH)(H_2O)^{2+} \quad (7a)$$

The coupling by $\cdot O_2\cdot$ with the carbon radical leaves an $[Fe(\cdot OH)]$ center, which goes to the observed $Fe^{III}(OH)^{2+}$ product. The peroxy radical $[PhC(O)OO\cdot]$ from the initiation step apparently abstracts a H-atom from a second $PhCH(O)$ and the resulting $Ph\dot{C}(O)$ radical couples with another $\cdot O_2\cdot$ in the propagation step (eq. 7b).

Progagation:

$$PhC(O)OO\cdot + PhCH(O) \longrightarrow PhC(O)OOH + Ph\dot{C}(O)$$
$$\qquad\qquad\qquad\qquad\qquad\qquad\quad \Big\downarrow O_2$$
$$\qquad\qquad\qquad\qquad\qquad\qquad\qquad PhC(O)OO\cdot \qquad\qquad\qquad (7b)$$

The Fe(II)-catalyzed oxygenation of another $PhCH(O)$ by the peracid represents a second progagation step (eq. 7c)

$$PhCH(O) + PhC(O)OOH \xrightarrow{\ Fe(II)\ } 2PhC(O)OH \qquad\qquad\qquad (7c)$$

The sum of these processes is a $Fe^{II}(H_2O_2)^{2+}$-catalyzed autoxidation of $PhCH(O)$ (eq. 8)

$$2PhCH(O) + O_2 \xrightarrow{\quad Fe^{II}(H_2O_2)^{2+} \quad} 2PhC(O)OH \qquad\qquad\qquad (8)$$

Table 1c summarizes the reaction efficiencies and dioxygenated products that result from the addition of 1 m$\underline{M}$ $[Fe^{II}(MeCN)_4](ClO_4)_2$ to a solution of 2 m$\underline{M}$ H_2O_2 and 2 m$\underline{M}$ substrate (RH) in dry MeCN. The results indicate that species 3 (Scheme 1) has the reactivity of the singlet $(^1\Delta_g)$ state; in the absence of substrate the overall stoichiometry is consistent with the disproportionation of H_2O_2

$$2H_2O_2 \xrightarrow{\ Fe(II)\ } 2H_2O + {}^3O_2 \qquad\qquad\qquad (9)$$

The extensive reactivity of diphenylisobenzofuran (DPBF), 9,10-diphenylanthracene, and rubrene to form exclusively dioxygenated products is consistent with the conclusion that the $Fe(II)-H_2O_2$ system produces a singlet oxygen-like intermediate $[Fe(H_2O_2)_2^{2+}]$.

The other substrates in Table 1c also undergo an initial dioxygenation. With cis-PhCH=CHPh, 0.26 m$\underline{M}$ of it is dioxygenated to give 0.52 m$\underline{M}$ PhCH(O). Because 1.0 m$\underline{M}$ H_2O_2 yields, at most, 0.50 m$\underline{M}$ O_2, the reaction efficiency is 52% for a one-to-one species 3-substrate dioxygenation via a dioxetane intermediate.

The monoxygenation of methyl styrene (PhCH=CHMe) to form the epoxide (Table 1c) appears to involve an O-atom transfer from the end-on configuration (2, Scheme 1) of the $Fe^{II}(HOOH)^{2+}$ complex (eq. 10)

$$PhCH=CHMe + Fe(II) + HOOH \longrightarrow [(PhCH=CHMe)2]^{2+} \longrightarrow$$

$$\overset{\displaystyle O}{\overset{\displaystyle \diagup\diagdown}{PhCH\!-\!\!-\!CHMe}} + Fe^{II}(OH_2)^{2+} \qquad\qquad\qquad (10a)$$

However, a significant fraction of the products from this substrate are the result of a dioxygenation to give PhCH(O) and MeCH(O), which indicates that the $Fe(II)/H_2O_2$ adduct has significant biradical character (1, Scheme 1). A reasonable mechanistic pathway that involves two HOOH molecules per PhCH=CHMe molecule is presented in eq. 10b.

PhCH=CHMe + Fe(II) + 2HOOH $\longrightarrow$

$$\left[(PhCH-CHMe)Fe^{II}(HOOH) \atop {\overset{|}{O}\ \overset{|}{O} \atop H\ \ H} \right] \longrightarrow \left[(PhCH \overset{OH}{\underset{OH}{\diagup}}\diagdown)(MeCH \overset{OH}{\underset{OH}{\diagup}}\diagdown)Fe^{II} \right]^{2+} \longrightarrow$$

$$PhCH(O) + MeCH(O) + Fe^{II}(OH_2)_2^{2+} \tag{10b}$$

The latter process is dominant when the HOOH concentration is greater than that for the Fe(II) catalyst. When H_2O_2 is in excess relative to Fe(II) and substrate, the disproportionation process of eq. 9 is favored via an activated dioxygen intermediate (3, Scheme 1), which dioxygenates aromatic olefins [e.g., PhCH=CHPh $\longrightarrow$ 2PhCH(O)].[1] Hence, PhCH=CHMe probably is subject to dioxygenation by this activated intermediate (Fe^{II}$(H_2O_2)_2$$^{2+}$] (eq. 11)

PhCH=CHMe + Fe(II) + 2H$_2$O$_2$ $\longrightarrow$ $\left[(PhCH=CHMe)3 \right. \longrightarrow$

$$\left[(PhCH-CHMe)Fe^{II}(H_2O)_2 \atop {\overset{O--O}{\overset{|}{}\ \overset{|}{}}} \right]^{2+} \longrightarrow PhCH(O) + MeCH(O) + Fe^{II}(H_2O)_2^{2+} \tag{11}$$

Fe^{III}Cl$_3$-INDUCED ACTIVATION OF H$_2$O$_2$

The observation[1] that iron(II) in ligand-free acetonitrile activates hydrogen peroxide to act as a monxygenase and dehydrogenase (but not as an initiator of radical reactions via Fenton chemistry) has prompted the consideration of other iron salts. Thus, anhydrous ferric chloride (Fe^{III}Cl$_3$) in dry acetontrile (MeCN) activates hydrogen peroxide to epoxidize alkenes, and to monoxygenate or dehydrogenate other organic substrates.[7]

Table 2 summarizes the conversion efficiencies and product distributions for a series of alkene substrates subjected to the Fe^{III}Cl$_3$-H$_2$O$_2$/MeCN system. The extent of the Fe^{III}Cl$_3$-induced monoxygenations is enhanced by higher reaction temperatures and increased concentrations of the reactants (subtrate, Fe^{III}Cl$_3$, and H$_2$O$_2$). For 1-hexene (representative of all of the alkenes) a substantial fraction of the product is the dimer of 1-hexene oxide, a disubstituted dioxane

$$\left(\overset{\overset{Bu}{|}}{\underset{\underset{Bu}{|}}{O \diagdown {CH_2 - CH \atop CH - CH} \diagup O}} \right).$$

With other organic substrates(RH) Fe^{III}Cl$_3$ activates H$_2$O$_2$ for their monoxygenation; the reaction efficiencies and product distributions are summarized in Table 2B. In the case of alcohols, ethers, and cyclohexane, a substantial fraction of the product is the alkyl chloride, and with aldehydes [PhCH(O))] the acid chloride represents one-half of the product. In the absence of substrate the Fe^{III}Cl$_3$/MeCN system catalyzes the rapid disproportionation of H$_2$O$_2$ to O$_2$ and H$_2$O.

Table 2. Products and Conversion Efficiencies for the Ferric Choride $(Fe^{III}Cl_3)$-induced Oxygenation/Dehydrogenation of Olefins and Organic Substrates (RH) by H_2O_2 in Acetonitrile.

Substrate (RH)	reaction[a,b] efficiency, %	products[c]
A. Olefins (-5°C, 10-min. reaction times)		
blank (H_2O_2)	100	O_2, H_2O
1-hexene	10	epoxide (1-hexene oxide) (71%), dimer (dioxane) (10%), others (19%)
1-hexene (+5°)	23	epoxide (55%), dimer (15%), others (30%)
1-octene	60	epoxide (53%), dimer (10%)
cyclohexene	25	epoxide (45%), dimer (30%)
$Me_2C=CMe_2$	40	$Me_2C\overset{O}{\overline{}}CMe_2$ (50%), dimers and others (50%)
B. Other substrates (+5°C, 20-min. reaction times)		
cyclohexanol	52	cyclohexanone (88%)
$PhCH_2OH$	63	PhCHO(O) (51%), $PhCH_2Cl$ (21%), PhC(O)OH (14%), PhC(O)Cl (14%)
$PhCH_2OCMe_3$	56	PhCH(O) (72%), $PhCH_2Cl$ (11%), PhC(O)OH (3%), PhC(O)Cl (14%)
PhCH(O)	75	PhC(O)OH (55%), PhC(O)Cl (45%)
$PhCH_3$ (25°C)	2	$PhCH_2OH$, PhCH(O), PhC(O)Cl, PhC(O)OH, creosols
cyclohexane	22	cyclohexylchloride (45%), cyclohexanol (40%), cyclohexanone (15%)
Ph_2S	58	Ph_2SO (100%)
Ph_2SO	60	Ph_2SO_2 (100%)
Ph_3P	80	Ph_3PO (100%)

[a] RH and $Fe^{III}Cl_3$ (1.0 mmol of each) combined in 10-20 mL dry MeCN, followed by the slow addition of 1 mmol H_2O_2 [1 $\underline{M}$ H_2O_2 (98%) in MeCN].

[b] Percentage of substrate converted to products.

[c] After the indicated reaction time, the product solution was quenched with water, extracted with diethylether, and analyzed by capillary gas chromatograph and GC-MS.

Because $Fe^{III}Cl_3$ is an exceptionally strong Lewis acid and electrophilic center, it activates H_2O_2 (which acts as a nucleophile) for the dehydrogenation of a second H_2O_2. On the basis of this disproportionation process, as well as the monoxygenation and dehydrogenation reactions of Table 2, the activation of H_2O_2 by $Fe^{III}Cl_3$ probably involves the initial formation of at least two reactive forms of an $Fe^{III}Cl_3$(HOOH) adduct that are in dynamic equilibrium (similar to Scheme 1)

$$\left[Cl_3Fe^{III} \begin{pmatrix} OH \\ | \\ OH \end{pmatrix} \;\rightleftharpoons\; Cl_3Fe^{III} \begin{pmatrix} O-O\diagdown{\overset{H}{}} \\ \diagup_{H} \end{pmatrix} \right].$$

The disproportionation of H_2O_2 probably occurs via a concerted transfer of the two hydrogen atoms from a second H_2O_2 to the $Fe^{III}Cl_3(H_2O_2)$ adduct. This dehydrogenation of H_2O_2 is a competitive process with the $Fe^{III}Cl_3$-substrate-H_2O_2 reactions. The controlled introduction of dilute H_2O_2 into the $Fe^{III}Cl_3$-substrate solution limits the concentration of H_2O_2 and ensures that the substrate-H_2O_2 reaction can be competitive with the second-order disproportionation process. The substrate reaction efficiencies in Table 2 are proportional to the relative rates of reaction $(k_{RH}/k_{H_2O_2})$. The mode of activation of H_2O_2 by $Fe^{III}Cl_3$ is analogous to that by $Fe^{II}(MeCN)_4^{2+}$; both are strong electrophiles in ligand-free dry MeCN and induce H_2O_2 to monoxygenate organic substrates.

The epoxidation of alkenes (Table 2A) appears to involve an O-atom transfer from the end-on configuration of the $Fe^{III}Cl_3$(HOOH) adduct. The electrophilicity of $Fe^{III}Cl_3$ promotes the initial activation of the alkene bond prior to the binding of H_2O_2. The resulting epoxides are rapidly dimerized to dioxanes. Hence, the complete conversion of an alkene to its epoxide is precluded; the more complete the conversion the higher the fraction of dioxane in the product mixture.

The results in Table 2B indicate that the $Fe^{III}Cl_3$(HOOH) adduct monoxygenates alkanes, alcohols, and aldehydes. A mechanism that is consistent with this involves the homolytic scission of the HO-OH bond in the side-on configuration, induced by the bound substrate, and the subsequent abstraction by one HO· of an H-atom from the α-carbon and addition of the second HO· to the resulting carbon radical (eq. 12).

$$PhCH_2OH + Fe^{III}Cl_3(H_2O_2) \;\longrightarrow\; [PhCH(OH)_2]Fe^{III}Cl_3(OH_2) \;\longrightarrow$$

$$PhCH(O) + Fe^{III}Cl_3(OH_2)_2 \tag{12}$$

An analogous process appears to occur for the oxygenation of benzaldehyde by the $Fe^{III}Cl_3$(HOOH) adduct, but 50% of the product is the acid chloride.

This result indicates that the activated side-on complex has some hypochlorous acid (HOCl) character and can add a chlorine atom to the carbon radical that results from the H-atom abstraction by the ·OH group. This also occurs with alkanes, alcohols, and ethers (Table 2B). Such chemistry is similar to the activation of chloride ion and H_2O_2 to HOCl by myeloperoxidase (a heme protein).[8,9]

Phosphines, dialkylsulfides, and sulfoxides are monoxygenated by the $Fe^{III}Cl_3(HOOH)$ adduct in a manner that appears to be analogous to that for the epoxidation of alkenes.

The Lewis acid-catalyzed (iron(II) and $FeCl_3$) reactions of H_2O_2 with various substrates exhibit parallels to reactions that are catalyzed by metalloenzymes. The Fe(II) and $FeCl_3$ catalyzed disproportionation of H_2O_2 in dry acetonitrile is analogous to that of catalase (eq. 9), and in the presence of appropriate substrates these Lewis acids display a peroxidase-like activity

$$H_2O_2 + RH \xrightarrow{\ Fe^{II}\ } H_2O + ROH \qquad\qquad (13)$$

that is illustrated by the oxidation of benzaldehyde to benzoic acid. The halogenation of benzaldehyde by the $Fe^{III}Cl_3/H_2O_2$ system is similar to the chemistry for myeloperoxidase and chloroperoxidase.

These results demonstrate that the chemistry of $Fe^{II}(MeCN)_4{}^{2+}$ and $Fe^{III}Cl_3$ is dramatically altered when water is removed to provide an aprotic and ligand-free environment, and support the thesis that oxygen-activation processes in aprotic solvents are useful models for the chemistry of dioxygen in biological membranes and in the hydrophobic regions of metalloproteins.

ACKNOWLEDGMENT

This work was supported by the National Science Foundation under Grant No. CHE-8212299.

REFERENCES

(1) H. Sugimoto, D.T. Sawyer, J. Amer. Chem. Soc., 106 (1984) 4283.

(2) C. Walling, Acc. Chem. Res., 9 (1976) 175.

(3) L.M. Dorfman, G.E. Adams, "Reactivity of the Hydroxyl Radical in Aqueous Solutions"; NSRDS-NBS 46, SD Catalog No. 13.48:46, U.S. Department Printing Office: Washington, D.C., U.S.A.; June, 1978.

(4) B.C. Gilbert, R.O.C. Norman, R.C. Sealy, J. Chem. Soc. Perkins Trans., 2 (1975) 303.

(5) C. Walling, Acc. Chem. Res., 8 (1975) 125-131.

(6) J.A. Howard, K.V. Ingold, Can. J. Chem., 45 (1967) 785.

(7) H. Sugimoto, D.T. Sawyer, J. Org. Chem., 50 (1985) 1784.

(8) H. Rosen, S.J. Klebanoff, J. Biol. Chem., 252 (1977) 4803.

(9) A.M. Held, J.K. Hurst, Biochim. Biophys. Res. Commun., 81 (1978) 878.

Accurate Synthetic Models for The Diiron Centers in Hemerythrin

Karl Wieghardt

Lehrstuhl für Anorganische Chemie I, Ruhr-Universität, D-4630 Bochum,

Federal Republic of Germany

Summary

Preparation, spectroscopic properties, structures and reactivity of accurate synthetic, low-molecular weight models of the diiron centers in hemerythrin are reviewed.

Introduction

The structure of the diiron centers in the oxidized forms of the non-heme, invertebrate respiratory protein hemerythrin (in particular that of methemerythrin and metazidohemerythrin) has in the past two decades been elucidated to an encouraging degree of certainty by a combination of spectroscopic methods(1) and, more recently, by high-resolution X-ray structure determinations(2). Two non-equivalent Fe(III) centers are connected by a μ_2-oxo- and two symmetrical carboxylato bridges as is depicted below:

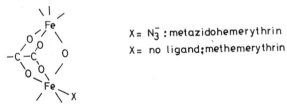

X = N_3^- : metazidohemerythrin
X = no ligand; methemerythrin

The situation is not quite so clear for the active form, deoxyhemerythrin, where two high-spin Fe(II) centers are proposed to be bridged by a μ_2-hydroxo- and two μ-carboxylato bridges(3). No high-resolution X-ray analysis is as yet available. The two iron centers are again not equivalent: one is hexa- and the other is five-coordinate.

Upon reaction with molecular oxygen oxyhemerythrin is formed. The structure of this form has been proposed to be as shown below(4). A hydroperoxo ligand

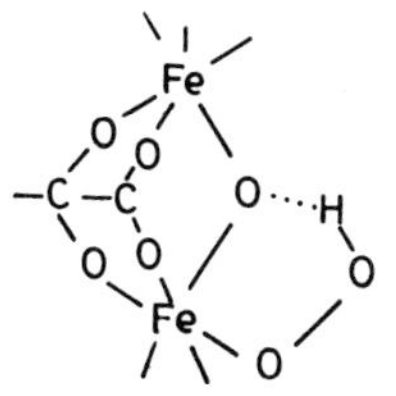

oxyhemerythrin

is coordinated to one of the two Fe(III) centers. Hydrogen-bonding of the end-on coordinated HO_2^- to the μ-oxo bridge has been invoked to account for the magnetic properties of oxyhemerythrin as compared to metazidohemerythrin(5).

Finally, Wilkins and coworkers(6) have identified further forms of the enzyme when deoxyhemerythrin is oxidized by outer-shere one-electron oxidants, or methemerythrin is reduced with $Na_2S_2O_4$. Semi-methemerythrins contain mixed-valence moieties of Fe(II), Fe(III) where the valencies are believed to be trapped.

The advancement of our knowledge of the intrinsic structural features and diversity of the diiron centers in the diffent forms of the enzyme hemerythrin has been - and still is - a challenge to preparative inorganic chemists, since-surprisingly enough - there had been no simple, low-molecular weight complexes of iron known, which could have served as accurate models. In particular, no co-ordination compounds of Fe(III) containing a μ_2-oxo-di-μ-dicarboxylato entity were characterized and no binuclear μ-hydroxo-bridged ferrous species were known. In this article synthetic routes to such complexes are reviewed.

Syntheses of Complexes with a $[Fe(III)_2(\mu_2-O)(\mu_2-R-CO_2)_2]^{2+}$ Core.

In 1983 two reports appeared in the literature describing the preparation, characterization and X-ray structures of two binuclear complexes of Fe(III) containing the desired $[Fe(III)_2(\mu_2-O)(\mu_2-R-CO_2)]^{2+}$ core(7,8). Armstrong and Lippard assembled this moiety using the tridentate, uninegative N-donor ligand tri-1-pyrazolylborate (1-), $HBpz_3$; whereas Wieghardt, Pohl and Gebert used the cyclic, saturated N-donor 1,4,7-triazacyclononane, tacn. The reaction of these ligands with $Fe(III)(ClO_4)_3 \cdot 6H_2O$ and sodium acetate in aqueous solution produces complexes 1 and 2 via "spontaneous self-assembly"(9) of the diiron core (Figure 1).

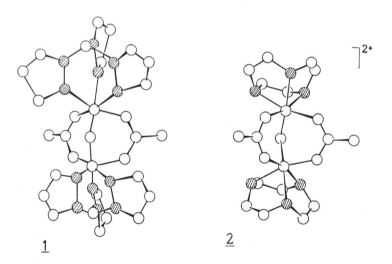

Figure 1: Molecular structures of 1 and 2

Alternatively, 1 may be prepared from $[Cl_3Fe-O-FeCl_3]^{2-}$ where the Fe-O-Fe structural unit is preformed(7b).   2 was originally obtained from mild hydrolysis of (tacn)$FeCl_3$ in saturated, aqueous solution of ammonium acetate. The crystal structures of 1 and 2 have been determined by X-ray analyses. In addition, μ-oxo-bis(μ-formato), 3, and μ-oxo-bis(μ-benzoato) derivatives of 1 have also been prepared and the structure of 3, $[Fe_2O(O_2CH)_2(HBpz_3)_2]$, has also been determined(7b).

Using derivatives of the macrocycle 1,4,7-triazacylononane,   namely

1,2-bis(1,4,7-triaza-1-cyclononyl)ethane (dtne) and N,N',N''-trimethyl-1,4,7-

triazacyclononane (Me-tacn), cationic binuclear μ-oxo-bis(μ-acetato)diiron(III)

complexes have been prepared following the above outlined synthetic routes

(10,11):

tacn   me-tacn   dtne

The structure of $\left[Fe_2(\mu\text{-}O)(\mu\text{-}CH_3CO_2)_2(Me\text{-}tacn)_2\right](ClO_4)_2$, 4, has recently been

determined by X-ray crystallography(12).

The ease with which these model compounds form under physiological condi-

tions may be taken as in indication for the inherent stability of the $\left[Fe_2(\mu\text{-}O)\right.$

$\left.(\mu\text{-carboxylato})_2\right]^{2+}$ core. Therefore, it was thought that this structural type

may also prevail with other trivalent transition metals. Indeed, $\left[Mn(III)_2(\mu\text{-}O)\right.$

$(\mu\text{-}CH_3CO_2)_2(tacn)_2\left](ClO_4)_2$, 5, and $\left[Mn(III)_2(\mu\text{-}O)(\mu\text{-}CH_3CO_2)_2(Me\text{-}tacn)_2\right](ClO_4)_2 \cdot$

H_2O, 6, have been synthesized from monomeric manganese(III) acetate and the ma-

crocyclic ligands(12) and their structures have been determined. They have

the same over-allgeometry as 1 and 4.

The following Table summarizes some structural data of the models and of

metazidohemerythrin.

Table of selected bond lengths $[\text{Å}]$ and - angles $[°]$ of the

$[M_2(\mu\text{-O})(\mu\text{-carboxylato})_2]^{2+}$ core

	M⋯M	M-O$_b$	M-O$_{ac}$	M-N$_t$	M-N	M-O-M	Ref.
1	3.145	1.785	2.043	2.19	2.15	123.6	(7)
2	3.064	1.78	2.03	2.21	2.16	118.3	(8)
3	3.168	1.78	2.05	2.18	2.147	125.5	(7)
4	3.125	1.80	2.03	2.20	2.27	120	(13)
6	3.084	1.81	2.05	2.23	2.13	121	(12)
A	3.25	1.89	2.22	2.22	2.26	135	(2)
		1.64		2.29			

A = metazidohemerythrin; M-N$_t$ denotes the M-N bond length in _trans_ position with respect to the Fe-O bond of the oxo-bridge.

The Fe-O and the Fe-N bond lengths are typical for high-spin Fe(III). It is noted that the Fe-N lengths in trans position with respect to Fe-O of the μ-oxo bridge are longer than those trans to Fe-O of μ-carboxylato bridges indicating a substantial trans-influence of the oxo-bridge. This does _not_ hold for 6, the manganese analogue(12).

Spectroscopic Properties and Reactivity of the Models

The elctronic spectra of the model compounds in the visible range have revealed a remarkable similarity among each other and with those of methemerythrin and of chloromethemerythrin(14) in a qualitative fashion. This observation indicates that the characteristic visible spectra of models and enzyme are not pertubed by possible ligand-to-metal charge transfer bands involving the pyrazolylborate ligands in 1, 3 or the histidin ligands in the enzyme. In Figure 2 the spectrum of 4 is shown; an additional absorption maximum is observed at 1031 nm ($\epsilon = 7 \text{ cm}^{-1}\text{Lmol}^{-1}$).

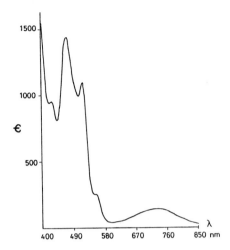

Figure 2: Electronic spectrum of 4 (methanol)

A further important feature of the model compounds and of the oxidized forms of the enzyme is the strong antiferromagnetic coupling of the Fe(III) centers via a superexchange mechanism mediated by the μ_2-oxo-bridge. The exchange coupling constant, J, between the two iron(III) atoms in methemerythrin has been determined to be -134 cm^{-1} whereas for oxyhemerythrin a reduced value of -77 cm^{-1} has been reported(5). For the models 1 and 4 J values of -121 cm^{-1}(7b) and -115 cm^{-1}(13) have been deduced from magnetic susceptibility measurements. These values are in excellent agreement with that of methemerythrin. It is interesting to note that protonation of the oxo-bridge in 1 leads to a μ-hydroxo bridged binuclear species $\left[(HBpz_3)Fe(OH)(O_2CCH_3)_2Fe(HBpz_3)\right]$ (ClO_4) 7,(15) (see below). This protonation of the oxo-bridge causes a dramatic decrease of the antiferromagnetic coupling (J = -17 cm^{-1} for 7(15)). These findings support strongly the structure proposed for oxyhemerythrin where a hydrogen-bond from the end-on coordinated HO_2^- ligand to the oxo-bridge has been invoked to account for the reduced value of J of -77 cm^{-1}(16).

Although the $\left[Fe_2O(carboxylato)_2\right]^{2+}$ moiety appears to be thermodynamically quite stable, studies of its reactivity have shown that the oxo- and carboxylato groups are kinetically labile. Aqueous solutions of 2 are not stable(7b). Addition of NaN_3 or NaNCS to such solutions under physiological conditions results in immediate precipitation of binuclear complexes of the type $(tacn)Fe(X)_2-O-FeX_2(tacn)$ $(X = N_3$ or NCS); at prolongued reaction times mononuclear complexes of the type $(tacn)FeX_3$ are formed. Thus the oxo-group is also replaced in protic media (11).

For $\underline{1}$ facile ^{18}O-exchange(7b) and protonation(15) reactions of the bridging oxygen have been observed. In addition, exchange reactions of the bridging carboxylate groups in $\underline{1}$ have been studied; e.g.

$$\underline{1} + 2(C_6H_5O)_2PO_2H \xrightarrow{CH_2Cl_2} \left[Fe_2O\{O_2P(OC_6H_5)_2\}_2(HBpz_3)_2\right] + 2CH_3COOH$$

The diphenylphosphate-bridged complex has been isolated and characterized by X-ray crystallography(17).

Synthesis of an Accurate Model of Deoxyhemerythrin

Attempts to reduce $\underline{1}$ and $\underline{2}$ electrochemically to produce a dinuclear carboxylato bridged complex of iron(II), which would serve as a model for deoxyhemerythrin, failed because in both instances the thermodynamically more stable complexes $Fe(HBpz_3)_2$ and $\left[Fe(tacn)_2\right]^{2+}$ formed rapidly(7b).

Using the more bulky N,N',N"-trimethyl-1,4,7-triazacyclononane the formation of this type of 1 : 2 complex is efficiently precluded. The reaction of this ligand with $Fe(ClO_4)_2 \cdot 6H_2O$ in the presence of sodium acetate in methanol affords pale yellow-green crystals of $\left[Fe_2(\mu-OH)(\mu-CH_3CO_2)_2(me-tacn)_2\right]$ $(ClO_4) \cdot H_2O$. Air-oxidation of this complex yields quantitatively $\underline{4}$. Figure 3 shows the structure of the Fe(II)-dimer and Table 2 summarizes pertinent bond lengths.

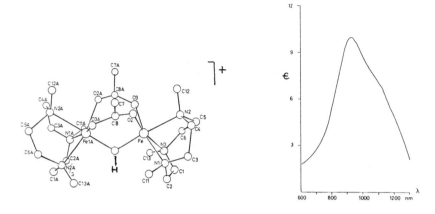

Figure 3: Molecular structure of $\left[Fe_2(\mu\text{-OH})(\mu\text{-CH}_3CO_2)_2(me\text{-tacn})_2\right]^+$ and its electronic spectrum (methanol)

Table 2: Mean bond lengths of model compounds

	Fe-O$_b$	Fe-O$_{ac}$	Fe-N	Ref.
$\left[L_2Fe(III)_2O(CH_3CO_2)_2\right]^{2+}$	1.80	2.03	2.23	(13)
$\left[L_2Fe(II)_2(OH)(CH_3CO_2)_2\right]^+$	1.99	2.13	2.28	(13)
$\left[L'_2Fe(III)_2(OH)(CH_3CO_2)_2\right]^+$	1.956	1.999	2.1o2	(15)

L = me-tacn; L' = HBpz$_3$

The electronic spectrum of the deoxyhemerythrin model complex in the visible (Figure 3) resembles very much that of the active enzyme(14). The most interesting aspect is the fact that the two high-spin iron(II) centers are weakly antiferromagnetically coupled . The calculated value of -14 cm^{-1} (13) is in excellent agreement with the value derived by Reem and Solomon(3) for the active enzyme.

Conclusion: The preparation of accurate model compounds for the diiron centers of the different forms of hemerythrin is possible. The similarities of spectroscopic properties is encouraging. It appears to be feasible to design ligands for dinuclear iron complexes which could mimic the reactivity of the enzyme towards oxygen. Therefore, it should be possible to prepare models for oxyhemerythrin and semimethemerythrin.

References
(1) a) I.M.Klotz; G.L.Klippenstein; W.A.Hendrickson
              Sience 192 (1976), 335.
    b) D.M.Kurtz,Jr.; D.Shriver; I.M.Klotz
              Coord.Chem.Rev. 24 (1977), 145.
    c) R.E.Stenkamp; L.H.Jensen
              Adv.Inorg.Biochem. 1 (1979), 219.
    d) J.Sanders-Loehr; T.M.Loehr
              Ibid. 1 (1979), 235.
    e) R.G.Wilkins; P.C.Harrington
              Ibid. 5 (1983), 51.
    f) I.M.Klotz; D.M.Kurtz, Jr.
              Acc.Chem.Res. 17 (1984), 16.
(2) a) R.E.Stenkamp; L.C.Sieker; L.H.Jensen; J.Sanders-Loehr
              Nature (London) 291 (1981), 263.
    b) R.E.Stenkamp; L.C.Sieker; L.H.Jensen
              J.Inorg.Biochem. 19 (1983), 247.
    c) R.E.Stenkamp; L.C.Sieker; L.H.Jensen
              Acta Cryst. B39 (1983), 697.
    d)R.E.Stenkamp; L.C.Sieker; L.H.Jensen
              J.Am.Chem.Soc. 106 (1984), 618.
(3) R.C.Reem; E.I.Solomon
              J.Am.Chem.Soc. 106 (1984), 8323.
(4) (a) R.E.Stenkamp; L.C.Sieker; L.H.Jensen; J.D.McCallum; J.Sanders-Loehr
              Proc.Natl.Acad.Sci. USA 82 (1985), 713.
    (b) A.K.Shiemke; T.M.Loehr; J.Sanders-Loehr
              J.Am.Chem.Soc. 106 (1984), 4951.
(5) J.W.Dawson; H.B.Gray; H.E.Hoenig; G.R.Rossman; J.M.Schredder; R.H.Wang
              Biochem. 11 (1972), 461.
(6) a) P.C.Harrington; D.J.A.DeWaal; R.G.Wilkins
              Arch.Biochem.Biophys. 191 (1978), 444.
    b) Z.Bradic; P.C.Harrington; R.G.Wilkins; G.Yoneda
              Biochem. 19 (1980), 4149.
    c) P.C.Harrington; R.G.Wilkins
              J.Am.Chem.Soc. 103 (1981), 1550.
(7) a) W.H.Armstrong; S.J.Lippard
              J.Am.Chem.Soc. 105 (1983), 4837.
    b) W.H.Armstrong; A.Spool; G.C.Papaefthymiou; R.B.Frankel; S.J.Lippard
              J.Am.Chem.Soc. 106 (1984), 3653.
(8) a) K.Wieghardt; K.Pohl; W.Gebert
              Angew.Chem. 95 (1983), 739.
              Angew.Chem.Int.Ed.Engl. 22 (1983), 727.
    b) A.Spool; I.D.Williams; S.J.Lippard
              Inorg.Chem., in press
(9) R.H.Holm; J.A.Ibers
              Science 209 (1980), 223.

(10) K.Wieghardt; I.Tolksdorf; W.Herrmann

Inorg.Chem. 24 (1985), 1230.

(11) K.Wieghardt; K.Pohl; D.Ventur

Angew.Chem. 97 (1985), 415.

(12) K.Wieghardt; U.Bossek; D.Ventur; J.Weiss

JCS Chem.Commun. 1985, 347.

(13) P.Chaudhuri; K.Wieghardt; B.Nuber; J.Weiss

Angew.Chem., in press

(14) a) J.Sanders-Loehr; T.M.Loehr; A.G.Mauk; H.B.Gray

J.Am.Chem.Soc. 102 (1980), 6992.

b) J.B.R.Dunn; A.W.Addison; R.E.Bruce; J.Sanders-Loehr; T.M.Loehr

Biochem. 8 (1977), 1743.

c) K.Garbett; D.W.Darnall; I.M.Klotz; R.J.P.Williams

Arch.Biochem.Biophys. 103 (1969), 419.

(15) W.H.Armstrong; S.J.Lippard

J.Am.Chem.Soc. 106 (1984), 4632.

(16) J.Loehr in "Bioinorganic Chemistry 85"; A.V.Xavier, Ed.,

VCH Publishers, Weinheim, 1985

(17) W.H.Armstrong; S.J.Lippard

J.Am.Chem.Soc., in press

Proteins of Iron Storage and Transport

Ferritin: A General View of The Protein, The Iron-Protein Interface, and The Iron Core

Elizabeth C. Theil

Department of Biochemistry, Box 7622, North Carolina State University, Raleigh, North Carolina 27695-7622, U.S.A.

SUMMARY

The need for ferritin in the iron metabolism of aerobic organisms and its function is described in terms of the constant and modifiable features of the **protein,** properties of the **iron-protein** interface related to nucleation and formation of the polymeric hydrous ferric oxide core, and the structure of the **iron core** itself. A large, soluble complex of Fe(III)-ATP (4:1) is described which contains phosphate throughout the complex of ca. 250 Fe atoms and which may serve as a model for iron-phosphate interactions in ferritin, in soils and in the ocean. Such complexes of iron and ATP may also be important in living systems for intracellular iron transport or, in the case of excess iron, for causing iron toxicity by sequestering nucleotide tri-phosphates and interfering with normal metabolism.

1 INTRODUCTION

Ferritin is a unique, bioinorganic complex containing Fe(III) both attached to the protein and in a bulk phase as a polymer of ferric oxyhy-droxide and ferric oxyphosphate (ca. 8:1); a single molecule can obtain up to 4500 Fe(III) atoms/ molecule (1-3). When cells first evolved, ferritin was not needed. However, the release of dioxygen into the earth's atmosphere, caused by the use of water as a source of reducing equivalents for photosyn-thesis, transformed iron from readily soluble ferrous to highly insoluble ferric. Then, life forms, dependent upon iron for proteins used in DNA syn-thesis and electron transport, required ferritin or a molecule with similar properties to achieve concentrations of iron compatible with metabolic need. Ferritin is found in higher plants, fungi, bacteria, invertebrates, and vertebrates, indicating that, in modern organisms, ferritin is the most common solution to the problem of storing ferric iron. Repetition of the conditions leading to ferritin formation in primitive times appears to recur during the formation of each ferritin molecule, since reconstitution proceeds by the oxidation of Fe(II) in the presence of the protein and air.

2 THE PROTEIN

Apoferritin, the protein without any iron, is a hollow sphere constructed of 24 subunits (ca. 20 Kdaltons) of similar or identical amino acid sequence. Requirements for assembly and/or function are sufficiently stringent that ferritin exhibits sufficient similarity for immunological crossreactivity between vertebrates as evolutionarily distant as fish and mammals (3, 4). Moreover, amino acid sequences are highly conserved among bullfrogs, rats, horses, and humans (5-9). In spite of the conservation of structure observed **between** animals, variations in apoferritin occur **within** an animal that are specific to a particular cell type, e.g. liver vs. red cell, and are super-imposed upon the canonical structure. The cell-specific differences in structure, which include variations in serine content and in accessibility to phosphorylation by protein kinase (10), correspond to differences in the availability of iron in vivo (11, 12). Since the DNA of rats, humans, and frogs contain multiple sequences which hybridize to sequences coding for ferritin (7, 9, 13), a multi-gene family may account for some of the cell-specific differences in ferritin structure.

Variations in the protein structure of ferritin can also occur by modify-ing the protein after synthesis. For example, ferritin from lamb macrophages contains **covalent, intramolecular crosslinks** that form pairs of subunits (14). However, when the animal is stressed by copper poisoning, e.g., macrophage ferritin has few detectable crosslinks. Intramolecular crosslinks between subunits have been found in a number of different types of ferritin (14, 15), but whether they can occur in all types of ferritin is not yet known. The scarcity of information about the natural crosslinks is probably explained by the fact that iron-loaded ferritin, which has few subunit crosslinks, is more abundant and thus has been more extensively studied. Although the nature of the amino acids in the crosslinks has not yet been determined, naturally occurring crosslinks are known in other proteins between glutamine and lysine (16) and between two tyrosine residues (17); changes in cellular levels of transglutaminases or free radicals could affect the formation of such crosslinks.

Synthetic subunit dimer crosslinks may be introduced into ferritin with the bifunctional reagent, 1,5-difluoro-2,4-dinitrobenzene; the functional effects are the same as for the natural crosslinks. For example, when ferritin is reconstituted from apoferritin and iron in vitro, natural crosslinks reduce the rate of iron uptake and increase the rate of iron release; synthetic crosslinks have the same effect (Table 1). If the intramolecular, subunit crosslinks were the major variable controlling the steady-state iron content of ferritin, the relative iron content of ferritin with crosslinks compared to that without crosslinks should be 0.31. Interestingly, the actual difference in the iron content of native ferritin without crosslinks, as isolated from macrophages of normal animals, is 0.39 compared to that of stress ferritin isolated from macrophages of copper-poisoned animals (14). Such a result indicates that the subunit crosslinks have a significant effect on the iron content of ferritin molecules in vivo. In addition, the enhanced ability of stress ferritin to sequester iron suggests that the structure of ferritin can itself affect the iron content of both the ferritin molecule and the cell.

Table 1.   The Effect of Subunit Dimer Crosslinks on Relative Rates of Reconstitution and Subsequent Iron Release in Lamb Spleen Ferritin

	Lamb spleen	
	Fe uptake	Fe release
	crosslinked/non-crosslinked	
Naturally crosslinked [a] subunit dimer (40%)	0.52 ± 0.09	1.68 ± 0.06
Synthetically crosslinked [b] subunit dimer (20-30%)	0.56 ± 0.13	1.51 ± 0.22

(a) Data from reference 14.

(b) Synthetic dimer crosslinks were introduced by reacting apoferritin with 1,5-difluoro-2,4-dinitrobenzene. The percentage of subunit dimer pairs was determined by densitometric analysis of stained protein after separation of dissociated subunits by electrophoresis in SDS containing polyacrylamide gels.

3 THE IRON-PROTEIN INTERFACE

Evidence for an iron-protein interaction in ferritin has been provided by ultra-high resolution electron microscopy, competition studies with other metals, and by x-ray and UV absorption spectroscopy. For example, examination of electron microraphs of native ferritin revealed regions where the iron core and the inside surface of the protein shell were in intimate contact (18). Reduction of rates of iron core formation by metals such as

Tb(III) and Zn(II), for which binding sites on the protein have been demonstrated (19-21), suggested competition between iron and the other metal ions
for sites on the protein. Disruption of a complex of vanadyl and apoferritin, detected by EPR spectroscopy, in the presence of Fe(II) and Fe(III)
also suggested binding sites for iron on the apoprotein (22).

Properties of an Fe-apoferritin complex, formed by the addition of small
numbers (2-8) of atoms of Fe(II) to apoferritin in the presence of air, have
been measured by difference spectroscopy at 310 nm (23). The spectra changed
with time, possibly due to oxidation of Fe(II) to Fe(III), and in the presence
of Tb(III) and Zn(II), confirming the earlier studies on the influence of
metal binding on the iron-protein interaction.

Fe(III)-apoferritin complexes have not been produced directly from Fe(III)
but rather from Fe(II) added in the absence of air and allowed to oxidize
in situ (22). Such a complex was used to determine the EXAFS and XANES of
apoferritin containing an average of 10 iron atoms/molecule (24). The
complex had spectral properties distinct from Fe(III) in the bulk core phase
and similar to an Fe(III)-oxalate complex with low Z atoms at 2.09 Å (O,N)
and 2.64 Å (C). Preliminary data analysis indicates the presence of an Fe-Fe
distance of ca. 3.4 Å. A similar Fe(III)-apoferritin complex made with ^{57}Fe
and examined by Mössbauer spectroscopy also showed the presence of Fe(III)
iron clusters (B. Huynh, personal communication), suggesting that iron in the
distinctive, carboxylate-containing environment detected by EXAFS may contain
multiple, neighboring Fe atoms attached to the protein.

The role of an iron-binding site on apoferritin could be obscured by the
fact that polymerization of hydrated Fe(III) can occur independently of the
protein. However, in ferritin the polymerization occurs **inside** the protein.
Thus, protein-binding sites most likely function as nucleation sites to orient
the growth of the hydrous ferric oxide polymer toward the hollow center of the
protein shell. Requirements of protein structure would then include, in
addition to those needed for assembly of subunits into the hollow shell, a
nucleation site or sites and channels in the shell through which Fe(II) may
pass. Two types of channels have been detected by P. Harrison and coworkers
in crystals of apoferritin, six of them hydrophobic and eight of them
hydrophilic (25). Conservation of amino acid sequence in ferritins from
mammals and amphibia (5, 9) in both regions suggests that the channels are
functionally important.

Detection of the iron site has not yet been possible in the x-ray diffraction data of apoferritin complexes, although sites for Cd, uranyl, and Tb have
been detected at several different locations (20, 25). However, the unusual

structural properties of the BB' interface (25) between subunit dimers (a
relatively impenetrable mass of amino acid side chains at the outer surface of
the molecule and a flexible groove on the inner surface), the conservation of
carboxylate ligands in the region now known to be at the dimer interface that
was first noted by R. R. Crichton and coworkers (26) and since confirmed by
others (6-9), the influence of crosslinked subunit dimer pairs on iron uptake
(14, Table 1), and a stoichiometry of metal binding near one/two subunits (22,
27, 28) suggests that the nucleation site(s) may be at the subunit dimer
interface(s). In contrast to nucleation at sites in the channels where the
addition of iron could lead to polymer growth through the pores in the protein
shell and to the outside, the addition of iron to a nucleation complex at the
subunit dimer interface would produce polymer growth toward the hollow center
of the molecule, which is where the iron core is in native ferritin.

4 THE IRON CORE

The three-dimensional structure of the hydrous ferric oxide in ferritin
resembles that of ferrihydrite, a natural hydrous ferric oxide which can be
formed experimentally by the hydrolysis of aqueous solutions of $Fe(NO_3)_3$ (29,
30). However, the structure of hydrous ferric oxides is influenced by the
presence of Cl^- and HCO_3^- present during hydrolysis (31, 32), in contrast to
the iron core formed by the reconstitution of ferritin; insensitivity of ferritin core structure to such anions in the environment during core formation
supports the idea that the protein controls the structure of the nucleus which
forms the core.

Examination of individual ferritin cores reveals that the crystallites in
an individual molecule may be single or multiple, suggesting that several
(12 ?) nucleation sites exist. No data exist that indicate the mechanism
which determines whether single or multiple nucleation sites will be used.
However, it is possible to imagine that such selection could easily be
affected by the presence of other metal ions at some of the sites and/or by
modifications in the structure of the protein shell. Since the surface area
of the iron core appears to influence the release of iron by reductants (35,
36), differences in surface area caused by the number of effective initiation
sites are likely to be physiologically significant.

Natural ferritin contains phosphate in the core (1, reviewed in ref. 3).
Although ferritin can be formed from apoferritin and Fe(II) in _vitro_ without
phosphate, the inclusion of phosphate in the reaction mixture yields a more
monodisperse core size (density) (36) and a smaller apparent size when measured by Mössbauer spectroscopy (37). The determination of where the phosphate
is in ferritin, and whether or not any phosphate is attached to the protein,

has been complicated by the slow exchange rates for many Fe(III)-phosphate complexes and by the fact that the conditions for the reductive removal of iron (and phosphate) from the ferritin core will also cleave phosphate esterified to protein side chains, such as serine (38-40). Recently, EXAFS analysis of Fe-P interactions in a 4:1 complex of Fe(III) and ATP, formed at pH 7, has provided some insight about possible sites of phosphate in the iron core of ferritin (41). The O and Fe distances about the average iron atom in the ATP complex were similar to ferritin, i.e. 1.95 Å and 3.34 Å, respectively. However, an Fe-P distance of 3.27 Å was also detected. Since the size of the complex appeared to be large, i.e. $\geq$ 250 Fe atoms, the presence of phosphate around the **average** iron atom indicates that phosphate was distributed throughout the large iron complex rather than only on the surface. The absence of any detectable ^{31}P resonances in NMR spectra of the complex suggests that all of the phosphorous in the ATP present in solution is influenced by the iron polymer, but whether any hydrolysis of ATP occurred during complex formation is not known. Figure 1 is a model of the environment around the average iron atom in the Fe(III)-ATP (4:1) complex. Note that the phosphate-Fe bond replaces an O bridge, adding potential irregularity to the structure. The Fe(III)-ATP complex can serve as a model for the phosphate distribution in the iron core of ferritin and in other iron-phosphate complexes such as those found in the ocean (42) and in soils (43). In addition, such complexes of Fe(III)-ATP could function to transport iron within cells or, in the case of excess iron, cause toxic effects by sequestering nucleotide triphosphate needed for normal metabolism.

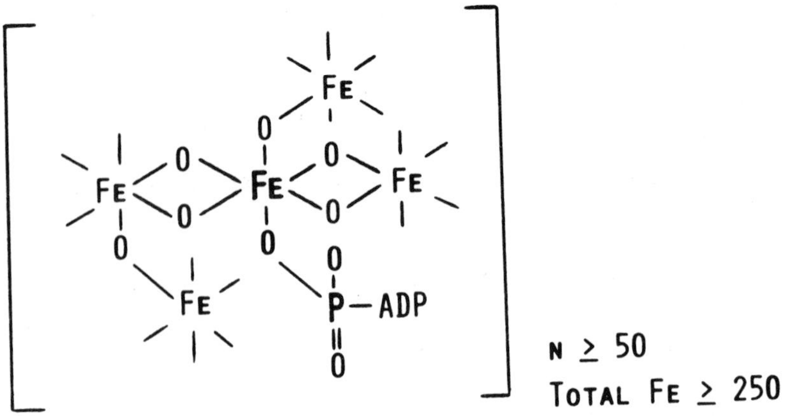

Fig. 1. Model of the Environment of the average iron atom in an Fe(III)-ATP (4:1) complex. The complex was formed from an acidic solution of $FeCl_3$ added to a solution of ATP with the pH maintained at 7.0. Concentrations of Fe(III) of 12 mM could be achieved (41).

Acknowledgement--The author's work described herein was supported by NIH grant AM20251 and by the North Carolina Agricultural Research Service.

5 REFERENCES

(1) S. Granick, P. F. Hahn, J. Biol. Chem. 155 (1944) 661-669.

(2) G. A. Clegg, J. E. Fitton, P. M. Harrison, A. Treffry, Prog. Biophys. Mol. Biol. 36 (1981) 53-86.

(3) E. C. Theil in E. C. Theil, G. L. Eichhorn, and L. G. Marzilli (Eds.), Advances in Inorganic Biochemistry, Vol. V, Iron Binding Proteins Without Cofactors or Sulfur Clusters, Elsevier, New York 1983, pp. 1-38.

(4) E. C. Theil, W. E. Brenner, Dev. Biol. 84 (1981) 481-484.

(5) C. Wustefield, R. R. Crichton, FEBS Lett. 150 (1982) 43-48.

(6) E. A. Leibold, N. Aziz, A. J. P. Brown, H. N. Munro, J. Biol. Chem. 259 (1984) 4327-4334.

(7) F. Costanzo, C. Santoro, V. Colantuoni, J. Bensi, G. Raugli, V. Romano, R. Cortese, EMBO J. 3, (1984) 23-27.

(8) J. M. Addison, J. E. Fitton, G. C. Ford, P. M. Harrison, W. G. Lewis, D. W. Rice, J. M. A. Smith, J. L. White in I. Urushizaki, P. Aisen, I. Listowsky, J. W. Drysdale (Eds.), Structure and Function of Iron Storage and Transport Proteins, Elsevier, Amsterdam 1983, pp. 17-23.

(9) J. R. Didsbury, E. C. Theil, R. E. Kaufman (in preparation).

(10) K. Ihara, K. Maeguchi, C. T. Young, E. C. Theil, J. Biol. Chem. 259 (1984) 278-283.

(11) J. E. Brown, E. C. Theil, J. Biol. Chem. 253 (1978) 2673-2678.

(12) H. Yamada, T. G. Gabuzda, J. Lab. Clin. Med. 83 (1974) 478-488.

(13) A. J. P. Brown, E. A. Leibold, H. N. Munro, Proc. Natl. Acad. Sci. 79 (1983) 5901-5905.

(14) J. R. Mertz, E. C. Theil, J. Biol. Chem. 258 (1983) 11719-11726.

(15) E. C. Theil, J. R. Mertz, K. Ihara, K. Maeguchi in (8), pp. 31-34.

(16) J. E. Folk, Ann. Rev. Biochem. $\underline{49}$ (1980) 517-531.

(17) P. Tressel, D. J. Kosman, (1980) Biochem. Biophys. Res. Commun. $\underline{92}$ (1980) 781-786.

(18) W. H. Massover, J. Mol. Biol. $\underline{123}$ (1978) 721-726.

(19) A. Treffry, S. H. Banyard, R. J. Hoare, P. M. Harrison in E. B. Brown, P. Aisen, J. Fielding, R. R. Crichton (Eds.), Proteins of Iron Metabolism, Grune and Stratton, New York 1977, pp. 3-11.

(20) S. H. Banyard, D. K. Stammers, P. M. Harrison, Nature $\underline{271}$ (1978) 282-284.

(21) E. C. Theil, D. E. Sayers, A. N. Mansour, F. J. Rennick, C. Thompson in K. O. Hodgson, B. Hedman, J. E. Penner-Halm (Eds.), EXAFS and Near Edge Structure III, Springer-Verlag, New York 1984, pp. 96-100.

(22) N. D. Chasteen, E. C. Theil, J. Biol. Chem. $\underline{257}$ (1982) 7672-7677.

(23) A. Treffry, P. M. Harrison, J. Inorg. Biochem. $\underline{21}$ (1984) 9-20.

(24) D. E. Sayers, E. C. Theil, F. J. Rennick, J. Biol. Chem. $\underline{258}$ (1983) 14076-14079.

(25) D. W. Rice, G. C. Ford, J. L. White, J. M. A. Smith, P. M. Harrison in (3), pp. 39-50.

(26) M. Heuterspreute, R. R. Crichton, FEBS Lett. $\underline{129}$ (1981) 322-327.

(27) M. Wauters, A. M. Michelson, R. R. Crichton, FEBS Lett. $\underline{91}$ (1978) 276-278.

(28) L. P. Rosenberg, N. D. Chasteen in P. Saltman, J. Hegenauer (Eds.), Biology and Physiology of Iron, Elsevier, New York 1982, pp. 405-407.

(29) U. Schwertmann, D. G. Schulze, E. Murad, J. Soil Sci. Soc. Amer. $\underline{46}$ (1982) 869-875.

(30) K. M. Towe, W. F. Bradley, J. Coll. Interface Sci. $\underline{24}$ (1967) 384-392.

(31) P. M. Harrison, F. A. Fischbach, T. G. Hoy, G. H. Haggis, Nature 216 (1967) 1188-1190.

(32) R. N. Sylva, Rev. Pure Appl. Chem. 22 (1972) 115-132.

(33) W. H. Massover, J. M. Cowley, Proc. Natl. Acad. Sci. U.S.A. 70 (1973) 3847-3851.

(34) P. M. Harrison, T. G. Hoy, I. G. Macara, R. J. Hoare, Biochem. J. 143 (1974) 445-451.

(35) T. Jones, R. Spenser, C. Walsh, Biochemistry 17 (1978) 4011-4017.

(36) A. Treffry, P. M. Harrison, Biochem. J. 171 (1978) 313-320.

(37) J. M. Williams, D. P. Danson, C. Janot, Phys. Med. Biol. 23 (1978) 835-851.

(38) C. Grant, G. Taborsky, Biochemistry 5 (1965) 544-555.

(39) R. W. Rosenstein, G. Taborsky, Biochemistry 9 (1970) 649-657.

(40) G. Taborsky in (3), pp. 235-279.

(41) A. N. Mansour, C. Thompson, E. C. Theil, N. D. Chasteen, D. E. Sayers, J. Biol. Chem. (1985) in press, June/July.

(42) R. A. Berner, Earth Planet. Sci. Lett. 18 (1973) 77-86.

(43) A. S. R. Juo, R. L. Fox, Soil Sci. 124 (1971) 370-376.

The Three-Dimensional Structure of Apoferritin: a Framework Controlling Ferritin's Iron Storage and Release

P.M.Harrison, G.C.Ford, D.W. Rice, J.M.A. Smith, A. Treffry and J.L. White.

Department of Biochemistry, The University of Sheffield, Sheffield, S10 2TN, U.K.

SUMMARY

   The iron-storage protein, ferritin, has an inorganic 'iron-core' of ferrihydrite-phosphate enclosed in a protein shell, apoferritin, composed of 24 symmetrically arranged polypeptide chains. To provide a storage and reserve function apoferritin must allow the passage of iron into the protein's internal cavity, its deposition inside and the subsequent mobilisation of this iron. These processes are discussed in relation to the known three-dimensional structure of the apoferritin shell.

1 INTRODUCTION

   Ferritin is a giant clathrate compound comprising a protein cage encompassing an 'iron-core' of the mineral ferrihydrite complexed with phosphate (1). The space for this mineral is a sphere of about 80Å diameter allowing the storage of up to 4500 Fe^{3+} atoms. The cage, apoferritin, is a nearly spherical protein shell of thickness about 25Å. This shell is composed of 24 polypeptide chains arranged in 432 symmetry, Fig. 1. Each chain is folded into a roughly cylindrical subunit (approximately 25 x 55Å), and antiparallel pairs of these subunits form the 12 faces of a rhombic dodecahedron.

2 DESCRIPTION OF STRUCTURE

   The apoferritin subunit is a bundle of 4 long antiparallel helices, A, B, C and D, with a shorter helix, E, lying at about 60° to this bundle. There is also a long strand running the length of the bundle

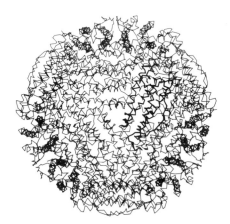

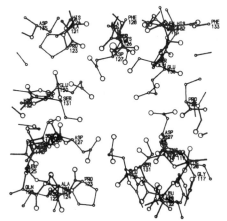

Fig.1   View of an apoferritin
molecule down one of its three-
fold axes. A three-fold axis
channel can be seen at the
centre of the molecule. Six
of the molecular two-fold axes
lie in the plane of the paper.
Subunits are drawn as connected
Cα atoms.

Fig. 2   View of the region
around a 3-fold channel
showing amino acid resi-
dues of three subunits.
Three aspartic acid and
three glutamic acid resi-
dues line this channel.

which forms a short stretch of antiparallel β-sheet with a 2-fold
related subunit. Subunits are arranged such that one end lies beside
a molecular 3-fold axis and the other points towards a 4-fold axis.
Around the latter axes four nearly parallel E helices from four subunits
are in close contact and form another, shorter bundle, with a small
hydrophobic central channel (diameter ca. 3-4Å, length ca. 15Å) which
passes through the protein shell. In the L-chains the amino acids
lining these channels, twelve leucines from four subunits, are conserved. Channels around the 3-fold axes are shorter (diameter ca. 3-4Å,
length ca. 8Å) and hydrophilic in character being lined by three aspartic acid residues towards the inside and three glutamic acid residues
towards the outside, Fig. 2. These are conserved in all available
sequences. Residues neighbouring these channels are also conserved or
conservatively replaced. On the internal surface of the molecule, the
rhomb face formed by each pair of subunits is flat except for an intersubunit groove which contains electron density attributable to water
molecules. Residues are predominantly hydrophilic, but less than half
of these are conserved in all available sequences (2). Electron
density for many of their side chains is weak suggesting flexibility.
Some of these residues may be in contact with the iron-core in ferritin
and be of importance in the initiation of ferrihydrite deposition
during ferritin formation.

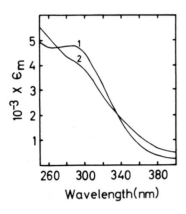

Fig. 3   U.V. Difference Spectra
         obtained (1) 2 mins and
         (2) 20 hrs. after the
         addition to apoferritin
         of 4 Fe atoms/molecule.

3   FORMATION OF IRON-CORE

How then do we envisage ferritin formation to proceed and iron
release to be achieved? Much more work has been done on the former.
Ferritin reconstitution occurs when Fe^{2+} is added to apoferritin in the
presence of O_2. The outcome is the deposition of the mainly crystalline
ferrihydrite mineral inside the apoferritin shell. Chemically this involves oxidation and hydrolysis. Early kinetic data suggested that,
overall, this occurs in two stages interpreted in terms of a 'crystal-
growth' model (3). The first, slow stage may be considered as
'nucleation' and this is followed by a rapid growth phase, during which
marked co-operativity gives an "all-or-none" distribution of ferrihydrite crystallites. Recent spectroscopic evidence (4) shows that
such clusters begin to form when only 2-4 Fe^{3+} atoms/molecule have been
added. As the first few Fe^{3+} are incorporated the g' = 4.3 EPR signal
is decreased by anti-ferromagnetic coupling (5). Changes in electronic
absorption spectra can also be seen after Fe^{2+} addition, Fig. 3 which
suggest that the first Fe^{3+} species formed migrate or rearrange to give
bi- and polynuclear hydroxy and/or μ-oxo bridged complexes (4).

Apoferritin catalyses the formation of its iron-core, its effect
being shown principally during the initial slow phase (6). This has
been explained as a chelation effect with carboxy ligands favouring
Fe^{2+} oxidation (3, 6). The provision by apoferritin of only limited
numbers of such ligands, of Fe^{3+} binding sites in proximity and of
groups which bind protons may also be important features in the catalysis of iron-core nucleation. During the second growth stage of
ferritin formation, Fe^{2+} oxidation may occur on the surfaces of ferrihydrite crystallites (3) and this may allow the four electron reduction
of dioxygen to water (6). Oxidant specificity is also relaxed at this

stage, $KIO_3/Na_2S_2O_3$ being as effective as dioxygen (7).

Table 1. Principal Metal Binding Sites on Apoferritin

No.	Residues	Metals	Location
1	ASP 80 GLN 82'	Cd, Tb, (Zn), (UO2)	Outside on 2-fold
2	ASP 127 ASP 127' ASP 127''	Cd, Zn, (Hg)	Inner 3-fold channel
3	GLU 130 GLU 130' GLU 130'' 3 H_2O	Cd, Zn	Outer 3-fold channel
4	HIS 132 ASP 135'	Cd, Zn, (Tb), (SO4)	Inside near 3-fold
5	ASP 38 GLU 45 CYS 48	Cd, Zn, (Tb), UO2 Hg	Inside near 2-fold
6	GLU 130 GLU 130' GLU 130'' ASP 127 ASP 127' ASP 127''	Tb	Middle 3-fold channel
7	GLU 53 GLU 56	Tb	Inside in 2-fold groove
8	GLU 57 GLU 60	Tb	Inside on B helix
9	CYS 126	Hg	Outer lip 3-fold channel
10	GLU 63 ARG 59 (GLU 56') (ARG 52')	UO2	Inside in 2-fold groove
11	GLU 57 H_2O GLU 136	UO2	Inside surface at BD interface

Hg = PCMB = $^+Hg-\emptyset-COO^-$

UO2 = $(UO_2F_5)^{3-}$ = UO_2^{2+}

Cd = Cd^{2+} Zn = Zn^{2+}

Tb = Tb^{3+} SO4 = SO_4^{2-}

( ) = Tentative or low occupancy

_____ = Residues conserved in known sequences

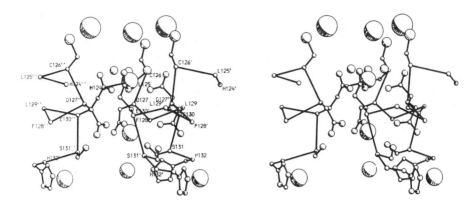

Fig. 4   Stereoview of the heavy metal binding sites in the region of
         the 3-fold axis.   Large spheres represent the Hg sites on the
         outside surface, the medium spheres the Cd sites within the 3-
         fold channel and on the inside surface and the small spheres
         the coordinated water molecules.

4   STRUCTURE-FUNCTION RELATIONS

How can these processes be related to the three-dimensional
structure of ferritin?   Unfortunately the lack of specific orientation
of the iron-core to protein and the very limited diffraction data for
ferrihydrite (1) prevent detailed description of its structure.   On the
other hand we might be able to pin-point sites at which Fe^{2+} and Fe^{3+}
bind during the initial stages of ferritin formation and identify the
channels through which iron penetrates the apoferritin shell.   However
we have as yet no information on iron binding sites, although we can
describe sites occupied by a number of other metals, namely Cd^{2+}, Zn^{2+},
Tb^{3+}, UO_2^{2+} and Hg.   The structure of horse spleen apoferritin was
derived from crystals grown from $CdSO_4$ solution.   Crystals have also
been grown from $TbCl_3$ solutions or $ZnSO_4$ solutions containing trace
amounts of $CdSO_4$.   Mercuribenzoate and UO_2^{2+} were used initially in
phase determination in apoferritin crystallized from $CdSO_4$. Zn^{2+} and Tb^{3+}
were studied because of their known effects on ferritin formation (4,6),
Zn^{2+} being an especially potent inhibitor. UO_2^{2+} also inhibits iron
incorporation but Hg is without effect.

Let us now consider the principal metal binding sites listed in
Table 1.   There are two Cd^{2+} ions bound on intermolecular 2-fold axes
near the molecular diad on the outside of the molecule, which, in the
crystals, make double intermolecular bridges (8).   These may be replaced by two Tb^{3+} or a single UO_2^{2+} ion.   It is unlikely that these
sites are directly involved in iron uptake or release processes.

Metals are found in the 3-fold channels shown in Figs. 1 and 2. Zn^{2+} and Cd^{2+} bind in the same two positions with either three aspartyl groups or three glutamyl residues plus three water molecules as ligands, Fig. 4. In crystals grown from $TbCl_3$ this double site is replaced by a single Tb^{3+} having all six carboxylates as ligands. These three metal sites each have a stoichiometry of 0.33 per subunit. It is likely, especially in view of the marked conservation of this intersubunit region, that these eight channels are the ports of entry (and exit) of iron and the observed ligand flexibility could be important for the channelling of iron into or out of the molecule. Several more metal positions have been identified, or tentatively identified, on the inner surface of the apoferritin shell. One of these has HIS 132 and probably ASP 135' (from a neighbouring subunit) as ligands and is found in Cd^{2+}, Zn^{2+} and Tb^{3+} containing crystals (at low occupancy in the latter). Although listed here as a metal site this may possibly be an anion site binding SO_4^{2-} or Cl^-. There are three of these sites (related by 3-fold symmetry) at about 5$\overset{\circ}{A}$ from the inner channel (Cd^{2+}/Zn^{2+}) position. In principle this could represent an Fe^{n+} binding site, either temporarily occupied by iron in transit to another centre, or as part of an actual nucleation site. A recent cDNA sequence shows that HIS 132 and ASP 135 are replaced by glutamic acid residues in embryonic amphibian red cell ferritin (Didsbury, Kaufman & Theil, J.Biol.Chem., submitted). Clusters of metal sites may also be identified on the inside surface on and around the B helix and BB' interface. These include two Tb^{3+} and two UO_2^{2+} ions which lie near the 2-fold axes relating B and B' helices of neighbouring subunits. One Tb^{3+} has ligands which are not conserved in some other known sequences (2). Another site further along the BB' groove may be occupied by several metals, but again only one of the available ligands is generally conserved. Invariant carboxyl ligands are glutamic acid residues 57, 60 and 63. The conservation of these residues, together with their capacity for binding several metal ions in proximity, makes this region attractive as an iron-core nucleation centre. Another feature of these sites is that they are 'one-sided' or 'open' sites, the number of ligands available on the protein being less than that required to complete the usual six co-ordination of Fe^{3+}. The retention of some water of hydration may provide a means of linking neighbouring Fe^{3+} ions through μ-oxo or hydroxy bridges. There are no actual pairs of sites within the 3.0-3.5$\overset{\circ}{A}$ distance expected for such bridged Fe^{3+} atoms, although, given ligand flexibility, it is not inconceivable that such bridging may occur.

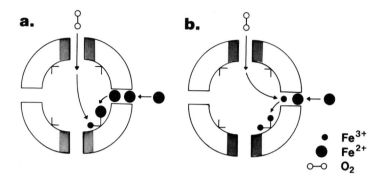

Fig. 5   Speculative Iron Uptake Mechanisms. Fe^{2+} enters and binds in
         the 3-fold channels, O_2 enters through the apolar (shaded) 4-
         fold channel. Oxidation occurs either (a) at a site on the
         inside surface or (b) at a site within the 3-fold channel.

5   SPECULATION ON IRON UPTAKE AND RELEASE MECHANISMS

     It is disappointing that we cannot at this stage be sure of where
and how the various processes involved in ferritin formation occur
within the apoferritin molecule. We can however, speculate on possibilities, Fig. 5. Apoferritin must be designed in order that Fe^{2+} oxidation and hydrolysis occurs more readily inside the molecule than
outside. It seems likely that Fe^{2+} enters at the 3-fold channels.
Binding of Fe^{2+} (or Fe^{3+}) in these channels must not be too tight since
ferrihydrite must be deposited within the inner cavity. The inner
channel site (three ASP residues) may have the higher binding affinity
for Fe^{2+}. Movement into the cavity could be facilitated by binding
a second Fe^{2+} in the outer channel site which would also prevent its
outward movement. Once the inner Fe^{2+} (or Fe^{3+}) has moved into the
cavity the second Fe^{2+} will move into the vacant channel site.
Alternatively if two Fe^{2+} are present in the channel two-electron oxidation may be possible. We may also hypothesise that O_2 enters apoferritin through the apolar 4-fold channels, so that oxidation takes
place inside the molecule, either in the channel or at one of the
nucleation centres we have discussed. One of the problems in defining
a mechanism of ferritin formation may indeed be that oxidation of Fe^{2+}
can take place in several different sites, especially after the iron-
core has started to form. Thus the initial species which we see,
Fig. 3, when about 4-8 Fe atoms/molecule are added is not seen if this
number is increased to 48. Presumably this is because the higher
number of Fe atoms leads to a more rapid formation of polynuclear
complex, aided, perhaps, by the greater efficiency of electron

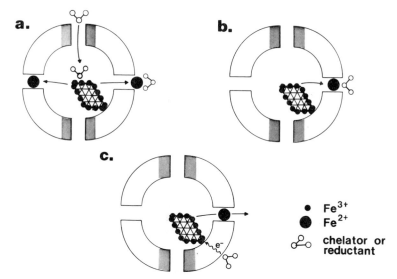

Fig. 6   Speculative Iron Release Mechanisms. (a) Small reductants
enter through the apolar (shaded) 4-fold channels and the released Fe^{2+} passes out through the 3-fold channel. (b) Fe^{2+}
chelators relieve a bottleneck of Fe^{2+} exciting through the 3-
fold channels. (c) Electron transfer through the protein
shell.

transfer to dioxygen now possible (6). In addition there may be subtle
structural changes after the initial Fe^{3+} species has formed, which
favour cluster formation.

Natural ferritin contains phosphate in association with its iron-
core (1). There are no obvious anion channels, so we may suppose that
phosphate enters through the apolar 4-fold axis channels. This may be
the route for other small anions and neutral molecules known to enter
apoferritin, although gaps may develop in other parts of the protein
shell as it undergoes dynamic fluctuations in structure. It is conceivable that binding of phosphate (sulphate in vitro?) could play a
role in core formation perhaps by binding to ARG 59 and 59'.

In vivo ferritin provides a reserve of iron for synthesis of haemoglobin and other iron-containing proteins. Little is known about iron
release from ferritin under physiological conditions. Several alternative means of release may be supposed, Fig. 6, each of which might
operate under different conditions. Small molecule reductants might
enter the molecule perhaps through the 4-fold channels, and the Fe^{2+}
released from the core may then pass out, presumably through the 3-fold
channels. Alternatively electrons might be passed through the protein
shell although it is about 25Å thick except in the vicinity of the

3-fold channels. Fe^{2+} chelators have been found to facilitate release
and actually to accelerate reduction. Such chelators might relieve a
bottleneck of Fe^{2+} exiting through the 3-fold channels or they might
enter the molecule and bring out Fe^{2+} as neutral complexes through the
4-fold channels. Fe^{3+} chelators might act in similar alternative ways
on the assumption that Fe^{3+} is found in the 3-fold channels in the
absence of reducing agents. A dynamic equilibrium between internal and
external Fe^{3+} was suggested many years ago (9).

6   BACTERIOFERRITIN

A last word should be said on the relationship between ferritins
and bacterioferritins. These are also multisubunit proteins with an
iron-core, but also with one haem per two protein chains. Although
their iron-cores are chemically different from those of ferritin (10)
having a higher phosphate : iron ratio, reconstitution to a ferritin-
like core is possible in the absence of phosphate (this has been shown
with bacterioferritin from Azotobacter vinelandii (11)). Thus these
molecules must also contain channels for iron and phosphate although
iron reduction may be mediated by their haem groups. Studies on the
structure and function of these fascinating proteins are in progress,

7   REFERENCES

(1) G. C. Ford, P. M. Harrison, D. W. Rice, J. M. A. Smith, A. Treffry,
     J. L. White & J. Yariv, Phil. Trans. Roy. Soc. Lond., B304, (1984)
     551-565.

(2) P. M. Harrison, J. L. White, J. M. A. Smith, G. W. Farrants, G. C.
     Ford, D. W. Rice, J. M. Addison & A. Treffry in R.R. Crichton (ed),
     Proteins of Iron Metabolism, Elsevier Science, Amsterdam, 1985,
     in press.

(3) I. G. Macara, T. G. Hoy & P. M. Harrison, Biochem. J., 126, (1972)
     151-162.

(4) A. Treffry & P. M. Harrison, J.Inorg.Biochem., 21, (1984), 9-20.

(5) L.P.Rosenberg & N. D. Chasteen in P. Saltman & J. Hegenauer (eds),
     The Biochemistry and Physiology of Iron, Elsevier Biomedical,
     New York, 1982, pp. 405-407.

(6) G. A. Clegg, J. E. Fitton, P. M. Harrison & A. Treffry, Progr. Biophys. Molec. Biol., 36, (1980), 53-86

(7) A. Treffry, J. M. Sowerby & P. M. Harrison, FEBS Lett., 95, (1979), 221-224.

(8) D. W. Rice, G. C. Ford, J. L. White, J. M. A. Smith & P. M. Harrison in G. L.Eichhorn,L. Marzilli & E. C. Theil (eds), Advances in Inorganic Biochemistry, vol. 5, Elsevier, New York, 1983, pp. 39-50.

(9) M. M. Jones & D. O. Johnston, Nature Lond., 216, (1967), 509-510.

(10) E.R. Bauminger, S.G. Cohen, D.P.E. Dickson, A. Levy, S. Ofer & J. Yariv, Biochim. Biophys. Acta, 623, (1980), 237-242.

(11) J. Yariv, J. M. A. Smith, J. L. White, A. Treffry, D.W. Rice, G. C. Ford, P. M. Harrison, J. M. Williams, G. D. Watt & E. I. Stiefel in I. Urushizaki, P. Aisen, I. Listowsky & J. W. Drysdale (eds), Structure and Function of Iron Storage and Transport Proteins, Elsevier Science, Amsterdam, 1983, pp.69-70.

The Release of Iron From Transferrin. An Overview

N. Dennis Chasteen, Carl P. Thompson, and Donna M. Martin

Department of Chemistry, University of New Hampshire, Durham,
New Hampshire, 03824 USA

SUMMARY

   Studies of the metal binding properties of the iron transport protein transferrin
have focused on identification of the ligands of the specific binding sites and
their role in the exchange of iron between the protein and its environment. In this
communication, the literature is briefly reviewed and evidence is presented for the
involvement of noncoordinating protein functional groups in the uptake and release
of iron by transferrin.

1 BACKGROUND

   The majority of body iron is associated with proteins of respiration, namely
hemoglobin, myoglobin and the cytochromes, and with the iron storage proteins
ferritin and hemosiderin (1). Although less than 1% of body iron is bound to
serum transferrin, all iron is transported by this protein at one time or another.
The role of the transferrins in the management of metabolic iron appears to be
greater than previously thought. In addition to being a transport protein for serum
iron, there is some evidence for the involvement of transferrin in the acquisition
of iron within the gut (2) and in the regulation of cell growth (3-7). Transferrin
also exhibits bacterial static activity as part of the defense mechanism against
pathogens (6,7).

   Human serum transferrin, human lactoferrin found in mother's milk and other body
fluids, and ovotransferrin from egg white are the most thoroughly studied of the
transferrins (6-9). These glycoproteins have molecular weights near 80,000, consist
of a single polypeptide chain with no subunits, and bind two Fe^{3+} along with two
carbonate anions at sites located in similar but separate globular domains of the
protein. Carbonate binding is required for iron binding. The two iron binding sites

are distant from one another, probably in excess of 30Å (10). The similar optical and EPR spectral properties of these proteins strongly suggest that their sites are composed of the same coordinating groups. The relatively small differences observed in the Fe^{3+} EPR spectra for the two sites of serum transferrin (11) probably arises from a slight difference in coordination geometry at the two sites. It has been demonstrated that one metal binding domain of the Cu^{2+} (12), VO^{2+} (13), Co^{2+} (14) and Th^{4+} (15) derivatives of transferrin undergoes a conformational transition near pH 10 causing an alteration in the metal binding site. The ability of transferrin to bind some 28 different metal ions (9) argues for considerable flexibility in its binding sites.

2 THE LIGANDS

The results of spectroscopic and chemical modification studies suggest that the metal site consists of two histidines (16-19), two tyrosines (18,20), hydroxide or water (20,21) and carbonate (22) to form a six or perhaps seven coordinate complex. The possibility that there is only one coordinating histidine cannot be completely excluded. Although once a matter of controversy, it is now generally accepted that the anion carbonate is bound directly to the iron and probably bridges between the iron and a cationic site on the protein (e.g. 8 and references therein).

The amino acid sequences of human serum transferrin (23,24), lactoferrin (25,26), and ovotransferrin (27,28) are now complete and provide insight into the identity of the iron ligands. Comparison of the sequences of the two domains of the three proteins indicates that only a few tyrosine, histidine, and arginine residues are conserved (Table 1) (26). The previous suggestion that tyrosine-185 is a ligand (29) appears to be incorrect since this residue is not conserved in lactoferrin (26). An iron binding fragment of molecular weight 18,000 has been isolated from lactoferrin and contains residues Tyr-93, Tyr-191, His-117, His-252, Arg-121, and Arg-257, but not Tyr-83, suggesting that Tyr-83 is not a ligand (26,30).

Conserved arginines are also included in Table 1 since a guanidinium group may constitute the site where carbonate binds to the protein (31). It has been suggested that Arg-124 in the N-terminal domain and its counterpart Arg-456 of the C-terminal domain of human serum transferrin are well positioned in the sequence to permit the simultaneous binding of carbonate to the protein and to the iron (29). Knowledge of the tertiary structure in the region of the metal site is needed to establish whether Arg-124 indeed participates in carbonate binding. The conserved residue Arg-254 near the potential iron ligand His-249 is in an alternate choice for the site of anion binding.

Table 1. Candidates for iron binding ligands in the transferrins (a)

Amino Acid	N-Domain	C-Domain
Tyrosine	85, 95, 188	412, 426, 517
	(83), (93), (191)	(427), (447), (540)
	[82], [92], [191]	[415], [431], [524]
Histidine	119, 249	451, 584
	(117), (252)	(472), (609)
	[116], [250]	[455], [592]
Arginine	124, 254	456, 589
	(121), (257)	(477), (614)
	[121], [255]	[460], [597]

(a) Conserved amino acid positions without parentheses are those of human serum
     transferrin. Positions given in parentheses and brackets are those of lacto-
     ferrin and ovotransferrin, respectively. Data taken from references 23
     through 28.

3 THE IRON EXCHANGE REACTION

Considerable progress has been made in recent years in understanding the cellular
processes by which iron is removed from transferrin (4,6,32-35). Following binding
to its receptor on the exterior of the cell, the transferrin-receptor complex is
internalized via endocytosis where it becomes incorporated into an endosome. Iron
appears to be released at this point; however, knowledge of the chemistry of iron
removal from the protein within the acidic milieu of the endosome is incomplete.
Apotransferrin bound to the receptor is recycled to the exterior of the cell where
the protein is released to the medium.

The marked decrease in the thermodynamic stability of the iron-transferrin-
carbonate complex with decreasing pH in-vitro is well documented (6,8,9) and is
consistent with the above mechanism for iron release to the cell. The rate of iron
removal by chelating agents is also greatly facilitated in acid, changing by an order
of magnitude with each unit change in pH (e.g. 36). However, in the absence of
of strong chelating agents, iron is known to be retained by the protein at pH 5.7
(37). Thus, intracellular chelating agents such as GTP or other phosphate compounds
may be required for iron removal from diferric transferrin within the acidic environment of the endosome. Such chelating agents conceivably participate as well in the
transport of the metal out of the endosomic vesicle into the cytosol for ultimate
incorporation into heme or deposition within ferritin.

Studies of the chelate mediated release of iron from transferrin have provided some insight into the molecular events which occur during iron removal. Much of the progress in this area can be attributed to the work of Bates and coworkers (38-41). The overall reaction is given by

$$Fe\text{-}TF\text{-}CO_3 + Chel \rightarrow \text{"}Chel\text{-}Fe\text{-}TF\text{-}CO_3\text{"} \rightarrow Chel\text{-}Fe + TF + CO_3{}^{2-}$$

where TF is apotransferrin and Chel is a chelating agent. Iron uptake is the reverse of the above reaction. Optical and EPR spectroscopic evidence has been obtained for the formation of mixed-ligand complexes of the type "Chel-Fe-TF-CO_3" where Chel is acetohydroxamic acid (38), pyrophosphate (39), or other chelators (40). In addition, kinetic data suggests that the Fe-TF-CO_3 ternary complex must first undergo a conformational change in which the iron becomes "exposed" prior to attack by the chelating agent Chel to form the mixed-ligand complex (38). The coordination sphere of the iron in this complex is unknown. These recent studies have revealed complexities of the protein which had not been appreciated previously.

4 THE IMPORTANCE OF PROTEIN STRUCTURE AND CONFORMATION

The binding and release of iron(III) by transferrin undoubtedly involves several factors in addition to the simple complexation of iron. Structural features other than the iron ligands themselves surely play a major role in the kinetic and thermo-dynamic properties of the protein. While iron coordination appears to be the same for all transferrins, these proteins differ substantially in their kinetic properties. The first-order rate constants for iron removal by 2,3-diphosphoglycerate follow the order: human serum transferrin > ovotransferrin >> lactoferrin with the rate constant for lactoferrin being four orders of magnitude lower than for serum transferrin (36). Moreover, the iron-lactoferrin-carbonate complex has remarkable stability in acid; the serum transferrin complex does not. The presence of cationic amino acids near the metal in serum transferrin but not found in lactoferrin may be partly responsible for the large differences between these proteins. In this connection, Shewale and Brew have found that 12 of the 59 amino groups in human serum transferrin exhibit reduced reactivity toward acetic anhydride implying that they are located in the region of the protein where iron binds (42).

Differences in properties between iron binding domains are also evident. For example, studies of iron removal from diferric transferrin using a variety of different mediating chelating agents show a curious dependence of the rate on salt concentration (43,44). Increasing the concentration of NaF, NaBr, NaI, $NaNO_3$, Na_2SO_4, or $NaClO_4$ causes the rate of iron removal for the N-terminal site to decrease whereas the rate for the C-terminal site increases. Similar behavior is observed for the

relative thermodynamic stability of iron binding to the two sites (45). These differences have been ascribed to conformational changes in the two iron binding domains
induced by the interaction of anions with the protein. EPR spectroscopy shows that
these effects are transmitted to the iron(III) centers (46,47). Cationic groups
near the metal, i.e. ε-amino group of lysine, the guanidinium group of arginine, or
the protonated imidazole of histidine, may serve as binding sites for anions, the
occupancy of which "trigger" a conformational transition leading to changes in the
iron binding properties of the protein. Such groups would not be expected to be
conserved among the domains of the various transferrins and could account for the
differences in their kinetic and thermodynamic properties. The presence of several
cationic groups in the proposed region of iron binding in serum transferrin has already been noted (24,29,42). These groups may serve to direct chelators to the
iron, thus facilitating the formation of a mixed-ligand complex and perhaps lending
stability to it.

The equilibrium distribution of iron between the two binding sites of serum
transferrin samples which have been 50% saturated with Fe(III) is markedly dependent
on pH, the occupancy of the C-terminal site being favored at low pH (11,45). In one
study, metal binding was shown to be coupled to the deprotonation of a functional
group(s) having an apparent pK_a near physiological pH 7.4 (45). The relative affinity
of iron for the two sites followed a pH titration curve in the pH range 7-9. However, in this pH range no significant change in the first coordination sphere of the
metal occurs as evidenced by EPR spectroscopy. Deprotonation of histidine and/or
tyrosine residues near the metal, but not coordinated to it, may be responsible for
the alteration in thermodynamic stability of iron binding near pH 7.4. Lysine or
tyrosine have been implicated in the conformational transition of the C-domain of
serum transferrin which occurs in the pH range 9-10 (13,14).

Studies of the properties of chemically modified transferrins have been initiated
in our laboratory to further elucidate the role of protein functional groups in the
kinetics of iron removal from transferrin by chelators. In order to examine those
groups which are not coordinated to the iron, the modification reactions were carried
out on the diferric protein. In this way the iron ligands are protected by the
metal from modification. Histidines and lysines were modified using the reagents
ethoxyformic anhydride and acetic anhydride, respectively. The apparent first-
order rate constants for iron removal from the two sites of the native and modified
proteins by pyrophosphate were measured spectrophotometrically by monitoring the
absorption band at 295 nm for the bound iron. The results are summarized in Table 2.

Large effects on the values of k_C and k_N for the C- and N-terminal binding sites,
respectively, are observed upon modification of the protein. Interestingly, lysine

Table 2. Rate constants for iron removal from the two sites of chemically modified
          human serum transferrin (a)

Protein	$k_N(min^{-1})$	$k_C(min^{-1})$
Control (b)	0.18	0.048
Lysine Modified (b) (83%)	0.007	0.195
Control (c)	0.16	0.056
Histidine Modified (c) (78%)	0.06	0.009

(a) Percent modification of the 58 lysines and 18 histidines of the protein are given
     in parentheses. Estimated relative errors in rate constants $\pm$ 10%.
(b) Conditions: 20 μM diferric transferrin, 2 mM pyrophosphate, 0.9 mM desferri-
     oximine B, 0.1 M Hepes, 0.02 M $NaHCO_3$, pH 6.9, 37°C.
(c) Conditions as in (a) except 3 mM pyrophosphate.

modification decreases k_N but has an opposite effect on k_C in a manner analogous to
the influence of salts on the protein (vide supra). This result is consistent with
the involvement of ε-amino groups in the binding of simple anions to the protein.
Both the N and C sites are stabilized kinetically upon modification of histidines
(Table 2). Similar trends are observed for the histidine modified protein when the
chelating mediators 2,3-diphosphoglycerate, ATP, GTP, citrate, or othophosphate are
employed. Thus, the phenomenon is not simply due to choice of mediator. These preliminary studies provide further evidence that amino acid residues which are not
coordinated to the iron play an important role in determining the kinetic properties
of transferrin.

5 CONCLUSION

It is evident that serum transferrin is more than a simple chelator of iron.
Structural features beyond the specific iron binding sites are clearly important in
governing the kinetic and thermodynamic properties of the protein. In one sense the
iron binding region might be considered an active site where an interplay between
protein ligands, other protein functional groups, and mediating chelators facilitate
the exchange of iron between transferrin and its environment. By exploiting the
differences between the transferrins, it should be possible to better understand the
complexities of the metal binding regions of these proteins.

6 ACKNOWLEDGEMENT

This work was supported by grant GM20194 from the National Institutes of Health.

7 REFERENCES

(1) R.R. Crichton, Struct. Bonding 17 (1973) 67-134.

(2) H.A. Huebers, E. Huebers, E. Csiba, W. Rummell, C.A. Finch, Blood 61 (1983)
     283-290.

(3) H. Broxmeyer, M. de Sousa, A. Smithyman, P. Ralph, J. Hamilton, J.I. Karlan,
     I.J. Bognacki, Blood 55 (1980) 324-333.

(4) R. Newman, C. Schneider, R. Sutherland, L. Vodinelich, M. Greaves, Trends Biol.
     Sci. 7 (1982) 397-400.

(5) M.G. Gaines, F.L. LaFleur, B.E. Holbein, Immun. Lett. 7 (1983) 51-53 and
     references therein.

(6) E.H. Morgan, Molec. Aspects Med. 4 (1981) 1-123.

(7) E.D. Weinberg, Physiol. Rev. 64 (1984) 65-102.

(8) N.D. Chasteen in E.C. Theil, G. Eichorn, L.G. Marzilli (eds.), Advances in In-
     organic Biochemistry, Vol. 5, Elsevier, New York, pp. 201-233.

(9) D.C. Harris and P. Aisen in T.M. Loehr (Ed.), Physical Bioinorganic Chemistry,
     Vol. 3, Addison-Wesley, New York, in press.

(10) P. O'Hara, S.M. Yeh, C.F. Meares, R. Bersohn, Biochemistry 20 (1981) 4704-4708.

(11) P. Aisen, A. Leibman, J. Zweier, J. Biol. Chem. 253 (1978) 1930-1937.

(12) J.L. Zweier, J. Biol. Chem. 253 (1978) 7616-7621.

(13) N.D. Chasteen, L.K. White, R.F. Campbell, Biochemistry 16 (1977) 363-368.

(14) I. Bertini, C. Luchinat, L. Messori, R. Monnanni, A. Scozzafava, Revista Port-
     uguesa de Quimica 27 (1985) 259.

(15) W.R. Harris, C.J. Carrano, V.L. Pecoraro, K.N. Raymond, J. Am. Chem. Soc. 103
     (1981) 2231-2237.

(16) B.M. Alsaadi, R.J.P. Williams, R.C. Woodworth, J. Inorg. Biochem. 15 (1981) 1-10.

(17) T.B. Rogers, B.A. Gold, R.E. Feeney, Biochemistry 16 (1977) 2299-2305.

(18) I. Bertini, C. Luchinat, L. Messori, A. Scozzafava, Eur. J. Biochem. 141 (1984) 375-378.

(19) J. Mazurier, D. Leger, V. Tordera, J. Montreuil, G. Spik, Eur. J. Biochem. 119 (1981) 537-543.

(20) V.L. Pecoraro, W.R. Harris, C.J. Carrano, K.N. Raymond, Biochemistry 20 (1981) 7033-7034.

(21) S.H. Koenig, R.D. Brown III in I. Bertini, R.S. Drago, C. Luchinat (Eds.), Coordination Chemistry of Metalloproteins, Rydale Press, 1983, pp. 19-33.

(22) M.R. Schlabach, G.W. Bates, J. Biol. Chem. 250 (1975) 2182-2188.

(23) R.T.A. MacGillivray, E. Mendiz, S.K. Sinha, M.R. Sutton, J. Lineback-Zins, K. Brew, Proc. Natl. Acad. Sci. USA 79 (1982) 2504-2508.

(24) R.T.A. MacGillivray, E. Mendez, J.G. Shewale, S.K. Sinha, T. Lineback-Zins, K. Brew, J. Biol. Chem. 258 (1983) 3543-3553.

(25) J. Mazurier, N.-H. Metz-Boutique, J. Jolles, G. Spik, J. Montreuil, P. Jolles, Experientia 39 (1983) 135-141.

(26) M.-H. Metz-Boutigue, J. Jolles, J. Mazurier, F. Schoentgen, D. Legrand, G.J. Spik, J. Montreuil, P. Jolles, Eur. J. Biochem. 145 (1984) 659-676.

(27) J.-M. Jeltsch, P. Chambon, Eur. J. Biochem. 122 (1982) 291-295.

(28) J. Williams, T.C. Elleman, I.B. Kingson, A.G. Wilkins, K.A. Kuhn, Eur. J. Biochem. 122 (1982) 297-303.

(29) N.D. Chasteen, Trends Biochem. Sci. 8 (1983) 272-275.

(30) D. Legrand, J. Mazurier, M.-H. Metz-Boutigue, J. Jolles, P. Jolles, J. Montreuil, G. Spik, Biochim. Biophys. Acta 787 (1984) 90-96.

(31) T.B. Roger, T. Borrensen, R.E. Feeney, Biochemistry 17 (1978) 1105-1109.

(32) K. Rao, J. van Renswoude, C. Kempf, R.D. Klausner, FEBS Lett. 160 (1983) 213-216.

(33) J. Van Renswoude, K. Bridges, J. Harford, R.D. Klausner, Proc. Natl. Acad. Sci. USA 79 (1982) 6186-6190.

(34) J.-N. Octave, Y.-J. Schneider, A. Trouet, R.R. Crichton, Trends Biochem. Sci. 8 (1983) 217-220.

(35) A. Brown-Mason, R.C. Woodworth, J. Biol. Chem. 259 (1984) 1866-1873.

(36) E.H. Morgan, Biochim. Biophys. Acta 580 (1979) 312-326.

(37) O. Zak, P. Aisen, Biochim. Biophys. Acta 742 (1983) 490-495.

(38) R.E. Cowart, N. Kojima, G.W. Bates, J. Biol. Chem. 257 (1982) 7560-7565.

(39) R.E. Cowart, S. Swope, T.T. Loh, N.D. Chasteen, G.W. Bates, submitted for publication.

(40) G.W. Bates in P. Saltman, J. Hegenauer (Eds.), The Biochemistry and Physiology of Iron, Elsevier, New York, 1982, pp. 3-18.

(41) N. Kojima, G.W. Bates, J. Biol. Chem. 254 (1979) 8847-8854.

(42) J.G. Shewale, K. Brew, J. Biol. Chem. 257 (1982) 9406-9415.

(43) J. Williams, N.D. Chasteen, K. Moreton, Biochem. J. 201 (1982) 527-532.

(44) D.A. Baldwin, D.M.R. de Sousa, Biochem. Biophys. Res. Commu. 99 (1981) 1101-1107.

(45) N.D. Chasteen, J. Williams, Biochem. J. 193 (1981) 717-727.

(46) D.A. Folajtar, N.D. Chasteen, J. Am. Chem. Soc. 194, (1982) 5775-5780.

(47) N.D. Chasteen, C.P. Thompson, J.P. Rines, in I. Urushizaki, P. Aisen, I. Listowski, and J.W. Drysdale (Eds.) Structure and Function of Iron Storage and Transport Proteins, Elsevier, New York, pp. 241-246.

Comparative Chemical and Biological Studies of Invertebrate Ferritins

J. Webb[1], K.S. Kim[1], V. Talbot[1], D.J. Macey[2], S. Mann[3], J.V. Bannister[4], R.J.P. Williams[4], T.G. St Pierre[5], D.P.E. Dickson[5], R. Frankel[6]

[1]School of Mathematical and Physical Sciences, and [2]School of Environmental and Life Sciences, Murdoch University, Perth WA 6150, Australia

[3]School of Chemistry, University of Bath, Bath BA2 7AY, UK

[4]Inorganic Chemistry Laboratory, University of Oxford, Oxford OX1 3QR, UK

[5]Department of Physics, University of Liverpool, Liverpool L69 3BX, UK

[6]Francis Bitter National Magnet Laboratory, Massachusetts Institute of Technology, Cambridge, Mass 02139, USA

SUMMARY

Ferritins have been isolated from the hemolymph of several species of chitons and limpets, marine invertebrates that actively generate tissue deposits of iron biominerals. High resolution electron microscopy, electron diffraction and Mössbauer spectroscopy studies indicate major points of difference between these and mammalian ferritin: the iron cores are larger but less crystalline; the cores contain less iron and have weaker exchange interactions together with a low superparamagnetic blocking temperature. Moreover, the proteins are immunologically distinct from mammalian ferritin and take up Fe(II) more rapidly. Ferritin is also shown to be the major high molecular weight zinc-binding protein in a tropical rock oyster containing elevated tissue levels of Zn.

1 INTRODUCTION

The iron-binding protein ferritin is of considerable bioinorganic interest since its metal-protein stoichiometry, although variable, is the largest yet reported. Horse spleen ferritin is a giant clathrate compound made up of a highly symmetrical protein shell of 24 identical subunits (MW 18,500) that encapsulates Fe(III) as a small particle of hydrous iron(III) oxide together with some phosphate. This central core can contain up to 4500 Fe atoms.

The molecular structure and behaviour of horse spleen ferritin has been described in some detail (1). Following earlier controversies (2), the core is now generally considered to have the structure of ferri-hydrite, $5Fe_2O_3.9H_2O$ with octahedral Fe(III) in a layer structure related to that of hematite, $\alpha-Fe_2O_3$. The manner by which Fe enters and leaves this clathrate compound has drawn considerable attention with at least seven possible mechanistic processes being identified (1). Not surprisingly, the kinetics of this heterogeneous and possibly auto-catalytic reaction are complex.

We have recently initiated studies of ferritins from the hemolymph of chitons and limpets, marine invertebrates whose teeth contain extensive biogenic deposits of iron(III) oxides and oxyhydroxides (3,4). Elsewhere in this volume (5) we describe the results of studies of these teeth at various stages of mineralization using the scanning proton microprobe to construct elemental composition maps at ~ 2 μm resolution and Mössbauer spectroscopy to follow the chemical transformations of the biogenic iron deposits. The major iron transport protein in the iron-rich hemolymph has been identified as ferritin (6) which is present at high concentra-tions, e.g. 400 μg/100 mL in the chiton Clavarizona hirtosa. Presumably the high iron binding capacity of ferritin makes it suitable for iron transport in these systems by providing the means by which a high flux of iron can be delivered to the mineralizing front.

2 ELECTRON MICROSCOPY

The size and crystallinity of the cores of chiton (C. hirtosa), limpet (Patella vulgata) and human ferritins have been determined at high resolution (0.25 nm, point-to-point) using a Jeol 200CX electron micro-scope (7). Human ferritin shows extensive lattice fringes indicating considerable regularity in its solid state structure. In contrast, both limpet and chiton ferritins show little if any crystallinity. These differences can be seen in the lattice images shown in Figure 1. The

cores of human ferritin appear as single domain crystallites while those
of limpet ferritin are poorly crystalline. Only few of these latter
cores show the resolved lattice fringes of Figure 1 b where the crystalline domains are much smaller than the overall size of the core.
Electron diffraction patterns from limpet ferritin cores consisted of
diffuse lines with, occasionally, a faint line at 1.4 - 1.5Å. In the
case of chiton ferritin, this line was not observed, suggesting that
this iron core is even less crystalline than is that of limpet ferritin.

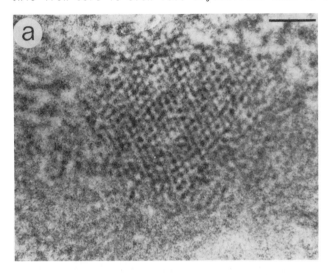

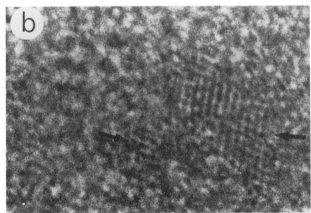

Fig. 1
(a) Lattice image of a 65Å single domain crystal of human spleen ferritin
    core with lattice fringe spacings of 2.7Å.
(b) Lattice image of a hemolymph ferritin core from the limpet Patella
    vulgata showing lattice fringe spacings of 3Å. Arrows indicate
    possible sites of crystallite growth.
Note: Bar = 20Å in both cases. Image detail is seen more clearly by
viewing the micrographs almost parallel to the plane of the page.

Measurements of the core diameters of the three ferritins indicate further differences. As shown in the histograms of Figure 2, the two invertebrate ferritin cores are appreciably larger in diameter than is that of human ferritin. The iron content of chiton ferritin is 23% and that of limpet ferritin is 22.5%. These are appreciably lower than that of human ferritin which analysed at 29%.

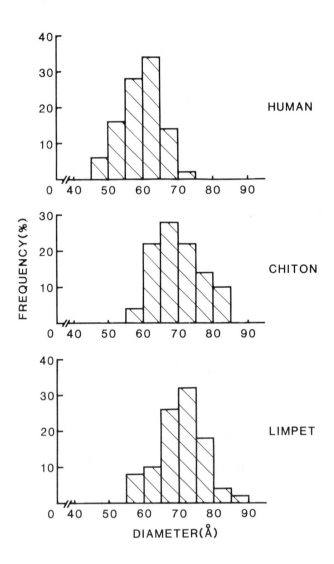

Fig. 2.   Size distribution of cores of human spleen ferritin, hemolymph ferritin from the chiton Clavarizona hirtosa and hemolymph ferritin from the limpet Patella vulgata.   Data shown are the results of ca. 50 determinations in each case.

3   MÖSSBAUER SPECTROSCOPY

Mössbauer spectra of limpet ferritin recorded from 1.3-77K show a more complex behaviour than has been reported for human ferritin (6). Spectra at 1.3, 15, 25 and 50K are shown in Figure 3.   At 1.3K, the Mössbauer spectrum of limpet ferritin consists of a magnetically split sextet with a hyperfine field of 47.7T which is close in value to that of human ferritin, 49.4T.

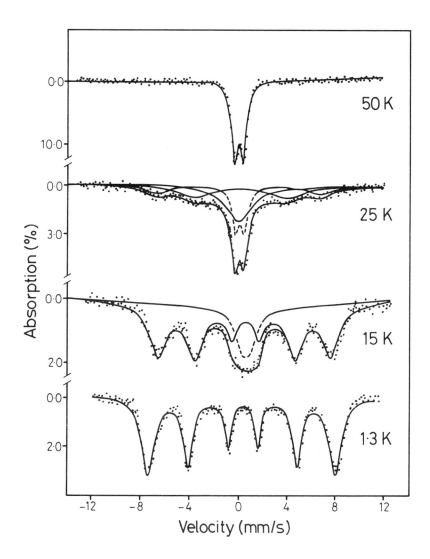

Fig. 3.   Mössbauer spectra of hemolymph ferritin from the limpet Patella vulgata in the temperature range 1.3-50K.

By 4.2K a doublet appears at the spectral centre, suggesting that the ferritin core is showing the superparamagnetic behaviour of small particles (9) as seen in human ferritin. However, as the temperature is raised, the limpet ferritin exhibits significant differences from human ferritin in its spectral behaviour. At these higher temperatures, the spectra differ from those of a superparamagnetic material. Thus by 25K the sextet is collapsing into the doublet rather than disappearing in the wings of the spectrum. This behaviour is more typically that observed at the transition from a magnetically ordered phase to a para-magnetic phase. At 50K the doublet is fully established.

Spectral fitting and analysis suggest that for limpet ferritin, the mean superparamagnetic blocking temperature and the magnetic ordering temperature are close in value, falling within the range 25-30K. For chiton ferritin, this value is 20-30K. In contrast, human ferritin exhibits comparatively straightforward superparamagnetic behaviour with a magnetic ordering temperature greater than 50K, well above the super-paramagnetic blocking temperature of ca. 40K (8).

The Mössbauer spectral behaviour of the invertebrate ferritins described here suggest that their iron cores differ significantly from those of mammalian ferritins. The lower ordering temperature in limpet ferritin (25-30K) compared to human ferritin (> 50K) indicates a weaker exchange interaction between iron(III) centres in the former case. This is consistent with the analytical and electron microscope data that show that limpet ferritin has a lower iron content but larger diameter than human ferritin. The iron density in limpet ferritin is appreciably less than in human ferritin. The lower crystallinity in the limpet ferritin core (Figure 1 b) is expected also to lower the ordering temperature.

This comparatively low crystallinity of the limpet ferritin core affects also the anisotropy energy barrier associated with the super-paramagnetic blocking temperature. Other factors involved include the shape, stress characteristics and surface properties of the iron core. For limpet ferritin the lowering of the blocking temperature and the lowering of the magnetic ordering temperature from the values observed for human ferritin render these two temperatures comparable (25-30K). The Mössbauer behaviour of limpet ferritin is then appreciably different from that of both mamallian and bacterial ferritins, as discussed in more detail elsewhere (10).

In summary, the electron microscopic and Mössbauer data, taken together, indicate that the iron cores in these two invertebrate ferritins, in comparison to that of human ferritin, are larger but are less crystalline. They have a lower iron content and hence iron density. Furthermore, with weaker exchange interactions, they exhibit comparatively low blocking temperatures.

4   IMMUNOCHEMISTRY

Consistent with these properties of the core, invertebrate apoferritins are generally of larger size than human apoferritin (11). For example, C. hirtosa apoferritin has a molecular weight of 550,000, subunits of molecular weights 28000 and 25000, but with pI values of 4.2-4.5 that are close to those of human ferritin. This invertebrate ferritin is, however, immunologically distinct from horse spleen ferritin as can be seen from the data shown in Figure 4. No precipitin lines were observed for the reaction of chiton ferritin with anti-horse ferritin antiserum, indicating that chiton and horse ferritins have no common antigenic determinants. In contrast, another molluscan ferritin, isolated from the oocytes of the snail Lymnae stagnalis, shows a partial cross-reaction with this antiserum (12). Ferritins from both the bivalve Corbicula sandai (molecular weight 503,000) and the earthworm Octolasium complanatum (460,000) are immunologically distinct from mammalian ferritins (13,14). Ferritins isolated from the hemolymph of the limpet species Patelloida alticostata and Patella peroni also have comparatively high molecular weights of 505,000 and 520,000 respectively (15,16).

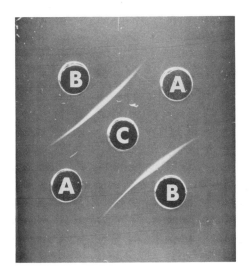

Fig. 4. Immunodiffusion of (A) hemolymph ferritin from the chiton Clavarizona hirtosa and (B) horse spleen ferritin against (C) antiserum to horse spleen ferritin.

5   IRON UPTAKE

The reactivity of the iron core in C. hirtosa ferritin has been
compared to that of horse spleen ferritin using measurements of the
initial rates of uptake of iron(II) in the presence of $KIO_3/Na_2S_2O_3$ as
oxidant.   The experimental procedure was basically that used (17,18) in
earlier studies that showed the rate of iron(II) uptake by horse spleen
ferritin to be dependent on the amount of iron present in the molecule.
The rate increased with iron content, supporting the reaction model in
which crystal growth is a dominant process.   When apoferritin from horse
spleen was compared with apoferritin and ferritin of known iron content
(up to 2000 atoms) from C. hirtosa, the chiton ferritin was found to take
up Fe(II) much more rapidly.   For example, under the same conditions,
when horse spleen apoferritin oxidized 300 μmoles of Fe(II)/min/mg
protein, the C. hirtosa ferritin oxidized 2.4 mmoles of Fe(II)/min/mg
protein.   This is an 8-fold increase in the rate of iron uptake.

As discussed earlier, the high resolution electron microscopy and
electron diffraction data indicate that the iron core in chiton ferritin
has very low crystallinity.   This structural character could well result
from the rapid uptake of iron(II) and hence the rapid growth of the iron
core.   Compared to human ferritin, chiton ferritin would have many
nucleation sites on the inner surface of the polypeptide shell, leading
to rapid formation of an essentially amorphous iron core.

The dependence of this rate on iron content (Figure 5) also shows
differences from that reported for horse spleen ferritin.   At low
[Fe(II)] the rate of uptake is low, increasing only slowly with increasing [Fe(II)].   This sigmoidal behaviour contrasts with that for horse
spleen ferritin of low iron content, which shows hyperbolic iron uptake
curves.

It would seem from this striking difference in kinetic behaviour that
the mechanism of incorporation of iron into the iron core differs
appreciably between the two proteins.   Further studies are required,
however, to discriminate in detail amongst the possible mechanisms (1).

In addition to the differences in the structure of the cores noted
earlier, this increased reactivity towards iron uptake can be linked to
the biological role of the chiton and limpet ferritins in the transport
of iron in the hemolymph to the mineralizing front (6,15).   In mammals,
a quite different iron-binding protein, transferrin, fulfills this
function (11) despite having a much lower iron binding capacity than

ferritin,binding only two iron atoms per molecule (MW 80,000).

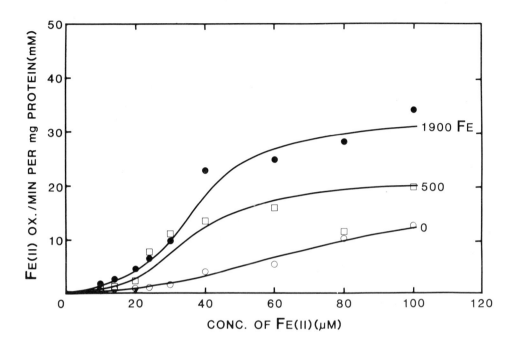

Fig. 5.   Initial rates of iron(II) uptake by hemolymph ferritin from the
chiton Clavarizona hirtosa for three preparations of iron content 0, 500
and 1900 Fe/protein.

6   OTHER ASPECTS

6.1 Invertebrate Transferrin

Recent studies have indicated that non-vertebrates can exhibit other
differences from the familiar situation of transferrin and ferritin
found in mammalian iron transport and storage respectively. Two examples
will serve as illustrations. Firstly, an unusual iron binding protein
has been isolated from the plasma of the ascidian Pyura stolonifera (19).
The protein binds only one iron atom in a polypeptide of MW 40,000.
Other biochemical and physiological data suggest strongly that this

protein is a "transferrin", with the larger transferrin from vertebrates being the product of gene duplication.

6.2 Zinc Binding

Secondly, in the tropical rock oyster Saccostrea cuccullata, the metal-binding proteins present include ferritin, whose MW of 550,000 is similar to that of other invertebrate ferritins. Fractionation of the proteins present in the body mass of oysters containing elevated levels of Zn (mean 1021 mg/kg wet wt) indicates that appreciable amounts of zinc are bound to ferritin (20). It is probable that ferritin may account for such protein-bound zinc in other bivalves. If so, then ferritin may also have a role, like metallothioneins, in binding and detoxifying increased body burdens of metals such as zinc and cadmium. In this regard it should be noted that a mammalian (i.e. rat) liver ferritin has been shown to bind Zn(II) under conditions of toxic Zn supply (21) and that Zn(II) is an efficient inhibitor of Fe(II) uptake by apoferritin (1,22). Single crystal x-ray structure analysis of horse spleen apoferritin has already revealed the presence of several binding sites for cadmium and zinc involving aspartate, glutamate and water as ligands (23). These sites are located in channels leading through the polypeptide shell to the iron core and thus may contribute to this inhibitory effect of Zn. However, the nature of the Zn binding sites in oyster ferritin has yet to be clarified.

In summary, invertebrate ferritins exhibit major points of difference from mammalian ferritins in their biological functions and the chemical structure and reactivity of their iron cores. Further differences in amino acid composition and immunological reactivity can be documented (11). There is of course sufficient similarity (14) for all these proteins to be termed ferritins. It is apparent that studies of these invertebrate ferritins can enlarge our understanding of how this protein with its high iron-protein stoichiometry can function in various biological environments. In this regard it is important to note that the invertebrate ferritins discussed here do not contain heme and hence can be compared more directly to mammalian than to bacterial ferritins. Single crystal analysis of the molecular structure of an invertebrate ferritin would substantially extend our understanding of this major iron binding protein.

7 <u>REFERENCES</u>

(1) G.C. Ford, P.M. Harrison, D.W. Rice, J.M.A. Smith, A. Teffry,
J.L. White and Yariv, J. Ferritin: design and formation of an iron-
storage molecule. <u>Phil. Trans. Roy. Soc. Lond. B.</u> <u>304</u> (1984)
551-565.

(2) J. Webb and H.B. Gray. Spectral studies of the ferritin core and
related iron(III) polymers. <u>Biochim. Biophys. Acta</u> <u>351</u> (1974)
224-229.

(3) J. Webb in P. Westbroek and E.W. De Jong (Eds), Biomineralization
and Biological Metal Accumulation, Reidel, Dordrecht (1983)
pp.413-422.

(4) H.A. Lowenstam. Minerals formed by organisms. Science <u>171</u> (1981)
487-490.

(5) J. Webb, T.G. St Pierre, D.P.E. Dickson, S. Mann, R.J.P. Williams,
C.C. Perry, G. Grime and F. Watt. Mössbauer and Pixe studies of
iron biominerals (1985). See this Volume.

(6) J. Webb and D.J. Macey in P. Westbroek and E.W. De Jong (Eds),
Biomineralization and Biological Metal Accumulation, Reidel,
Dordrecht (1983) pp.423-427.

(7) S. Mann, J.V. Bannister and R.J.P. Williams. Structure and
composition of ferritin cores isolated from human spleen, limpet
(<u>Patella</u> <u>vulgata</u>) hemolymph and bacterial (<u>Pseudomonas</u> <u>aeruginosa</u>)
cells. Submitted for publication.

(8) S.H. Bell, M.P. Weir, D.P.E. Dickson, J.F. Gibson, G.A. Sharp and
T.J. Peters. Mössbauer spectroscopic studies of human haemosiderin
and ferritin. <u>Biochim. Biophys. Acta</u> <u>787</u> (1984) 227-236.

(9) S. Mørup, J.A. Dumesic and H. Topsoe in R.L. Cohen (Ed.),
Applications of Mössbauer Spectroscopy Vol. 2, Academic Press,
New York (1980) pp.1-53.

(10) T.G. St Pierre, S.H. Bell, D.P.E. Dickson, S. Mann, J. Webb,
J.V. Bannister, G.R. Moore and R.J.P. Williams. Mössbauer
spectroscopic studies of the cores of human, limpet and bacterial
ferritins. Submitted for publication.

(11) E.H. Morgan in A. Jacobs and M. Worwood (Eds), Iron in Biochemistry and Medicine II. Academic Press, London (1980) pp.641-687.

(12) W. Bottke, Isolation and properties of vitellogenic ferritin from snails. J. Cell Sci. 58 (1982) 225-240.

(13) A. Baba, M. May and W.W. Fish. The properties of Corbicula sandai apoferritin. Biochim. Biophys. Acta 491 (1977) 491-496.

(14) P. Arosio, S. Levi, E. Gabri, S. Stafanini, A. Finazzi-Agro and E. Chiancone. Properties of ferritin from the earthworm Octolasium complanatum. Biochim. Biophys. Acta 787 (1984) 264-269.

(15) M.A. Burford, D.J. Macey and J. Webb in I. Urushizaki, P. Aisen, I. Listowsky and W. Drysdale (Eds), Structure and Function of Iron Storage and Transport Proteins. Elsevier, Amsterdam (1983) pp.219-220.

(16) M.A. Burford, D.J. Macey and J. Webb. Hemolymph ferritin and radula structure in the limpets Patelloida alticostata and Patella peroni (Mollusca: Gastropoda). Submitted for publication.

(17) S.M. Russell and P.M. Harrison. Heterogeneity in horse ferritins. A comparative study of surface charge, iron content and kinetics of iron uptake. Biochem. J. 175 (1978) 91-104.

(18) I.G. Macara, T.G. Hoy and P.M. Harrison. The formation of ferritin from apoferritin. Kinetics and mechanism of iron uptake. Biochem. J. 126 (1972) 151-162.

(19) A.W. Martin, E. Huebers, H. Huebers, J. Webb and C.A. Finch. A mono-sited transferrin from a representative deuterostome: the ascidian Pyura stolonifera. Blood 64 (1984) 1047-1052.

(20) J. Webb, D.J. Macey and V. Talbot. Identification of ferritin as a major high molecular weight zinc-binding protein in the tropical rock oyster Saccostrea cuccullata. Arch. Environ. Contam. Toxicol. (1985) in press.

(21) D. Price and J.G. Joski. Ferritin: a zinc detoxicant and a zinc ion donor. Proc. Nat. Acad. Sci. USA 79 (1982) 3116-3119.

(22) A. Treffry and P.M. Harrison. Spectroscopic studies on the binding
     of iron, terbium and zinc by apoferritin. J. Inorg. Biochem. 21
     (1984) 9-20 and references therein.

(23) P.M. Harrison, G.C. Ford, D.W. Rice, J.M.A. Smith, A. Treffry and
     J.L. White. The three-dimensional structure of apoferritin: a
     framework controlling ferritin's iron storage and release. Rev.
     Port. Quim. 27 (1985) 119-121.

Kinetics in
Bioinorganic Chemistry

Steady State and Burst Kinetic Studies on Peroxidases

H. Brian Dunford, Anne-Marie Lambeir, Cornelia Bohne[*] and Wilhelm J. Baader[*]

Department of Chemistry, University of Alberta, Edmonton, Alberta, Canada T6G 2G2

[*]Instituto de Química, Universidade de São Paulo, C.P. 20.780, São Paulo, Brasil

SUMMARY

Three halogenation reactions are examined: (i) the uncatalyzed iodination of tyrosine by molecular iodine, (ii) the horseradish peroxidase-catalyzed iodination of tyrosine by H_2O_2 and iodide ion and (iii) the chlorination of monochlorodimedone by peracetic acid and chloride ion catalyzed by chloroperoxidase. It is concluded in (i) that iodination is accomplished by HOI. In (ii) either HOI or Fe•OI is active. The latter may be regarded as enzyme-activated

---

Abbreviations: HTOH: tyrosine with its replaceable o-hydrogen; ITOH: o-substituted monoiodotyrosine; HTO⁻: tyrosinate ion; HITO: quinoid intermediate in which H and I share an o-position; $HTOCH_3$: methyl ether formed from tyrosine; HRP: horseradish peroxidase; Fe•OI: iodinating species formed from compound I and I⁻; HA: substrate; IA: iodinated substrate; HClD: monochlorodimedone with its replaceable H; Cl_2D: dichlorodimedone; ROOH and ROH: peracetic and acetic acids; ClP: chloroperoxidase; Fe•OCl: chlorinating species formed from compound I and Cl⁻; $(CH_3)_2C=O^*$: triplet state acetone.

hypoiodous acid formed by addition of iodide ion to the ferryl oxygen atom of compound I. In (iii) Fe·OCl is the chlorinating reagent. An example of burst kinetics is provided by the light emitting reaction which occurs spontaneously when isobutyraldehyde is added to an aerated solution of horseradish peroxidase.

1   INTRODUCTION

In this paper we examine some halogenation reactions, both uncatalyzed and catalyzed by peroxidases, and a light-emitting reaction from isobutyraldehyde and molecular oxygen catalyzed by horseradish peroxidase. These provide examples of reactions amenable to study by steady-state and burst kinetics.

2   PEROXIDASE-CATALYZED HALOGENATION

We examine three problems to determine to what extent they are related: (i) the uncatalyzed iodination of tyrosine by iodine, (ii) the horseradish peroxidase-catalyzed iodination of tyrosine by iodide ion and hydrogen peroxide and (iii) the chloroperoxidase-catalyzed chlorination of monochlorodimedone catalyzed by chloride ion and peracetic acid.

2.1   The Uncatalyzed Iodination of Tyrosine by Iodine

The overall reaction is:

$$HTOH_{(total)} + I_{2(total)} \xrightarrow{k_{app}} H^+ + I^- + ITOH_{(total)} \quad (eq.\ 1)$$

The relevant equilibria (1) are:

$$I_2 + I^- \rightleftharpoons I_3^- \quad (eq.\ 2)$$

$$I_2 + H_2O \rightleftharpoons H_2OI^+ + I^- \quad (eq.\ 3)$$

$$H_2OI^+ + H_2O \rightleftharpoons HOI + H_3O^+ \quad (eq.\ 4)$$

At high pH a slow conversion of hypoiodite to iodate occurs (2). The overall process is

$$3OI^- \rightarrow IO_3^- + I^- \qquad \text{(eq. 5)}$$

for which the mechanism appears to be

$$2IO^- \rightarrow IO_2^- + I^- \qquad \text{(eq. 6)}$$

$$2IO_2^- \rightarrow IO_3^- + IO^- \qquad \text{(eq. 7)}$$

This kinetically-controlled process can be eliminated or corrected for by using carefully defined experimental conditions. The iodate is inert in the iodination of tyrosine.

In a classic study of the iodination of tyrosine (1) the three most plausible mechanisms were determined to be:

$$HTO^- + I_2 + H_2O \rightarrow ITO^- + I^- + H_3O^+ \qquad \text{(eq. 8)}$$

$$HTO^- + H_2OI^+ \rightarrow ITO^- + H_3O^+ \qquad \text{(eq. 9)}$$

$$HTOH + HOI \rightarrow ITOH + H_2O \qquad \text{(eq. 10)}$$

The iodination by molecular iodine was eliminated because it did not fit the observed rate constant _versus_ pH profile (1). Recently it was shown that iodination by H_2OI^+ could be eliminated because the rate constant would have to exceed the diffusion-controlled limit which is physically impossible (3). Therefore the most likely iodinating reagent is hypoiodous acid, HOI.

A less likely possibility (4,5) is

$$HTO^- + I_2 \rightleftarrows HITO + I^- \qquad \text{(eq. 11)}$$

$$HITO + base \xrightarrow{\text{slow}} ITO^- + Hbase \qquad \text{(eq. 12)}$$

H and I occupying the same ortho- position in HITO formed in a rapid equilibrium. Evidence for this mechanism consists of a positive kinetic isotope effect (k_H/k_D) in the iodination of 2,4,6-trideuterophenol (4) and 4-nitrophenol-2,6-d_2 (5) compared to the undeuterated compounds. In the former case iodination by acyl hypoiodite formed from buffer was ignored (6) and in the latter a slowly reacting substrate was chosen where a change in mechanism might not be surprising.

It was demonstrated that the reaction

$$HTOCH_3(total) + I_2(total) \xrightarrow{\quad\times\quad} ITOCH_3 + H^+ + I^- \qquad (eq. 13)$$

did not occur (7). This could be an indication that the species

might occur along the reaction coordinate for the reaction of hypoiodous acid with tyrosine. Base catalysis would be necessary for final product formation from the HITO quinoid species. The temporary formation of H_2OI^+ not present in sufficient concentration in bulk solution, would provide a derivative I^+ species of great potency. There appears to be no evidence for I^+ itself as the iodinating species (8).

This rather detailed discussion provides tentative evidence that the iodinating species is HOI. In the physiological iodination of tyrosine catalyzed by mammalian peroxidase, as discussed below, it would appear that HOI is also utilized. Therefore the mechanisms are similar. An important question is whether the enzyme merely generates the same reagent or whether it activates it to a more potent form.

2.2   The Peroxidase Catalyzed Iodination of Tyrosine

The physiological source of iodine is the iodide salt in our diets. The first major deviation from the conventional peroxidase cycle was demonstrated in the reaction of iodide ion with hydrogen peroxide catalyzed by horseradish peroxidase (9). The overall process is

$$H_2O_2 + 2I^- + 2H^+ \xrightarrow{\text{HRP}} I_2 + 2H_2O \qquad (eq. 14)$$

The two most plausible mechanisms are

Mechanism I: HRP + H_2O_2 → Compound I + H_2O (eq. 15)

Compound I + I^- + H^+ → HRP + HOI   (eq. 16)

HOI + I^- + H^+ → I_2 + H_2O (eq. 17)

Mechanism II: HRP + H_2O_2 → Compound I + H_2O (eq. 15)

Compound I + I^- → Fe·OI   (eq. 18)

Fe·OI + I^- + $2H^+$ → HRP + I_2 + H_2O (eq. 19)

In either case there is no intermediate formation of compound II. Iodination of substrate would occur either by the reaction

HOI + HA → IA + H_2O (eq. 20)
or
Fe·OI + HA + H^+ → IA + HRP + H_2O (eq. 21)

In a system with little iodide present either of eqs. 20 or 21 would predominate over eq. 17 or 19. At present it is not possible to make a clear choice between eqs. 20 and 21.

A definitive answer as to whether an enzyme halogenating species can exist is provided below.

2.3 The Chloroperoxidase Catalyzed Chlorination of Monochlorodimedone

The overall reaction is

$$HClD + Cl^- + H^+ + ROOH \xrightarrow{\text{ClP}} Cl_2D + ROH + H_2O \qquad \text{(eq. 22)}$$

The reaction will also occur when H_2O_2 is used in place of peracetic acid, but the catalatic reaction of chloroperoxidase interferes with the chlorination reaction.

The two most plausible mechanisms for the chloroperoxidase-catalyzed chlorination of monochlorodimedone are (10):

$$\underline{\text{Mechanism I}}: \quad \text{ClP} + \text{ROOH} \rightarrow \text{Compound I} + \text{ROH} \qquad (\text{eq. 23})$$

$$\text{Compound I} + \text{Cl}^- + \text{H}^+ \rightarrow \text{ClP} + \text{HOCl} \qquad (\text{eq. 24})$$

$$\text{HOCl} + \text{HClD} \rightarrow \text{Cl}_2\text{D} + \text{H}_2\text{O} \qquad (\text{eq. 25})$$

$$\underline{\text{Mechanism II}}: \quad \text{ClP} + \text{ROOH} \rightarrow \text{Compound I} + \text{ROH} \qquad (\text{eq. 23})$$

$$\text{Compound I} + \text{Cl}^- \rightarrow \text{Fe} \cdot \text{OCl} \qquad (\text{eq. 26})$$

$$\text{Fe} \cdot \text{OCl} + \text{HClD} + \text{H}^+ \rightarrow \text{Cl}_2\text{D} + \text{H}_2\text{O} \qquad (\text{eq. 27})$$

In either mechanism chloride ion also inhibits the reaction by binding weakly to the ferric ion of the native enzyme. This inhibition is readily taken into account and does not detract from the analysis. Without going into details, the first mechanism predicts linear plots of the two steady-state parameters versus chloride ion concentration, the second hyperbolic plots. Clearly hyperbolic plots were obtained (10). Of greater importance, the first mechanism leads to a prediction of a steady-state rate which is independent of monochlorodimedone concentration; the second predicts a dependence. The rate constant for eq. 27 is greater than 10^8 $M^{-1}s^{-1}$ compared to $\sim 10^5$ $M^{-1}s^{-1}$ for eq. 26. This implies that detection of Fe·OCl would be difficult as would proof of a dependence upon monochlorodimedone concentration. However the latter was attained by minimizing chloride ion inhibition, maximizing formation of Fe·OCl and keeping monochlorodimedone concentration as low as possible consistent with the observation of steady-state kinetics.

Recently a chain reaction for the halogenation of monochlorodimedone has been proposed (11). A chain reaction is not consistent with the observation of Michaelis-Menten type of kinetics.

3 CHEMILUMINESCENCE FROM ISOBUTYRALDEHYDE AND OXYGEN

The reaction of isobutyraldehyde with molecular oxygen catalyzed by horseradish peroxidase provides a unique example of burst and steady-state kinetics. The overall process is (12)

$$H_3C-\underset{\underset{H}{|}}{\overset{\overset{CH_3}{|}}{C}}-C\overset{O}{\underset{H}{\diagdown}} + O_2 \xrightarrow{HRP} HCOOH + (CH_3)_2\ C=O^* \qquad (eq.\ 28)$$

$$(CH_3)_2C=O^* \rightarrow (CH_3)_2C=O + h\nu \qquad (eq.\ 29)$$

Most of the elementary reactions recently have been identified (13,14). The cause of the burst is the autoxidation of isobutyr-aldehyde, which occurs despite careful purification. It is difficult to make a preparation of isobutyraldehyde which does not contain an amount of its autoxidation product

$$H_3C - \underset{\underset{H}{|}}{\overset{\overset{CH_3}{|}}{C}} - C\overset{O}{\underset{OOH}{\diagup}}$$

which is in excess of the amount of HRP used in experiments. This peracid produces a concentration of compound I in excess of its steady-state concentration, followed by a higher-than-steady-state concentration of compound II. Both compounds react with the enol form of isobutyraldehyde. The product is a free radical reactive towards molecular oxygen which leads to a dioxetane-type of intermediate species which decays to the final products, electronically excited acetone and formic acid. As the reaction progresses, the concentrations of compounds I and II decline from their maximum to their steady-state values; the burst ends and the steady state phase begins. Light emission may be observed for several minutes. With great precautions, the amount of peracid present in an isobutyraldehyde preparation can be lowered to the point where a lag phase, rather than a burst phase, is observed. The burst can be restored by the addition of H_2O_2.

4   REFERENCES

(1)   W.E. Mayberry, J.E. Rall and D. Bertoli, J. Amer. Chem. Soc. 86 (1964) 5302-5307.

(2)   O. Haimovich and A. Treimin, J. Phys. Chem. 71 (1967) 1941-1943.

(3)   H.B. Dunford and I.M. Ralston, Biochem. Biophys. Res. Commun.
      116 (1983) 639-643.

(4)   E. Grovenstein Jr. and D.C. Kilby, J. Amer. Chem. Soc. 79
      (1957) 2972-2973.

(5)   E. Grovenstein Jr. and W.S. Aprahamian, J. Amer. Chem. Soc. 84
      (1962) 212-220.

(6)   B.S. Painter and F.G. Soper, J. Chem. Soc. (1947) 342-346.

(7)   W.E. Mayberry, J.E. Rall, M. Berman and D. Bertoli,
      Biochemistry 4 (1965) 1965-1972.

(8)   C.K. Ingold, "Structure and Mechanism in Organic Chemistry,"
      Cornell University Press, Ithaca, 1953, pp. 288-295.

(9)   R.S. Roman and H.B. Dunford, Biochemistry 11 (1972) 2076-2082.

(10) A.-M. Lambeir and H.B. Dunford, J. Biol. Chem. 258 (1983)
      13558-13563.

(11) B.W. Griffen and P.L. Ashley, Arch. Biochem. Biophys. 233
      (1984) 188-196.

(12) E.J.H. Bechara, O.M.M. Faria Oliveira, N. Durán, R. Casadei de
      Baptista and G. Cilento, Photochem. Photobiol. 30 (1979) 101-
      110.

(13) H.B. Dunford, W.J. Baader, C. Bohne and G. Cilento, Biochem.
      Biophys. Res. Commun. 122 (1984) 28-32.

(14) W.J. Baader, C. Bohne, G. Cilento and H.B. Dunford, J. Biol.
      Chem. In press.

Pseudomonas Cytochrome Oxidase:
Structural Features, Catalytic Properties and The Reaction with Oxygen

M. Brunori,, A. Colosimo (+), M.C. Silvestrini and M.G. Tordi

Inst. of Chemistry (Fac. of Medicine) and CNR Centre for Molecular
Biology, 1st University of Rome - 00185 Rome, Italy
(+) Dept. of Exp. Medic. and Biochem. Sci., 2nd University of Rome
(Tor Vergata).

SUMMARY

Some recently acquired informations on the structural and functional
properties of Pseudomonas cytochrome oxidase (EC 1.9.3.2. Ferrocytochrome c_{551}:oxygen oxidoreductase) are reviewed and, whenever possible,
related to each other in an unitarian framework. Emphasis is given to
the mechanisms of the oxidizing and reducing reactions with macromolecular substrates (cytochrome c_{551} and azurin) and dioxygen, respectively, paying particular attention to the dimeric structure of the enzyme
and to some functional features shared with the cytochrome oxidase of
mitochondrial origin.

1. INTRODUCTION

Among bacterial oxidases, the one purified from Pseudomonas aeruginosa seems to have been a particularly attractive subject of investigations since it was originally purified (1) (for some recent reviews,
see 2-4). Possibly this interest is justified on the basis of the following considerations: i) the multiplicity of its oxidizing substrates,
which demand the monoelectronic reduction of nitrite or the tetraelec-
tonic reduction of oxygen, implying different and alternative mechanisms; ii) the direct involvement in the nitrogen cycle of the biosphere through the gas-reducing, anaerobic destruction of nitrite; iii) the
inducibility in the presence of nitrate, related to the interesting

question of gene(s) activation triggered by small molecules; iv) the
relatively simple quaternary structure, consisting of two identical
subunits within which the existence of cooperative interactions has
been proposed; v) the hydrosolubility of the dimeric unit which, at
difference with mitochondrial oxidases, avoids the use of detergents
during the purification. These interesting features are partially coun-
terbalanced by the relatively complex purification procedure or the
ease with which catalytic activity may be lost due to the detachment
of the d_1 haem.

In this paper the functional properties of the enzyme will be reviewed in the light of the recent progresses in the knowledge of its struc
tural features. The aim of the review, however, is not to be exhaustive in covering the pertinent literature, but to present a rational
survey of the kinetic data which have been produced in a number of laboratories (including that of the authors).

2. GENERAL PROPERTIES

Pseudomonas cytochrome oxidase or nitrite reductase (E.C.1.9.3.2)
was firstly purified by Horio and coworkers (1, 5) from Pseudomonas
aeruginosa grown on a nitrate containing medium under quasi anaerobic
conditions. Since then, other purification procedures, based on traditional (6, 7, 8) or immunological (9) methods have been proposed. Moreover, it was verified that strict anaerobiosis is not required for the
biosynthesis while nitrate is essential (8, 10, 11). It is now generally accepted that the enzyme is a water soluble dimer of ~ 120 kDa,
composed of two identical subunits, each containing a c haem, the site
of entrance of electrons, and a d_1 haem which transfers electrons to
external oxidizing agents (6, 7, 12).
The enzyme is able to reduce oxygen (K_m=2.8 x 10^{-5}M) to water (10,
13, 14); the finding that it could reduce nitrite (K_m=5.3 x 10^{-5}M) to
nitric oxide (15) accords much more favorably, however, with the circumstances under which the enzyme is produced in bacterial culture.
Both the nitrite reductase and the oxidase activity are inhibited by
cyanide, although only the latter function is inhibited by carbon monoxide (10); cells are able to grow, in fact, in a normal way under flux
of CO instead of N_2 (11).
There is general agreement now that nitrite reduction is the physiological function of the enzyme. A mechanism for the latter reaction
based upon the existence in the catalytic cycle of NO-bound forms for
both the oxidized and the reduced enzyme was reported by Shimada and
Orii (16). Recently, evidence has been obtained for the production of

N_2O either through an NO intermediate (17) or directly from nitrite (18) with a 2 electron step but at a very low rate (1/100 as compared to NO production). The production of N_2O at a higher rate (1/10 as compared to NO production) has been reported by Bessières and Henry (19), possibly through a NO intermediate.

The reduction of hydroxylamine to ammonia (20) has very low efficiency and probably no physiological role.

The physiological electron donors are generally thought to be azurin and cyt c_{551} (5), two relatively small and single site redox proteins purified from the same bacterium. The enzyme can easily be reduced in vitro by ascorbate and quinol (21). Dithionite ($Na_2S_2O_4$) is also a good reducing agent, but the reaction products bind to the d_1 haem, and thus its use is not recommended (22).

The redox potentials for the c and the d_1 haems under various conditions are reported in Table 1.

Table 1. Redox potentials of c and d_1 haems in Ps. cytochrome oxidase

	Em^7		pH	Method	Ref.
c haem	288		?	?	23
	290		6.6	Kin	24
	294		7.0	Pot	25
	288	(°)	7.0	Kin	26
	255	(°)	9.1	"	"
d_1 haem	287		7.0	Pot	25
c haem - d_1 haem	73		6.0	Pot	27
	40÷100		6.6	Kin	24
	-24		7.0	Pot	28
	-28÷+9		7.0	Pot	29
	60		7.0	Kin	30

(°) These values drop of at least 80 mV upon ligation of CO to the d_1 haem. Pot = potentiometric data; Kin = kinetic data.
Experimental conditions: room temperature and phosphate buffer, except pH 9.1 (2% borate).

Fig. 1 shows the absorption bands assigned to each haem in the visible and Soret regions (4).

On the basis of anaerobic reduction spectrophotometric titrations (30), cooperative interactions between the two subunits have been proposed. This finds an echo in the value of 1.4 for the Hill coefficient calculated by Parr et al. (31) from CO binding equilibrium isotherms.

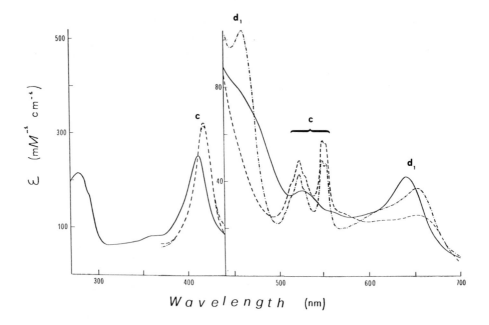

Fig. 1.Absorption spectra of Ps. cytochrome oxidase.
(——) oxidized, (-·-) reduced by sodium ascorbate and (--) CO-
bound forms, in phosphate 0.1 M pH 7.0.

3. STRUCTURAL FEATURES

Within each subunit the c̲ haem is covalently bound while the d_1 haem
is not and hence can be reversibly removed by HCl-aceton extraction
with complete loss of enzymatic activity (32). The dimeric structure is
physiological and associated in vivo with the inner surface of the cytoplasmic membrane (33). The forces holding together the subunits are
mainly hydrophobic (34). The AA composition of the subunits is known
(35,9) and a 57 residue fragment, binding the c̲ haem, has been sequenced
(36) and showed to contain two Cys in homology with cyt c. Information
on the overall secondary structure obtained by CD (37) indicates that
the molecule has a rather low α-helical content (16%) and a high β-
structure content (48% for the oxidized and 35% for the reduced derivative).

The quaternary structure has been investigated by electron microscopy (38), with results consistent with the dimeric structure formed by

identical subunits, as well as by small angle X-ray diffraction (39)
which indicates that the enzyme is constituted by two ellipsoids of rotation with a long axis of 40 Å and a short axis of 20 Å for the oxidized molecule and 30 Å and 25 Å, respectively, for the reduced one (see
Fig. 2). In the dimeric structure all the haems are located at one end
of the molecule, as deduced from emission spectroscopy (40).

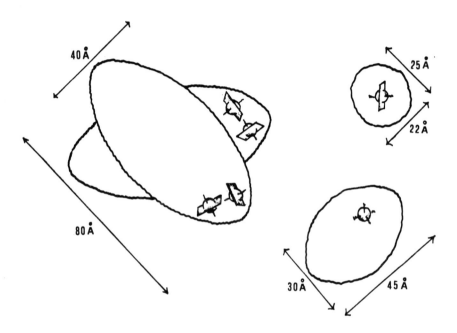

Fig. 2. Molecular shape and dimensions of Ps. cytochrome oxidase.
The relative geometry of the monomers in the functional dimeric
unit and their dimensions are depicted according to ref. 38,39,
42. Notice the apical position of the heam carrying regions (40).
The two macromolecular reducing substrates,azurin (lower
right) and cyt c_{551} (upper right) are shown for comparison.

Crystals, firstly prepared during enzyme purification (41) have been
characterized (42, 43) in terms of space groups and cell dimension.
Crystals of the oxidized protein were reported either to disrupt (43)
or to be stable upon reduction (44). Anyway, the bulk of information
reported above and the thermal denaturation studies on the enzyme as a
function of its redox state (45), suggest that the overall conformation
of the reduced and oxidized species are different. Polarized single
crystal absorption studies have shown that in each subunit the two
haems (c and d_1) are oriented perpendicularly to each other (44). This

structural feature has been correlated to the electron transfer rate inside the molecule.

4. REACTIONS WITH AZURIN AND CYTOCHROME c_{551}

4.1 Pre steady-state

Azurin and cyt c_{551}, two globular metalloproteins carrying a copper ion and a c haem as prosthetic groups, respectively, and extracted from Ps. aeruginosa, are generally regarded as the physiological electron donors for Ps. aeruginosa Cytochrome oxidase. A great deal of information is available on their structure and function (46, 47).

The electron transfer from reduced (Cu I) azurin to oxidized Ps. oxidase can be easily followed due to the different absorption bands of the chromophores on the two molecules. Rapid kinetic methods have been extensively used to elucidate the reaction mechanism. The first report on the subject (24) indicated the existence of: i) a fast process conforming to bimolecular behaviour and approaching a plateau at high Az concentrations, which was interpreted as the formation of a complex between the two proteins within which reduction of the c haem on the oxidase occurs, and ii) a much slower monomolecular process involving electron transfer from the c haem to the d_1 haem within the enzyme. These conclusions were confirmed by subsequent, more extensive investigations by both T-jump and stopped flow methods (48, 29) which pointed out the noticeable complexity of the process. Looking at the electron transfer in the two directions (i.e. from reduced Azurin to oxidized oxidase and vice versa), under both conditions three kinetic phases were observed, the first two of which reflecting bimolecular processes occurring at the c haem and the slowest one (monomolecular) involving the d_1 haem moiety (for the numeric values of the rates, see Table 2). The biphasic reaction at the level of the c haem would be consistent with the idea of the non equivalence of the two sites in the dimer, although at the time this was excluded in favour of a possible heterogeneity in the enzyme molecular population. In the same papers (48,29), studies with the CO derivative of the reduced oxidase are also reported, which confirmed that the initial bimolecular process is somewhat heterogeneous, and led to the proposal of the reaction scheme 1 where the complex between azurin (A) and cyt oxidase (C) is represented before and after the electron transfer (X_1 and X_2 respectively).

Table 2. Kinetic parameters for the electron transfer reactions between Ps. cytochrome oxidase and azurin/Cyt $\underline{c}_{551}$.

	Oxidation of red. oxidase			Oxidation of red. and CO bound oxid.		Reduction of oxidized ox.			Ref.
	Phase 1 $(M^{-1} s^{-1})$	Phase 2 $(M^{-1} s^{-1})$	Phase 3 (s^{-1})	Phase 1 $(M^{-1} s^{-1})$	Phase 2 $(M^{-1} s^{-1})$	Phase 1 $(M^{-1} s^{-1})$	Phase 2 $(M^{-1} s^{-1})$	Phase 3 (s^{-1})	
Reaction with Azurin	3.2×10^5 3×10^6 (pH 6.6)	2×10^4 /	0.35 10 (pH 6.6)	1.3×10^6(✱) / 2×10^6 (pH 9.1)	2.4×10^4 / /	4.8×10^5(✱) 1×10^6 (pH 6.6) 1.5×10^5 (pH 9.1)	1.5×10^4 (✱) / /	0.25 $0.2 \div 2$ (pH 6.6) 1 (pH 9.1)	(29) (24) (26)
Reaction with Cyt $\underline{c}_{551}$				4×10^6 1.3×10^7 (pH 9.1)					(26) (26)

The temperature was between 20 and 25°C and the pH = 7 (unless otherwise stated); (✱) = calculated from the data reported in the original paper.

Scheme 1. Electron transfer reactions between Ps.cytochrome oxidase
          and Azurin.

$$C^{3+} + A^{+} \rightleftharpoons X_1 \rightleftharpoons X_2 \rightleftharpoons C^{2+} + A^{2+}$$

$$\Updownarrow$$

$$(A^x)^{+}$$

X_1 and X_2 represent forms of a molecular complex between Azurin (A)
and Ps. cytochrome oxidase (C), and (A^x) is the catalytically incom-
petent form of Azurin. The d_1 haem is not present in the scheme since
it was removed from the reaction by combination with CO.

Direct observations of electron transfer with cyt $\underline{c}_{551}$ as a substrate is difficult because of the very great similarity in the absorption
spectra of this cytochrome and the c haem moiety of the oxidase. In
spite of that, a second order rate constant could be estimated for the
reduction of cyt $\underline{c}_{551}$ by the reduced and CO-bound form of the enzyme
(see Table 2 (26)). The kinetics of the reverse reaction:

$$2 \text{ cyt } \underline{c}_{551}{}^{2+} + c^{3+}\text{-}d_1{}^{3+} \rightleftharpoons 2 \text{ cyt } \underline{c}_{551}{}^{3+} + c^{2+}\text{-}d_1{}^{2+}$$

although more difficult to be analyzed, were also measured and found to
be biphasic, as expected from the more extensively studied azurin kinetics (24,29,48). The initial rapid phase, which corresponds to the reduction of the c haem, has a $t\frac{1}{2}= 0.1$ s at µM concentrations of both
reagents. These studies (26) indicated that Cyt $\underline{c}_{551}$ and azurin are not
equally efficient as reducing substrates, since the rate of electron
donation from cyt $\underline{c}_{551}$ appeared 3-4 times greater than that of azurin
under the same conditions. Extending these conclusions to the situation
'in vivo' demands, however, a reliable estimate of the concentration of
the three redox proteins in the cell.

4.2 Steady-state

Electron transfer between Ps. oxidase and its physiological reductants have been studied extensively under steady-state conditions (5,
21,49) indicating large similarities and some differences in the overall behaviour of azurin and cyt $\underline{c}_{551}$ (see Table 3).   A more recent
investigation by Tordi et al. (14) confirmed substantially the previous
results, assigning to cyt $\underline{c}_{551}$ the higher affinity for the enzyme, and
to azurin a slightly higher catalytic rate. In the same study, extending cyt $\underline{c}_{551}$ concentrations well beyond the apparent k_m, the observed
initial velocity of oxidation increased and eventually almost doubled
at a substrate concentration $\geqslant$ 100 µM. This observation has been
interpreted in terms of a 'half-hearted' behaviour of the enzyme, since
at relatively low cyt $\underline{c}_{551}$ concentrations only one of the two identical
binding sites of the dimer is catalytically active, possibly because of
unfavourable interactions depressing the formation of the enzyme-substrate complex at the second site. This interpretation is not inconsi-

stent with the structural organization of the protein, in which the active sites are segregated at one extreme of the dimer (see fig. 2) and
therefore possible steric and/or electrostatic negative interactions
between the molecules of substrate are envisaged.

Table 3. Steady-state parameters for oxidation of Cyt c_{551} and azurin
catalyzed by Ps. cytochrome oxidase.

		Azurin		Cyt c_{551}		Ref.
pH	T	Km	T.O.N.	Km	T.O.N.	
	(°C)	(μM)	(min^{-1})	(μM)	(min^{-1})	
7.5	18	39	67	19	64	(5)
7.0	30	49	128	5.6	112	(21)
7.0	22	42	64	2.2	27.2	(49)
7.0	25	15+3	154+12	2.1+0.2	132+5	(14)

The turnover numbers (T.O.N.) have been normalized taking into account
the differences in the extinction coefficients reported in the original papers on the basis of the now commonly accepted value of M.W. =
= $30x10^5$/Fe for Ps. oxidase (12).

When reduced azurin and cyt c_{551} were simultaneously exposed to Ps.
oxidase in air, the observed steady-state oxidation kinetics is complex,
as expected taking into account the rapid electron transfer between the
two substrates in the free state (50). In spite of these difficulties,
it seems likely that a mechanism involving a simple competition between
the two substrates for the same active site on the enzyme is indeed ope
rative (14).

5. REACTIONS WITH OXYGEN

The ability of Ps. cytochrome oxidase to reduce oxygen to water was
firstly analyzed by Yamanaka et al. (41); in the last decade, however,
only a few attempts to understand the mechanism of the reaction have
been reported. Shimada and Orii (28) using rapid scanning spectrophoto
metry to observe the reduction of the enzyme by an excess ascorbate in
the presence of oxygen, obtained evidence for the formation of a transient 'oxygenated' species of the enzyme. Wharton and Gibson (51) carried out a more direct study monitoring the oxidation of the ascorbate-
reduced enzyme by excess oxygen using the stopped-flow method. These
authors postulated a sequential transfer of electrons to oxygen and
stated that the oxidation of the c haem lags behind the reaction of
the d_1 haem. However, it was later shown by Greenwood et al. (52) that
the time course of the oxygen reaction is more complex consisting of

three phases only the fastest of which (second order rate constant =
= $3.3 \times 10^4 M^{-1} s^{-1}$) was oxygen concentration dependent. The two slower
processes were first order reactions with rate constants of $1.0 \pm 0.4 \ s^{-1}$
and $0.1 \pm 0.03 \ s^{-1}$, respectively. In order to assign the kinetic phases
kinetic difference spectra were determined and it was unequivocally
shown that the events occurring during the initial bimolecular phase
are simultaneous at both the c and the d_1 haem absorption bands. Kinetic titration experiments reported in the same paper confirmed that
the dimeric enzyme has a relatively low affinity constant for oxygen,
approximately $10^4 M^{-1}$, which impairs the determination of the O_2 stoichiometry.

In order to clarify the mechanism of the O_2 reaction, a study has
been undertaken in our laboratory on a monomeric form of the enzyme,
obtained after succynilation of the native molecule under controlled
conditions. The derivative is somewhat unstable, tending to loose the
d_1 haem more easily than the native form, and some degree of structural heterogeneity and variability among different preparations was
observed. In spite of that, preliminary results of rapid mixing experiments clearly show that: i) a single kinetic phase is observed, which
is O_2 concentration dependent; ii) this process has the same spectral
features of the first phase observed by Greenwood et al. (52), thus
the reaction involves the d_1 haem; iii) it has essentially the same
2nd order constant ($3-5 \times 10^4 M^{-1} s^{-1}$), thus it can be identified with the
faster phase observed with the native enzyme; iv) the affinity of the
monomer for O_2 is at least two order of magnitudes higher than that of
the dimer, the titration curve being essentially stoichiometric (1 oxygen molecule/monomer). In terms of reaction mechanism, these results
would imply that 2 oxygen molecules bind to the native dimer and that
reduction of O_2 goes through a peroxide intermediate (see Scheme 2). A
complete study of this reaction is at present in progress (Tordi et al.,
in preparation).

Scheme 2. Oxygen binding stoichiometry for the monomeric (A) and the
dimeric (B) forms of Ps. cytochrome oxidase.

$$A) \quad M \xrightarrow{O_2, \ 2e^-} M - O_2^{2-} \xrightarrow[\text{fast ?}]{} M + O_2^{2-}$$

$$B) \quad \begin{matrix} M \\ | \\ M \end{matrix} \xrightarrow{2O_2, \ 4 \ e^-} \begin{matrix} M - O_2^{2-} \\ | \\ M - O_2^{2-} \end{matrix} \xrightarrow{2 \ H^+} \begin{matrix} M \\ | \\ M \end{matrix} + O_2 + 2H_2O$$

If the d_1 haem is the site of attack for oxygen, the fast oxygen-de

pendent oxidation of the c haem observed by Greenwood et al. (52) implies that the internal electron transfer occurs with a rate constant
$\geqslant$ 100 s^{-1}. This value is greatly in excess of those that have been
observed for the initial oxidation of the c haem from the d_1 haem in
the anaerobic reduction of the oxidized enzyme by azurin (i.e. 0.25 s^{-1},
See Table 2).

This conclusion indicates that, although the rate of the reaction
with oxygen of the bacterial enzyme is much lower than that of the mitochondrial oxidases, its behaviour appears to parallel that of mammalian cytochrome oxidase, in which the presence of the physiological
substrate, oxygen, greatly enhances the electron transfer rates within
the protein (53, 54). This is tentatively described in Scheme 3 where
for both Pseudomonas (A) and mammalian (B) oxidases the presence of
oxygen opens a different (faster) pathway for the intramolecular electron transfer from the electron accepting (c and a haems, respectively)
sites to the electron donating (d_1 and a_3 haems, respectively) sites.

Scheme 3. Alternative pathways for the intramolecular reduction of the
oxygen binding sites in Ps. (A) mammalian (B) cytochrome oxidase in the absence and presence of oxygen.

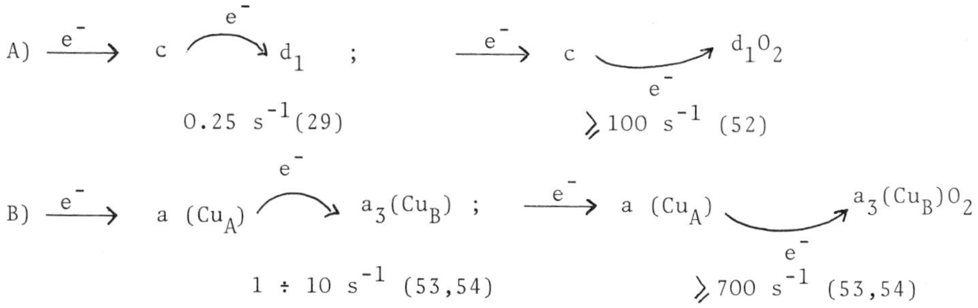

A) $\xrightarrow{e^-}$ c $\xrightarrow{e^-}$ d_1 ; $\xrightarrow{e^-}$ c $\xrightarrow{e^-}$ d_1O_2

$\qquad$ 0.25 s^{-1}(29) $\qquad$ $\geqslant$ 100 s^{-1} (52)

B) $\xrightarrow{e^-}$ a (Cu$_A$) $\xrightarrow{e^-}$ a_3(Cu$_B$) ; $\xrightarrow{e^-}$ a (Cu$_A$) $\xrightarrow{e^-}$ a_3(Cu$_B$)O$_2$

$\qquad$ 1 ÷ 10 s^{-1} (53,54) $\qquad$ $\geqslant$ 700 s^{-1} (53,54)

---

c, d_1, a, a_3 indicate the corresponding haems, and Cu$_A$, Cu$_B$ the associated copper ions in the case of mammalian oxidase. The rates of the process involved in the electrons leaving and entering the oxidases are
omitted for the sake of clarity, as well as the oxidation states of the
metal centers.

The above results also imply that the perpendicular orientation of
c and d_1 haems is not a structural feature responsible for the slow
electron transfer in multihaem oxidases, as proposed by Makinen et al.
(44), since there are conditions under which the transfer can be fast
and which surely do not imply a macroscopic rearrangement of the haems
in the molecule.

6. REFERENCES

(1) T. Horio, J. Biochem. (Tokyo), 45, (1958), 267-279.

(2) T.E.Mayer and M.D. Kamen, Adv. Prot. Chem. 35, (1982), 167-170.

(3) R.K. Poole, Biochim. Biophys. Acta, 726, (1983), 205-243.

(4) Y. Henry and P. Bessières, Biochimie, 66, (1984), 259-289.

(5) T. Horio, T. Higashi, T. Yamanaka, H. Matsubara and K. Okunuki, J. Biol. Chem., 236 (1961), 944-951.

(6) T. Kuronen and N. Ellfolk, Biochim. Biophys. Acta, 275, (1972), 308-318.

(7) J.C. Gudat, J. Singh and D.C. Wharton, Biochim. Biophys. Acta, 292, (1973), 376-390.

(8) S.R. Parr, D. Barber, C. Greenwood, B.W. Phillips and J. Melling, Biochem. J., 157, (1976), 423-430.

(9) M.C. Silvestrini, G. Citro, A. Colosimo, A. Chersi, R. Zito and M. Brunori, Anal. Biochem., 129, (1983), 318-325.

(10) T. Yamanaka, Ann. Rep. Scient. Works Fac. Sci. Osaka Univ. 11, (1963), 77-115.

(11) M.C. Silvestrini and L. Tuttobello, personal communication.

(12) M.C. Silvestrini, A. Colosimo, M. Brunori, T.A. Walsh, D. Barber and C. Greenwood, Biochem. J., 183, (1979), 701-709.

(13) R. Timkovich and M.K. Robinson, Biochem. Biophys. Res. Comm., 88, (1979), 649-655.

(14) M.G. Tordi, M.C. Silvestrini, A. Colosimo, L. Tuttobello, and M. Brunori, Biochem. J., submitted.

(15) T. Yamanaka, A. Ota and K. Okunuki, Biochim. Biophys. Acta, 53, (1961), 294-308.

(16) H. Shimada and Y. Orii, FEBS Letters, 54, (1975), 237-240.

(17) D.C. Wharton and S.T. Weintraub, Biochem. Biophys. Res. Comm., 97, (1980), 236-242.

(18) C.H. Kim and T.C. Hollocher, J. Biol. Chem., 258, (1983),4861-4863.

Three sources of the [2Fe-2S] protein from parsley (most extensively studied) and spinach (6)-(7), and from the blue-green algae Spirulina platensis (8), have been used. The latter represents a different type of organism in order to maximise variations in [2Fe-2S] composition. Its inclusion is also important since the only [2Fe-2S] crystal structure at present determined is for the S. platensis protein (9). The [2Fe-2S] ferredoxins have a single peptide chain of 98 amino-acid residues

(A)   (B)

(M.Wt.10,500), and an active site bound by four cysteine side chains (RS) as in (A). The active site is one-electron active (E^0 =-0.42V), (1).

$$[Fe_2S_2(SR)_4]^{2-} + e^- \rightleftharpoons [Fe_2S_2(SR)_4]^{3-} \qquad \text{(eq. 1)}$$

A feature of the structure is the closeness of the $[Fe_2S_2(SR)_4]^{2-}$ cluster to the surface, Figure 1, with both Fe atoms within 5Å of the surface. Clostridium

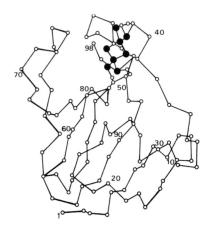

Fig.1 The cluster and polypeptide chain for S. platensis [2Fe-2S] ferredoxin (9)

pasteurianum has been used (10), as the source of 2[4Fe-4S] ferredoxin (M.Wt. 6000). An x-ray crystal study of the 2[4Fe-4S] protein from Peptococcus aerogenes has confirmed (11) a structure in which a single peptide chain of 55 amino acids binds the [4Fe-4S] clusters as in (B), with centres~12Å apart. Each cluster is one electron active (E^0 = -0.40V), (2)

$$[Fe_4S_4(SR)_4]^{2-} + e^- \rightleftharpoons [Fe_4S_4(SR)_4]^{3-} \qquad \text{(eq. 2)}$$

A particularly striking property of the ferredoxins is the high negative charge of the protein at pH 7, which for the [2Fe-2S] plant ferredoxins (e.g. parsley) is -17, and for the somewhat smaller 2[4Fe-4S] ferredoxin from Clostridium pasteuranium is -10 (both proteins in the oxidised state).

Experimental details were as previously described (6)-(8),(11). Rate constants were determined by stopped-flow spectrophotometry with the inorganic reactant in large (>10-fold) excess of protein ($\sim 10^{-5}$M). All reactions were at 25°C with ionic strength adjusted to I = 0.10M (NaCl). The buffer used was tris(hydroxymethyl) methylamine, abbreviated to Tris or Tizma (Sigma).

2 RESULTS AND DISCUSSION

2.1 Reactions of Parsley [2Fe-2S] with Oxidants

A range of complexes of charge 3- to 5+ were used as oxidant for $[Fe_2S_2(SR)_4]^{3-}$ (6)-(7). Experimental first-order rate constants (k_{obs}) gave linear dependences on the oxidant with the negative and zero charge reactants enabling $k(M^{-1}s^{-1})$ to be determined. With the 2+ through 5+ charged oxidants a 'non-linear' dependence on oxidant concentration consistent with (3)-(4) is obtained (where P is the protein).

$$P + \text{oxidant} \xrightarrow{K} P, \text{oxidant} \qquad \text{(eq. 3)}$$

$$P, \text{oxidant} \xrightarrow{k_{et}} \text{Products} \qquad \text{(eq. 4)}$$

This gives the expression (5).

$$k_{obs} = \frac{Kk_{et}[\text{oxidant}]}{1 + K[\text{oxidant}]} \qquad \text{(eq. 5)}$$

Results obtained are summarised in Table 1, where the product Kk_{et} is equivalent to k ($M^{-1}s^{-1}$). No dependence on rate constant k on pH 7.0-9.0 was observed.

Positively charged redox inactive complexes associate with the protein $[Cr(NH_3)_6]^{3+}$ ($K=464M^{-1}$), and $[Cr(en)_3]^{3+}$ ($K=590M^{-1}$), and block reaction with the positively charged oxidants (7). The blocking is complete, and K is the same in all cases suggesting specificity of site. The same complexes only partially block reaction with three neutral complexes one of which is included in Table 1, and accelerate the reaction with $[Co(edta)]^-$. Direct interaction of 3+ and 3- complexes makes it difficult to carry out a similar meaningful test with the 3- oxidant. The pattern of behaviour which emerges, including the magnitude (and trend) of all K values, clearly indicates that electrostatics are contributing significantly. Using equations which enable K for the interaction of two small oppositely charged

Table 1. Oxidation of [2Fe-2S] (parsley) ferredoxin. Rate constants at $25^{\circ}C$, pH 8.0, I = 0.10M (NaCl)

Oxidant	K (M^{-1})	k_{et_1} (s^{-1})	k $(M^{-1}s^{-1})$
$[(NH_3)_5CoNH_2CO(NH_3)_5]^{5+}$	26,400 [a]	214 [a]	5.6×10^6 [b]
$[Pt(NH_3)_6]^{4+}$	21,000	3.29	6.9×10^4 [b]
$[Co(NH_3)_6]^{3+}$	998	19.2	1.9×10^4 [b]
$[Co(NH_3)_5Cl]^{2+}$	(194)	(2300)	4.1×10^5 [b]
$[Co(NH_3)_5C_2O_4]^+$			5.7×10^3
$[Co(acac)_3]$			4.3×10^3
$[Co(edta)]^-$			7.2×10^3
$[Co(C_2O_4)_3]^{3-}$			3.9×10^3

[a] Extrapolated from data $0-7^{\circ}C$

[b] $k = Kk_{et}$

reactants to be calculated, it has been possible to estimate local effective protein binding site charges on the [2Fe-2S] proteins, which give a scatter of results in the -3 to -4.5 range (12). The average value is close to -4.

2.2 Comparisons with Other [2Fe-2S] Proteins

Similar studies have been carried out for spinach and S. platensis [2Fe-2S] ferredoxins (6)-(8). Rate constants k ($=Kk_{et}$) with different charged oxidants are shown in Table 2.

Table 2. Rate constants ($M^{-1}s^{-1}$, $25^{\circ}C$) for the Oxidation of $[Fe_2S_2(SR)_4]^{3-}$, pH 8.0, I = 0.10M (NaCl)

Oxidant	$10^{-3}k$ (parsley)	$10^{-3}k$ (S.platensis)
$[Co(NH_3)_6]^{3+}$	19.0	8.4
$[Co(acac)_3]$	7.0	3.6
$[Co(edta)]^-$	7.2	4.4

A comparison of K and k_{et} for the reactions with $[Co(NH_3)_6]^{3+}$ is made in Table 3.

Table 3.   Data ($25^{\circ}C$) for the oxidation of $[Fe_2S_2(SR)_4]^{3-}$, pH 8.0, I = 0.10M (NaCl).

Source of [2Fe-2S]	K/M^{-1}	k_{et}/s^{-1}
Parsley	998	19.2
Spinach	993	15.9
S. platensis	2070	4.9

From both sets of data it is concluded that there is little change resulting from the variation in protein source.

2.3 Amino-acid Sequences

Sequences are known for 27 different [2Fe-2S] ferredoxins (13). There are twenty-two invariant positions most of which are close to the [2Fe-2S] cluster. Four of these are the cysteine residues 41,46,49 and 79 which bind the two Fe atoms. The other invariant residues are believed to be structurally and functionally important, and it is to these regions one looks in attempting to identify binding sites which are relevant to the in vivo redox processes. Whether it is these same sites which are influential in reactions with inorganic complexes remains to be established. Certainly in the case of the more extensively studied plastocyanin and cytochrome c reactions the same sites would seem to be relevant, but this need not always be the case. The parsley sequence has recently been determined. There are 34 different amino acids on comparing S. platensis and parsley [2Fe-2S] (14).

2.4 Location of Binding Sites

Of the four cysteinyl S-atoms that of residue 49 lies inside the molecule, 41 and 46 are slightly covered with peptide, and 79 is accessible to solvent (9). Both inorganic S-atoms are buried inside the molecule.

Four regions on parsley ferredoxin having three consecutive acidic residues are to be noted. These same regions are largely conserved in all plant ferredoxins and S. platensis. They are at positions 21-23, 31-33, 67-69 and around 94-96, Table 4.

Table 4. Conserved acidic and other relevant residues for [2Fe-2S] ferredoxins. The
numbering is as given for S. platensis (1-98 residues) in ref. 9. For many plant
sequences numbers have to be adjusted by adding one or two to adjust the alignments.

	21	22	23		31	32	33	
Parsley	Asp	Asp	Asp		Glu	Glu	Glu	
Spinach	Asp	Asp			Glu	Glu	Glu	
S. Platensis	Asp	Asp	Asp		Glu	Glu		

	67	68	69		92	93	94	95	96
Parsley	Asp	Asp	Glu		His	Lys	Glu	Glu	Glu
Spinach	Asp	Asp	Asp		His	Lys	Glu	Glu	Glu
S. Platensis	Asp	Asp	Asp		His	Glu	Glu	Glu	

The conserved negative patches at 67-69 and 94-96 are close to the active site,
Figure 2. Those at 21-23 and 31-33 are some 25Å away, and at

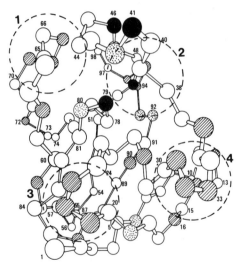

Fig. 2 The structure of S. platensis   [2Fe-2S] ferredoxin (as in Figure 1) with
circles representing amino-acids,● for cysteines attached to active site,⊖ for
negatively charged residues, and ⊗ for positively charged residues. The broken line
circles indicate the 3- negatively charged regions.

such a distance as to question their possible effectiveness as electron transfer
binding sites. The effect of paramagnetic $[Cr(NH_3)_6]^{3+}$ on the ^1H and ^{13}C NMR of
oxidised Anabaena variabilis [2Fe-2S] has been studied by Markley and colleagues
(15). They observed selective line broadening of Tyr25 and Tyr82 (the latter is 83
in Markley's paper) and concluded that residues 22,23 and 62 interact with the

$[Cr(NH_3)_6]^{3+}$. This result raises questions as to why 31-33, 67-69 and 94-96 are not also effective. The availability of nearby aromatic residues to monitor line broadening is a possible contributing factor. Another is the possible effect on the NMR of the [2Fe-2S] active site in close proximity. One of the negative patches (94-96) has positively charged residues nearby which may well reduce its influence. Association of redox partners such as $[Co(NH_3)_6]^{3+}$ at the 21-23 site will no doubt occur, but this is not expected to give other than a small contribution to electron transfer. Association at the 67-79 and 94-96 sites, where the negative charge is reinforced by that of the active site, is expected to lead to a much greater contribution to electron transfer.

A final point is that spinach [2Fe-2S] is now known to consist of a mixture of ferredoxin I and II components which can only be separated after carboxymethylation (16). Results obtained for many if not all ferredoxins may have this complication The ferredoxin II component in the spinach case is ~ 20% of the total. It has 25 residues different, but retains with minor changes negative patches. No biphasic kinetics attributable to these components have yet been observed (6).

2.5 Reactions of 2[4Fe-4S] with Different Oxidants

First-order plots for the $[Co(NH_3)_6]^{3+}$ oxidation of the reduced 2[4Fe-4S] protein give excellent linearity (> four half-lives) and behaviour consistent with either a two stage (relatively) slow-fast oxidation of the [4Fe-4S] clusters or statistical kinetics (10). The latter interpretation requires identical (within 20%) absorbance changes and rate constants for the two reaction sites. Relevant information has been obtained using the pulse radiolysis method to convert oxidised protein to ~10% partially reduced protein (17). In the presence of excess $[Co(NH_3)_6]^{3+}$ reoxidation is observed with the same rate constant as in the stopped-flow experiments. This corresponds to oxidation of the second cluster. It can be concluded therefore that there is no co-operativity between the two [4Fe-4S] sites, and that statistical kinetics apply.

Results obtained for stopped-flow reaction with 5+, 4+ and 3+ positively charged oxidants are shown in Table 4,(10).

Association constants are noticeably less and rate constant (k_{et}) greater than for the [2Fe-2S] protein. From calculations (12) the charge on the protein binding site is estimated to be -3. However there are no negative patches on the protein Figure 3. From the temperature dependence of the $[Co(NH_3)_6]^{3+}$ oxidation, parameters for K (ΔH^o = 0.3 kcal mol^{-1}; ΔS^o = 13.4 cal $K^{-1}mol^{-1}$) differ considerably from those for the [2Fe-2S] protein (10.2; 47.9), (6)(10). Similarly for the 2[4Fe-4S] protein activation parameters for k_{et} ($\Delta H^{\ddagger}$ = 15.3 kcal mol^{-1}; $\Delta S^{\ddagger}$ = 1.9 cal $K^{-1}mol^{-1}$) differ from those for [2Fe-2S] (8.5; -24.1). These suggest different

Table 5. Association constants K and electron-transfer rate constants k_{et} (25°C) for the oxidation of the 2[4Fe-4S] protein at pH 8.0, I = 0.10M (NaCl). Numbers in parentheses are for the corresponding parsley [2Fe-2S] reactions.

Oxidant	K/M^{-1}	k_{et}/s^{-1}
$[Co(NH_3)_6]^{3+}$	466	98
	(998)	(19.2)
$[Pt(NH_3)_6]^{4+}$	2400	111
	(21000)	(3.3)
$[(NH_3)_5CoNH_2Co(NH_3)_5]^{5+}$	< 4000	> 200
	(26400)	(214)

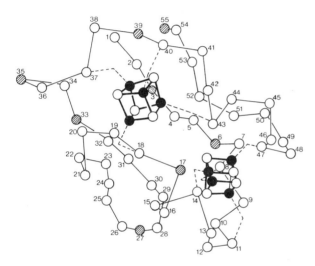

Fig. 3 The 2[4Fe-4S] ferredoxin structure with ⊖ representing negatively charged residues, and ⊙ for the positive residue. There are no negatively charged patches except those provided by the [4Fe-4S] clusters.

mechanistic features. One possible explanation is that a negative patch or patches are involved in the [2Fe-2S] case, but that the exposed cluster and its charge of 3- is influential in the 2[4Fe-4S] case. Different degrees of solvation could be relevant at these two sites. The distance over which electrons are transferred may be less for the [4Fe-4S] clusters, consistent with the bigger k_{et} values.

2.6 Inner-sphere Reductions

The Cr(II) complex of the 1,4,5,12-tetraazacyclopentadecane saturated macrocylic ligand, here designated as $[Cr(15aneN_4)(H_2O)_2]^{2+}$, $(E^O = -0.58V)$, has labile axial ligands. Following reduction of the two proteins, product analyses have demonstrated that the Cr(III) remains attached, and therefore that the reactions fall within the definition of inner-sphere electron transfer (18). There are three observations to make. First of all for 2[4Fe-4S] the kinetic plots remain uniphasic for reduction of both redox centres. This rules out a single electron entry site which might have been expected anyway in view of the marked similarity between the first and second halves of the sequence. Secondly the reduction is not blocked by redox inactive $[Cr(en)_3]^{3+}$ at a level where 55% inhibition might have been expected. Therefore it would appear that for these inner-sphere reactions the Cr(II) reductant expresses some affinity for, and there is bond formation, at an alternative site. Unfortunately ~40% of the protein is denatured by Cr(III) attachment and further experiments aimed at identifying this point of attachment have not been possible. Some similar studies have been carried out with the [2Fe-2S] protein.

Finally, it is interesting that for the $[Cr(15aneN_4)(H_2O)_2]^{2+}$ reduction of 2[4Fe-4S], rate constants at pH 8 $(1.03 \times 10^3 M^{-1} s^{-1})$ increase by 30% on decreasing the pH to 7 giving a pK_a of 7.46. The effect is clearly not explained by the electrostatic effect of adding a proton. The same pK_a (7.4) has been observed in potentiometry experiments (19). Protonation of $[Fe_4S_4(SR)_4]^{2-}$ rather than adjacent amino-acids is indicated from properties observed for the $[Fe_4S_4(SCH_2CH_2CO_2)_4]^{6-}$ analogue $(pK_a$ 7.4) (20). However no effects of protonation on UV-VIS/NMR/EPR/CD spectra have yet been detected (18)(19). One possible explanation for 2[4Fe-4S] proteins is that hydrogen-bonding of the cysteinyl S-atom to adjacent groups is replaced by outright protonation as the pH is decreased.

7 REFERENCES

(1) S.K. Chapman, C.V. Knox, A.G. Sykes, J. Chem.Soc. Dalton Trans (1984), 2775-2780 and earlier papers in series.

(2) O. Faver, Y. Shahak, I. Pecht, Biochem 21 (1982), 1885-

(3) H.B. Gray, unpublished work with electronically excited $[Cr(bipy)_3]^{3+}$ and $[Ru(bipy)_3]^{2+}$ complexes.

(4) J. Butler, S.K. Chapman, D.M. Davies, A.G. Sykes, S.H. Speck. N. Osheroff, E. Margoliash, J.Biol.Chem., 258 (1983), 6400-6404.

(5) M.A. Augustin, S.K. Chapman, D.M. Davies, A.G. Sykes, S.H. Speck, E. Margoliash, J.Biol. Chem. 258 (1983), 6405-6409.

(6) F.A. Armstrong, A.G. Sykes, 100, J. Amer. Chem. Soc., 100, (1978) 7710-7715.

(7) F.A. Armstrong, R.A. Henderson, A.G. Sykes, J. Amer. Chem. Soc., 101, (1978), 7710-7715.

(8) I.K. Adzamli, A. Petrou, A.G. Sykes, K.K. Rao, D.A. Hall, Biochem. J., 211, (1983), 219-226

(9) T. Tsukihara, K. Fukuyama, M. Nakamura, Y. Katsube, N. Tanaka, M. Kakudo, K. Wada, T. Hase, H. Matsubara,J. Biochem., 90, (1981), 1763-1773.

(10) F.A. Armstrong, R.A. Henderson, A.G. Sykes, J. Amer. Chem. Soc., 102, (1980) 6545-6551.

(11) E.T. Adman, L.C. Sieker. L.H. Jensen, J. Biol. Chem., 248 (1973), 2987-3996.

(12) S.K. Chapman, J.D. Sinclair-Day, A.G. Sykes, S.C. Tam, R.J.P. Williams, J. Chem. Soc. Chem. Comm., (1983), 1152-1153.

(13) H. Matsubara, T. Hase, S. Wakabayashi, K. Wada, D.S. Sigman, M.A.B. Branzier (Eds), in The Evolution of Protein Structure and Function, Academic Press, 1980, pp 245-266.

(14) T. Nakano, T. Hase, H. Matsubara, J.Biochem. 90, (1981), 1725-1730.

(15) T.-M. Chan. E.L. Ulrich, J.L. Markley, Biochem., 22 (1983), 6002-6007.

(16) Y. Takahashi, T. Hase, K. Wada, H. Matsubara, Plant Cell Physiol., 24 (1983), 189-198.

(17) I.K. Adzamli, H. Ong Wah Kim, A.G. Sykes, J. Inorg. Biochem., 16, (1982), 311-317 and J. Butler, R.A. Henderson, F.A. Armstrong, A.G. Sykes, Biochem. J., 183, (1979), 471-474.

(18) I.K. Adzamli, R.A. Henderson, J.D. Sinclair-Day, A.G. Sykes, Inorg. Chem., 23, (1984), 3069-3073.

(19) R.S. Magliozzo, B.A. McIntosh, W.V. Sweeney, J.Biol.Chem., 257, (1982), 3506-3509.

(20) R.C. Job, T.C. Bruice, Proc. Natl. Acad. Sci. (U.S.A.), 72, (1975), 2478-2482.

Reduction of Hemerythrin, Myoglobin and Derivatives by Radicals

Z. Bradić, K. Tsukahara, P.C. Wilkins, R.G. Wilkins

Department of Chemistry, New Mexico State University
Las Cruces, NM 88003 USA

SUMMARY

   The value of the kinetics approach in <u>detecting</u> discrete species during chemical reactions will be emphasized. This will be illustrated by reference to our work on the respiratory protein hemerythrin (1). In addition, the reduction of hemerythrin by a number and variety of radicals will be compared with that of its iron porphyrin-containing counterpart, myoglobin.

1   INTRODUCTION

   Hemerythrin is an iron-containing respiratory protein in certain marine organisms (1). In the coelemic fluid of most species examined, it is octameric. From the retractor muscle of <u>Themiste zostericola</u>, it is a monomer. Each subunit of hemerythrin contains two non-heme irons, bridged by two aminoacids and an oxy group. The deoxy form contains both irons in the oxidation state +2, and this interacts reversibly with O_2 to give the oxy form. Both deoxy and oxy forms are easily oxidized to a met species containing +3 irons. This met form reacts with a number of anions to form adducts. Recently (2), two semi-met forms have been characterized, in which the two irons are present in the +2 and +3 oxidation states. These have characteristic EPR signals at liquid He temperatures (3), and interest in the protein has been heightened by the reporting of similar EPR signals shown by reduced iron proteins from a number of disparate sources. These include purple acid phosphatases from beef spleen and from pig allantoic fluid, as well as component A of methane monooxygenase from <u>Methylococcus capsulatus</u> (Bath) (4).

2   REDUCTION OF HEMERYTHRIN AND DERIVATIVES BY RADICALS

2.1   Dithionite Reduction

It was the study of the dithionite reduction of methemerythrin (2) which led to the identification of the (semi-met)$_R$ form [Fe(III)Fe(II)]$_8$ with a distinctive spectrum and affinity towards N$_3^-$ ion. The reduction of methemerythrin to (semi-met)$_R$ by SO$_2^-$ required stopped-flow study. The further reduction to deoxyhemerythrin was much slower, independent of S$_2$O$_4^{2-}$ concentration, and appeared biphasic, with the first portion accounting for a much larger spectral amplitude (2). No species with distinctive properties could be discerned along the reaction profile between semi-met and deoxy. The loss of N$_3^-$ binding by, and the EPR signal for, semi-methemerythrin paralleled the build-up of deoxy as monitored by O$_2$ uptake. All protein present could be accounted for after the loss of met by (semi-met)$_R$ and deoxy. In this respect, our results differ from those of Armstrong, Ramasami and Sykes (5), who employed a series of metal(II) complexes as strong reducing agents. As well as confirming the (semi-met)$_R$ form, they suggested the presence of a discrete quarter-met form, [Fe(III)Fe(II)]$_4$[Fe(II)Fe(II)]$_4$.

In the reduction of anionic adducts of methemerythrin by dithionite, the fast stage (met → semi-met) is markedly slowed because reduction has to await dissociation of the anion from the adduct (6). Thus, the whole sequence (1) can be observed, e.g.,

$$\text{met.SCN}^- \;\rightleftharpoons\; \text{SCN}^- + \text{met} \longrightarrow \text{semi-met} \longrightarrow \text{deoxy} \qquad (1)$$

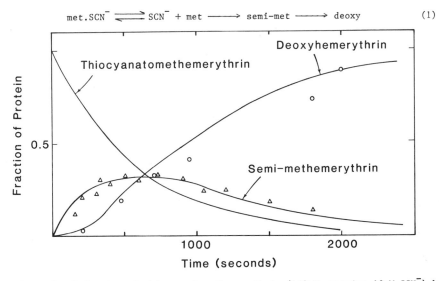

Figure 1.   Reduction of thiocyanatomethemerythrin (158μM protein; 10mM SCN$^-$) by dithionite (0.5mM) at pH 6.1, I=0.46M. Full curve on basis of met. SCN → semi-met (k=1.6x10^{-3}s^{-1}) and semi-met → deoxy (k=2.1x10^{-3}s^{-1})

All three species can be separately analysed (Fig. 1). Again, the semi-met → deoxy transformation is clean until the last 10-15% reaction, an explanation for which has been given (2).

2.2 Reduction by Other Radicals

The results of a study of the reduction of methemerythrin by a number of radicals are shown in Table 1. Except where indicated, all data refer to protein from Phascolopsis gouldii, pH 6.0-6.4, and I = 0.50M. Studies with methemerythrin from T. zostericola gave similar results. A casual glance at the Table shows a correlation between reducing power of the radical and its reactivity towards methemerythrin (through reduction to semi-methemerythrin). We can apply the simple Marcus treatment (7) as embodied in equation (2) to the results,

$$k_{12} = (k_{11}k_{22}K_{12}f_{12})^{\frac{1}{2}} \tag{2}$$

where k_{12} is the rate constant for the reduction, k_{11} is the self-exchange rate constant for the radicals (assumed $10^8 M^{-1}s^{-1}$) and k_{22} is the corresponding value for the protein (assumed $10^{-3}M^{-1}s^{-1}$ (8)). K_{12} is obtained from the radical reduction potential (Table 1) and $E°$ for met → semi-met (+0.11 volts (8)).

$$\ln f_{12} = \frac{(\ln K_{12})^2}{4 \ln (k_{11}k_{22}/10^{22})} \tag{3}$$

Agreement between the rate constant calculated on the basis of (2) and that observed (Table 1) is remarkably good, bearing in mind that we have ignored work term corrections and charges differences among the radicals. There is little direct reduction of met.SCN$^-$ by MV$^+$ or PDQ$^+$ radicals. Reduction of (semi-met)$_R$ by the viologen-type radicals is slow, although some direct reduction appears to take place, $k(MV^+) \sim 9 \times 10^4 M^{-1}s^{-1}$. Reduction of (semi-met)$_o$ [the other mixed oxidation form, obtained by one-electron oxidation of deoxyhemerythrin (2)] in contrast, is rapid, $k(MV^+) = 2.3 \times 10^7$; $k(DQ^+) = 1.4 \times 10^7 M^{-1}s^{-1}$. This behavior resembles that displayed by dithionite ion.

We have recently studied a number of reductions by O_2^- by using KO_2 as a source of O_2^- ion (9). Solutions of KO_2 at pH $\geq$ 11.5 are relatively stable. In one syringe of a stopped-flow apparatus, such solutions are mixed with oxidant from the other syringe. Employing a similar technique we have studied the reactions of hemerythrin with O_2^-. The results have been disappointing. No reaction within the disproportionation time of O_2^- (approx. 5 sec at pH $\sim$9) is observed with any of the forms--met, (semi-met)$_R$ or oxy-hemerythrin. This sets a second-order rate constant of $\leq 10^3 M^{-1}s^{-1}$. Further, superoxide ion ($\sim$1mM) does not compete with oxygen (0.1mM) for deoxyhemerythrin when a O_2^-/O_2 mixture is added to deoxyhemerythrin.

Table 1. Data for reduction of methemerythrin by radicals at 25°C.

Radical	$E°$ volts	$k(obsd)$ $M^{-1}s^{-1}$	$k(calc)$ $M^{-1}s^{-1}$
e_{aq}^{-}	-2.9	1.0×10^{9a}	----------
CO_2^{-}	-2.0	6.8×10^{7ab}	----------
	-0.55	6.2×10^{6}	1.4×10^{7}
	-0.49	5.4×10^{6}	6.2×10^{6}
MV	-0.45	3.8×10^{6}	3.7×10^{6}
DQ	-0.35	1.1×10^{6}	8.7×10^{5}
SO_2^{-}	-0.26	1.5×10^{5}	2.1×10^{5}
PTQ	-0.19	8.0×10^{5}	7.1×10^{4}
	-0.19	7.2×10^{4}	7.1×10^{4}
Riboflavin (fully reduced)	-0.12	7.2×10^{4}	2.1×10^{4}
	+0.2	9.9×10^{3}	7.9×10

[a] $I = 0.03M.$ [b] Themiste zostericola.

3 INTERACTION OF LIGANDS WITH DEOXYHEMERYTHRIN

Extensive data are available for the uptake of oxygen by deoxyhemerythrin (10). On the basis of the high rate constant for reaction of deoxymyohemerythrin with O_2 ($7.8 \times 10^7 M^{-1} s^{-1}$) it was suggested (10) that one iron(II) has a vacant site--now likely in view of the x-ray structure of methemerythrin (11). The anions NCO^- and N_3^- bleach oxyhemerythrin (HrO_2) and from the kinetics of the $HrO_2 + X^-$ interaction, kinetic and thermodynamic data for deoxyhemerythrin (Hr^0) interaction with these anions (Eqn (4)) could be determined (Table 2 (12))

$$Hr^0 + X^- \rightleftharpoons Hr^0X^- \qquad k_1, \; k_{-1}, \; K_1 \qquad\qquad (4)$$

It is apparent that it is the protonated form HX which is the reactive species. Dissociation of the anion is remarkably slow, with a half-life, for example, of about a minute for the F^- and CNO^- adducts.

Recently, CD and MCD spectra of deoxyhemerythrin and anionic adducts have been described (13). Binding constants of N_3^- and CNO^- ($K_1 \sim 70M^{-1}$ at pH 7.7) are in good agreement with our data (12). We (12) now confirm the weak F^- binding ($K_1 = 7M^{-1}$ at pH = 7.7 (13)). The competition of potential ligands with oxygen for deoxyhemerythrin (Hr^0) is a sensitive, spectral method for detecting Hr^0-X^- interaction. We find little binding by Cl^-, ClO_4^-, CN^-, SCN^-, HCO_3^-, HCO_2^-, $CH_3CO_2^-$ imidazole or $Fe(CN)_6^{4-}$ (12). Autoxidation to met accompanies reaction (4) and it is not always easy to separate the two steps (12). We see no semi-met formed during

Table 2. Data for primary interaction of deoxyhemerythrin with X^- (Eqn 4) at I = 0.15M or 0.5M and 25°C.

X^-	pH	k_1, $M^{-1}s^{-1}$	k_{-1}, s^{-1}	K_1, M^{-1}
N_3^-	5.3	1.9×10^3	~ 0.1	$\sim 1.9 \times 10^4$
	6.3	1.6×10^2	0.10	1.6×10^3
	7.7	~ 9	0.10	~ 90
	7.7	---------	------	$\sim 70^a$
CNO^-	6.3	59	0.019	3.1×10^3
	7.7	---------	------	$\sim 70^a$
	8.7	~ 0.24	0.012	~ 20
F^-	5.8	4.6	0.012	380
	6.3	1.25	0.012	104
	7.7	0.046	0.012	3.8
	7.7	---------	------	$\sim 7^a$

[a] Reference (13).

the autoxidation of oxyhemerythrin in the presence of SCN^- ion. This suggests that autoxidation is simply a replacement of O_2^{2-} (oxy can be considered $Fe(III)Fe(III)O_2^{2-}$ (14)) by SCN^- ion.

Finally, it should be stressed that a number of reactions of hemerythrin, including substitution, pH-promoted changes, and redox reactions, appear controlled by a slow conformational change ($k \sim 10^{-2}-10^{-3}s^{-1}$) (Table 3) (4). This includes the disproportionation of semi-methemerythrin (1). Electron transfer is, therefore, even faster than $10^{-2}s^{-1}$ over 26-28 Å, but this is not unreasonable in the light of recent findings (15).

Table 3. Reactions of Hemerythrin Dominated by a First-Order Conformational Change

Protein Form	Reactant (pH)	Rate Constant s^{-1}
octamer (P. gouldii)	acid ↔ base	
methemerythrin	interconversion (8.2)	3.3×10^{-3}
	SCN^- (9.0)	5.0×10^{-3}
	$S_2O_4^{2-}$ (9.0)	2.7×10^{-3}
	thiol reagents (9.0)	2.0×10^{-3}
	SDS (7.8)	$2 - 11 \times 10^{-3}$
semimethemerythrin	0 → R forms and $Fe(CN)_6^{3-}$ oxidation (8.2)	1.3×10^{-3}
semimethemerythrin (T. zostericola)	intramolecular dispropor-tionation (8.2)	2.2×10^{-3}
monomer (T. zostericola)	acid ↔ base	
metmyohemerythrin	interconversion (7.0)	7.2×10^{-3}
	SCN^- (8.2)	3.2×10^{-3}
	$S_2O_4^{2-}$ (8.2)	3.5×10^{-3}
semimetmyohemerythrin	0 → R forms (8.2)	1.0×10^{-2}

4 REDUCTION OF METMYOGLOBIN AND DERIVATIVES BY RADICALS

The reduction of metmyoglobin by a number of derivatives is shown in Table 4. Unlike hemerythrin, whose adducts are not reduced directly (eqn (1)), metmyoglobin (Mb^+) complexes with CN^-, imidazole and pyridines are reduced directly by SO_2^- (16), DQ^+, PTQ^{2+} (18), and even the bulky macrocycle cobalt(II) sepulchrate (17). It is believed that SO_2^- attacks the ligand and transfers its electron through the π-system to the metal ion (16). The much bulkier reductants such as PTQ^{2+} and Co(II) sepulchrate may react by contrast at some point on the periphery of the protein, and this is then followed by transfer to the metal ion.

Table 4. Second-order rate constants for reduction of Mb^+ derivatives by radicals at I = 0.15M or 0.50M and 25°C

Protein	Reductant	k (obsd) $M^{-1}s^{-1}$	k(calc) $M^{-1}s^{-1}$
Mb^+OH_2	SO_2^-	4.5×10^6	2.7×10^6
	MV^{+}	5.4×10^{7a}	4.1×10^7
	DQ^{+}	1.3×10^7	1.1×10^7
	PTQ^{2+}	1.3×10^6	9.0×10^5
	Co(II)sepulchrate	3.5×10^3	1.5×10^3
Mb^+OH^-	SO_2^-	$< 10^4$	---------
	DQ^{+}	$< 10^5$	---------
Mb^+ imidazole	SO_2^-	8.8×10^7	9.6×10^7
	DQ^{+}	3.4×10^7	1.3×10^8
	PTQ^{2+}	$>5 \times 10^6$	9.3×10^6
	Co(II)sepulchrate	3.1×10^4	1.6×10^4
Mb^+F^-	SO_2^-	$< 2 \times 10^2$	---------
	DQ^{+}	1.1×10^3	---------
	Co(II)sepulchrate	$< 2 \times 10^2$	---------
Horseradish peroxidase	SO_2^-	5.0×10^5	---------
	DQ^{+}	1.5×10^5	---------

[a]J.W. Van Leeuwen, C. Van Dijk, H.J. Grande, C. Veeger, Eur. J. Biochem. 127 (1982) 631-637

Once again, we can apply Marcus treatment to the reduction by five radicals of Mb^+OH_2 (E° = +0.06 volts (19)) and Mb^+imidazole (E° = -0.10 volts (19)). Using a value of 10^8 $M^{-1}s^{-1}$ for k_{11}, the self-exchange rate constants for the radicals, and 1 $M^{-1}s^{-1}$ and 3×10^4 $M^{-1}s^{-1}$ for k_{22}, the self-exchange rate constants for metMb/deoxyMb and metMb.imidazole/deoxyMb.imidazole, respectively, the calculated

rate constants are in very good agreement with those observed (Table 4). The value
1 $M^{-1}s^{-1}$ was used as the result of some experiments on the cross-reaction between
horse heart deoxymyoglobin and sperm whale metmyoglobin. Spectral changes are
small, the reaction is slow and does not proceed to completion so that only
approximate second-order rate constants could be obtained. The value chosen for the
imidazole adduct best fitted the experimental data and indicates the profound
influence of coordinated imidazole on the electron transfer rate. Using the
recently determined self-exchange rate constant for azurin (P. aeruginosa), 4.3 x
10^3 $M^{-1}s^{-1}$ at pH = 7.3 (20), we estimate from eqn (2) that the second-order rate
constant for reduction of azurin by deoxymyoglobin is 5.3 x 10^3 $M^{-1}s^{-1}$. We find
experimentally that k = 3.7 x 10^4 $M^{-1}s^{-1}$. How about that?

5   ACKNOWLEDGEMENTS

This work was supported by National Science Foundation and National Institutes
of Health grants and this is gratefully acknowledged.

6   REFERENCES

(1) R.G. Wilkins, P.C. Harrington, Adv. Inorg. Biochem. 5 (1983) 51–85.

(2) P.C. Harrington, D.J.A. deWaal, R.G. Wilkins, Arch. Biochem. Biophys. 191
    (1978) 444–451; Z. Bradić, P.C. Harrington, R.G. Wilkins, G. Yoneda,
    Biochemistry, 19 (1980) 4149–4155.

(3) B.B. Muhoberac, D.C. Wharton, L.M. Babcock, P.C. Harrington, R.G. Wilkins,
    Biochim. Biophys. Acta, 626 (1980) 337–345.

(4) For references see P.C. Harrington, R.G. Wilkins, Biochemistry, 24 (1985)
    210–214.

(5) G.D. Armstrong, T. Ramasami, A.G. Sykes, J.C.S. Chem. Commun. (1984) 1017–1019.

(6) E. Olivas, D.J.A. deWaal, R.G. Wilkins, J. Inorg. Biochem. 11 (1979) 205–212.

(7) R.A. Marcus, J. Phys. Chem. 72 (1968) 891–895.

(8) F.A. Armstrong, P.C. Harrington, R.G. Wilkins, J. Inorg. Biochem. 18 (1983)
    83–91; P.C. Harrington, R.G. Wilkins, J. Inorg. Biochem. 19 (1983) 339–344.

(9) Z. Bradić, R.G. Wilkins, J. Am. Chem. Soc. 106 (1984) 2236–2239.

(10) A.L. Petrou, F.A. Armstrong, A.G. Sykes. P.C. Harrington, R.G. Wilkins, Biochim. Biophys. Acta 670 (1981) 377–384.

(11) R.E. Stenkamp, L.C. Sieker, L.H. Jensen, J. Am. Chem. Soc. 106 (1984) 618–622; R.E. Stenkamp, L.C. Sieker, L.H. Jensen, J.D. McCallum, J.S.-Loehr, Proc. Natl. Acad. Sci. USA 82 (1985) 713–716.

(12) Z. Bradić, R. Conrad, R.G. Wilkins, J. Biol. Chem. 252 (1977) 6069–6075 and unpublished current experiments.

(13) R.C. Reem, E.I. Solomon, J. Am. Chem. Soc. 106 (1984) 8323–8325.

(14) I.M. Klotz, D.M. Kurtz, Jr. Acc. Chem. Res. 17 (1984) 16–22.

(15) H.B. Gray, Plenary Lecture, 2nd International Conference on Bioinorganic Chemistry, Algarve, Portugal, April 1985.

(16) E. Olivas, D.J.A. deWaal, R.G. Wilkins, J. Biol. Chem. 252 (1977) 4038–4042; D.R. Eaton, R.G. Wilkins, J. Biol. Chem. 253 (1978) 908–915.

(17) R.J. Balahura, R.G. Wilkins, Biochim. Biophys. Acta, 724 (1983) 465–472.

(18) M. Furue, S. Nozakura, Bull. Chem. Soc. Jpn. 55 (1982) 513–516. These interesting bisviologen compounds can be doubly reduced. The potential shown in Table 1 refer to that for singly to doubly reduced species, estimated from a comproportionation constant and the overall $PTQ^{4+} \rightarrow PTQ^{2+}$ potential.

(19) E. Antonini, M. Brunori, Hemoglobin and Myoglobin in their Reactions with Ligands, North-Holland, Amsterdam, 1971, p. 332.

(20) K. Ugurbil, S. Mitra, Proc. Natl. Acad. Sci. USA 82 (1985) 2039–2043.

Kinetics and Reaction Pathways for The Autoxidation of Cobalt Polyamine Complexes through Dioxygen Complex Formation

Arthur E. Martell, Carl J. Raleigh, Arup Basak

Department of Chemistry, Texas A&M University, College Station, Texas 77843 U.S.A.

SUMMARY

Kinetic measurements of the oxidative dehydrogenation of coordinated poly-amines in binuclear, μ-peroxo dioxygen complexes show the reactions to be second order, first order in the dioxygen complex, and first order in hydroxide ion. The reaction pathway for conversion of the dioxygen complexes to inert species is very sensitive to the conformation of the coordinated polyamine. The results are interpreted in terms of a reaction mechanism in which homolytic O-O fission is concerted with double bond formation, transfer of the α-proton to the coordin-ated oxygen, and electron transfer from the polyamine ligand to the coordinated oxygen through the metal ion.

1 INTRODUCTION

A few examples of oxidative dehydrogenation of coordinated amines through dioxygen complex formation have been described in the literature. It was found by Harris et al. (1,2) that binuclear cobalt dioxygen complexes with coordinated de-protonated dipeptides such as glycylglycine and analogus ligands undergo oxidative dehydrogenation at the N-terminal positions to form the corresponding iminoacyl-amino acids. Autoxidation of a 4-N cobalt(II) macrocyclic complex related to salcomine to give a cobalt(III) complex in which the ligand has two additional double bonds, reported by Black and Hartshorn (3), is believed to occur through di-oxygen complex formation. Also, the mechanism proposed by Burnett et al. (4) for the Cu(I)-catalyzed autoxidation of an $N_6O_4(30)$ macrocycle involves the formation of binuclear dioxygen complexes as intermediates, although in this case the binu-clear μ-peroxobiscopper(II) complex is too unstable to be isolated and identified.

2 OXIDATIVE DEHYDROGENATION OF PYRIDYL-CONTAINING PENTAMINES

Initial studies on the oxidative dehydrogenation of a coordinated polyamine through cobalt dioxygen complex formation have recently been reported (5,6). In this case the binuclear, μ-peroxo-bispolyamine-dicobalt(III) complex was isolated and characterized, and its kinetics of conversion to an inert complex was followed quantitatively. Extension of this study to Co(II) complexes of a series of polyamines, 1 - 5, has led to determination of reaction pathways and partial elucidation of the requirements for the promotion of intramolecular ligand attack by coordinated dioxygen, resulting in dehydrogenation of the polyamine.

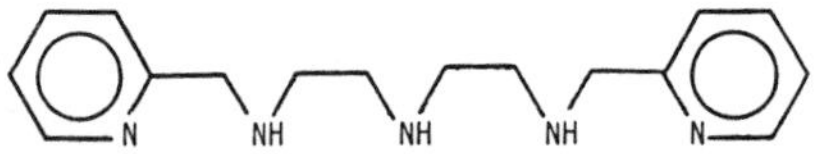

1 PYDIEN

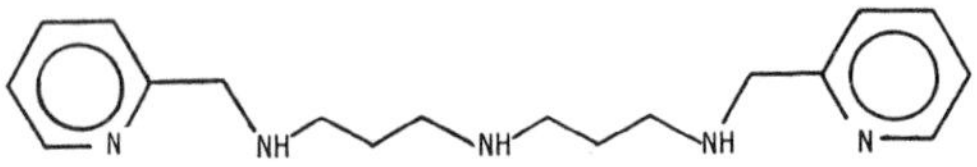

2 PYDPT

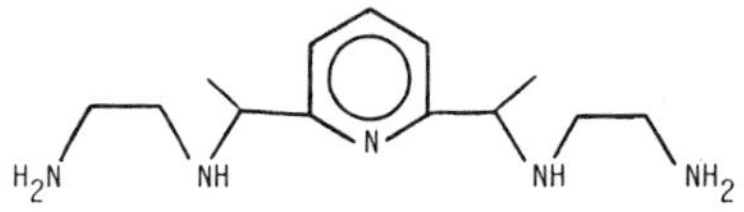

3 EPYDEN

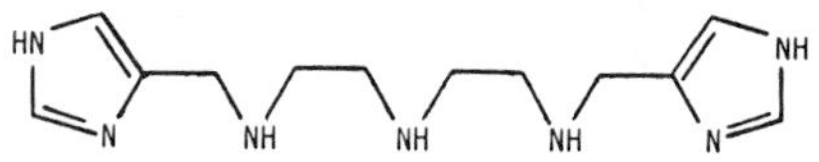

4 IMDIEN

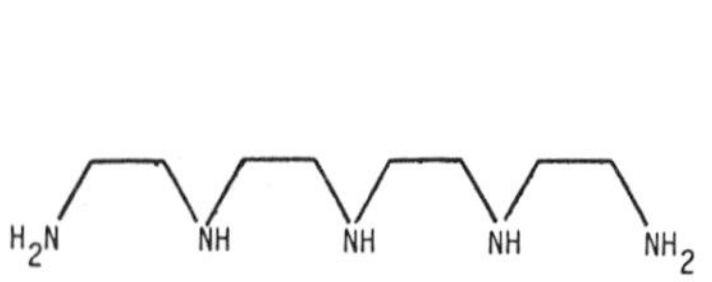

5 TETREN

The binuclear cobalt dioxygen complexes derived from PYDIEN, 1, and PYDPT, 2, are rapidly converted to Co(II) complexes of dehydrogenated polyamines containing one imine group conjugated with a pryidine ring. Experimentally, kinetics of reaction were measured by preparing the dioxygen complex in solution at pH values where it has high thermodynamic stability, removing excess oxygen, and raising the temperature to 35°C. The monoimine was isolated and identified by its IR spectrum, and by quantitative hydrolysis to 2-pyridinecarboxaldehyde. The evidence obtained in determining the nature of the reaction pathway and stoichiometry of the oxidative dehydrogenation reaction is summarized in Table 1. The cobalt(II) complex of the monoimine formed in the first oxidative dehydrogenation step forms a dioxygen complex which is thermodynamically somewhat less stable than the original complex, but is sufficiently stable to work with in the same manner. This complex in turn undergoes a second oxidative dehydrogenation to form a Co(II) complex of a coordinated di-imine, which hydrolyzes spontaneously to a complex of diethylenetriamine and 2-pyridinecarboxaldehyde. When the reaction is carried out in the presence of excess oxygen the sequential dehydrogenation reactions overlap and only the final products can be isolated from the reaction mixture. These reactions are second order, first order in dioxygen complex and first order in hydroxide ion. Deprotonation of the aliphatic amino group undergoing dehydrogenation is therefore considered to be an essential part of the reaction mechanism.

Table 1. Evidence for formation of Co(II) complex of oxidatively dehydrogenated ligand.

1.   DC sampled polarograms indicate Co(II) complex formed.
2.   Monoimine determined by hydrolysis to aldehyde and by TLC separation.
3.   Uv-visible and IR spectra similar to those of synthetic imine complex.
4.   No H_2O_2 formed in reaction mixture.
5.   Product formed after anaerobic dehydrogenation forms a new dioxygen complex with O_2.

The fact that the cobalt dioxygen complex involving the coordinated pentamine EPYDEN does not undergo oxidative dehydrogenation throws considerable light on the constitutional requirements of this reaction. In this case a so-called metal-centered oxidative degradation takes place for which the products are inert Co(III) complexes of the original polyamine, and hydrogen peroxide. The evidence obtained for the nature of this reaction is summarized in Table 2.

Table 2. Evidence for metal centered oxidation of the cobalt EPYDEN dioxygen complex

1. H_2O_2 formed.
    a.   Detected polarographically
    b.   Determined semiquantitatively by iodide titration
2.   Co(III) complex of unchanged ligand formed
    a.   Identified by measurement of electronic absorption spectrum
    b.   Polarographic reduction of reaction product gives the same half-wave potential as that of the initial Co(III) EPYDEN complex
    c.   The complex formed does not combine with dioxygen

The change in reaction pathway for the cobalt dioxygen complex containing **3**, relative to that of the dioxygen complexes containing coordinated **1** and **2**, was interpreted in terms of the probable conformation of the EPYDEN ligand in the cobalt dioxygen complex formed (7). The folded arrangement of the ethylenediamine moieties in **6** prevents the formation of an imine group conjugated to the pyridine ring. This interpretation has been more recently supported by the crystal structure determination of the iodide obtained from a concentrated solution of **6** in the presence of excess iodide ion (8), as indicated by Figure 1.

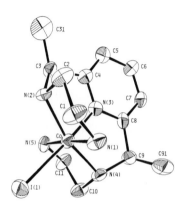

Fig.1

6 Proposed conformation of EPYDEN in its cobalt dioxygen complex

This new evidence led to a reinspection of the crystal structures of the dioxygen complexes containing coordinated ligands **1** and **2**, which had been reported earlier (9,10). These structures clearly showed that the coordinated ligands in both dioxygen complexes have conformations of the aliphatic triamine bridges (see **1** and **2**) that are fairly close to the conformations required for the imine formed as the result of oxidative dehydrogenation.

The experimental work described above on the oxidative degradation of the cobalt dioxygen complexes containing pentamine ligands establishes the sensitivity of the dehydrogenation reaction to the conformation of the coordinated ligand. The kinetic studies described below on mixed ligand cobalt dioxygen complexes (11) now reveals still another requirement for oxidative dehydrogenation - that the amino group undergoing oxidative dehydrogenation must be proximal to the coordinated dioxygen.

3 OXIDATIVE DEHYDROGENATION OF 2-AMINOMETHYLPYRIDINE

In the mixed ligand system containing a 1:1:1 ratio of cobalt(II), 2-amino-methylpyridine (**7**, AMP) and diethylenetriamine (**8**, DIEN) the binuclear dioxygen complex **9** is present from p[H] 7 to 11, while other possible components have

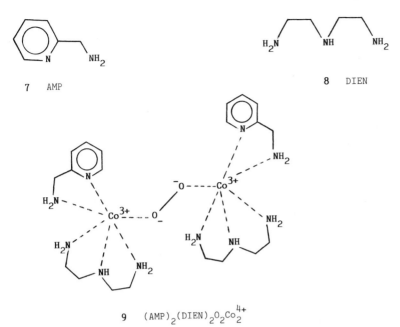

7   AMP

8   DIEN

9    $(AMP)_2(DIEN)_2O_2Co_2^{4+}$

Scheme 1. Dehydrogenation of AMP in Co(II)-AMP-DIEN-dioxygen system

REACTION STOICHIOMETRY

Oxygenation

$$2[(DIEN)(AMP)Co(OH_2)]^{2+} + O_2 \rightleftharpoons [(DIEN)(AMP)Co^{3+} \overset{{}^-O}{\diagdown}\underset{O^-}{\diagup} Co^{3+}(DIEN)(AMP)]^{4+}$$

A, B

Dehydrogenation

$$[(DIEN)(AMP)Co^{3+}\overset{{}^-O}{\diagdown}\underset{O^-}{\diagup}Co^{3+}(DIEN)(AMP)]^{4+} \longrightarrow 2[(DIEN)(IMP)Co]^{2+} + 2H_2O$$

A, B   C

Hydrolysis

$$[(DIEN)(IMP)(H_2O)Co]^{2+} \longrightarrow [(DIEN)(NH_3)Co]^{2+} + \underset{}{\bigcirc}-CHO$$

C

Note: The dioxygen complex consists of two reactive forms: A, which dehydrogenates
      rapidly; and B, which dehydrogenates slowly, to the imine C. It is assumed
      that the molar absorptivities of A and B are equivalent.

negligible concentrations. The degradation of this dioxygen complex under anaerobic conditions gave the imine derived from AMP, whereas the DIEN ligand was found
to be inert. Kinetic measurements at 35°C revealed a fast rate and a slow rate,
characterized by rate constants differing by over an order of magnitude. The
stoichiometry of this reaction is indicated by Scheme I in which the species
undergoing rapid oxidative dehydrogenation is represented by A, and all other
possible species are represented by B. The rate law developed for this system
is based on the reasonable approximation that all mixed-ligand dioxygen complexes
formed have molar absorptivities of equal magnitude, and is presented in the
form of equations (1) - (5).

$$-d[A]/dt \ = \ k_1^f[A] + k_2^f[OH][A] \tag{1}$$

$$-d[B]/dt \ = \ k_1^S[B] + k_2^S[OH][B] \tag{2}$$

$$-d([A] + [B])/dt = k_{obs}^i([A] + [B])$$

$$= (k_1^f + k_1^S)([A] + [B]) + (k_2^f + k_2^S)[OH]([A] + [B]) \tag{3}$$

EARLY STAGE

$$k_{obs} \ = \ k_1^f + k_2^f[OH] + k_1^S + k_2^S[OH] \tag{4}$$

FINAL STAGE

$$k_{obs} \ = \ k_1^S + k_2^S[OH] \tag{5}$$

Consideration of the possible conformations of the mixed ligand dioxygen
complex 9 reveals several possibilities, three of which are indicated by 10,
11, and 12. Of these only 10 is considered capable of homolytic fission of the
O-O bond, concerted with double bond formation and proton transfer to both coor-.
dinated oxygens. Therefore 10 is selected as the mandatory complex through which
the oxidative dehydrogenation reaction must take place, and is the species that
takes part in the fast reaction, A → C. It is therefore suggested that the slow
reaction consists of rate-determining conversion of the several species presented
by B (11, 12, etc.) to the reactive species A.

The experimental evidence favoring the concerted mechanism described above
is summarized in Table 3. The kinetic deuterium isotope effect is not yet available, and is awaiting the synthesis of a sample of completely α-deuterated amino-
methylpyridine (AMP) in our laboratory.

All the essential features of the proposed reaction mechanism, described
above in narrative form, may be expressed in terms of two graphic formulas: the
AMP-deprotonted dioxygen complex, 13, and the proposed transition state 14. As
indicated above, all changes in positions of atoms and movement of electrons,
including the conversion of 13 to 14, are presently assumed to be concerted.

Table 3. Evidence for mechanism of dehydrogenation of coordinated polyamine ligand
in binuclear cobalt dioxygen complexes

1. All dehydrogenation reactions are base catalyzed.

2. Imine group formed is conjugated with an aromatic ring (no dehydrogenation
    with aliphatic polyamines).

3. Conformation of polyamine in dioyxgen complex must be compatible with forma-
    tion of trigonal R-C=N-R' group (R = aromatic).

4. When isomers possible only configuration with α-CH- adjacent to coordinated
    dioxygen undergoes dehydrogenation.

5. (Large deuterium isotope effect).

Conclusion: Concerted O-O bond scission, imine double bond formation, and proton
            transfer to coordinated peroxo oxygen.

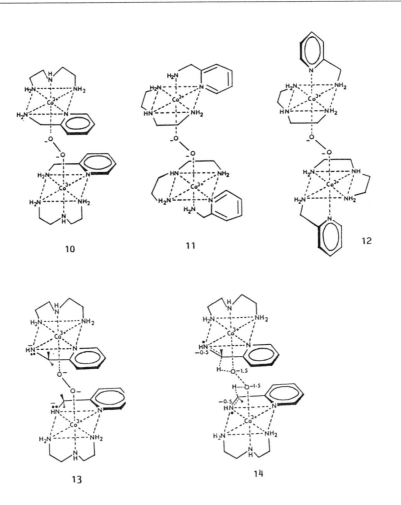

4 ACKNOWLEDGEMENT

The work described in this paper was supported by The Robert A. Welch Foundation under research grant No.A-259, and by the Petroleum Research Fund of the American Chemical Society under research grant No.15093-AC3.

5 REFERNCES

(1) W. R. Harris, A. E. Martell, J. Coord. Chem. 10, 107-113 (1980).

(2) W. R. Harris, R. C. Bess, A. E. Martell, T. H. Ridgeway, J. Am. Chem. Soc. 99, 2958-2965 (1977).

(3) D. S. Black, A. J. Hartshorn, Tetrahedron Lett., 25, 2157-2160 (1974).

(4) M. G. Burnett, V. McKee, S. M. Nelson, M. G. Drew, J. Chem. Soc. Chem. Commun., 829-830 (1980).

(5) C. J. Raleigh, A. E. Martell, Inorg. Chem., 24, 142-148 (1985).

(6) C. J. Raleigh, A. E. Martell, Inorg. Chem., in press.

(7) C. J. Raleigh, A. E. Martell, J. Chem. Soc. Chem. Comm., 335-336 (1984).

(8) C. J. Raleigh, A. E. Martell, J. Coord. Chem., in press.

(9) J. H. Timmons, A. Clearfield, A. E. Martell, R. H. Niswander, Inorg. Chem., 18, 1042-1047 (1979).

(10) J. H. Timmons, R. H. Niswander, A. Clearfield, A. E. Martell, Inorg. Chem., 18, 2977-2982 (1979).

(11) A. Basak, A. E. Martell, Inorg. Chem., to be submitted.

Metals in Medicine

Clinical Disorders of Zinc Metabolism and Their Treatment

Kenneth H. Falchuk, M.D.

Center for Biochemical and Biophysical Sciences and Medicine,
Department of Medicine, Brigham and Women's Hospital, Boston, MA 02155

SUMMARY

Zinc is involved in nearly all aspects of normal metabolism.
However, under pathological conditions, it induces diseases in humans,
animals and plants. The signs and symptoms of the diseases it produces
vary; they are dependent on the tissues or organs affected and whether
the mechanisms underlying the resultant disorders are the consequences
of a deficiency, imbalance or excess. Zinc deficient animals and
humans manifest abnormalities in organs with a high cellular turnover;
for example, skin (parakeratosis, acrodermatitis), intestine (loss of
mucosal cell lining, fibrosis), gonads (hypogonadism and aspermia) or
in organs which are undergoing rapid growth (dwarfism). In addition,
in the developing fetus there are extensive malformations (over 90%) of
all organs. Zinc deficiency can be a) hereditary in nature
(acrodermatitis enteropathica), or b) acquired by dietary deficiency,
ingestion of compounds which bind to and prevent zinc absorption,
surgical removal of the small intestine, administration of
hyperalimentation fluids with no added zinc, etc. Interactions between
zinc and either calcium, copper or cadmium can also lead to disease.
Toxic effects of zinc depend on the route of entry; when inhaled it
causes pulmonary disease, when given intravenously it causes anemia and
fever. The possible molecular bases underlying the effects of
deficiency and toxicity are discussed.

INTRODUCTION

The importance of zinc to biochemistry, biology, pathology, and clinical and veterinary medicine is now generally recognized. Humans contain about 2-3 gms Zn/70 kg. Approximately 10-20 mg zinc are believed to be required and obtained daily through dietary intake. The developing fetus, the pregnant female and the growing child or adolescent have a higher zinc requirement than adult men or nonpregnant females. Most of ingested zinc is excreted in the feces. The fraction which is absorbed enters through the small intestine. The absorptive mechanisms are not well understood. The metal binding protein, metallothionein, has been thought to be involved in the process but unambigous evidence is lacking. Excretion occurs principally through secretions from the gastrointestinal, renal, pancreatic and other exocrine systems. The excretion from the gastrointestinal system occurs mainly through pancreatic secretions and amounts to as much as 1-2mg/day. Zinc normally is excreted in the urine at a rate of 500-800 µg/24hrs and in sweat at 550 µg/24 hrs (1,2).

Nearly all of the element absorbed is distributed within cells which contain over 99% of the total body zinc (2). However, no special tissue storage site for zinc appears to exist. Most tissues contain from 10 to 200 µg/gm wet weight except for the prostate, prostatic secretions and sperm which have even higher amounts. In the cells, it is incorporated into more than 200 metalloenzymes involved in nucleic acid, protein, carbohydrate and lipid metabolism (1,2). It is found in cell membranes, nuclei and other organelles, where it may serve other non-enzymatic functions (3). For example, in the E. gracilis nucleus, the metal has been found to be involved in the regulation of chromatin composition, structure and function (3-9). The generality of these findings to other cell lines needs to be established. Within membranes zinc may be involved in cellular functions such as e.g. phagocytosis, platelet aggregation etc. (10).

1.1 Serum Zinc

Less than 1% of the total zinc is found in the extracellular fluid. Serum contains between 90 to 120 µg% (11). Normally, the serum zinc content is maintained constant. It decreases in conditions of reduced intake or absorption (e.g. regional enteritis) or of increased urinary losses (e.g. nephrotic syndrome, post-alcoholic cirrhosis, during administration of penicillamine, and other chelating agents, diuretics, following trauma, burns, surgery and other high catabolic states, hemolytic anemias, sickle cell disease) (12). It also decreases during the acute phases of diseases involving all organ systems, for example, myocardial infarctions, infections, malignancies, hepatitis and others (Table 1). The low values are restored on recovery from any of these illnesses (11).

Table 1   Serum Zinc Content in Health and Disease

Category	Serum Zinc (μg/100 ml)	PValue
Health	96+20(20)*	
Convalescence	98+20(31)	†
Disease:		
Infectious	44+20(14)	<0.001
Cardiac	67+28(14)	<0.001
Hepatic	46+26(10)	<0.001
Renal	50+20(7)	<0.001
Acute leukemia	65+24(10)	<0.001
Carcinoma	66+20(14)	<0.001
Pulmonary	67+20(8)	<0.001
Neurologic	77+24(10)	<0.02

* Mean + 2 SD, with no. of subjects in parentheses.
† Not significant.

The mechanism for the decreases in these diseases may involve redistribution from plasma to liver and other organs, a process which is believed to be under humoral control. ACTH, adrenal corticosteroids and a protein released from leukocytes are among the humoral components which may be involved (11). The total serum zinc can be separated into two fractions. Approximately 30% is tightly associated with alpha-2-macroglobulin. The remaining, major fraction (70%) is loosely bound to one or more proteins; albumin is believed to be the predominant one. This fraction is accessible to cells and serves as the sole source of metal for their metabolic needs. All of the decreases in serum zinc associated with disease states originate from this fraction, that bound to alpha-2-macroglobulin being stable in these conditions (11).

The decreases in serum zinc which occur in acute diseases (Table 1) usually are associated with concomittant increases in serum copper (13,14) (Fig. 1). On recovery of the acute disease the serum content of both metal returns to normal.

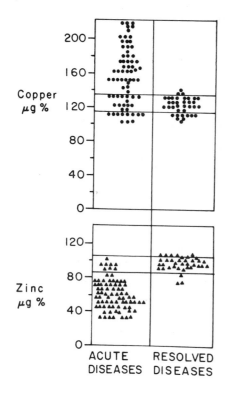

Figure 1. Serum Zinc (▲) and Copper (●) in acute and resolved
diseases.

The relationship is not a fixed one, however. There are conditions
under which decreases in zerum zinc are not associated with
concomittant increases in copper content. Thus, in a population of
patients with low serum zinc suffering from a variety of malignant
diseases, including adenocarcinomas, sarcomas, melanomas, lymphomas,
leukemias, etc, the serum copper is distributed in at least three
distinct groups; those with high, normal or low copper contents. The
physiological, pathological and/or diagnostic significance of the
changes in the two metals is unknown and needs to be elucidated
(Figure 2).

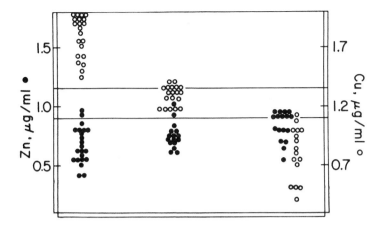

Figure 2. Serum Zinc (●) and copper (O) contents in patients with various malignancies (Falchuk, K.H. and Lokich, J.J., unpublished observations).

2.   Diseases of Zinc Metabolism

2.1 Zinc Deficiency

While it had been known since the 1930s that zinc is an essential nutrient for animals (15), deficiency states in humans were believed to be unlikely. This was thought to be due to the presumed availability of sufficient zinc in all diets. However, a series of reports on Egyptian and Iranians villagers, whose diets were either phytate rich or contained clay and who developed hypogonadal dwarfism reversed with oral zinc supplementation, led to the recognition of zinc deficiency as a clinical entity (16,17).

Zinc deficiency has now been reported in humans with diverse disease conditions. The clinical findings which are now known to be typical of zinc deficiency are listed in (Table 2).

Some cases of deficiency are acquired, others are genetically determined. Acquired deficiency states usually result when dietary intake is inadequate or when intake is adequate but other conditioning factors come into play (Table 3).

Table 2
Signs and Symptoms of Zinc Deficiency

A. General

Decreased zinc content of serum, hair and other tissues.
Decreased activity of some zinc enzymes - alkaline
phosphatases, ? others

B. Tissue specific

Dermatological
Parakeratosis, acrodermatitis, alopecia

Gastrointestinal
Diarrhea and malabsorption

Endocrinological
Failure to develop secondary sexual characteristics
(hypogonadism, aspermia, etc.)

Skeletal
Retardation of growth, bone development

Developmental
Extensive congenital malformations of nearly all fetal organs

Immunological
Thymic aplasia, dysfunction of humoral and cell mediated
immunolgical reactions

Neurological
Behavioral disorders (confusion, apathy)

Acquired deficiencies can be caused by zinc malabsorption in
chronic diarrheal diseases, or formation of metal complexes with
dietary components, e.g. phytates, which are not readily absorbed.
Patients who had undergone surgical removal of their small intestines
and were given intravenous hyperalimentation without zinc
supplementation developed, within weeks, a classic set of
dermatological abnormalities (Table 2). They were cured by zinc
supplementation and were diagnosed as having acquired zinc deficiency
(18). Similar clinical findings have been observed in other patients
who had not had bowel resections but were on long term intravennous
hyperalimentation without zinc supplements. Zinc deficiency also can
result from increased losses through urinary, pancreatic or other
exocrine secretions or from metabolic imbalances produced by
antagonistic or synergistic interactions between metals. Large amounts
of Ca, for example, decrease its absorption and induce deficiency (19).

A genetically determined condition, named acrodermatitis
enteropathica, also is associated with zinc deficiency. It is
transmitted as an autosomal recessive trait in which abnormalities in
zinc absorption are thought to exist. The onset of deficiency often
appears when an affected infant is weaned from human to cow's milk.

The disease was initially described by Brandt in 1936 who reported dermatitis in children with malabsorption syndromes (20). However, it was classified as a discrete entity in 1942 by Danbolt and Closs (21). They described a disease which was characterized by total alopecia, symmetrical, erythematous and vesicopustular dermatitis localized around the mouths, eyes, nostrils, and extremeties. In addition, there was diarrhea, growth retardation, and emotional disturbances. Some suffered from opthalmological disorders such as blepharitis, conjunctivitis, photophobia and/or corneal opacities. Pathological examination of the affected tissues and organs do not reveal abnormalities which can be ascribed to any specific injurious agent. The gastrointestinal tract is mostly normal but there is scattered flattening of intestinal villi and mucosal ulcerations. The lamina propia is infiltrated by lymphocytes. The skin is edematous, there is congestion with lymphocytic infiltration. There is focal necrosis of the dermis. The lymph nodes and spleen show absence of germinal centers and both immature and mature plasma cells in paracortical areas. There is thymic aplasia.

The disease is fatal unless treated. The first major breakthrough in its treatment was with diodoquin, the halogenated derivative of the chelating agent 8-hydroxyquinoline (22). Subsequently, it was replaced by oral zinc supplementation which, on the one hand, was curative and, on the other, confirmed that all of the manifestations of the disease derived from zinc deficiency (23).

Table 3
Human Zinc Deficiency

I. Acquired
       Inadequate Intake or Absorption with Normal Requirements
       Low Dietary zinc content
       Presence of agents in diet that bind zinc and prevent
       absorption (phytates)
       Excessive metals (Ca,Cu) in diet competing for absorption
       pathways
       Post-surgical removal of small bowel
       Malabsorption syndromes

       Total parenteral nutrition without zinc supplementation

II. Acquired
       Standard Intake with Increased Requirements or Excretion
       Chelation Therapy (Penicillamine)
       ?Cirrhosis
       ?Burns
       ?Acute diseases

III. Genetically Induced
       Acrodermatitis Enteropathica

A number of animal models exist which have served to define experimentally the consequences of zinc deficiency in vertebrates. The most extensively studied are those in which nutritional zinc deprivation has been induced, for example, the rat (24). Two other models, of genetic origin, include the lethal trait A46 of cattle (25) and the lethal milk mutation in mice (26,27).

In these systems, zinc deficiency leads to increased abortions or to early death of newborns. The fetus manifests high frequency of congenital malformations of nearly all organ systems (24). Tissues with a high cellular turnover including skin, gastrointestinal mucosa, chondrocytes, sperm and thymocytes are characteristically, but not exclusively, affected (19,24-27). The dermatological abnormalities, hyperkeratosis and parakeratosis, are the most prominent. The usual distribution of the parakeratotic lesions is in areas which are readily traumatized, but they can develop in other areas as well. They can become pustular and/or crusting red scaly plaques. Infections are common with either fungi or bacteria.

2.2 Zinc Toxicity

Toxic effects are dependent on the chemical form, the size of the dose, the route of entry into the body, the biological ligands associated with the metal, the distribution, concentration and excretion within and from organs. Toxicity follows inhalation of zinc fumes by e.g. welders, oral ingestion, intravenous, intramuscular or intratesticular administration (Table 4).

Table 4
Manifestations of Zinc Toxicity

Route of Entry	Effects
Oral	Gastric ulceration and bleeding, nausea, vomiting, diarrhea, pancreatitis
Respiratory	Respiratory distress, pulmonary inflamation and fibrosis.
Intravenous (or by hemodialysis)	Fever, anemia, nausea, vomiting acute tubular necrosis (renal), liver failure, lethargy
Intratesticular	Teratomata
Skin	Contact dermititis (papulopustular eczema)

Zinc toxicity following hemodialysis has been reported and represents an important clinical problem for patients undergoing this treatment. Dialysis fluids can be contaminated with zinc from the adhesive plaster used on the dialysis coils or from galvanized pipes. Its uptake into the blood has led to the development of a toxic syndrome characterized by anemia, fever and central nervous system disturbances (28). Toxic amounts of zinc also decrease chemotaxis, phagocytosis and pinocytosis. Platelet aggregation is reduced as well (10).

3. Molecular Mechanisms of Deficiency or Toxicity

The molecular mechanisms of toxicity include inhibition of enzyme activity by virtue of binding to essential amino acid residues, alterations in nucleic acid function and structure, protein synthesis, membrane permeability, inhibition of phosphorylation, among others (Table 5).

Table 5

Toxic Effects of Zinc on Biological Systems

Molecules	Effect	
	Biochemical	Biological
Nucleic Acids	Altered Structure, Template Function	Carcinogenesis Mutagenesis
Proteins and Enzymes	↓Proteolysis ↓Collagen Formation	?
Lipids	Altered membrane Permeability and Functions	↓Chemotaxis ↓Phagocytosis ↓Pinocytosis ↓Platelet aggregation ↑Lymphocyte ↑mitosis

The metabolic basis for the clinical disorders induced by zinc deficiency still need to be defined. It has not been possible to account for them on the basis of alterations of the functions of zinc in any one, or combinations, of its known metalloenzymes (3). Recent

studies with experimental model systems, however, suggest a role for
zinc in the regulation of the structure, composition and function of
the genome which differs from that of its function in enzymatic
catalysis. The identification of this role for zinc might provide the
molecular mechanism to account for the above clinical manifestations in
terms of effects on genome function induced by its deficiency (3-9).

4. REFERENCES

1. Li, T.K. and Vallee, B.L. (1980) in Modern Nutrition in
    Health and Disease, VI. ed. Goodhart, R.S. and Shils, M.E., Lea
    and Febiger, Phila. Penn., 408-441.
2. Vallee, B.L. (1959) Physiol. Rev., 39:443.
3. Vallee, B.L. and Falchuk, K.H. (1981) Phil. Trans Royal Soc., 185.
4. Falchuk, K.H., Mazus, B., Ulpino, L. and Vallee, B.L. (1976)
    Biochem., 15, 4468.
5. Falchuk, K.H., Fawcett, D.W. and Vallee, B.L. (1975) J. Cell Sci.
    17, 57.
6. Falchuk, K.H., Mazus, B., Ber, E., Ulpino-Lobb, L. and Vallee,
    B.L. (1985) Biochem., 24:2576.
7. Crossley, L.G., Falchuk, K.H. and Vallee, B.L. (1982) Biochem,
    22:5351.
8. Stankiewicz, A.J., Falchuk, K.H. and Vallee, B.L. (1984) Biochem.,
    22:5150.
9. Mazus, B., Falchuk, K.H. and Vallee, B.L. (1985) Biochem., 23:42.
10. Chapvil, M., Zukoski, C.F., Hattler, B.G. et al., (1976) in Trace
    Elements in Human Health and Diseases, Vol. 1, ed. Prasad A.S. and
    Oberleas, D., Academic Press, N.Y., 269-281.
11. Falchuk, K.H. (1977) New Eng. J. Med. 269:1129.
12. Cuthberton, D.P., Fell, A.S., Smith, C.M. et al., (1972) Br. J.
    Sing. 59:925.
13. Fell, G.S., Canning, E., Husain, S.L. and Scott, R. (1972) in
    Trace Elements in Environmental Health, ed. Hemphill, D.D.,
    University of Missouri, Columbia, Missouri, 293-301.
14. Karcinoglu, Z.A., Karcioglu, G.L., Sarper, R.M. and Hrgovcic, M.
    (1980) in Zinc and Copper in Medicine, ed. Karcioglu, Z.A. and
    Sarper, R.M., 464-534, Charles C. Thomas, Springfield, Ill.
15. Todd, W.R., Elvejheim, C.A., and Hart, E.B. (1934) Am. J.
    Physiol.107:146.
16. Prasad, A.S. (1966) in Zinc Metabolism, ed. A.S. Prasad, 250-303
    Charles C. Thomas, Springfield, Ill.

17. Halsted, J.A., Ronaghy, H.A., Abadi, P., Haghshenass, M., Amirhakemi, G.H., Barakat, R.M., Reinhold, J.G., (1972) <u>Am. J. Med.</u>, <u>53</u>:277.

18. Kay, R.G., Tasman-Jones, C., Pybus, J., Whiting, R., and Black, H. (1976) <u>Ann. Surg.</u>, <u>183</u>(4):331.

19. Tucker, H.F. and Salmon, W.D. (1955) <u>Proc. Soc. Exp. Biol. Med.</u>, 1955 88:613.

20. Brandt, T. (1936) <u>Acta Derm.-Veneneol.</u>, <u>17</u>:513.

21. Danbert, N. and Closs, K. (1942) <u>Acta Derm. Vener Stockh.</u>, <u>22</u>:17.

22. Dillaha, C.Z., Lorincz, A.L., Aarvik, O.N. (1953) <u>J. Am. Med. Ass.</u> <u>152</u>:509.

23. Barnes, P.M. and Moynaham, E.J. (1973) <u>Proc. R. Soc. Med.</u>, <u>66</u>:327.

24. Hurley, L.S. and Swenerton, H., (1966) <u>Proc. Soc. Exp. Biol. Med.</u>, <u>123</u>:692.

25. McPherson, E.A., Beatlis, I.S., Young, G.B. (1964) <u>Nord Vet. Med.</u>, 16 (Suppl 1) 533.

26. Green, M.C. and Sweet, H.O. (1973) <u>Mouse News Letter</u>, <u>48</u>:35.

27. Piletz, J.E. and Ganschow, R.E. (1978) <u>Science</u>, <u>199</u>:181.

28. Gallery, E.D.M., Blomfield, J. and Dixon, S.R. (1972) <u>Br. Med. J.</u>, <u>4</u>:331.

From Theory to Therapy: How to Make a New Drug Out of a New Idea

Karl H. Beyer, Jr.

Department of Pharmacology, The Milton S. Hershey Medical Center, The Pennsylvania State University, Hershey, Pennsylvania, USA

SUMMARY

The better the clinical correlates of a disease are understood, the more closely they are approximated in the laboratory, the more carefully primary and secondary attributes and safety assessment of an interesting new compound have been studied and the more thoroughly they are understood at the preclinical level, the more likely it is to survive thoughtful clinical study in well selected patients and to become a useful new drug - if it has survived such studies to merit that distinction.

1 INTRODUCTION

In the Abstract of this talk I mentioned words like luck, serendipity, designed discovery as part of the history of drug therapy. Today, I shall explain how you might go about making a new drug out of an interesting idea or agent - the excitement, the pitfalls, the time, the cost.

I wrote a book entitled "The Discovery, Development and Delivery of New Drugs" (1) and have used it in a course to teach graduate students in Pharmacology what this is all about. Their professors usually don't know any more about this subject than you; few people do.

I hope that what I shall have to say about drug discovery and development will be helpful. This general subject has been my career from the time I started preparing for it, when I was 12 years old, until the other day when Mrs. Beyer and I left home for this meeting and the beautiful Country of Portugal. In other words, drug discovery and development is the way I live. It is my way of combining a dedication to Medicine with a love for Chemistry.

Anyone who has been so fortunate as to share in the discovery and development of a useful new drug knows this to be one of the most self-rewarding experiences imaginable.

2 PERSPECTIVE

Most people who become involved in the discovery of a new drug just happen to do so. Just as in the past most drugs just happened to be discovered. Serendipity is the more elegant expression of such happenstance. Some people declare drug discovery is all luck - even my friends who have never discovered a new drug.

There is nothing wrong in happening to become interested in whether a new compound might be a useful drug. Such an interest outside the structure of the pharmaceutical industry is likely to be the province of an alert, inquisitive mind in an individual who wants to do something worthwhile. His or her reasons for wanting to become involved in bringing that new concept or observation to fruition as a new drug are likely to be personal, professional, seldom pecuniary.

But, regardless of how good a chemist, a bioinorganic chemist for instance, that person is he must realize rather soon that getting from theory to therapy is something for which he is not entirely prepared.

The purpose of this lecture is to help such an individual make that transition from theory to therapy. I hope each of you will be that person, sooner or later.

Each of you knows something about the early history of heavy metals in medicine and about the empirical medicinal use of botanical concoctions. Whole areas of knowledge had to be developed before organic and inorganic chemistry could be put together in synthesis of organometalic compounds so that the metals might be carried reasonably safely to where they were usefully effective. Of course, a whole phylogeny of organisms had done this sort of very sophisticated bioinorganic chemistry since their very beginnings, to catalyse specific bioorganic reactions. You and I call such compounds enzymes. You know that sulfur, zinc, copper, iron all serve such a catalytic role in enzymes, and that most of the elements in the periodic chart are either essential to normal life or are useful to us in our role as normal person or patient.

Some of the more simple remedies you know as formulations of elements would include ferrous carbonate for iron deficiency anemia. The doctors of old prescribed this as Blaud's Pills dating back to the French physician by that name who introduced the pills in 1831 for the treatment of chlorosis. Zinc oxide ointment has been as much a part of dermatology as aspirin has been the pediatrician's standby. Back when I was a youngster most everyone who went to an Ear, Nose and Throat Doctor came out of his office with a purplish black mouth, his throat having been swabbed with a silver proteinate formulation called Argyrol. I'm not sure how much Argyrol helped our sore throats, but at least it was not well absorbed or my sisters and I still would have argyrism, which is a bluish cast to one's skin. Argyrol is gone today, but the originator left behind the Barnes Collection of Art, French Impressionists mostly, in Philadelphia that is as well known among artists as his silver proteinate product used to be among physicians.

At an international meeting like this we could spend hours swapping such stories native to our homelands. Any list of such products would serve as an introduction to what you need to understand if you are going to try to develop a new drug.

In truth, a new drug should be effective and it should be safe. These are its principal attributes; efficacy and safety. Having made this declaration that the new drug should be safe and effective or effective and safe, I should like to pass along to you a quotation I hope you never forget. It is a part of my philosophy of research - of life. To quote: "Science progresses by successive approximations to the truth."

In the framework of this lecture the statement that science progresses by successive approximations to the truth means that we evaluate and understand both the utility and safety of our new drugs within the limits of knowledge and methodology of the day. This does not necessarily mean that your own insight into your new concept or new compound has to comply with knowledge commonly believed by those versed in your art. New drug research is innovative, it is discovery. The basis for your contribution has its roots in common knowledge, but don't let it bother you if your best friend doesn't really believe you are right; so long as your command of that area of knowledge in which your inventions is rooted is sound. Indeed, you may find it difficult at first to express your new idea or concept of what your new substance does, or where it might be useful. Never mind, you and ultimately your collaborators may have to develop a whole body of knowledge to support your work, but that is part of the fun of it all. In other words, don't dismiss your new idea or new observation just because it may be inconsistent with what you were taught or the experts believe to be true. Even if your dream comes true and you discover a new drug, you probably will never understand how it works or what it does as thoroughly as you would like.

What you must do is carry out thoroughly as much of the research on your new idea as is within your expertise. This is a must, if you are going to convince others to participate in making a new drug out of your new idea.

3 BACKGROUND FOR YOUR NEW OBSERVATION

I hesitate to take an example to illustrate the processes that go into the development of a new drug in the field of bioinorganic chemistry, but I will try. From the foregoing examples everybody knows that administration of an iron salt is necessary to correct an iron deficiency anemia. Ferrous salts are better than ferric salts, but iron is not well absorbed when administered in oral dosage forms. Intramuscular and intravenous iron formulations have their problems too, from a safety standpoint. If you give too much iron over too long a period of time it gets stored in the liver as hemosiderosis, etc., etc.

4 YOUR DISCOVERY

Everybody knows that iron, to be useful, must be in the form of hemoglobin, ultimately. But let's assume you have told me that from your own research you have found that copper seems to facilitate the synthesis of hemoglobin and so does zinc. You find it fascinating that the rate of hemoglobin synthesis is greatest if the iron-containing culture medium for your experiments is first charged with an organic copper salt and then with zinc. This facilitation of hemoglobin synthesis does not occur if the two, zinc and copper, are presented in the reverse order or when the system is charged with copper and zinc concurrently! (Now please understand I don't know a thing about hemoglobin synthesis. After all, this is your research, not mine. It's your idea, your area of expertise!) I note that this research of yours is being done in tissue culture. This is fine. I gather that you have worked with the technique for years.

As you continue to explore this interesting phenomenon, you find that it is characteristic of cells known to synthesize hemoglobin, but not of other tissues. Characteristics that determine rate optima vary somewhat with corresponding tissue from the several species you have studied, including human. In other words, the basic observation wherein iron and copper salts are added to the medium, followed by the addition of zinc within a certain time frame obtains in the corresponding tissue of several species, as a generalization. You probably have some thoughts about your discovery, about what is happening. It's time for a next step along the road to your new drug.

5 YOUR CONCEPT OF INVENTION

(For the moment, we shall refer to this observation, your discovery, as your invention. You and I don't think of our work this way, but the patent attorney does.)

When you get to the point where you feel the observation is real and may have therapeutic application, you should write what is called a "Concept of Invention," date and sign it, explain what it means to someone who will respect your confidence, and have that person sign and date the document, also. (If you are a chemist trained in biology, you are likely to date and at least initial the experiments in your notebook. If you are a biologist who knows some chemistry, you are more likely to neglect this nicety. A dated notebook and Concept of Invention may be needed to establish your priority in case your patent application is thrown into interference with a similar patent application filed by someone else.)

Your Concept of Invention only needs to state briefly your observation and your anticipation that it facilitates the synthesis of hemoglobin, important to the treatment of iron deficient anemias. This helps establish that the invention is yours, that it may have an utility, that the Patent Application will be in your name. All this is important to you and to the institution in which you work.

6   THE PRECLINICAL EVALUATION

Having done this basic research in tissue culture, you are a long, long way from trying it out on your friends or anyone else. First, you should be able to show that the invention can be reduced to practice, that it works, in one or more laboratory animals. If this is beyond your capability, you will need to convince someone who knows how to create iron deficient anemia in laboratory animals that your discovery is worth his collaboration. There actually are ways to create the appropriate anemia in animals, but unless your associate has already confirmed the literature that illustrates the reversal of anemia by iron, you certainly will want assurance (i.e., data) that he can reproduce those results. That should not be a serious problem, but you may have great difficulty in finding the proper conditions for demonstrating your new phenomenon in animals. You are going to learn a lot more than you thought you wanted to know about your basic discovery before you have completed an adequate Preclinical Evaluation, as this phase of the work is called. What you do at this stage should help to determine the conditions for Clinical Trial and whether it is even safe to go to Clinical Trial.

Each Preclinical Experiment should be so designed that it yields helpful information toward designing the next experiment. For instance, if you give the iron and copper salts and then the zinc salt orally and nothing happens to the anemia, all may not be lost. Did you design the experiment so you know that the several elements were actually absorbed and got to where you wanted them, and in effective concentrations? You might think that an intramuscular or intravenous route of administration would be more appropriate. This is not necessarily so.

You had better talk to a respected Internist friend in your Medical Department

before you get too far along with your "Preclinical." You need to know the realities
of current treatment of anemias. Your clinical consultant may tell you that deficiency of iron is probably the most common nutritional disorder in the world. Although this deficiency is more common in underdeveloped countries of the world, their
problem is nutrition. Elsewhere medical causes are the more important. In either
case there is effective, cheap iron therapy. To be an outstanding innovation, your
new therapy will have to be better tolerated. It will have to work faster and be
more effective when administered orally once-a-day as a capsule or tablet than current therapy. The market potential for such a product could be tremendous, but it
would have to be truly innovative to be of much interest. Knowing all this helps as
one designs the preclinical research.

The design of the experiments in anemic animals needs to incorporate (1) untreated
controls, (2) other controls employing an iron salt commonly used in therapy and (3)
variations in the combination of iron, copper and zinc salts. It is not important at
this stage that the formulation of iron, copper and zinc salts be what is ultimately
employed clinically, or that the mode of administration is the practical one in
therapy. What you need to do is to show in anemic animals that the proper sequencing
of copper and zinc salts facilitates the synthesis of hemoglobin. If you can do
this, you may have the basis for a patent.

7 THE PATENT APPLICATION

It is time to discuss the invention with your patent attorney, but not the time to
publish. If you do not file your patent application in the USA within one year of
publication, it will not be allowed. If you publish before you file in the USA, your
application will usually not be accepted in other countries. Moreover, the attorney
may want the assurance that you actually have a formulation suitable for clinical
trial. Indeed, he may advise you to wait until the first clinical tests support your
claim structure; that the proper combination or sequence of iron, copper and zinc
does work better, faster and is well tolerated. Hopefully, your biochemical research
indicates a rationale for why it works. For instance, whereas you have shown that
both copper and zinc are required in the catalysis of hemoglobin synthesis in the
anemic state, you may have found that zinc catalysed systems actually divert or block
copper-catalysis in a cascade synthesis of hemoglobin, if both are available concurrently, or zinc is available first. The reason for going this far before filing
your patent is that unless some really novel salt of one or more of these metals is
required in the formulation of your potential product, you may end up with a process
patent rather than a product patent, in this example. Either one is fine, but a
product patent is usually the stronger; but enough of that.

Your Preclinical Studies need to include what's good about the formulation and
what's bad about it. Another way of looking at the matter is that (1) in addition to

studying its primary attribute (the effect on anemia), you should assess (2) its
secondary attributes; like whether it produces diarrhea, or hypotension, or changes
in the animal's behavior. (3) One more critical type of study at the preclinical
level is the safety assessment of your formulation.

8 PRODUCT FORMULATION

A word about your formulation and its safety assessment. Remember, I said it
should be in a single dosage form; capsule or tablet. Since you found you need iron
and copper available at the same time, a rapid-released double salt of an organic compound might be suitable with the zinc being released from a second organic complex
more slowly. Another way to do this would be to put suitable organic salts of iron
and copper in separate fast-release microencapsulated form and the zinc salt in a
similar but slow-release form; all these put together in a single conventional capsule. Whatever the formulation for clinical trial, this is the one that should be
submitted for safety assessment before clinical trial.

9 COLLABORATION WITH A PHARMACEUTICAL COMPANY

At this point, I am a little ahead of my story. When you have demonstrated your
principle that sequential availability of copper and zinc increases the rate of hemoglobin synthesis in laboratory animals convincingly, you have done your job. You
should go then to a pharmaceutical company that has the research capability to develop the rest of the preclinical, including formulation and safety assessment, and
ultimately the clinical assessment of your new therapy for you.

How you go about developing this relationship with such a company, what your ar-
rangements, both research and financial should be, who should assume responsibility
for getting your patents for you, the involvement of your institution as well as
yourself in the agreements, etc., is more than enough for another few hours, more
time than we have here. Your Agreement, if it comes to that, will be with the
company, not the nice people who were excited about your data, except as they have
input to corporate management. It may cost the company between twenty-five and one-
hundred-million dollars and ten years of staff time to develop your product and to
build the facilities to bring it to a world market. Quite a risk for even a big
company, but no greater than for the fruits of its own research efforts. Then, too,
companies like people vary a great deal in their understanding of a technical situation (like yours), in their resources, and in their willingness to accept financial
risks.

10 OVERVIEW OF NEW DRUG ASSESSMENT

There are four steps that may help at the research level of product development that should be mentioned.

(1) <u>Do what you know how to do</u> and for which you have the capacity and leave the rest to people who have the other talents. Time was when you could have given ferrous carbonate to an anemic patient and discovered that it helped. That was a long, long time ago when preclinical and clinical research capabilities were no better developed than your own science, and when government regulatory agencies had not yet been invested with authority to assure the safety and efficacy of new drugs.

(2) <u>Safety assessment is no place to experiment with a new drug</u>. Neither is it a place to cut corners with respect to adequacy of assessment. The less expertly safety assessment is done the greater the likelihood of creating imponderable observations the uncertainty of which can haunt the clinical study and the interactions with regulatory agencies for years.

(3) <u>The more thorough the preclinical assessment</u> of primary and secondary attributes of a new drug the more likely a sensible explanation and successful handling of vicissitudes that are bound to occur in the clinical trials. Be prepared!

(4) <u>The proper selection of subjects and patients</u> for the <u>clinical studies</u> is paramount. It has been said that the proper study of man is man, but this implies that the clinical studies be well conceived and clearly interpretable. The understatement of this talk would be that not all clinical studies qualify as definitive for many good reasons as well as bad. Moreover, the regulatory agents seem to require more and more studies on more and more patients for longer and longer periods of time. Only a pharmaceutical company can afford the millions of dollars and years of effort it takes to get the product to the practicing physician.

I have selected a relatively simple example (it says here) for your new therapeutic agent in that we know iron is necessary for hemoglobin synthesis, and that iron deficient anemia can be relieved by ferrous salts. Things are frequently much more complex. For instance, clinical research reports on the use of lithium in clinical depression range from effective to ineffective. Part of the problem is our poor understanding of clinical depression. In a way it would be like assessing penicillin in pneumonia if we had no knowledge of microbiology. Gold salts can be useful or devastating in arthritis and platinum seems to have such a record in cancer chemotherapy. I teach my students that organomercurials are useful diuretics when injected intramuscularly, but to inject them intravenously is to invite sudden cardiac death. Fortunately, that disaster doesn't happen often. <u>Luck</u> is more likely to be bad luck than good in drug research, and <u>serendipity</u> is a lovely word but a lonely way to discovery.

I hope that I have helped you understand what is ahead if you undertake to discover and develop a new drug. You really should not be discouraged. Much of modern therapy has progressed the course I have described, and I have followed this trail many times. You can do it too, with lots of help from others.

I can wrap up all this in one sentence, one bit of advice. It is this. The better job and the better understanding at each step of the way the more likely your success as you proceed "From theory to therapy." It can be a wonderfully exciting experience most of the time - but some days it may seem more like only some of the time.

11 REFERENCES

(1) K. H. Beyer, Discovery, Development and Delivery of New Drugs, Spectrum Publica-
    tions, Inc., 1978.

Gold Drugs

Susan J. Berners Price, Peter J. Sadler

Department of Chemistry, Birkbeck College,
Malet Street, London WC1E 7HX, U.K.

SUMMARY

   The intriguing coordination chemistry of gold related to its use as an injectable or orally-active antiarthritic drug and potential anti-cancer agent is reviewed.

1 INTRODUCTION

   Current interest in the pharmacology of gold drugs centres on the continued use of injectable gold(I) thiolates for the treatment of rheumatoid arthritis, and the recent approval by the FDA for clinical use of the orally-active, anti-arthritic gold(I) phosphine drug, auranofin, "Ridaura" [(2,3,4,6-tetra-O-acetyl-1-thio-β-D-glucopyranos-ato-S)(triethylphosphine)gold].

   Several reviews have been published in recent years summarising the biochemistry and inorganic chemistry of these and related gold compounds (1-4). This review updates the current state of the art with respect to characterisation, and to biologically-relevant reactions of gold, including recent studies of the cytotoxicity and anti-tumour activity of auranofin.

2 HISTORY

   Modern interest in the medicinal chemistry of gold can be traced

back to Robert Koch's discovery in 1890 of the in vitro antitubercular
activity of gold cyanide. This was too toxic for clinical use, but during the next 30 years several gold(I) thiolates were introduced for the
treatment of tuberculosis. The period 1925-35 has been termed the "gold
decade" in tuberculosis treatment. It was during this period that Landé
first introduced gold compounds for the treatment of non-tubercular infections. He mistakenly believed that a relationship existed between
polyarthritis and tuberculosis, but nevertheless reported that gold therapy brought about significant reductions in joint pain in arthritic
patients. This prompted Forestier, in 1935, to investigate the use of
gold drugs in rheumatoid arthritis, and gold(I) thiolates have been in
clinical use ever since (1-4).

3 GOLD IN RHEUMATOID ARTHRITIS

3.1 Gold(I) thiolates

Despite the long history of gold(I) thiolates in arthritis therapy,
their mechanism of action is still uncertain. Furthermore, it is only
within the last few years that the solid state and solution structures,
and biologically relevant ligand-exchange reactions of these compounds
have been investigated in detail.

The two gold compounds most commonly employed in chrysotherapy are
aurothiomalate ("Myocrisin") and aurothioglucose ("Solganol"). Neither
of these compounds appears to crystallise and so it has not yet been
possible to elucidate their structures by X-ray diffraction techniques.
Two groups have used EXAFS measurements to study both solid and solution
structures of Myocrisin and Solganol (5,6). In all cases, gold was
found to be coordinated by two sulphur atoms 2.3 Å away, which provided
convincing evidence that these compounds are polymeric with bridging
sulphurs. The degree of polymerisation is not certain but some molecular
weight measurements have suggested hexamer formation (7). There are no
examples of crystalline 1:1 gold(I) thiolate complexes, but a twisted
double-strand chain structure has been determined for a crystalline 1:1
silver(I) thiolate complex ($AgSCMeEt_2$) in the solid; this dissociates
into octameric cyclic units in solution (8).

Grootveld and Sadler have recently put forward evidence to show that
up to 23% of gold in solid samples of aurothiomalate is structurally
different to the remainder (9). The existence of non-equivalent gold
environments was also suggested from both the EXAFS (5,6) and [197]Au
Mössbauer spectra (10). In the latter case the high-velocity line was

broader and of reduced intensity compared to the other one.   Dissolution
studies have shown that structural changes occur immediately after
dissolution of aurothiomalate in water (9).   The solution is initially
yellow, but becomes colourless over a period of about 30 minutes at room
temperature.   These spectrophotometric changes can be reversed by the
addition of salts.   It is possible that the yellow colour is associated
with short gold-gold contacts and the coiling of chains.   Structural
changes dependent on ionic strength were also detected by ^{1}H and ^{13}C
NMR (7) and interpreted as an interconversion between compact and more
flexible forms of the polymer.

The characterisation of Myocrisin and interpretation of its ligand-
exchange reactions have been further complicated by the recent discovery
that the clinically-used drug contains a gold:thiomalate ratio of less
than 1:1.   Perrett and coworkers have separated excess thiomalate from
Myocrisin by HPLC methods (11), and Grootveld and Sadler have used a
spectrophotometric method, involving the reduction of ferric cytochrome
c, to estimate that solid samples of aurothiomalate contain a 9.4% molar
excess of thiomalate over gold (12).   The excess thiolate is
probably bound to gold, giving chain species containing both bridging
and terminal thiomalates (Figure 1).

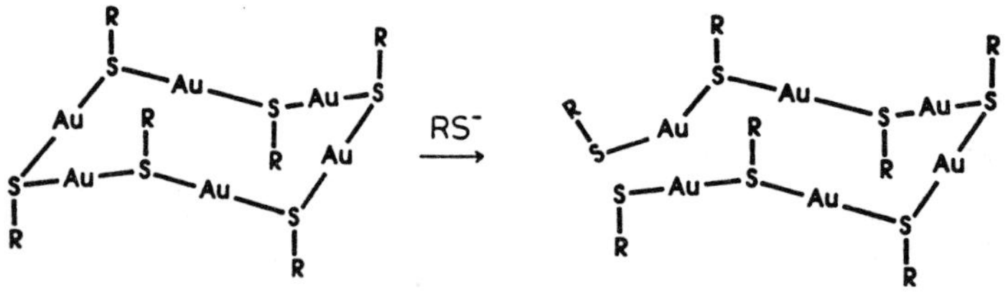

Fig. 1   A possible ring structure for a 1:1 gold:thiomalate complex
         showing how addition of a small excess of thiomalate   may lead
         to chain species (12).

Several groups have studied the ligand exchange reactions of aurothiomalate with excess thiols.   Isab and Sadler originally suggested
that the reaction of Myocrisin with excess thiomalate (tm) produced
$[Au_4tm_7]^{3-}$ clusters (13,14).   However, if the result is corrected to
take into account the presence of excess thiomalate in the Myocrisin
sample, then the Au:S stoichiometry of the product is close to 1:2, as
expected for $[Au(tm)_2]^{-}$.   A variety of other thiols, including glutathione and cysteine, react with aurothiomalate (14,15,16,17) according
to the equations:

$$\frac{1}{n}(Autm)_n + RSH \rightleftharpoons [tm - Au - SR]^- + H^+$$

$$RSH + [tm - Au - SR]^- \rightleftharpoons [RS - Au - SR]^- + tmH$$

Thus, thiomalate is released in the presence of excess thiol and this may account for the observation of free thiomalate in the plasma and urine of aurothiomalate-treated patients (18).

Thiol-exchange reactions are expected to play a significant role in the biochemistry of gold thiolate drugs. Most of the circulating Au in blood is localised in the plasma fraction and is bound to albumin (2). Shaw and coworkers have investigated the binding of aurothiomalate to bovine serum albumin using ^{197}Au Mössbauer and X-ray absorption spectroscopy (19). They proposed that gold binds tightly to cys-34 of albumin to form Alb-Cys-S-Au-tm, with additional weaker binding of gold, perhaps via bridging thiomalate.

Red cells from patients treated with Myocrisin usually have a low gold content (20), but gold levels are considerably higher for smokers rather than non-smokers. Cyanide is inhaled in tobacco smoke, and reaction of aurothiomalate with cyanide may break down polymeric Au(tm) and enhance the uptake of gold into red cells (21). Reactions of cyanide with aurothiomalate in vitro lead to $[Au(CN)_2]^-$ and $[Au(tm)(CN)]^-$ as products (22).

3.2 Gold(I) phosphines and auranofin

Perhaps the most significant advance in the use of gold therapy for rheumatoid arthritis has been the development of the orally-active gold(I) phosphine complexes. Gold(I) thiolates are administered by injection, and cause toxic side-effects in approximately 40% of patients. The most severe problem is nephrotoxicity, which occurs as a result of a large accumulation of gold in the kidneys. In the mid 1960's, Sutton and coworkers at SK & F Laboratories began a search for orally-active gold compounds. They hoped that these would allow gold levels to be maintained by a low daily dose, thus preventing the large build up of gold in tissues which follows large injected doses.

A series of phosphino gold(I) complexes, R_3PAuCl, were found to exhibit oral antiarthritic and antiinflammatory activity in animal models. The maximum absorption and activity was observed when the coordinated phosphine was Et_3P (23). However, diarrhoea was a troublesome side-effect in initial clinical trials on Et_3PAuCl, and it was abandoned

in favour of the acetylated thioglucose derivative auranofin, which was
selected for clinical development. Under the tradename "Ridaura", it
received approval by the FDA on 24 May 1985 for marketing for drug use
in the United States.

The results of clinical trials on auranofin to date suggest that its
efficacy approaches that of aurothiomalate, and that is relatively well
tolerated in most patients. The most common side-effects are diarrhoea
and skin rash (20,24). Auranofin appears to have a contrasting pharmo-
kinetic profile to aurothiomalate (Table 1), and this is primarily a
result of the greater lipophilicity of the drug, which is presumably
responsible for its oral absorption.

Table 1 Comparative pharmacokinetic data for auranofin and auro-
         thiomalate (adapted from (20))

	auranofin	aurothiomalate
Oral absorption	ca 25%	< 1%
Blood distribution: cell-bound	ca 40%	< 1%
protein-bound	ca 60%	ca 99%
Steady state blood [Au]	3-3.5 μM^a	15-36 μM^b
Excretion: faecal	85%	30%
renal	15%	70%
Body retention after 6 months (1 dose)	< 1%	25-42%

[a] 6 mg oral/day   [b] 50 mg intramuscular/week

In contrast to the gold(I) thiolate drugs, auranofin is crystalline,
and its structure has been determined in the solid state by X-ray
diffraction (25), and in solution by NMR methods (26). It is monomeric
with almost linear coordination P-Au-S (Figure 2).

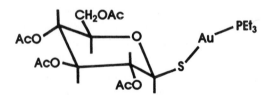

Fig. 2 The structure of auranofin ("Ridaura") as determined by X-ray
        crystallography (25)

Little is known about the site of auranofin absorption or the form
of the drug circulating in patients after its administration. The fate

of auranofin in the presence of acid has been investigated by several
groups, in an attempt to predict the likely form of the drug in the
stomach. Hydrolysis of acetyl groups was observed by ^{1}H (17) and ^{13}C
(27) NMR. At 298 K in 0.1 M HCl the half-life for hydrolysis is about
6 hours. In acidic-methanol solution the reaction is much more rapid.
Hempel and Mikuriya (28) identified four products from a 1:1 mixture of
auranofin:HCl in MeOH:H_2O (95:15 v/v), 20 minutes after mixing: auranofin itself, tetracetylthioglucose, Et_3PAuCl, and a bis-gold(I) sulo-
phonium compound $[(TATG)Au(PEt_3)_2]^+$. The kinetics of the reaction have
been investigated by spectrophotometric titrations (29). The intestinal absorption of auranofin has been studied, in vitro, by the everted
sac method (30). The drug was found to be deacylated on passing through
the rat gut wall.

The Au-P bond has been shown to be stable at pH 7 by ^{31}P NMR (26),
and release of phosphine does not occur readily in most model reactions.
However, studies with ^{195}Au-, ^{35}S- and ^{32}P-radiolabelled auranofin in
dogs (31), have shown that ^{35}S and ^{32}P are excreted more rapidly than
^{195}Au, and Et_3PO has been identified as a major metabolite in the urine
of auranofin-treated patients (20). Razi and coworkers have observed
release of Et_3P in whole human blood, in vitro, using ^{31}P NMR (12,15).
After incubation of 0.7 mM auranofin in whole blood for 5.5 hours, the
^{31}P NMR spectrum showed peaks for Et_3PO and two types of gold-bound
phosphine. The plasma fraction contained all the Et_3PO, whereas the
red-cell fraction contained both types of gold-bound PEt_3 (Figure 3).
The ^{31}P NMR chemical shifts suggested that the gold is bound to thiolate sulphurs. ^{1}H NMR studies show that intracellular glutathione is
involved, the other site may be in the cell membrane. The rate at
which Et_3P was displaced from auranofin-treated red cells was found to
be greatly enhanced by treatment with a lipophilic dithiol, dimercapto-
propanol (15). Endogenous thiols in hydrophobic (membrane) sites may
play an important role in phosphine release reactions. Once the
phosphine has been released the products of auranofin metabolism could
be similar to the products of the metabolites of Myocrisin. However,
the phosphine may deliver the gold to hydrophobic sites not available
to Myocrisin-derived gold and the phosphine, once released, may exhibit
biological activity in its own right (vide infra).

3.3 Mechanisms of action

Although the discovery of auranofin has brought about renewed interest in the pharmacology of gold drugs, their mode of action is not yet
understood. This is perhaps not unexpected in view of the fact that

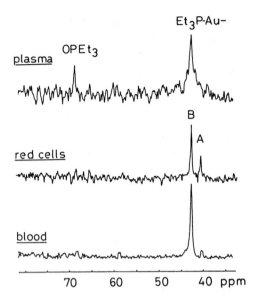

Fig. 3 $\{^1H\}^{31}P$ NMR spectra of <u>A</u> whole blood containing 0.7 mM auranofin; <u>B</u> the separated red cells, and <u>C</u> the separated plasma. The two types of Et$_3$PAu species observed in red cells may correspond to binding to intracellular glutathione and to thiolate sulphurs in the cell membrane. A small amount of Et$_3$P is released into the plasma as Et$_3$PO.

the exact etiology and pathogenesis of rheumatoid arthritis are also unclear. Gold drugs have been shown to have an effect on many aspects of the disease state and consequently a number of different mechanisms have been proposed (Table 2).

Table 2 Some possible mechanisms of action of gold drugs

(1)	Modulation of the immune responses: humoral or cell-mediated
(2)	Inhibition of the formation of immune complexes
(3)	Inhibition of synovial cell proliferation and collagen synthesis
(4)	Inhibition of lysosomal enzyme synthesis, release or activity
(5)	Inhibition of prostaglandin synthesis
(6)	Regulation of copper and zinc metabolism

The most prominent theories suggest that gold acts by immunological mechanisms and alters lysosomal enzyme activity (24). Both
humoral and cell-mediated responsiveness are thought to play a role in
the pathogenesis of the disease and gold interacts with various components of the immune system producing immunosuppressive and immuno-
enhancing effects (32). Mechanisms involving alteration of lysosomal
enzyme activity are favoured because gold accumulates within the syn-
ovium in the lysosomes of synovial cells and macrophages. The gold-
laden deposits are referred to as aurosomes. Using X-ray absorption
spectroscopy, Elder and coworkers (6) have investigated the form of gold
in aurosomes following treatment of rats with both aurothiomalate and
$[AuCl_4]^-$. The spectra were analysed in terms of gold(I) bound to two
sulphur atoms at a distance of 2.3 Å. It is conceivable that this is
a form of gold metallothionein. Trace metal interactions may be important in gold biochemistry. Abnormal copper and zinc metabolism is
associated with rheumatoid arthritis, and Shaw and coworkers (33) have
shown that gold displaces these metals from horse kidney and rat liver
metallothionein.

4 ANTITUMOUR ACTIVITY OF GOLD COMPOUNDS

An important difference between the pharmacological profiles of
auranofin and aurothiomalate is that auranofin exhibits potent in vitro
cytotoxic activity against a variety of tumour lines (34,36). Lorber
and coworkers investigated the in vivo tumour activity of auranofin
and found increased survival times of mice with P388 leukaemia (35).
Recently auranofin has been screened in 15 tumour models (36). It was
active only in i.p. (intraperitoneal) P388 leukaemia, and required i.p.
administration for activity. A number of other phosphino gold(I)
complexes including Ph_3PAuCl have also shown antitumour activity (37,38),
and there is current interest in investigating the likely mechanisms
of action of these compounds.

It seems unlikely that cytotoxicity will involve the binding of gold
to O- or N-donor atoms of DNA. DNA-binding interactions are generally
accepted to be involved in the antitumour activity of Pt(II) complexes,
but Au(I) is a very much softer metal ion than Pt(II) and there are
very few examples of stable gold(I) complexes containing N-ligands.
Blank and Dabrowiak (39) have investigated the interactions of a series
of gold(I) complexes with calf thymus DNA using absorption and circular
dichroism spectroscopy. They observed no interaction for auranofin but
Et_3PAuCl and Et_3PAuBr did bind, showing a preference for guanine and
cytosine residues.

We have recently prepared a series of triethylphosphine gold(I) complexes with imido ligands (40,41). Of particular interest is a new riboflavin complex which was highly active in the carrageenan anti-inflammatory assay. Through the use of ^{15}N-labelled complexes and the observation of $^2J(^{31}P-^{15}N)$ couplings by ^{31}P (and ^{15}N) NMR, we were able to establish P-Au-N coordination for these imido complexes in solution (Figure 4). Similar NMR studies should prove useful for investigating possible binding interactions of R_3PAu^+ species with nucleic acid bases. Our studies have shown that P-Au-N bonds are stable in solution, but N-ligands are readily displaced by softer S-containing ligands in model reactions (40).

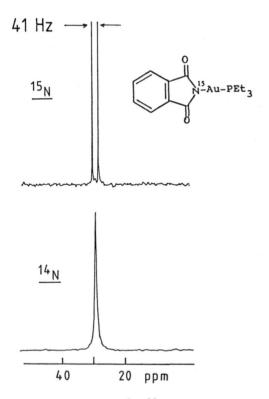

Fig. 4   24.2 MHz $\{^1H\}^{31}P$ spectra of Et$_3$PAuN(phthalimide) in CDCl$_3$ with (A) ^{15}N in natural abundance (0.4%) and (B) ^{15}N enriched to 98.9%.

It has been reported that the cytotoxic cellular response to auranofin is rapid (36). B16 melanoma cells treated with auranofin at concentrations as low as 1 μM for 2 h showed extensive morphological alterations, including surface membrane pitting, cell rounding and

membrane lysis. This suggests that the cytotoxicity of auranofin is
due to its effects on cellular processes other than DNA, RNA or protein
synthesis. It is possible that the phosphine ligand is involved in the
cytotoxic process and that the role of the gold is to transport the
ligand inside cells. K[Au(CN)$_2$] has been shown to exhibit significant
activity in several tumour models including a 50% cure rate for Lewis
lung carcinoma. Similarly, it has been suggested that the function of
the gold is merely to transport CN$^-$ inside cells, where it inhibits
essential enzymes (38).

It is known that Et$_3$P is oxidised to Et$_3$PO during the metabolism of
auranofin (20), but it is not known when the P-Au bond breaks, and what
is reduced during phosphine oxidation. We have shown that [Au(PEt$_3$)$_2$]Cl
reductively cleaves disulphide linkages of albumin with the release of
the phosphine oxide (42). [Au(PEt$_3$)$_2$]Cl caused whole blood samples to
solidify within a few hours as a result of the denaturation of the protein. The reduction of essential cellular components by phosphines or
the generation of reactive radical species during phosphine oxidation,
perhaps involving redox-active metal ions, may be important cytotoxic
events.

Finally, it is worth mentioning the potential of Au(III) complexes
as anticancer agents. Au(III) is isoelectronic with Pt(II) (d^8) and
complexes are generally square-planar. Stable complexes are formed
with N-donor ligands and Au(III) nucleotide complexes are known (43).
It is perhaps surprising, therefore, that Au(III) is the only d^8 square-
planar system to have escaped extensive evaluation for anticancer activity. A number of Au(III) amine complexes, for instance [AuCl$_3$(pyridine)] and [Au(en)$_2$]Cl$_3$, have been tested, but showed no activity (38).
Ligand-exchange reactions for Au(III) are very much more rapid than for
Pt(II) and since many Au(III) complexes are strong oxidising agents they
are likely to undergo rapid reduction to Au(I) in vivo, and the resultant species may bind to plasma proteins and not enter cells. There is
scope for the design of Au(III) complexes with tightly bound ligands
as potential antitumour agents. We have recently described NMR methods
for mapping the coordination spheres of some Au(III) complexes in solution (40). It is notable that the only Au(III) complexes with antitumour activity, tested by the NCI, are [AuMe$_2$Cl$_2$]$^+$ and
[Me$_2$Au(SCN)$_2$AuMe$_2$], which both contain inert alkyl ligands.

The possibility that broad-spectrum gold anticancer agents can be
designed which are less carcinogenic and mutagenic than Pt compounds
provides an exciting prospect for future research.

Acknowledgements

   We are indebted to many colleagues who have stimulated our thinking
in this area, especially those at SKF Laboratories (Philadelphia).

5 REFERENCES

(1)(a) P.J. Sadler, Struct. Bonding (Berlin) 29 (1976) 171-214.
   (b) P.J. Sadler, Gold. Bull. 5 (1976) 110-118.

(2)   C.F. Shaw III, Inorg. Perspect. Biol. Med. 2 (1979) 287-355.

(3)   D.H. Brown, W.E. Smith, Chem. Soc. Rev. 9 (1980) 217-239.

(4)   K.C. Dash, H. Schmidbaur, Metal Ions in Biol. Syst. 14 (1983)
       180-205.

(5)   M.A. Mazid, M.T. Razi, P.J. Sadler, G.N. Greaves, S.J. Gurman,
       M.H.J. Koch, J.C. Phillips, J. Chem. Soc. Chem. Commun. (1980)
       1261-1262.

(6)   R.C. Elder, M.K. Eidsness, M.J. Heeg, K.G. Tepperman, C.F.
       Shaw III, N. Schaeffer, A.C.S. Symp. Ser. 209 (1983) 385-400.

(7)   A.A. Isab, P.J. Sadler, J. Chem. Soc. Dalton Trans. (1981)
       1657-1663.

(8)   I.G. Dance, L.J. Fitzpatrick, A.D. Rae, M.L. Scudder, Inorg.
       Chem. 22 (1983) 3785-3788.

(9)   M.C. Grootveld, P.J. Sadler, J. Inorg. Biochem. 19 (1983) 51-64.

(10)(a) D.T. Hill, B.M. Sutton, A.A. Isab, M.T. Razi, P.J. Sadler,
       J.M. Trooster, G.H.M. Calis, Inorg. Chem. 22 (1983) 2936-2942.
    (b) K. Brown, R.V. Parish, C.A. McAuliffe, J. Am. Chem. Soc. 103
       (1981) 4943-4945
    (c) A.K.H. Al-Sa'ady, K. Moss, C.A. McAuliffe, R.V. Parish,
       J. Chem. Soc. Dalton Trans. (1984) 1609.

(11)   S.R. Rudge, D. Perrett, A.J. Swannell, P.L. Drury, J. Rheumatol.
       11 (1984) 150.

(12)   M.C. Grootveld, M.T. Razi, P.J. Sadler, Clinical Rheumatol.
        3 (Suppl. 1) (1984) 5-16.

(13)   A.A. Isab, P.J. Sadler, Chem. Comm.   (1976) 1051-1052.

(14)   A.A. Isab, P.J. Sadler, J. Chem. Soc. Dalton Trans. (1982) 135-141.

(15)   M.T. Razi, G. Otiko, P.J. Sadler, A.C.S. Symp. Ser. 209 (1983)
        371-384.

(16)   C.F. Shaw III, Proc. Symp. Bioinorg. Chem. Gold Coord. Compounds
        SK & F Laboratories, Philadelphia 1983 98-123.

(17)   N.A. Malik, G. Otiko, M.T. Razi, P.J. Sadler in (16) pp. 82-97.

(18)   E. Jellum, E. Munte, Ann. Rheum. Dis. 209 (1982) 385-400.

(19)   C.F. Shaw III, N.A. Schaeffer, R.C. Elder, M.K. Eidsness, J.M.
        Trooster, G.H.M. Calis, J. Am. Chem. Soc. 106 (1984) 3511-3521.

(20)   R.C. Blodgett Jr., M.A. Heuer, R.G. Pietrusko, Seminars in Arth-
        ritis and Rheumatism 13 (1984) 25-273.

(21)   G.G. Graham, T.M. Haavisto, H.M. Jones, C.D. Champion, Biochem.
        Pharmacol. 33 (1984) 1257-1262.

(22)   G.G. Graham, J.R. Bales, P.J. Sadler, J. Inorg. Biochem. (1985)
        in press.

(23)   B.M. Sutton, E. McGusty, D.T. Walz, M.J. DiMartino, J. Med. Chem.
        15 (1972) 1095-1098.

(24)   M. Chaffman, R.N. Brogden, R.C. Heel, T.M. Speight, G.S. Avery,
        Drugs 27 (1984) 378-424.

(25)   D.T. Hill, B.M. Sutton, Cryst. Struct. Comm. 9 (1980) 679-686.

(26)   M.T. Razi, P.J. Sadler, D.T. Hill, B.M. Sutton, J. Chem. Soc.
        Dalton Trans. (1983) 1331-4.

(27)   I.C.P. Smith, A. Joyce, H. Jarrell, B.M. Sutton, D.T. Hill in
        (16) pp. 47-57.

(28) J. Hempel, Y. Mikuriya in (16) pp. 37-46.

(29) R.F. Pasternack, J. Hempel, Rev. Port. Quim. 27 (1985) 31-32

(30) K. Tepperman, R. Finer, S. Donovan, R.C. Elder, J. Doi, D. Ratliff, K. Ng, Science 225 (1984) 430-431.

(31) A.P. Intoccia, T.L. Flanagan, D.T. Walz, L. Gutzait, J.E. Swagdis, J. Flagiello Jr. et al., J. Rheumatol. 9 (Suppl. 8) (1982) 90-98.

(32) A.J. Lewis, D.T. Walz, in G.P. Ellis, G.B. West (Eds.), Progress in Med. Chem. Vol. 19, Elsevier Biomedical Press, Amsterdam 1982, pp. 2-58.

(33) G. Schmitz, D.J. Minkel, D. Gingrich, C.F. Shaw III, J. Inorg. Biochem. (1980) 12 293-306

(34) T.M. Simon, D.H. Kunishima, G.J. Vibert, A. Lorber, Cancer 44 (1979) 1965-1975,

(35) T.M. Simon, D.H. Kunishima, G.J. Vibert, A. Lorber, Cancer Res. 41 (1981) 94-97.

(36) C.K. Mirabelli, R.K. Johnson, C.M. Sung, L. Faucette, K. Muirhead, S.T. Crooke, Cancer Res. 45 (1985) 32-39.

(37) K.C. Agrawal, K.B. Bears, S. Marcus, H.B. Jonassen, Proc. Am. Assoc. Cancer Res. 19 (1978) 28.

(38) P.J. Sadler, M. Nasr, V.L. Narayanan in M.P. Hacker, E.B. Douple, I.H. Krakhoff (Eds.), "Platinum Coordination Complexes in Cancer Chemotheraphy", Martinus Nijhoff Pub., Boston 1984, pp. 290-304.

(39) C.E. Blank, J.C. Dabrowiak, J. Inorg. Biochem. 21 (1984) 21-29.

(40) S.J. Berners Price, M.J. DiMartino, D.T. Hill, R. Kuroda, M.A. Mazid, P.J. Sadler, Inorg. Chem. (1985) in press.

(41) S.J. Berners Price, P.J. Sadler, R. Kuroda, M.J. DiMartino, B.M. Sutton, D.T. Hill, Rev. Port. Quim. 27 (1985) 397-398.

(42) N.A. Malik, G. Otiko, P.J. Sadler, J. Inorg. Biochem. 12 (1980) 317-322.

(43) D.W. Gibson, M. Beer, R.J. Barrett, Biochemistry 10 (1971) 3669-3679.

Environmental
Bioinorganic Chemistry

A Comparative Study of Nickel and Aluminum Transport and Toxicity in Freshwater Green Algae

Brian R. Folsom, Andrei Popescu, Peter B. Kingsley-Hickman and John M. Wood

Gray Freshwater Biological Institute/University of Minnesota

Summary

The transport and toxicity of metals in Eukaryotic algae, nickel in Chlamydomonas UTEX 89 and aluminum in Chlorella saccarophila have been examined. In Chlamydomonas it was found that nickel transport involves the ATP-dependent Mg^{++} transport system, and nickel toxicity can be prevented by increasing the concentration of Mg^{++} relative to Ni^{++}. This protection by Mg^{++} was specific for this fast exchange ion in that Ca^{++} did not prevent Ni^{++} from reaching toxic levels in the cytoplasm. In Chlorella Al^{+++} transport apparently involves the ATP-dependent Ca^{++} transport system, as aluminum toxicity can be reversed by increasing the ratio of Ca^{++} to Al^{+++}. Preliminary experiments using ^{27}Al NMR and ^{31}P NMR with algal suspensions in vivo demonstrated that aluminum transport involves complexation with cytoplasmic phosphates. Furthermore ^{31}P NMR indicated that glucose metabolism may be inhibited by Al^{+++} early in the glycolytic pathway of Chlorella.

1. Introduction

The biochemical basis for resistance to metal toxicity is complicated by the great variety of reactions at the molecular and cellular levels even in closely related organisms and tissues. Several strategies for resistance to intoxication have been identified (1-4).

Metal ion interactions in biology can be divided into three classes:

1. Ions in fast exchange with biological ligands.
2. Ions in intermediary exchange with biological ligands.
3. Ions in slow exchange with biological ligands.

Examples of those elements in fast exchange include the alkali metals Na^+ and K^+, the alkali earth metals Ca^{2+} and Mg^{2+}, and, of course, H^+. In this study the transport and toxicity of one essential element (nickel) and one non-essential element (aluminum) are considered. These elements can be either in slow or intermediary exchange and can compete for binding sites with the fast exchange ions calcium and magnesium.

More than ten years ago Zerner's group in Queensland, Australia showed that nickel can function as an essential element (5). Since that time nickel has been found to play a very important role in the metabolism of C_1 compounds in the anaerobic bacteria. Nickel-containing coenzymes function in the active sites of the enzymes which fix molecular hydrogen (i.e. the hydrogenases), in the terminal enzyme for methane biosynthesis (i.e. a nickel-containing B_{12}-analog or corrin macrocycle), and in the hydration of carbon monoxide by those organisms which utilize CO as sole carbon and energy source (4).

In sediments nickel forms stable and insoluble complexes with sulfide ions and with thiolates to give nickel sulfides and stable coordination complexes with organic compounds which contain thiolgroups. However, at the sediment/water interface nickel forms weaker coordination complexes with oxygen donors such as carboxylate, hydroxyl, and other oxy-ligands (e.g. humic acids, fulvic acids, clays, metal oxides etc.). Slightly stronger complexes are formed with oxygen donors at the cell surfaces of bacteria and algae which have many anionic functional groups from both proteins and polysaccharides (e.g. polygalacturonic acids at the surface of green algae). These complexes to the weaker oxygen donors are unstable enough for nickel to be exchanged rapidly with Ca^{2+} and Mg^{2+}, releasing Ni^{2+} into the water. Thus, Ni^{2+} has an intermediate exchange rate with Ca^{2+} and Mg^{2+} and so Ni^{2+} cannot be removed entirely from industrial wastewater by traditional treatment methods.

Contamination of industrial wastewaters by nickel is of special concern because certain nickel complexes have been shown to be carcinogenic (6). Nickel is one of the most toxic of the transition metals, showing toxicity in low doses to both animals and plants (7). Substantial information is available on the toxicity of nickel towards algae (8-10). Also, studies have been performed on the toxic effects of nickel in combination with other cations (11-13). However, little attention has been given to other important environmental factors which determine nickel toxicity in the algae.

Aluminum is the third most abundant element in the earth's crust (1). The chemistry of this element under both aerobic and anaerobic conditions makes it unavailable for uptake by living organisms unless those organisms grow at low pH (14). The median background concentration of aluminum in the rivers of North America is 230 µg/liter with a range from 12-2,550 µg/liter (15). An EPA study of the continuing acidification of 1,050 lakes on the Laurentian shield in Northeastern Minnesota, North Central Wisconsin and the upper peninsula of Michigan shows increasing concentration of Al^{+++} in water with increased acidification (15). Similar results have been found in acidified lakes in the Adirondacks (14) and by Hutchinson and Stokes for most acidified lakes in the Province of Ontario, Canada (15). All of this work supports the data first published in Sweden and Norway from a study of over 5,000 lakes (15). Clearly, the abundance of aluminum in the earth's crust and its solubility in water below pH 6.0 indicates the impact of fossil fuel utilization on the mobilization of this non-essential yet toxic element. To date the analytical methods for this element have relied on total element methods without regard for the importance of individual inorganic chemical speciation, even though it is recognized that toxicity depends on the precise chemical structures of these complexes. Chronic toxicity studies in rats indicate the importance of the ingested chemical species of aluminum (16). For example, $Al(OH)_3$ is non-toxic at extremely high doses, but $AlCl_3$ has a very low LD_{50} dose.

It is important to understand the transport mechanisms for aluminum complexes in acidified water, because the presence of aluminum in drinking water supplies has been implicated in both the epidemiology and physiology of Alzheimer's disease (15). An epidemic of Alzheimer's disease in a region of Guam, where the soils were primarily bauxite (AlF_3), has been correlated with Al in the local drinking water supplies, even though the chemical speciation of Al in this drinking water supply has never been established, nor was the pH of the water supply determined. However, it is clear from our results that pH has a profound effect on the uptake and toxicity of metal ions in the green algae.

1.1. Results

Chlamydomonas was grown in modified Cramer-Myers medium at 20°C with constant irradiation without shaking (17). This organism will tolerate up to 10 ppm of Ni^{++} without any effect on its growth rate (Fig. 1). In fact this organism will

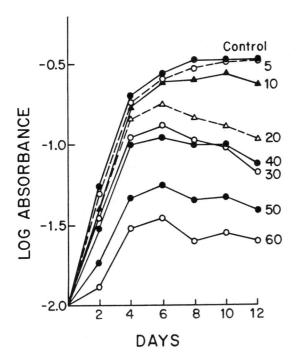

Figure 1. The effect of different $^{63}Ni^{2+}$ concentrations on the growth of Chlamydomonas at pH 7.0.

even grow slowly in the presence of up to 150 ppm Ni^{2+}, with toxicity only being expressed at doses in excess of 200 ppm. This nickel tolerance depends on the age of the culture, with older cells being more resistant than younger cells, and on the pH. Below pH 5.5 nickel was found to be toxic at much lower concentrations. Further examination of this nickel tolerance showed that there is a correlation between the concentration of Mg^{++} in the culture medium and the cytotoxic effects of nickel (Fig. 2). Similar competition between Ca^{2+} and Ni^{2+} could not be shown, indicating that Ni^{2+} transport may be specific to the ATP-dependent Mg^{2+} channel.

Similar experiments were performed with Al^{+++} in Chlorella saccarophila. This organism was chosen due to its acid tolerance thus allowing us to study the transport and toxicity of soluble aluminum species. Chlorella was grown in bold basal medium with 0.1% glucose added at 20°C with agitation in an incubator shaker (18). Aluminum toxicity to this species of Chlorella was shown to be dependent on the concentration of Ca^{2+} in the growth medium (Figure 3).

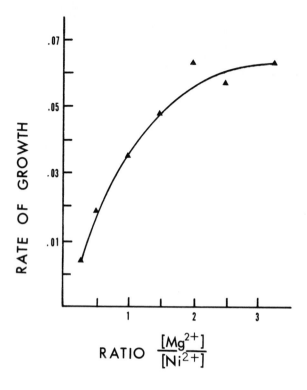

Figure 2. The effect of Mg^{2+} on Ni^{2+} toxicity in <u>Chlamydomonas</u>.

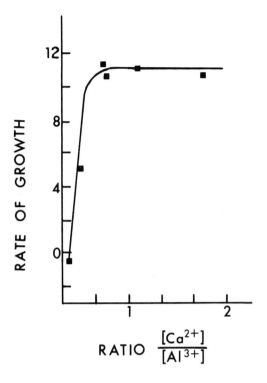

Figure 3.   The effect of Ca^{2+} on Al^{+++} toxicity in <u>Chlorella</u>.

Advantage was taken of the natural abundance of ^{27}Al to follow the uptake of soluble aluminum salts by cell suspensions of <u>Chlorella</u> using NMR with an 8.7 Tesla magnet (94 MHz for ^{27}Al, 146 MHz for ^{31}P). Simultaneously the impact of aluminum transport on phosphate metabolism in whole cells could be monitored by ^{31}P NMR.

Figure 4a shows a ^{31}P NMR of a cell suspension of acid-tolerant <u>Chlorella</u> grown at pH 3.0. Based on previous results (19) intracellular phosphate-containing compounds can be assigned. The intense resonance at C represents extracellular inorganic orthophosphate. Resonances at A and B are inorganic orthophosphate in chloroplasts and in cytoplasm, respectively. These are distinguishable due to the pH difference between chloroplasts and cytoplasm. The broad resonance at SP is from sugar phosphates. The resonance at pp is intracellular polyphosphate. The resonances for the 3 phosphates on ATP are not well resolved due to our inability to provide sufficient light intensity to these thick cell suspensions in the NMR cavity.

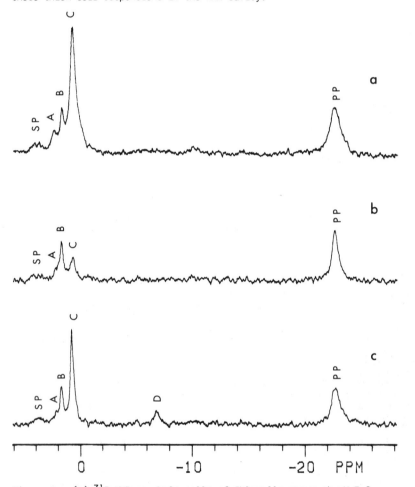

Figure 4.   (a) ^{31}P NMR on whole cells of <u>Chlorella</u> grown at pH 3.0.
            (b) ^{31}P NMR spectrum showing the decreases in extracellular ortho-
                phosphate concentration due to uptake by <u>Chlorella in vivo</u> upon
                the addition of glucose.
            (c) ^{31}P NMR spectrum showing a buildup of extracellular orthophos-
                phate after the additon of AlCl$_3$.

Figure 4b shows the change due to the addition of glucose which is rapidly metabolized by <u>Chlorella</u> causing the intracellular orthophosphate concentration to increase due to phosphate uptake. Figure 5 shows the ^{27}Al spectrum after the addition of AlCl$_3$. The sharp AlCl$_3$ resonance decreases in intensity rapidly upon addition of this salt and the broad signal which appears is consistent with complexation to phosphate compounds, thus indicating that Al may interfere directly with phosphate metabolism in the cytoplasm. After the addition of AlCl$_3$ the ^{31}P NMR (Figure 4c) shows that intracellular orthophosphate builds up again even in the presence of glucose, indicating that glycolysis may be inhibited by intracellular Al^{+++}. Since the Al-ATP complex is known to inhibit hexokinase in mammalian cells (21), these preliminary results suggest that aluminum toxicity in <u>Chlorella</u> may be due to inhibition of glycolysis.

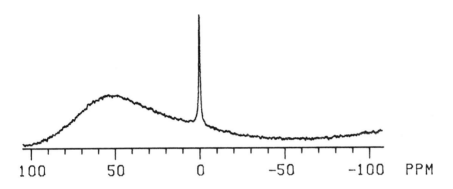

Figure 5. ^{27}Al NMR spectrum showing the uptake of AlCl$_3$ (sharp resonance) and complexation of Al^{+++} to phosphate groups (broad resonances).

1.1.1 Discussion

Previously we have shown that there are fundamental differences in the transport and in the resistance mechanisms employed by the photosynthetic Prokaryotes (Cyanobacteria) and Eukaryotes (Green Algae) (2-4). The resistance to toxic metal ions in the Prokaryotes have evolved which either prevent metal transport across the cytoplasmic membrane, or which actively transport unwanted elements from the cytoplasm to the external environment (4). In the Eukaryotes both essential and non-essential metals compete with the fast exchange ions for transport through their specific ATP-dependent channels. In this comparative study we have found that nickel uptake is determined by its competition with magnesium, and aluminum uptake by competition with calcium. Accordingly, the toxic effects of nickel and aluminum can be alleviated by increasing concentrations of magnesium and calcium, respectively.

The most significant contributor to metal ion transport and toxicity is the external pH. Acidic conditions are responsible for increasing the concentrations of such metal ions so that they can compete with the calcium and magnesium active transport systems to increase intracellular concentrations to toxic levels. Clearly the acidification of both aquatic and terrestrial ecosystems can mobilize toxic elements, and these elements can reach toxic levels in all Eukaryotes in areas where fast exchange ions are depleted.

Acknowledgements

This research was supported by a grant from Atlantic Richfield Company.

References

(1) Hong-Kang Wang, J.M. Wood. Environ. Sci. and Technol. 17 (1983) 582A-590A.

(2) J.M. Wood. Chem. Scripta 21 (1983) 155-162.

(3) J.M. Wood. Evolutionary Aspects of Metal Ion Transport - Metal Ions in Biology. H. Siegel Ed. Marcel Dekker N.Y. 18 (1984) 223-237.

(4) J.M. Wood. Microbial Strategies in Resistance to Metal Ion Toxicity. Metal Ions in Biology. H. Sigel Ed. Marcel Dekker, N.Y.

(5) N.E. Dickson, C. Gazzola, R.L. Blakeley, B. Zerner. J. Am. Chem. Soc. 97 (1975) 4131-4133.

(6) F.W. Sunderman. Env. Health Perspectives 40 (1981) 131-141.

(7) C.G. Chumbly. A.D.A.S. Advisory Paper 10 (1971).

(8) D.F. Spencer. Environ. Pollution (Series A) 25 (1981) 241-247.

(9) J.S. Fezy. Environ. Pollution 20 (1979) 131-139.

(10) Jerome O. Nriagu. Nickel in the Environment. A Wiley-Interscience Publication. (1980).

(11) P.T.S. Wong, Y.K. Chau, P.L. Luxon. J. Fish. Res. Board. Can. 35 (1978) 479-481.

(12) Glenn W. Stratton, Charles T. Corke. Chemosphere 8-10 (1979) 731-740.

(13) P.V. Deviprasad, P.S. Deviprasad. Water, Air and Soil Pollution 17 (1982) 263-268.

(14) J.M. Wood. Proceedings of a Conference sponsored by NIEHS on "The Health Effects of Acid Rain". Research Triangle, N.C. November 16-19, 1984. To be published in Env. Health Perspect. Ed. R. Goyer (1985).

(15) S.E. Jorgenson, A. Jensen. Processes of Metal Ions in the Environment. (1985) Chapter 3, pp. 61-100. Metal Ions in Biological Systems. Volume 18. H. Sigel Ed. Marcell Dekker, New York.

(16) O. Wawschinek, Pogglitsch. Aluminum Toxication bei Dialyspatienten. Proceedings of the First Graz Symposium on Spurenelemente and Gesundheit Graz. Austria. Sept. 11-15, 1984.

(17) M. Cramer, J. Meyer. Arch. Mikrobiol. 17 (1952) 384.

(18) H.W. Nichals, H.C. Bold. J. Phyco. (1965) 1, 34-38.

(19) Mitsumori Fumiyuki, Ito Osamu. FEBS Letters (1984) 174.2, 248-252.

Arsenic in The Environment

Kurt J. Irgolic

Department of Chemistry, Texas A&M University, College Station, Texas 77843 U.S.A.

SUMMARY

Arsenic, an ubiquitous element, has found many uses. Arsenic has the ability to be trivalent or pentavalent and form stable bonds with carbon. A variety of arsenic compounds (arsenite, arsenate, methylarsonic acid, dimethylarsinic acid, arsenobetaine, arsenocholine, arsenic-containing riboses and lipids) occur in nature and participate in a biologically mediated arsenic cycle. The organic compounds of arsenic thus far found in nature are less toxic than inorganic derivatives. The biochemical pathways leading to and connecting these compounds are not known with certainty. Recently, evidence was found for the essentiality of arsenic. Much work is needed to elucidate the transformations and biological functions of arsenic compounds. This work will be aided by liquid chromatographic methods using arsenic specific detection systems.

1 INTRODUCTION

Arsenic is an ubiquitous element notorious as a poison but nevertheless essential for life (1). Arsenic ranks twentieth among the elements in abundance in the earth's crust. The average concentration of arsenic in the continental and oceanic crust is approximately 2 mg/kg (2,3). The amount of arsenic in the solid crust (total mass 2×10^{19} t) has been estimated to be 4×10^{13} t. Arsenic is rarely encountered in nature as the free element. Arsenic is enriched in sulfidic ores occurring mainly in form of arsenides of cobalt, nickel, copper, lead, and iron, and as the sulfides As_4S_4 (realgar) and As_2S_3 (orpiment). Arsenopyrite, FeAsS, found frequently in small but rich deposits, was the main source of arsenic for mankind during most of its history (4). Weathering of primary arsenic minerals forms

arsenic trioxide, arsenites, and arsenates. Many metal arsenates occur in the
oxidation zone of sulfidic ores. The natural process of weathering mobilizes
arsenic compounds and disperses them in soil, freshwater, ocean water, sediments,
and sedimentary rocks. The natural concentration of arsenic in fresh- and ocean
water is a few μg/L. The concentration in sediments, sedimentary rocks, and coal
may reach several thousand milligrams per kilogram (3).

Industrial societies use a variety of arsenic compounds to preserve wood (36%),
manufacture herbicides (31%), dessicate cotton (15%), enrich ores by flotation (8%),
and improve the quality of glass (5%). The percentages in parentheses indicate how
much of the total amount (25,000 short tons) of arsenic trioxide consumed annually
in the United States is used for a particular purpose (5,6). Arsenic trioxide, the
starting material for all arsenic-containing products, is obtained as by-product of
the smelting of lead, zinc, and copper ores.

The arsenic compounds mobilized by "natural" processes and "human" activities are
dispersed in the environment, are changed via purely chemical or biologically
mediated reactions, and interact with organisms causing beneficial and detrimental
effects.

2 THE CHEMISTRY OF ARSENIC

Arsenic, a metalloid, has a rich chemistry. In its inorganic compounds, arsenic
may be pentavalent (e.g., in arsenates, NaH_2AsO_4) or trivalent (e.g., in arsenites,
$NaAsO_2$). Arsenic forms bonds with organic groups, in which the As-C bonds are
stable in aqueous, oxidizing, and reducing environments. Arsenic may be linked in
organic arsenic compounds to one, two, three, or four organic groups. In most of
these organic compounds arsenic may be trivalent or pentavalent. Other elements -
in addition to carbon - that are important for the chemistry of arsenic are
identified in Figure 1. For the environmental chemistry of arsenic, compounds of
arsenic with organic groups, oxygen, sulfur, and selenium are of special importance.
The great affinity of arsenic for sulfur is of special significance. Compounds with
As-H bonds are important for the analytical chemistry of arsenic (7). Arsenic
derivatives with As-alkali metal, As-halogen, and As-N (P or As) bonds are useful
for the synthesis of organic arsenic compounds. The ability of triorganylarsines to
react with transition metal compounds is responsible for the existence of a huge
number of coordination compounds.

3 ARSENIC COMPOUNDS IN NATURE

The richness of arsenic chemistry suggests that a variety of arsenic compounds
may be present in the environment and may participate in a global arsenic cycle.
During the past few years several new and unexpected arsenic compounds were

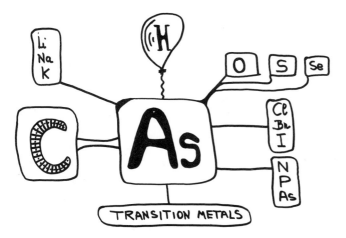

Fig. 1. Elements important in arsenic chemistry.

discovered in organisms that grew in unpolluted environments.

Until very recently the arsenic cycle (Fig. 2) consisted of methylation and demethylation reactions changing inorganic arsenite to methylarsonic acid, dimethylarsinic acid, and trimethylarsine oxide. The methylarsenic compounds are

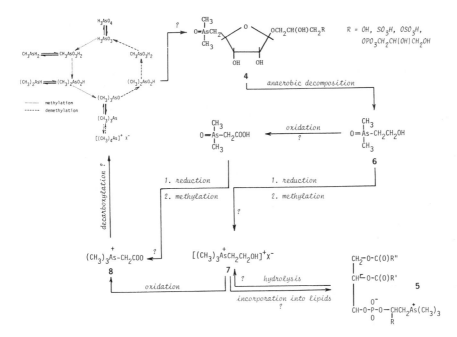

Fig. 2. Suggested (?) and experimentally proven reactions for the cycling of arsenic.

then demethylated stepwise to arsenite. Biological methylation of arsenic compounds is ubiquitous in nature and is carried out by microorganisms such as *Scopulariopsis brevicaulis* and *Candida humicola* (8). However, higher organisms including mice, rats, monkeys (8) and men (9) can also methylate inorganic arsenic compounds. Pentavalent arsenic compounds can be reduced under appropriate conditions to trivalent arsenic derivatives, for instance, by strains of the genus *Pseudomonas* (10) and by Methanobacterium (11). These reduction reactions [arsenate → arsenite; $(CH_3)_nAsO(OH)_{3-n} \rightarrow (CH_3)_nAs(OH)_{3-n}$, $n = 1, 2$] are important, because pentavalent arsenic compounds cannot be methylated (12). The mechanisms of these methylation and demethylation reactions are not yet known with certainty. S-Adenosylmethionine 1 and methylcobalamine 2 have been shown to methylate trivalent arsenic compounds. Tetrahydrofolic acid 3 may also serve as a methyl donor in these reactions.

NMR experiments with a model system fo the methylation of trivalent arsenic compounds consisting of methylcobaloxime and methyldihaloarsines in chloroform showed the methylation reaction to be more complex than expected (13). The NMR data suggest that the arsine coordinates to the cobalt atom, the methyl group migrates to an equatorial position in the cobaloxime, and the equatorial methyl group is then transferred to arsenic. The primary product appears to be a dimethyldihaloarsonium salt of a cobaloxime anion. Knowledge about the in-vitro and in-vivo methylation of arsenic compounds is important, because these methylation reactions provide the starting material for more complex organic arsenic compounds that are formed by organisms.

Marine organisms (14) appear to accumulate and transform arsenic compounds more efficiently than land-based organisms. Most of the organic arsenic compounds more complex than simple methylarsenic derivatives were therefore found in lobsters, shrimp, sharks, sea cucumber, crabs, and other marine organisms. Arsenobetaine, $(CH_3)_3As^+CH_2COO^-$, was identified in sever.1 marine organisms (Fig. 3) and might be

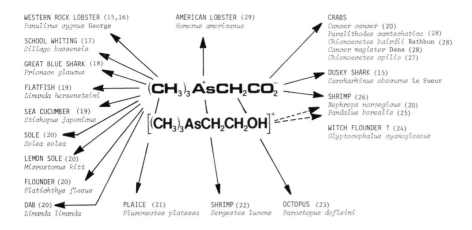

WESTERN ROCK LOBSTER (15,16)
Panulirus cygnus George

SCHOOL WHITING (17)
Sillago bassensis

GREAT BLUE SHARK (18)
Prionace glaucus

FLATFISH (19)
Limanda herzensteini

SEA CUCUMBER (19)
Stichopus japonicus

SOLE (20)
Solea solea

LEMON SOLE (20)
Microstomus kitt

FLOUNDER (20)
Platichthys flesus

DAB (20)
Limanda limanda

AMERICAN LOBSTER (29)
Homarus americanus

CRABS
Cancer cancer (20)
Paralithodes camtschatica (28)
Chionoecetes bairdii Rathbun (28)
Cancer magister Dana (28)
Chionoecetes opilio (27)

DUSKY SHARK (15)
Carcharhinus obscurus Le Sueur

SHRIMP (26)
Nephrops norvegicus (20)
Pandalus borealis (25)

WITCH FLOUNDER ? (24)
Glyptocephalus cyanoglossus

PLAICE (21)
Pluronectes platessa

SHRIMP (22)
Sergestes lucens

OCTOPUS (23)
Paroctopus dofleini

$(CH_3)_3\overset{+}{As}CH_2CO_2^-$

$[(CH_3)_3AsCH_2CH_2OH]^+$

Fig. 3. Organisms in which arsenobetaine or arsenocholine was identified.

present in many more. Arsenocholine, $[(CH_3)_3As^+CH_2CH_2OH]^+X^-$, was found in shrimp (Fig. 3). Derivatives of dimethyl(ribosyl)arsine oxide **4** were detected in brown kelp and the giant clam. The biochemical pathways leading to these arsenic

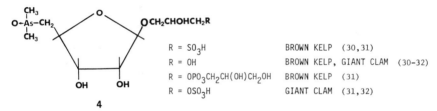

R = SO₃H   BROWN KELP (30,31)
R = OH   BROWN KELP, GIANT CLAM (30-32)
R = OPO₃CH₂CH(OH)CH₂OH   BROWN KELP (31)
R = OSO₃H   GIANT CLAM (31,32)

4

Brown Kelp: *Ecklonia radiata*   Giant Clam: *Tridacna maxima*

compounds are unknown. The discovery that the arsenic-containing ribose **4** is converted to hydroxyethyldimethylarsine oxide **6** (Fig. 2) in anaerobically incubated brown kelp (33) suggests that the ribose might be a precursor of arsenocholine **7** and arsenobetaine **8**. The reactions required for the conversion of hydroxyethyl-dimethylarsine oxide to arsenocholine should not pose any difficulties to organisms. Arsenocholine can then be incorporated into phospholipids. In these arsenolipids **5** arsenic replaces nitrogen in the choline moiety. Evidence for the formation of arsenolipids by algae growing in an arsenate-containing medium is available (34).

CH₂OCOR
|
CH-OCOR
|
CH₂OPO◄R

5

R = $-CH_2CH_2\overset{+}{As}(CH_3)_3$

= $-\underset{COO^-}{CH}-CH_2\overset{+}{As}(CH_3)_3$

= $-CH_2CH(OH)CH_2O$ ... $CH_2\overset{CH_3}{\underset{CH_3}{As\rightarrow O}}$

The hydrolysis of these lipids would release arsenocholine that could be oxidized to arsenobetaine. Such an oxidation reaction has been shown to occur in mice, rats, and rabbits (35). Arsenocholine could be decarboxylated to a tetramethylarsonium compound that would provide a reentry into the methylation–demethylation cycle (Fig. 2). The methylation–demethylation cycle would then deliver a dimethylarsenic species that could be used to synthesize the arsenic–containing ribose **4**.

Benson and coworkers claimed that the arsenic moiety forming phospholipids is a 2-carboxy-2-hydroxyethyltrimethylarsonium salt (trimethylarsoniolactic acid) (see structure 5). An extensive series of reactions and chromatographic experiments seemed to confirm the identity of this arsenic compound (36). Subsequently, lipids containing trimethylarsoniolactate were detected frequently (37) and found their way into the literature. It appears now, that trimethylarsoniolactate is not the arsenic compound incorporated into lipids. The nearly identical chromatographic and pH–dependent electrophoretic mobilities of trimethylarsoniolactate and the arsenic–containing ribose 4 led to the erroneous structural assignment for the phospholipid (37,38). The suggestion that trimethylarsoniolactate is replaced in the arsenolipids by the arsenic–containing ribose (38) has not yet been firmly proven by experiment.

The misidentification of trimethylarsoniolactate shows that chromatographic and electrophoretic results cannot be taken as conclusive proofs. The properties of a compound found in nature must be compared with synthetic materials of known composition and structure. Arsenobetaine (39,40), arsenocholine (40), and some derivatives of these compounds were prepared. Work is in progress to synthesize the arsenic–containing riboses and phospholipids. These synthetic samples will allow the development of chromatographic techniques for the efficient detection of arsenic compounds, the exact determination of their properties, and the evaluation of their toxicity.

4 THE TOXICITY AND ESSENTIALITY OF ARSENIC

The environmental threats posed by toxic elements and the amounts of essential elements required by organisms are generally expressed in terms of total element concentrations or quantitites without consideration of the nature of the compounds in which these elements occur. However, the effects of trace elements are caused by particular trace element compounds that interact with biologically important molecules. A thorough understanding of the role of trace elements including arsenic can be achieved only when the identities and concentrations of trace element compounds in the environment are known and their transformations have been studied. Arsenic, for instance, well known as a poison, is found in crabs at concentrations of 10 mg/kg (27,28). An opulent meal of crabs or other marine organisms could provide a dose of arsenic sufficient for toxic symptoms to appear if all the arsenic were present as inorganic arsenite, the most toxic of the common compounds of arsenic. Fortunately, the predominant arsenic compound in crabs is arsenobetaine that was found to be nontoxic in mice (16,41), rats, and rabbits (41). Therefore, marine foods do not appear to be hazardous to man because of their arsenic content. Organisms use their biochemical apparatus to detoxify inorganic arsenic compounds. The organic arsenic derivatives formed might serve useful purposes that are, however, completely unknown. It is conceivable, that arsenolipids become incorporated into membranes. Whether membranes with arsenolipids function better or worse than arsenic-free membranes must be explored.

Inorganic and some organic arsenic compounds are toxic. Their chronic and acute effects are well known (42,43). However, recent experiments with animals indicate that arsenic is an essential element (1). Almost nothing is known about the metabolic function of arsenic. An arsenic requirement for man cannot yet be estimated with any certainty. In three experimental animal species an arsenic concentration of 50 ng/g of diet was considered to be just adequate. Mertz (44) stated recently: "If such findings could be extrapolated to man (50 ppb in 500-600 grams of dry diet), a minimum daily requirement would be estimated at 25 to 30 μg, an amount not furnished by the typical diet (in the US) of which the Market Basket Survey is representative. Although the initial, immediate consequences of deficiency of most new trace elements are mild, the fact that severe disease, sudden heart death, appeared in the third generation of arsenic-deficient goats, should serve as a strong motivation for intensive future research." Perhaps, the arsenic eaters of Austria, who consumed relatively large amounts of arsenic trioxide, satisfied their arsenic demand in an unusual way (45).

The essentiality of arsenic should provide strong incentives to explore the transformation of arsenic compounds in nature. Analytical techniques are now available for such a task (46,47). Liquid chromatographic methods using graphite furnace atomic absorption spectrometers or inductively coupled argon plasma emission spectrometers as arsenic-specific detectors were developed and used for the speciation of arsenic. Extensive use of these techniques and cooperative efforts between analytical chemists, microbiologists, nutrition experts, and toxicologists will rapidly advance our knowledge of arsenic in the environment.

Acknowledgement: Support by the Robert A. Welch Foundation of Houston, Texas, and by Texas A&M University's Center for Energy and Mineral Resources is gratefully acknowledged.

5 REFERENCES

(1) F. H. Nielsen and E. O. Uthus, "Arsenic" in "Biochemistry of the Essential Ultratrace Elements," E. Frieden, Ed., Plenum Press, New York, 1984, pp. 319-340; and references therein.

(2) K. H. Wedepohl, "Die Zusammensetzung der oberen Erdkruste und der natürliche

Kreislauf ausgewählter Metalle. Ressourcen," in "Metalle in der Umwelt," E. Merian, Ed., Verlag Chemie, Weinheim, FRG, 1984, pp. 1-10.

(3) "Arsenic" U.S. National Academy of Sciences, Washington, D.C., 1977, p. 16.

(4) R. M. Allesch, "Arsenik" Verlag Ferd. Kleinmayr, Klagenfurt, Austria, 1959.

(5) L. D. Fitzgerald, "Arsenic Sources, Production and Applications in the 1980's," in "Arsenic: Industrial, Biomedical, Environmental Perspectives," W. H. Lederer and R. J. Fensterheim, Eds., Van Nostrand Reinhold Co., New York, 1983, pp. 3-9.

(6) W. H. Lederer and R. J. Fensterheim, Eds., "Arsenic: Industrial, Biomedical, Environmental Perspectives," Van Nostrand Reinhold Co., New York, 1983, pp. 43-111.

(7) K. J. Irgolic, R. A. Stockton and D. Chakraborti, "Determination of Arsenic and Arsenic Compounds in Water Supplies," in "Arsenic: Industrial, Biomedical, Environmental Perspectives," W. H. Lederer and R. J. Fensterheim, Eds., Van Nostrand Reinhold Co., New York, 1983, pp. 282-308.

(8) J. S. Thayer, "Organometalic Compounds and Living Organisms," Academic Press, New York, 1984, pp. 189-194; 199-202.

(9) E. A. Crecelius, Environ. Health Perspect. 19 (1977) 147-150.

(10) C. N. Cheng and D. D. Focht, Appl. Environ. Microbiol. 38 (1979) 494-498.

(11) B. C. McBride and R. S. Wolfe, Biochemistry 10 (1971) 4312-4317.

(12) R. A. Zingaro and K. J. Irgolic, Science 187 (1975) 765-766.

(13) K. J. Irgolic, C. H. Banks, N. R. Bottino, D. Chakraborti, J. M. Gennity, D. C. Hillman, D. H. O'Brien, R. A. Pyles, R. A. Stockton, A. E. Wheeler and R. A. Zingaro, NBS Spec. Publ. 618 (1981) 244-263.

(14) M. O. Andreae, "Biotransformation of Arsenic in the Marine Environment," in "Arsenic: Industrial, Biomedical, Environmental Perspectives," W. H. Lederer and R. J. Fensterheim, Eds., Van Nostrand Reinhold Co., New York, 1983, pp. 378-392.

(15) J. R. Cannon, J. S. Edmonds, K. A. Francesconi, C. L. Raston, J. B. Saunders, B. W. Skelton and A. H. White, Aust. J. Chem. 34 (1981) 787-798.

(16) J. R. Cannon, J. B. Saunders and R. F. Toia, Sci. Total Environ. 31 (1983) 181-185.

(17) J. S. Edmonds and K. A. Francesconi, Mar. Pollut. Bull. 12 (1981) 92-96.

(18) S. Kurosowa, K. Yasuda, M. Taguchi, S. Yamazaki, S. Toda, M. Morita T. Uehiro and K. Fuwa, Agric. Biol. Chem. 44 (1980) 1993-1994.

(19) K. Shiomi, A. Shinagawa, M. Azuma, H. Yamanaka and T. Kikuchi, Comp. Biochem. Physiol. 74C (1983) 393-396.

(20) J. B. Luten, G. Riekwel-Booy, J. Van der Greef and M. C. ten Noever de Brauw, Chemosphere 12 (1983) 131-141.

(21) J. B. Luten, G. Riekwel-Booy and A. Rauchbaar, Environ. Health Perspect. 45 (1982) 165-170.

(22) K. Shiomi, A. Shinagawa, T. Igarashi, H. Yamanaka and T. Kikuchi, Experientia 40 (1984) 1247-1248.

(23) K. Shiomi, A. Shinagawa, H. Yamanaka and T. Kikuchi, Nippon Suisan Gakkaishi 49 (1983) 79-83; Chem. Abstr. 98, 120745.

(24) G. K. H. Tam, S. M. Charbonneau, F. Bryce and E. Sandi, Bull. Environ. Contam. Toxicol. 28 (1982) 669-673.

(25) H. Norin, R. Ryhage, A. Christakapoulos and M. Sandstroem, Chemosphere 12 (1983) 299-315.

(26) H. Norin and A. Christakopoulos, Chemosphere 11 (1982) 287-298.

(27) S. Matsuto, R. A. Stockton and K. J. Irgolic, Sci. Total Environment, 1985, in press.

(28) K. A. Francesconi, P. Micks, R. A. Stockton and K. J. Irgolic, Chemosphere, submitted.

(29) J. S. Edmonds and K. A. Francesconi, Chemosphere 10 (1981) 1041-1044.

(30) J. S. Edmonds and K. A. Francesconi, Nature 289 (1981) 602-604.

(31) J. S. Edmonds and K. A. Francesconi, J. Chem. Soc. Perkin Trans. I (1983) 2375-2382.

(32) J. S. Edmonds, K. A. Francesconi, P. C. Healy and A. H. White, J. Chem. Soc. Perkin Trans. I (1982) 2989-2993.

(33) J. S. Edmonds, K. A. Francesconi and J. A. Hansen, Experientia 38 (1982) 643-644.

(34) N. R. Bottino, E. R. Cox, K. J. Irgolic, S. Maeda, W. J. McShane, R. A. Stockton and R. A. Zingaro, ACS Symp. Ser. 82 (1978) 116-129.

(35) E. Marafante, M. Vahter and L. Dencker, Sci. Total Environ. 34 (1984) 223-240.

(36) R. V. Cooney, R. O. Mumma and A. A. Benson, Proc. Natl. Acad. Sci. USA 75 (1978) 4262-4264.

(37) A. A. Benson and P. Nissen, Dev. Plant Biol. 8 (1982) 121-124 (Biochem. Metal. Plant Lipids); references therein.

(38) A. A. Benson, "Phytoplankton Solved the Arsenate-Phosphate Problem," in Proc. 5th ESCB Conference, Taormina, Sept. 1983, R. Gilles, Ed., Springer Verlag, Berlin, in press.

(39) J. S. Edmonds, K. A. Francesconi, J. R. Cannon, C. L. Raston, B. W. Skelton and A. H. White, Tetrahedron Lett. (1977) 1543-1546.

(40) W. J. McShane, "The Synthesis and Characterization of Arsenocholine and Related Compounds," Ph.D. Dissertation, Texas A&M University, December 1982.

(41) M. Vahter, E. Marafante and L. Dencker, Sci. Total Environ. 30 (1983) 197-211.

(42) Ref. 3, p. 117, 173.

(43) J. Savory and M. R. Wills, "Arsen," in "Metalle in der Umwelt," E. Merian, Ed., Verlag Chemie, Weinheim, FRG, 1984, pp. 319-334.

(44) W. Mertz, "Implications of the New Trace Elements for Human Health," in "Arsen," Proc. 3. Spurenelement Symp., 7.-11. Juli 1980, M. Anke, H.-J. Schneider and Chr. Bruckner, Eds., Friedrich-Schiller-Universität, Jena, G.D.R., 1980, pp. 11-15.

(45) K.-H. Most, "Arsen als Gift und Zaubermittel in der deutschen Volksmedizin mit besonderer Berücksichtigung der Steiermark," Ph.D. Dissertation, University

Graz, Austria, July 13, 1939, Doktorats-Akten Z-2430.

(46) K. J. Irgolic, "Environmental Inorganic Analytical Chemistry," in "Environmental Inorganic Chemistry," K. J. Irgolic and A. E. Martell, Eds., VCH
Publishers, Inc., Deerfield Beach, Florida, 1985, pp. 547-564.

(47) K. J. Irgolic and F. E. Brinckman, "Liquid Chromatography - Element Specific
Detection Systems for Molecular Speciation," Report, Dahlem Conference "The
Importance of Chemical Speciation in Environmental Processes," Sept. 2-7, 1984,
Berlin, F. E. Brinckman and M. Bernhard, Eds., Springer-Verlag, Berlin, in
press.

Plutonium Speciation from Disposal Vault to Man

J.E.Cross, D.Read, G.L.Smith and D.R.Williams

Department of Applied Chemistry, University of Wales Institute of
Science and Technology, PO Box 13, Cardiff CF1 3XF, UK.

SUMMARY

Plutonium is the major transuranic by-product of the nuclear fuel
cycle and radioactive wastes may contain significant quantities of this
element. Plutonium's long half-lives, α-activity and chemical toxicity
make this element of paramount importance in radiological assessments.
The disposal of any radioactive material involves its encapsulation
within a suitable matrix and its subsequent placement in a repository,
known as a vault. It is intended that this barrier will contain the
waste until it no longer poses an environmental threat. However, the
situation where the vault fails and the radioelements enter the surrounding geosphere must be considered. Therefore, it is essential that
both the physical and chemical behaviour of each radioelement is
known. Computer simulation may be used to predict this information.
In this paper the chemical speciation of plutonium is followed. In the
vault, which is modelled as a concrete solution, plutonium speciation
is dominated by plutonium(IV) hydrolysis products, dictated by the high
pH conditions. As it moves into the geosphere, near neutral pH conditions are encountered and competitive complexing by inorganic ligands
(such as carbonate and fluoride) and organic material becomes important. The extent to which plutonium is incorporated in the biosphere
and, ultimately, man, is also determined by its chemical speciation.
The major routes for plutonium uptake are discussed together with its
distribution _in vivo_ and its removal from man using chelating agents.
The work presented illustrates the importance of a knowledge of chemical speciation and how computer simulation modelling may be used for
its investigation.

1   INTRODUCTION

The safe disposal of radioactive waste arising from the nuclear
industry is a major concern of the modern age. The wastes occur as
complex mixtures of approximately sixty main isotopes, each of differing radiotoxicity, and comprehensive site assessment procedures are
required before they may be emplaced in an underground repository. For
the purpose of disposal, waste forms in the UK are broadly classified
into very low, low, intermediate, and high level wastes based on their
activities and heat generating capacities.

Plutonium is potentially a major contributor to the risk caused by
leaching of buried radioactive material. The α-emitter ^{239}Pu, in particular, has a half-life long enough (24,390 years) to suggest that
decay would not sufficiently reduce levels before breaching of even a
high integrity vault. A detailed knowledge of the likely behaviour of
plutonium in the disposal system is, therefore, essential. This paper
attempts to trace the effects of a changing chemical environment on the
element as it migrates from a disposal vault through the geosphere to
the human population.

2   CHEMICAL SPECIATION

In order to predict the behaviour of plutonium in any radioactive
waste disposal scenario, a knowledge of the chemical speciation of the
system is essential. Chemical speciation may be defined as the different chemical forms of an element which together comprise its total
concentration in a given sample (1). Speciation data may provide
considerable information concerning the fate of radioelements since
different species will have varying solubilities, be adsorbed onto
solid surfaces to a differing extent and have different toxicities.
The type of information which may be gained from a knowledge of the
chemical speciation along the path from vault to biosphere is illustrated in Figure 1.
   The experimental study of speciation is problematical. The techniques employed are usually highly sophisticated, time-consuming and
tedious. In order to avoid the disruption of the labile equilibria
involved, they must also be non-invasive. The system under investigation generally contains a large number of species, all at very low
concentrations, hence insensitivity is often a serious problem. This
is particularly true for plutonium which has a very low solubility at
high pH. Techniques for studying the speciation of actinides, such as

photoacoustic laser-induced spectrometry (2), are currently being developed. However, it is too early to assess how much information on the species present such techniques will be able to provide.

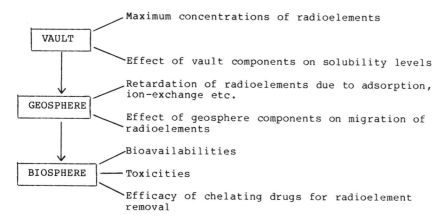

Figure 1   Speciation in Radioactive Waste Disposal

In view of the problems associated with the experimental study of chemical speciation, the alternative approach of computerised modelling has been developed.

3   COMPUTER SIMULATION

3.1   Introduction

Computer simulation is increasingly used to investigate systems which are either very difficult, expensive, or not feasible to study experimentally. In chemical speciation studies, computer simulation can enable the important components in a system to be identified without unnecessary experimental work, and allow a more rapid appreciation of their significance.

The first stage in computer simulation must be to fully characterise the system being studied to establish a chemical model. The concentrations of each component (e.g. Mg^{2+}, Ca^{2+}, CO_3^{2-}) are required, together with the pH and redox state (Eh) of the system. These data are then used as input to the chemical model. In general, the computer codes use a formation constant approach to compute the speciation. Large thermodynamic databases are employed which contain formation constants (β) for all the species which could possibly be formed by the components in the system. These are used together with mass balance equa-

tions for each component in a series of iterative calculations until
the equilibrium distribution of the chemical species is reached.   The
output from the simulation is typically designed to give the equilibrium concentration of each chemical species considered, from which the
total solubility of a component (e.g. plutonium) may be obtained. Some
computer codes are more sophisticated than others, allowing a better
representation of the system to be modelled.   The available codes,
their thermodynamic databases, and a selection of examples using this
simulation approach to chemical speciation in plutonium studies are
described more fully below.

3.2 Computer programs available for modelling chemical speciation

There are a large number of codes available for modelling chemical
speciation in aqueous systems;   these have been developed for use in a
wide variety of applications.   The most suitable codes for modelling
radioactive waste are those originally developed for geochemical
systems, since they can consider solid phases in addition to aqueous
species.   Also, they can incorporate redox reactions, temperature
variation, ion-exchange and, in some cases, adsorption;   all important
processes when radioelements are considered.

The codes fall into two main categories, chemical speciation codes
(e.g. MINEQL and SOLMNQ) and reaction path codes (e.g. PHREEQE and
EQ3/6). The former group are static models, which calculate the chemical equilibrium distribution of aqueous species in a solution and the
saturation indices for solid phases.   The latter group may perform the
same function but, in addition, they may be used as dynamic models,
capable of predicting the path of a reacting system.   For example, mass
transfer in and out of a system, or changes in the distribution of an
aqueous species, either as a reaction progresses or with time.   A reaction path calculation contains at least one process or reaction which
is not in a state of thermodynamic equilibrium and, hence, "drives" the
reaction.   Reaction path capabilities enable a code to be used to model
a wider variety of systems than the equilibrium models.   However, the
choice of program is entirely dependent on the particular system to be
modelled.   In some cases, the simpler codes may be sufficient;   in
others, they may be used first to indicate the important components in
a system, and then more detailed modelling may be undertaken using a
pathways code.

3.3 Verification and validation

Code verification and validation are essential in all modelling exercises. Verification ensures that the code is calculating correctly and does not contain any "bugs". One of the simplest methods of verification is by comparison of the different results obtained from different codes on a common problem. Two intercode comparison exercises have now been performed using several of the geochemical codes (3,4), and results indicate good mathematical agreement.

Codes and database validation, however, is a much harder problem. In a validation exercise the code is used to model a well-characterised system and the predicted and experimentally observed properties are compared. In general, there has been only limited validation undertaken using these codes, basically due to the experimental difficulties encountered when attempting to characterise a system. Some validation of the codes is being done by comparing predicted solubilities and speciation with some relatively simple experimental results, but considerably more effort is required. The entire simulation can never be fully validated, however, owing to the long time-scales involved.

4   DATA AND DATABASES

4.1   Introduction

The quality of all results from computer modelling depends solely upon the quality of the data used, irrespective of the level of sophistication of modern programs. Four primary data sets are required for simulating the processes operating during and following release of plutonium from an underground waste repository:
(a) Thermodynamic:- stability constants, ΔH_r.
(b) Retardation/sorption:- sorption coefficients (K_d), Freundlich/ Langmuir isotherms, etc.
(c) Hydrogeologic:- flow type, advective velocity, diffusion, porosity, permeability.
(d) Site-specific:- characteristics of groundwater, mineralogy and waste.

The thermodynamic stability constants used by the speciation programs are the basis of the work. It is essential that values are critically assessed prior to incorporation into the models and desirable that respective databases from around the world are consistent to facilitate inter-code and inter-laboratory comparisons. A review of the chemical data available for studying plutonium migration from a disposal vault is given below.

4.2 Thermodynamic data

Plutonium is an extremely difficult element to study experimentally owing to its high radiotoxicity, the difficulty of maintaining a particular oxidation state, and its tendency to polymerize under environmental conditions. Except at pH $\approx$ 1, Pu^{3+} is very readily oxidised to Pu^{4+}, whereas the plutonyl ion, PuO_2^{2+}, is easily reduced by complexing agents. The PuO_2^{+} ion co-exists with the other oxidation states and is normally at much lower concentrations than either PuO_2^{2+} or Pu^{4+}.

A large volume of data has been assembled over the last 40 years and several recent compilations and critical evaluations of plutonium redox and complex chemistry are available (5,6). Values with a high degree of accuracy are scarce, however, and valid only for the media in which they are measured; almost invariably low pH solutions with high concentrations of plutonium. Caution is needed when applying these data to predict the chemical speciation of plutonium in neutral or alkaline solution and at low environmental concentrations.

In cases where stability constants of plutonium complexes are not known, it is possible to obtain a rough estimate by comparison with analogous metal ions, e.g. La^{3+} for Pu^{3+}, Th^{4+} for Pu^{4+}, NpO_2^{+} for PuO_2^{+} and UO_2^{2+} for PuO_2^{2+}. These estimated constants may differ from the corresponding plutonium values but it is imperative that all species likely to exist are included in any simulation of speciation and solubility in natural systems.

Areas of particular relevance to natural systems where experimental work is urgently needed are described below:-

(a) The CO_3^{2-} ion is known to be one of the strongest complexing agents for plutonium in aqueous solutions (7,8) but information on plutonium-carbonate complexes is still very limited, especially the formation constants with Pu(III) and Pu(IV). The existence of Pu(III) and Pu(IV) complexes with mixed $OH-CO_3^{2-}$ ligands is uncertain, and for $Pu_2(CO_3)_3{}_{(s)}$, the only data available have been extrapolated from lanthanide analogues.

(b) Only a few measurements have been made of the Pu(III) and Pu(IV) hydrolysis products $Pu(OH)_2^{+}$, $Pu(OH)_3^{0}$, $Pu(OH)_2^{2+}$ and $Pu(OH)_3^{+}$. The existence of $Pu(OH)_5^{-}$ has not been verified; constants being based on tentative observation of U(IV), and data for the solid phase $Pu(OH)_3$ is available only by extrapolation from americium or lanthanide values.

(c) Experimental measurements of halide complexes in aqueous solution are limited in number and scattered over a wide range of ionic strengths.

(d) Little is known about plutonium complexation by humic or fulvic acids.

Substantial improvements to the existing plutonium thermodynamic database have been made in recent years and the element is currently under review by the OECD/NEA. Their compilation of stability constants is expected to be ready during 1985.

4.3 Sorption data

The retardation of a radionuclide migrating from a waste repository may be defined as:

$$R_f = \frac{V_w}{V_n} = 1 + K_d \rho_r (1 - \varepsilon) a_f / \rho_w \varepsilon a_p$$

where R_f is the retardation or retention factor, V_w is the velocity of the groundwater, V_n the velocity of the nuclide, K_d the distribution coefficient, ρ_r the density of rock (kg/m^3), ρ_w the density of water (kg/m^3), a_f the specific surface of fissures in the bedrock (m^2/m^3), a_p the specific surface of particles used in K_d determinations (m^2/m^3) and ε the porosity. The distribution coefficient is an equilibrium parameter which does not differentiate between the numerous mechanisms likely to induce mass transfer between solution and solid phases, e.g. physical adsorption, ion-exchange, co-precipitation, colloid formation and flocculation. Concentrating on measurement of K_d, plutonium uptake on geologic media from groundwater has been studied extensively during the last few years. Unfortunately, data from various experiments are rarely directly comparable owing to differences in experimental techniques, failure to control conditions and failure to determine the speciation of plutonium in the solution phase. This has resulted in plutonium K_ds varying by 3 orders of magnitude in an inter-laboratory study (9), even with standardised rock samples. Accurate K_ds can only be obtained in pH/Eh invariant systems, otherwise the effect of polymerization/precipitation reactions may result in very high apparent K_d values. A compilation of all available plutonium sorption data with detailed documentation of the experimental conditions used is being prepared by the OECD/NEA. This project termed ISIRS (International Sorption Information Retrieval System) is at an early stage of development but will prove invaluable to modellers of radionuclide migration in the future.

It is imperative that an adequate knowledge of the above has been obtained before starting the final stages of an assessment.

The refinement of databases and the use of internally consistent data sets are necessary to put computer simulation modelling on a firm footing. The latter will not alone provide a meaningful model of real systems, however, unless the problem to be solved has been correctly defined and the processes modelled are reasonably well understood.

5   PLUTONIUM IN THE VAULT

In the UK it is proposed that low and intermediate level radioactive wastes will be suitably packaged and then placed in either shallow or deep land repositories according to their radioactive content. All current repository designs envisage extensive use of cement and concrete for vault construction, grouting and waste packaging. Therefore, it is essential that the chemical behaviour of these materials and their interactions with the radioelements is thoroughly understood before long-term radiological site assessments are made.

Cementitious materials may undergo changes over a long period of time. First, there are changes within the cement itself; for example, the continued slow hydration of calcium silicate matrix, the crystallisation of amorphous phases and reactions with the aggregate leading to internal structural changes (10). Secondly, there are reactions of the concrete with the environment, such as its dissolution by leaching with groundwater or interaction with groundwater components, such as SO_4^{2-} or CO_3^{2-} to form new phases. Finally, there are changes resulting from wet/dry cycles, corrosion of the metal reinforcement, effects of radiation and the action of micro-organisms. In a recent assessment of the long-term durability of concrete in radioactive waste repositories, sulphate attack and $Ca(OH)_2$ leaching were identified as the most likely processes to cause degradation of the repository (11). Hence, the structural integrity of the vault has been estimated at between 380 and 3000 years, depending on its design. During this period, many of the radionuclides will undergo radioactive decay; however, the longer-lived components, such as the actinides, [129]I and ^{99}Tc, will still be present. If it is assumed that the vault is eventually breached and becomes saturated with water, then it is the chemistry of the aqueous phase which will determine the subsequent release of the radionuclides into the geosphere.

At a first approximation, the vault may be modelled as a solution in equilibrium with the solid phases of concrete. Then, using the chemical equilibrium codes described above, the maximum solubilities and chemical speciation of each of the radioelements in this concrete solution are modelled. For example, some results for plutonium are given in Table 1. These clearly show the influence of the high pH on its speciation.

TABLE 1   Computed Plutonium Solubility in a Typical Concrete Solution

pH	Plutonium Solubility/ mol dm^{-3}	Solubility Limiting Phase	Dominant = Aqueous Species	% of Aqueous Plutonium
8.0	3.16×10^{-9}	$Pu(OH)_4$	$Pu(OH)_4^0$	100
10.0	3.29×10^{-9}	$Pu(OH)_4$	$Pu(OH)_4^0$	96
			$Pu(OH)_5^-$	4
12.0	1.64×10^{-8}	$Pu(OH)_4$	$Pu(OH)_5^-$	80.7
			$Pu(OH)_4^0$	19.3

The long-term ageing of concrete will be accompanied by a gradual decrease in the pH from 13 to about 10, as the alkali salts are leached from the matrix. Chemical modelling may be used to predict the effect on the solubility of the radioelements in this changing vault environment. Figure 2 shows the results obtained for plutonium and it is interesting to note the very small effect that pH causes on the maximum solubility. Modelling also enables the relative effects of other vault components on the speciation of the radioelements to be observed. For example, the waste matrix may contain organic components, such as EDTA and citric acid, which originate from decontamination operations. These organic ligands can be included in the model and their relative importance assessed. In Figure 2, the solubility of plutonium over a range of pH values is plotted for solutions containing no EDTA, 1 x 10^{-6} mol dm^{-3} EDTA and 1 x 10^{-4} mol dm^{-3} EDTA. It is clearly seen how the increased solubility at pH = 8 reflects the formation of the PuEDTA$^-$ complex. Hence, chemical modelling is a powerful tool for near-field investigations, enabling good predictions to be made concerning both the maximum solubilities and the chemical speciation of radioelements leaving the vault and entering the geosphere.

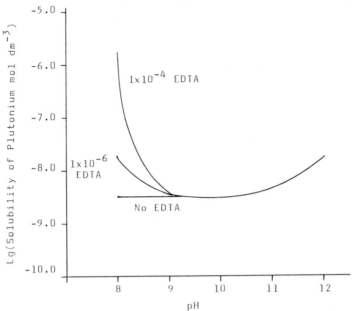

Figure 2   Solubility of plutonium in a concrete solution and the effect
of different EDTA concentrations (unit = mol dm^{-3})

6   PLUTONIUM IN THE GEOSPHERE

6.1   General plutonium geochemistry

Plutonium in natural aqueous solutions can exist in four oxidation
states, (III), (IV), (V) and (VI), the latter two as dioxo species,
PuO_2^+ and PuO_2^{2+}. The oxidation potentials of the Pu(III-IV), (IV-V) and
(V-VI) couples are so close that all of these states and their hydrolysis products may co-exist under environmental conditions. The presence
of complexing ions may stabilize one particular oxidation state, but
briefly, the stability of the four plutonium oxidation states may be
summarised as follows. Pu^{3+} is stable in acidic solution but easily
undergoes oxidation by autoradiolysis if ^{239}Pu is present, to Pu^{4+}.
Pu^{4+} is also stable in acid solutions but, unlike Pu^{3+}, persists at
higher pH owing to stabilization through hydrolysis reactions. At high
concentrations it disproportionates to Pu^{3+} and PuO_2^+ in weak acids and
alkaline systems. PuO_2^+ may be the species which governs the total plutonium solubility at low concentrations, near neutral pH and in the
absence of strong complexing agents (12), whereas Pu(VI) species are
likely to be dominant in seawater and brines (13,14). The above generalizations can be negated by factors such as strong complexation which

can reverse the above trends and the relative stabilities of the different states.

According to Costanzo et al. (15), all plutonium in natural waters at neutral pH is probably in the polymeric state, a view largely shared by Kim et al. (16). Thus, it is to be expected that migration rates will be affected, not only by the oxidation state of the soluble plutonium, the sorptive properties of geologic media and the solubility of the solid phases, but also by the stability of plutonium suspensions, colloids and pseudocolloids in the percolating groundwater.

6.2 Complexation of dissolved plutonium

Plutonium cations in all oxidation states exist in aqueous solution as highly charged ions which can undergo hydrolysis and interact with anionic species by ionic bonding. Where different oxidation states of plutonium have been complexed by the same ligand, the sequence of complex strength most commonly follows that of the hydrolysis reactions, i.e. $Pu^{4+} > PuO_2^{2+} \geqslant Pu^{3+} > PuO_2^+$.

The complexing of plutonium in aqueous solutions by inorganic ligands has been reviewed (17,18). Multiply-charged anions form more stable complexes with plutonium than those of single charge and for ligands of major environmental significance the following sequence generally holds - $CO_3^{2-} > SO_4^{2-} > F^- > NO_3^- > Cl^-$. Taking inorganic complexes only, the anion concentration ranges of groundwaters and the magnitude of the corresponding plutonium stability constants suggest that the solution chemistry of plutonium should be almost entirely dominated by hydroxide and carbonate complexation at neutral to alkaline pH under oxic conditions. Based on thermodynamic considerations, Allard and Rydberg (18) state that under aerobic conditions, plutonium solubility is controlled by PuO_2, with $Pu(OH)_4^0$ as the dominant species in solution between pH 6 and 9. Below pH 5 to 6, PuO_2^+ dominates and below pH 3 to 4, Pu^{3+} would be the major species. Hexavalent species are not thought to contribute significantly. Under reducing conditions, the solubility limiting phase is still thought to be PuO_2 at high pH (>7) but $Pu_2(CO_3)_3$ becomes stable in acidic waters. The overall solubility of plutonium is likely to be considerably higher than in oxic systems with trivalent species dominating over the environmental range of pH.

How well the above predictions compare with computed speciation and solubility levels of plutonium in a typical clay groundwater may be

assessed from Figures 3-5. The MINEQL program was used for all calculations.

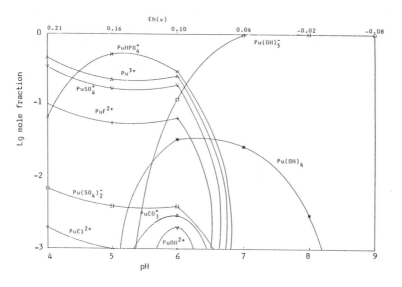

Figure 3   Plutonium speciation in a typical clay groundwater

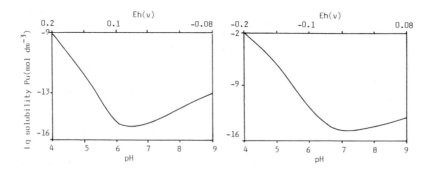

Figures 4 and 5 The variation of plutonium solubility as a function of
pH and Eh in a clay groundwater

The pH was scanned from 4 to 9 with Eh, in the first instance, assumed to follow the siderite(Fe(II))/goethite(Fe(III)) reaction. Hydroxy species dominate between pH 6 and 9 (Fig.3) with carbonate complexing of relatively little importance at this carbonate level (5 x 10^{-4} mol dm^{-3}). Phosphate, fluoride and sulphate are significant ligands at lower pH. Under reducing conditions, the pattern is similar with the Pu^{3+} ion exerting an even greater influence at low pH. As predicted (18), plutonium solubility is higher in a reducing environment (Figs. 4,5) by up to seven orders of magnitude at pH 4. The solubility limiting phase (PuO_2), however, does not vary with either pH or Eh.

The results give lower values than expected for total plutonium solubility in neutral to alkaline conditions. Estimates are generally of the order of 10^{-8} mol dm^{-3} (12,19) rather than 10^{-13} mol dm^{-3} but it must be noted that the calculations above take no account of organic ligands likely to be present in the waste or rock-soil matrix and do not allow for the effect of colloids.

6.3 Colloid formation

The equilibria discussed above and implied in all thermodynamic calculations are useful in characterising and predicting plutonium behaviour in aqueous systems but are only directly applicable if equilibrium is maintained and aqueous species are in "true" solution. While this may be the case for Pu(V) and Pu(VI), it is less probable for Pu(III) and Pu(IV) which show a strong tendency for hydrolysis, and, with the latter, polymerization. The occurrence of polymeric or colloidal plutonium results in higher concentrations of plutonium in the "aqueous" phase than would otherwise be expected. According to Bulman (20), at a concentration of 6.8 x 10^{-8} mol dm^{-3} Pu(IV) exists in anionic form up to pH 2.8, as a "pseudocolloid" at pH 2.8 to 7.5, and as a "true" colloid above pH 7.5. Generally, polymerization is an irreversible process owing to "ageing" by crystallization or the replacement of hydroxyl by oxybridges (21). Depolymerization is slow, even for freshly formed polymer but may be brought about by <u>Thiobacillus ferroxidans</u> growing in iron-rich waters (20).

As noted in the previous section, Pu(IV) forms stable complexes with many organic and inorganic ligands which, by competition, retard the formation of colloids. The uranyl ion may also retard polymerization by binding through hydroxyl bridges to active sites in the polymer network, thereby functioning as a chain terminating unit (22). Once formed, however, the ageing process renders the colloidal Pu(IV) resistant to complexing species, even at environmental plutonium levels ($<10^{-8}$ mol dm^{-3}).

While the presence and form of colloidal plutonium has been established in numerous experimental studies, its behaviour in natural systems is still very poorly understood. The colloids could be either true radiocolloids (aggregates of the radionuclide itself) or pseudocolloids (colloid material already present in the groundwater onto which the radioelement has sorbed) (23). Pseudocolloidal transport is thought to be the dominating plutonium migration mechanism in many environmental waters (18). For colloidal material to move through rocks and soils it must not be adsorbed onto the surface of these materials, the suspensions must be stable and, in porous media, "polymer particles" must be smaller than the pore size of the geomatrix. In the geosphere, therefore, colloids have a much slower diffusion rate than ionic or molecular species and if plutonium exists predominantly in this form, its mobility would be governed by the colloid solubility and the nature of the soluble plutonium species. Polymeric plutonium is more soluble than crystalline PuO_2 but less soluble than amorphous $Pu(OH)_4$ (24) and its precipitation by nitrate has been found to closely resemble a solubility product mechanism (25). If this holds in other media, one may be justified in using such a simple approach when modelling colloidal processes but clearly a great deal of further work is needed.

6.4 Sorption

The retardation of plutonium during migration through the geosphere depends upon the stability of the waste form and sorption/desorption reactions of the leached plutonium with geologic material. Although sorption reactions may be occurring, the equilibrium plutonium concentration in leached waters will be determined by the solubility of a plutonium solid phase as long as this solid exists (19). Therefore, in the immediate vicinity of stored wastes, plutonium concentrations in solutions percolating through PuO_2-contaminated media would be expected to be similar to PuO_2 solubility under the pH/Eh conditions prevailing and unrelated to equilibrium distribution coefficients (K_d) measured at lower plutonium levels. If the leachate percolates soils or rocks containing no PuO_2, plutonium levels will be governed by sorption reactions (26). These, in turn, are affected by solution pH, Eh, ionic strength, complexing ligands and temperature - all controls on pluton-ium speciation, and the nature of the sorbing phases. Until now, efforts to predict plutonium uptake from groundwaters have focused on determining distribution coefficients (K_d) between synthetic waters and various rock types. Watters (27) stated that the sorption of plutonium was an equilibrium process, modified primarily by the oxida-tion state of the soluble plutonium and by the presence of dissolved organic carbon (DOC). At pH ≈ 7 and low DOC, he considered K_d values to be very similar (within 1 to 2 orders of magnitude). Most recent work, however, suggests that for such a complex, multivalent element K_d values are limited in use unless experimental conditions are very strictly controlled and the species present in the system are identi-fied (9).

According to Erickson (28), two sorption mechanisms control the distribution of plutonium between solid and solution phases. An ion-exchange phenomenon, associated with silicates, dominates at high solution phase concentrations ($>10^{-3}$ mol dm^{-3}), whereas at lower concentrations ($<10^{-4}$ mol dm^{-3}), sorption is associated with hydrous metallic oxides. This could have important implications for modelling the migration of plutonium through the geosphere. In the case of an ion-exchange mechanism, the migration pattern follows the theory of diffusion of soluble species in a porous medium. If precipitation or co-precipitation on hydrous oxides dominates, mobility will be governed by the behaviour of colloidal particles passing through a filtrating medium. It is, therefore, essential that the sorption processes are characterized before transport modelling is attempted.

7   PLUTONIUM IN THE BIOSPHERE

Organic environmental contaminants are ultimately degraded in nature. Such a process is not possible for metal ions and the only detoxification mechanism is that of immobilisation. The extent to which metal ions are accumulated in food chains and passed on to man depends on the physico-chemical forms of that element. Thus, a know-ledge of the speciation of plutonium in the biosphere is essential in order to be able to predict its bioavailability to man. In particular, consideration must be given to the presence of both naturally occurring and synthetic chelating agents which may enhance the movement of the actinides through the food chain.

Plutonium is readily polymerised at pH > 2 which retards its movement through food chains. However, the presence of chelating agents, such as citrate, suppresses this hydrolysis and retains the metal ion in solution (29). Pu(IV) shows the greatest tendency to form complexes and this is the most stable oxidation state of the metal under normal environmental conditions.

Investigations into the chemical form of plutonium in the soil environment suggest the metal is complexed to humic and fulvic acids in the +4 oxidation state (20). It is postulated that these organic acids participate in the uptake of cations by plant roots. Alternatively, they may act as a slow-release mechanism for the actinide cations.

Chelating agents, natural or synthetic, have a significant effect on the distribution of actinides in the biosphere. Complexing agents, such as nitrilotriacetate (NTA) and ethylenediaminetetraacetate (EDTA) are being used in increasing quantities in agriculture and as decontaminating agents by nuclear authorities. Research into the migration of ^{239}Pu from the Maxey flats disposal trenches in USA indicates that the radionuclide migrates as an EDTA complex (30).

The major routes of entry of plutonium into man are by inhalation into the lungs or via cuts, abrasions, and wounds. In the case of inhalation, the rate of clearance from the lungs depends very much on the chemical form of the plutonium. Insoluble compounds, such as oxides and fluorides, may take years, soluble compounds (e.g., nitrates, citrates) several weeks, and stable complexes like those with EDTA or DTPA, only a few days to be removed from the lungs. Similarly, the clearance from the blood of plutonium ingested via wounds is dependent on the chemical speciation of the metal. Colloidal particles or insoluble compounds are rapidly removed from the blood by phagocytosis, being concentrated to a large extent in the liver, but with some going to the spleen, skeleton and other reticuloendothelial tissues.

Soluble plutonium becomes rapidly associated with transferrin and is then cleared relatively slowly to the liver and skeleton where it is bound in ferritin and hemosiderin, respectively. Only a very small amount of the plutonium ingested is excreted, the majority of the metal being immobilised in the tissues. However, this may lead to radioactive 'hot spots' which may cause tumour growth.

Regardless of its mode of administration, plutonium attains the same oxidation state in vivo. All available evidence points to that being

Pu(IV).   The distribution of plutonium in vivo bears marked similarities to that of iron, being predominantly associated with the iron
transport and storage proteins.   Plutonium is stored in the body as
insoluble deposits (e.g. oxides, fluorides, hydroxides and other polymeric aggregates), as ferritin complexes in the liver lysosomes (31) or
as hemosiderin in the bone (32).   This fraction is essentially inert.
The three remaining fractions are in labile equilibrium and, thus,
there is exchange of plutonium between them.   These consist of a labile
protein complex with transferrin (33) low-molecular-weight (LMW)
species in which the metal ion is predominantly bound to citrate (34),
and a small amount of aquated Pu(IV) ions.   The LMW species are of
particular importance in vivo since they are involved in the transport
of the metal around the body and thus influence the distribution of the
metal ion.   The LMW speciation of plutonium(IV) in blood plasma has
been computed using the ECCLES program (35).   ECCLES computes the
equilibrium distribution of a metal ion amongst the LMW ligands of
normal blood plasma.   LMW plutonium is almost entirely complexed to
citrate, $Pu(C_6H_5O_7)(OH)_2^-$ and $Pu(C_6H_5O_7)(OH)^0$ species predominating.

In addition to quantifying the LMW distributions of metal ions in
plasma, the ECCLES model may also be used to evaluate the efficacy of
chelating agents in mobilising toxic metal ions from plasma.   This is
quantified in terms of a Plasma Mobilising Index (P.M.I.) (36):

$$P.M.I. = \frac{\text{Concentration of LMW species in presence of drug}}{\text{Concentration of LMW species in normal plasma}}$$

The abilities of a range of chelating agents to mobilise plutonium
from the plasma proteins have been investigated using the ECCLES
program (35).   The PMI curves for these agents are illustrated in
Figure 6.   CDTA, DTPA and EDTA were all shown to be effective agents,

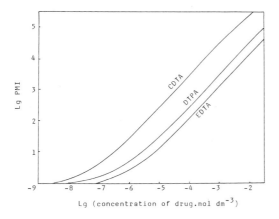

Figure 6   Plasma Mobilization of Plutonium by Chelating Agents

the order of decreasing efficacy being CDTA > DTPA > EDTA.   Although
CDTA appears to mobilize plutonium to the greatest extent, the major
species formed (Pu(CDTA)) is neutral and, thus, may simply redistribute
the metal round the body.   DTPA is the most widely accepted therapy for
plutonium intoxication (37).   However, there are certain limitations
associated with this drug.   The drug is more toxic when given as the
calcium salt rather than the zinc salt, due to the ligand's affinity
for Zn(II) ions.   However, the zinc complex is less effective at mobilising plutonium.   In view of this, DTPA is best given as the calcium
salt and the zinc status of the patient monitored and compensated for.
Moreover, DTPA is a hydrophilic drug and is thus confined to the extracellular spaces.   As plutonium is rapidly incorporated into tissues and
bone, this drug will be ineffective at removing the metal if treatment
is delayed.   Attempts have been made to synthesise lipophilic derivatives of DTPA.   One such agent, Puchel, showed considerable promise in
early animal experiments (38) but has subsequently been shown to have
less affinity for plutonium than does DTPA.   It also appears to have a
high toxicity.

The best way forward in developing a more effective regime for
plutonium decorporation is that of synergistic chelation therapy.   This
involves the use of a lipophilic agent to mobilise the metal from the
tissues followed by a hydrophilic agent which effectively competes for
the metal ion and causes excretion of the metal in the urine.   DTPA
appears to be the most suitable hydrophilic agent available;   whether
or not Puchel is an effective lipophilic drug is yet to be determined.
Even if a suitable synergistic therapy could be developed, there is
still the problem of the insoluble deposits of plutonium for which
there is no effective treatment.

8   CONCLUSIONS

The work reviewed in this article clearly indicates how the behaviour of plutonium is strongly influenced by its ambient environment.
During its movement along the pathway from vault to man, it undergoes a
series of chemical reactions which dictate its ultimate fate.   In the
vault, plutonium speciation is dominated by the high pH of the concrete
environment and the solubility is controlled by Pu(IV) hydrolysis
products.   On entering the geosphere, the solubility of plutonium
increases in response to this reduction in pH.   The redox conditions
encountered in the groundwater are critical in determining the
distribution of plutonium oxidation states and, hence, in turn, the

products of aqueous competitive complexation, the extent and type of sorption reactions and the importance of colloid formation. The movement of plutonium through the biosphere is influenced considerably by the presence of organic ligands, both naturally occurring and synthetic. However, the major route of entry of plutonium into man is by inhalation or via wounds, rather than through food chains. The distribution of plutonium in vivo closely mimicks that of iron, the radioelement being complexed to the iron transport and storage proteins. Investigations into the efficacy of chelating agents for plutonium decorporation therapy indicate that DTPA is still the most effective agent available. Synergistic chelation therapy holds promise for the future if suitable drugs can be identified.

Computer simulation of chemical speciation is a powerful tool for use in radioactive waste studies. It provides a relatively simple, fast, and cost-effective method of investigation enabling a greater understanding of the processes than would otherwise be possible.

9. ACKNOWLEDGEMENT

We would like to acknowledge the financial support of the UK Department of the Environment, and NIREX (Nuclear Industry Radioactive Waste Executive).

10. REFERENCES

(1) P.W.Linder et al., Analysis Using Glass Electrodes, Open University Press, Milton Keynes 1984, pp.71-86.

(2) W.Schrepp et al., Appl.Phys. B32 (1983) 207-209.

(3) D.K.Nordstrom et al., in E.A.Jenne (ed.), Chemical Modelling in Aqueous Systems, ACS Symposium Series 93, American Chemical Society, Washington D.C. 1979, pp.857-892.

(4) T.W.Broyd et al., A Comparison of Computer Programs which Model the Equilibrium Chemistry of Aqueous Systems, presented at the Third Plenary Meeting of the CEC project "MIRAGE", Brussels, 1985.

(5) J.M.Cleveland, The Chemistry of Plutonium, American Nuclear Society 1979, pp.82-90.

(6) S.L.Phillips, LBL-14313, Lawrence Berkeley Lab., USA 1982.

(7) J.J.Katz, G.T.Seaborg, The Chemistry of the Actinide Elements, Wiley, New York 1957, pp.477.

(8)   B.Allard, in N.Edelstein (ed.), Actinides in Perspective, Pergamon Press, New York 1982, pp.553-579.

(9)   J.F.Relyea, R.J.Serne,   PNL-2872, Pacific Northwest Lab., USA, 1979.

(10)   F.P.Glasser et al., Proceedings of the Materials Research Society Conference, Nov.26-30, Boston 1984.

(11)   A.Atkinson, J.A.Hearne. AERE-R11465, Harwell U.K., 1984.

(12)   A.Saltelli et al., Proceedings of the OECD/NEA Workshop on the Migration of Long-lived Radionuclides in the Geosphere, Brussels 1979.

(13)   D.M.Nelson, M.B.Lovett, Nature (London) 276 (1978) 599-601.

(14)   S.R.Aston, Mar.Chem. 8 (1980) 319-325.

(15)   D.A.Constanzo et al., J.Inorg.Nucl.Chem. 35 (1973) 609-622.

(16)   J.I.Kim et al., Mat.Res.Soc.Symp.Proc. 26 (1984) 31-40.

(17)   J.M.Cleveland, The Chemistry of Plutonium, Gordon and Breach, New York 1970, pp.653.

(18)   B.Allard, J.Rydberg in W.T.Carnall and G.R.Choppin (eds.), Behaviour of Plutonium in Natural Waters, ACS Symposium Series 216, American Chemical Society, Washington D.C. 1983, pp.275-295.

(19)   R.G.Strickert, D.Rai, Sci.Basis Nucl.Waste Manag. 6 (1982) 215-221.

(20)   R.A.Bulman, Structure and Bonding 34 (1978) 39-77.

(21)   G.L.Johnson, L.M.Toth, ORNL/TM-6365, Oak Ridge National Lab, USA, 1978.

(22)   L.M.Toth et al., J.Inorg.Nucl.Chem. 43 (1981) 2929-2934.

(23)   U.Olofsson et al., Sci.Basis Nucl.Waste Manag. 5 (1982) 753-764.

(24)   D.Rai, J.L.Swanson, Nucl.Tech. 54 (1981) 107-112.

(25)   J.T.Bell et al., J.Inorg.Nucl.Chem. 35 (1973) 623-628.

(26)   D.Rai et al., Soil Sci.Soc.Am.J. 44 (1980) 490-495.

(27)   R.L.Watters in (18), pp.275-295.

(28)   K.L.Erickson, Sci.Basis Nucl.Waste Manag. 2 (1980) 641-646.

(29)   A.Lindenbaum, W.Westfall, Int.J.Appl.Rad.Isotopes, 16 (1965) 545-553.

(30)   J.M.Cleveland, T.F.Rees, Science 212 (1981) 1508-1509.

(31)   G.Boocock et al., Radiat.Res. 42 (1970) 381-396.

(32)   P.W.Durbin, Health Phys. 29 (1975) 495-510.

(33)   G.Boocock, D.S.Popplewell, Nature (London) 20 (1965) 282-283.

(34)   D.S.Popplewell. Diagnosis and Treatment of Incorporated Radio-nuclides, IAEA, Vienna 1976, p.25.

(35)   J.R.Duffield et al. J.Inorg.Biochem. 20 (1984) 199-214.

(36)   P.M.May, D.R.Williams. FEBS Lett. 78 (1977) 134-138.

(37)   N.L.Spoor, NRPB-R59, HMSO, London 1977, pp.1-21.

(38)   J.W.Strather et al., NRPB/R and D-2, HMSO, London 1978, 115-117.

Biological Mineralization

The Inorganic Chemistry of Bio-Minerals

Robert J.P. Williams

University of Oxford, Inorganic Chemistry Laboratory, South Parks Road,
Oxford OX1 3QR, U.K.

SUMMARY

The study of bio-minerals although a very old topic is new for the community of
the bioinorganic chemist. This allows him to bring his expert knowledge of
inorganic chemistry into a new area, that of solid state bioinorganic chemistry.
Apart from the use of structural tools, mainly based on the electron microscope, new
analytical methods based on NMR and PIXE must be valuable. The examination of
nucleation and growth by kinetic methods, the detection of defects and the study of
the physical chemistry of the surfaces of a vast range of crystalline and amorphous
materials is required. The work will need analysis of the organic molecules which
stabilise the particular solids in their special forms. New synthetic procedures,
chemistry on films and in vesicles, will be valuable. The research connects with
material science as much as it connects with functional use of shape and form in
biology. The present paper illustrates these points from some of our own work.

1 INTRODUCTION

A biological object has to be analysed with its function in mind since the object
has been refined by evolution. The functions of bio-minerals are as protective
devices (outer shells), structural supports (bones), aids to attack (teeth), as
various kinds of sensors (magnetic or gravitational) or as concentrated deposits of
required elements, wastes or poisons. These minerals have fascinated biologists for
hundreds of years but only recently has the inorganic chemist turned his attention
to them. I shall describe what is of interest for the inorganic chemist, especially

those who also have an interest in material science. Good introductory reviews are given by references (1) and (2).

2 METHODS

The crystallites of biominerals are usually very small and there is often little that can be done by X-ray diffraction above powder pattern level. An electron microscope study is necessary not only for the analysis of the small crystals but to establish that so-called amorphous deposits have in fact no repeat structure, i.e. that they are truly amorphous. The level of resolution must be pursued to below 3.0Å in the electron microscope in order to establish this point. The electron microscope in the scanning mode (SEM) reveals the three dimensional space filling form of the objects while in the transmission (TEM) mode it yields both diffraction patterns and lattice images. These are computer analysed. Used on the biological object it also shows the orientation and size of crystallites. Attached to the modern electron microscope it is usual to have an X-ray and Energy Loss detectors for element analysis. The inorganic part of biological minerals is not simple, $CaCO_3$ has often Sr in it; so called apatite $Ca_2(OH)PO_4$ contains carbonate and magnesium; silica is differentially hydrated in different biological minerals; iron oxide may contain phosphate, and so on. The need for very sensitive analysis locally for a wide range of elements has led us to use PIXE, a scanning proton microscope for analysis (see other articles in this book) as well as the electron microscope. Unfortunately PIXE has not yet the resolution to a grid of 1,000Å which is required. None of these methods will analyse for protons. The structural role of OH groups as opposed to 0 or H_2O can be uncovered using a number of solid state NMR methods (3) or by switching to neutron diffraction methods.

The definition of the inorganic matrix is the easy part of the battle as in all bio-inorganic chemistry. The difficult part is the organic material present for various purposes. The obvious purpose is the bonding together of the inorganic material in a composite. Most bio-minerals are composites and the polymer is a protein or a polysaccharide. None have been thoroughly defined. Organic molecules are also thought to be used as nucleating agents for crystallisation, possibly as crystal growth promotors, and finally as inhibitors, e.g. of ice nucleation. A few are known. To appreciate the state of the art I give one or two illustrations mainly from our own work.

3 THE SILICA IN PLANTS: AN AMORPHOUS MINERAL

Silicon has a huge turn-over by life. It is associated particularly on land with the grasses, where it functions as a structural support and as a protective device. We have examined during formation the silicified hairs of <u>phalaris canariensis,</u> a

Fig. 1(a). The seed and capsule of phalaris canariensis showing the fine heavily silified (SiO_2) hairs. (b) A view of the hair (x4,000) showing the concentric cylindrical form.

Fig. 1(c). A view of a broken end of a hair (left), see above (x10,000). The pictures on the right (x50,000) show the different packings of silica opals at the right edge (bottom), a quarter of the way along (middle) and in the centre (top) of the hair.

type of millet, Fig. 1. The hair is first formed as the organic outer cell wall hair emerges it starts to silicify between the primary cell wall and the cell membrane depositing a variety of polysaccharides and silica simultaneously in this space. The hair space is finally filled with this silica composite and a sharp hard needle is produced. During the hardening and in-filling of the hair the cell withdraws. We have monitored the changes in the elements using both EM and PIXE as the silicification proceeds looking both at the hardening hair and the cellular contents (4). Here I refer only to the structure of the silica which is seen (by SEM) to be laid down in concentric cylinders. The silica is formed from minute opals (100Å diameter) which by TEM are amorphous to 5.0Å resolution. The opals are arranged in different patterns at different stages of the in-filling, Fig. 1. (5). We do not understand this but it is related to differential depositions of the organic matrix. Investigation of the silica by NMR shows it to be $SiO_n(OH)_{4-2n}$ where we can only define the phase by the number of Si atoms which have 0, 1, 2 or 3 OH groups (3).

This brief summary of silica in one apparently rare plant should not be allowed to hide the global significance of the turnover of silicon in life. It is one tenth that of carbon. The structures seen in the above millet are present in all grasses to some degree. Nor should it hide the delicate way in which silica can be handled in hundreds of algae, protozoa, plants and animals to make minute shells. Silica impregnated organic matrices may be very interesting materials and they also occur in some very strong materials, such as the teeth of limpets (6).These observations raise a fundamental point about shape and form in biology and especially with regard to their inorganic minerals.

The fact that the hydrated silica of biology is <u>not</u> crystalline means that the observed shape is that of an organic mould and no epitaxial relationship is required. The surface energy of the hydrated silica is undoubtedly reduced by the organic polymers, probably polysaccharides, but there is no possibility of structural matching. The silica conforms to the volume shape of the polymers.

The silica is readily redissolved and may be transferred from site to site as in the lorica of choanoflagellates (2). The transfer is down a thermodynamic gradient of surface energy (or solution energy) and is in the opposite sense to the original deposition which required the silica, probably as $Si(OH)_4$, to be pumped into the vesicular mould. The control of the hydration and dehydration is not a phase transformation but a continuous process and as such is likely to be facile and rapid. We do not know which small organic molecules if any are involved in silica transfer.

4 THE GROWTH OF A CRYSTAL: IRON OXIDES

Features of crystal growth which are obvious are (1) the major resultant planes found by diffraction and lattice image methods, (2) the final size of the crystallite (3) the defect structure which includes both impurity chemical defects and physical faults.

As illustrations we have observed that some crystals of magnetite from magnetic bacteria are almost perfect. It should be noted that since a cooperative property is required here (bulk magnetism) then a single domain crystal, defect free, is the optimum device which will serve. In contrast Mann has shown that the FeO(OH) of ferritin (supposed ferrihydrite) is far from perfect and in some species is so heavily loaded with phosphate that it becomes an amorphous precipitate. Finally in limpet teeth FeO(OH) is found as perfect needle-like single crystals in the form of goethite growing along the c-axis. These needles now have an orientation to the cutting edge of the tooth in order to make optimal the cutting power of the teeth. Here iron oxides are being used in three ways - as sensors, as stores and in weapons. The growth pattern has evolved to produce the material in three different forms suitable for three different functions. Magnetite domains had to become permanent magnets at ~100° C; Goethite had to become, as is apatite in bone, oriented strong needles; but ferritin had a very different requirement - to redissolve as easily as possible. The low crystallinity and the particular allotropic form of ferritin, ferrihydrite, see to it that this state of iron hydroxide is the most soluble form of iron as is required for its function - a useful store. Of course in every case the domain structure can be and has been analysed further by measurement of spectroscopic properties - e.g. Mossbauer or EXAFS and by examination of magnetic properties.

If we ask how this control is exerted over crystallisation then we must seek the answer in the accompanying organic matrices. Ferritin is laid down in a protein core, magnetite in a bilayer vesicle and goethite in a glycoprotein matrix heavily impregnated with amorphous silica (see above). The control exerted by the polymers is complete. We have been modelling these growth conditions in vesicles for several years since it leads to the prospect of controlled materials for man's use in catalysts and drugs (7,8). Completely parallel studies of calcites show how skillfully nature controls crystal growth. We have investigated in detail the gravity sensors of many species, otoliths and otoconia (9), Fig. 2. The skill in making uniform weights (not single crystals) from composites is totally intriguing. We have also studied shells, coccoliths of single cell organisms showing how in part they are flat single crystal plates and in part very beautifully shaped composites (10). Finally Runnegar has shown that the calcite of sea shells is grown along quite unusual faces (11).

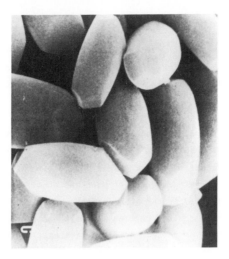

Fig. 2. The otoliths of the gravity device of the inner ear (x1,000). The
calcite is seemingly crystalline but each object is in fact a composite of
thousands of true calcite crystals built into an organic preformer which decides
the crystalline appearance, see ref.(9).

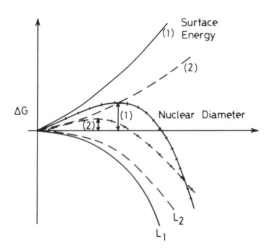

Fig. 3. The free energy changes during nucleation. The full lines are for the
more insoluble allotrope e.g. calcite, while the broken lines are for the more
soluble salt, e.g. vaterite. The combination of surface energy and lattice energy
generate a higher barrier to crystallisation for calcite, see refs. (13) and (14).

Amongst apatites major interest is in human bones and teeth. A recent study of
the nature of tooth enamel shows that this highly crystalline material which is not
a simple apatite contains interesting defects in the crystal lattice along particular lines (12). The defect structure could well be related to the risk of dental
decay. Of course incorporation of fluoride into this lattice is one way in which to
reduce decay.

5 NUCLEATION AND INHIBITION

The theory and experimental approaches to spontaneous nucleation have been considerably advanced by the work of Nancollas and his group over several years (13).
The reader is advised to refer to his work. In biology it is usually the organic
matrix which controls nucleation deciding the precise chemical allotropic form, and
its shape, which will appear. For example calcium carbonate can precipitate as
calcite, aragonite, vaterite or amorphous calcium carbonate. All occur in specific
ways in nature sometimes all three in the same shell. The secret of controlled
nucleation is the control the polymers exert on the surface energy (14). It is the
surface energy that is the barrier to nucleation and it is usually the higher the
more insoluble the salt. Thus it is the more soluble salt which precipitates most
readily, Ostwald-Lussac Law of Stages. We have offered an explanation of this phenomenon (14) and it is this preferred kinetic route which allows the control over the
form of crystallisation in biology.

Inhibition is again a surface phenomenon. Organic molecules can block growth.
The shape of many biological objects depend on this mixture of inorganic and organic
chemistry. For example the enamel of teeth may well be protected by a range of inhibitors. Perhaps the best example is the control over ice precipitation.

The temperature of the blood of fish in far northern or southerm waters is such
that ice should be deposited. They live with blood temperatures about $0.5^{\circ}C$ below
the blood freezing point and the blood remains liquid. The nucleation of ice crystals can not be prevented as random fluctuations but apparently before they can
grow and while they are so small that they are unstable (thermodynamically) they are
bound to a polymer which prevents growth. The unstable nucleus, a fluctuation, then
must melt. This is a kinetic control over crystal growth, an inhibition. Work in
my laboratory using NMR has given an outline structure of one of the antifreeze
glycopeptides and in a forthcoming paper we shall indicate how the peptide may
function (14).

The nucleation process is usually thought of as a fluctuation requiring in a
supersaturated solution the development of an unstable nucleus of some 50-100 atoms
before the adverse surface energy can be overcome by favourable lattice terms. The

chance of such fluctuations can be biased in the presence of organic polymers such that ion pairs or multiplets can be the initial steps, complex ion reactions, which help to lower the adverse barriers seen in Fig. 3. Such steps may involve very few atoms. An example could be the formation of the ferritin core where a probable initiation site is the pair of zinc sites in the protein channels (Harrison and Williams). These sites could be occupied firstly by Fe(II) and then oxidised to a structure such as Fe(III).O.Fe(III).OH. Such binuclear stable units could in principle greatly increase the probability of crystallisation of Fe(III).O.OH from a starting solution of Fe(II). We have shown in studies of vesicular precipitation of Fe(OH)$_3$ or a related basic hydroxide that starting from Fe(III) ions only amorphous materials resulted. However starting from Fe(II) ions in the vesicle we obtained crystalline Fe(III) compounds. The control due to phospholipid surfaces is complex but like the ferritin core they can generate selective pathways to crystalline products.

6   CONTROL OVER SHAPE AND FORM

The manufacture of functional objects for mechanical purposes demands control over shape and form. Biology has achieved this end in material science. We may be stunned by the beauty of the creations, Fig. 4, but we must not miss the functional value - the true achievement. It is more to the point to ask how is the control achieved. The central answer is the laying down of an ordered matrix of organic polymers. The polymers may just form a container, a vesicle, which means that the exterior of the object is controlled, but also the chemistry, or they can form a fantastic pattern - a lacework in three dimensions - within some contained volume to which the inorganic material is added. We do not know if the interaction is truly epitaxial, atom by atom, or if some large region of matrix matching is involved. A return by the inorganic chemist to the study of simple materials such as NaCl, CaCO$_3$, SiO$_2$, Ca$_2$(OH)PO$_4$, FeO(OH) and even ice and their interaction at the surface with organic molecules is long overdue. This return will bring rewards in the field of bio-minerals but it will bring new ideas into material science - the study of composites such as modern cements, clays and ceramics.

The fact that the minerals are controlled by containing polymers and vesicles must not hide the chemical control which a vesicle container generates. The membranes of the vesicles pump ions so as to control degrees of super-saturation. Ions that are pumped include, proteins, sodium, phosphate, and calcium. We do not know how silica is handled.

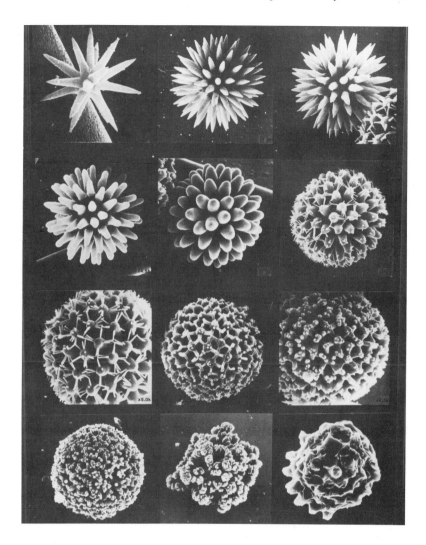

Fig. 4. The growth and decay of a sterrosperaster spicule in the sponge _Aurora Rouri_. The object is made of silica. (Reproduced with permission from the British Natural History Museum).

7 REFERENCES

(1) H.A. Lowenstam, Science, 211, (1981) 1126-1131.

(2) S. Mann, Structure and Bonding, 54, (1983) 125-174.

(3) S. Mann, , C.C. Perry, R.J.P. Williams, C.A. Fyfe, G.C. Gobbi, and G.J. Kennedy, J. Chem. Soc. (London) Chem. Comm. (1983) 168-170.

(4) C.C. Perry, S. Mann, and R.J.P. Williams, Proc. Roy. Soc. (London) (1984) 222B, 427-438.

(5) C.C. Perry, S. Mann, and R.J.P. Williams, Proc. Roy. Soc. (London) (1984) 222B, 439-446.

(6) G.W. Grime, G. Watt, S. Mann, C.C. Perry, J. Webb, and R.J.P. Williams, Trends in Biochemical Sciences, (1985) 10, 6-10.

(7) S. Mann, and R.J.P. Williams, J. Chem. Soc. (London) Dalton Trans., (1983) 311-316.

(8) S. Mann, M.J. Kime, R.G. Ratcliffe, and R.J.P. Williams, J. Chem. Soc. Dalton Trans., (1983) 771-774.

(9) S. Mann, S.B. Parker, M.D. Ross, A.J. Skarnulis and R.J.P. Williams, Proc. Roy. (London) 218B (1983), 415-424.

(10) S.B. Parker, A.J. Skarnulis, P. Westbroek, and R.J.P. Williams, Proc. Roy. Soc. (London) 219B, (1983) 111-117.

(11) B. Runnegar, Alcheringa 8, (1984) 273-290.

(12) E.F. Bres, J.C. Barry, and J.L. Hutchinson, J. Ultrastructure Research, (1985) to be published.

(13) G.H. Nancollas, Adv. Colloid Interface Sci., 10, (1979) 215-252.

(14) R.J.P. Williams, Proc. Roy. Soc. (London) 304B, (1984) 411-424.

(15) S.B. Parker, and R.J.P. Williams, (1985) to be published.

Mössbauer Spectroscopic and Scanning Proton Microprobe Studies of Iron Biominerals

J. Webb[1], T.G. St Pierre[2], D.P.E. Dickson[2], S. Mann[3], R.J.P. Williams[4], C.C. Perry[4], G. Grime[5], F. Watt[5], N.W. Runham[6]

[1]School of Mathematical and Physical Sciences, Murdoch University, Perth WA 6150, Australia

[2]Department of Physics, University of Liverpool, Liverpool L69 3BX, UK

[3]School of Chemistry, University of Bath, Bath BA2 7AY, UK

[4]Inorganic Chemistry Laboratory, and [5]Department of Nuclear Physics, University of Oxford, Oxford OX1 3QR, UK

[6]Department of Zoology, University College of North Wales, Bangor LL57 2DG, UK

SUMMARY

   The lateral teeth of the radulas of the marine invertebrates - chitons and limpets - have been studied using proton-induced X-ray emission (PIXE) analysis and Mössbauer spectroscopy. Using the Oxford scanning proton microprobe, the PIXE analyses reveal complex compositional maps of the several elements present in these biomineralized structures. The changes in these elemental maps as mineralization progresses have also been determined. Mössbauer spectroscopy of the teeth and of teeth fragments has revealed at least two different iron components - goethite (α-FeOOH), most of which is in the tooth cusp, and a minor component, which shows unusual superparamagnetic behaviour, and is predominantly localized in the base of the teeth. These two types of data are compared and related to the nature of the organic matrix present in the teeth.

1   INTRODUCTION

1.1 Biomineralization of Iron

Biomineralization of iron is now known to be a widespread phenomenon, having been reported in all five living Kingdoms, ranging from Animalia to Monera (1-3). Prominent examples include magnetite (Fe_3O_4) reported in magnetotactic bacteria and several higher organisms such as chitons, pigeons, tuna and honey bees; ferrihydrite ($5Fe_2O_3.9H_2O$) present in the central core of the protein ferritin; and two phases of FeOOH: goethite (α-FeOOH) and lepidocrocite (γ-FeOOH), which occur in the teeth of different groups of marine molluscs. Lepidocrocite has been reported in the magnetite-containing teeth of some species of chitons, while goethite occurs in the teeth of limpets. Other biominerals can occur in the same tooth as these iron minerals, e.g. a poorly crystalline form of a calcium phosphate apatite mineral in chiton teeth (4) and amorphous silica (SiO_2) in limpet teeth (5). The spatial organization of these various bio-minerals and their biosynthesis are of particular interest since the teeth represent in many cases composite bioinorganic materials of exquisite morphology and design (2,3).

1.2 Characteristics of Chiton and Limpet Radulas

Chitons and limpets occur widely in the intertidal and shallow water molluscan community, feeding on fine algae, sponges or other encrusting organisms using a specially developed tongue or radula. The radula teeth are mineralized allowing the animals to excavate to a limited extent, the rocks over which they browse (4). The teeth are progressively mineralized along the radula and are continually replaced as the mature mineralized teeth are lost during feeding. Thus the radula of chitons and limpets offers a sequence of mineralization in both space and time which can be studied within a single biological organ.

In the mature radula teeth, these hard mineralized phases are present within an organic matrix. In contrast the immature teeth are of similar gross morphology but are soft organic structures devoid of biomineral deposits.

The anatomical location of the radula in the chiton Clavarizona hirtosa is shown in Figure 1a. For the limpet Patella vulgata the comparable section is shown in Figure 1b. The similarities in the anatomy of the two species are apparent. The radula of C. hirtosa is approx. 30 mm long and contains about 70 transverse rows of teeth, while

in P. vulgata the radula is much longer (70 mm) and contains 200 rows.
Examination of the radulas from both molluscs reveals biomineral deposits
of iron that are clearly visible in the prominent lateral teeth of the
radula.   In general these teeth can be subdivided into the top or cusp,
the base (lower down) and the radula membrane.   A major (but not
necessarily the only) component of the biomineralized tissue in C. hirtosa
is magnetite while in P. vulgata it is goethite, consistent with observations on other chiton and limpet species (7-10).

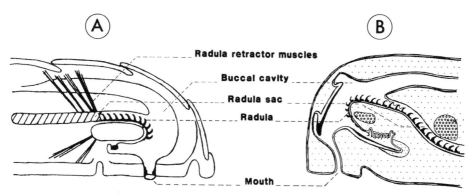

Fig. 1.   Anatomical view, showing diagrammatic longitudinal section of
(a) the chiton Clavarizona hirtosa and (b) the limpet Patella vulgata,
adapted from refs. 8 and 10. The lateral teeth of the radula are shown
in profile.

2   SPM AND PIXE ANALYSIS

The distribution of elements within these different types of teeth -
which are simply teeth at different stages of the complex biomineralization process - has recently been determined using a scanning proton
microprobe (SPM).   This proton induced X-ray emission (PIXE) analysis is
rapidly emerging as a powerful multi-elemental analytical technique (11,
12).

The incident proton beam used in the SPM produces very little background X-ray radiation, allowing analytical sensitivities at the ppm
level to be achieved. With the beam focussed to small dimensions and
then scanned over the sample, the characteristic X-rays produced allow
two-dimensional elemental maps of the sample to be obtained.   In studies
of chiton and limpet radulas, the Oxford proton microprobe was operated
in the scanning mode with a spatial resolution of ca. 2 µm using a proton
beam of 4 MeV energy and an intensity of 100 pA/µm^2.   The X-ray energy
spectrum of a mature lateral tooth from the chiton C. hirtosa and the
limpet Patelloida alticostata are shown in Figure 2.

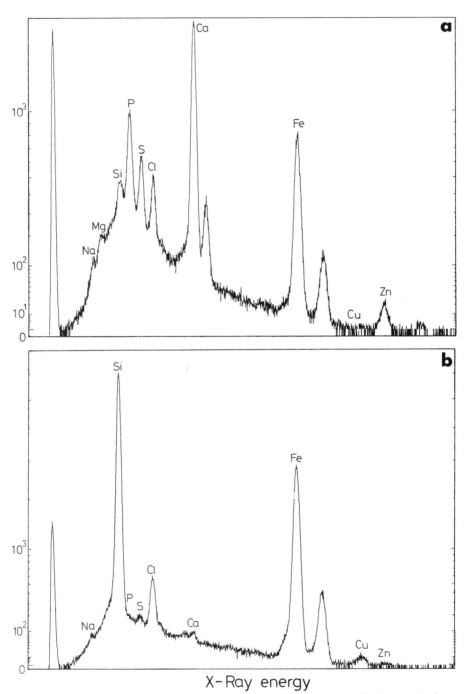

Fig. 2.   The X-ray energy spectrum of a mature mineralized tooth from (a) the chiton <u>Clavarizona hirtosa</u> and (b) the limpet <u>Patelloida alticostata</u> obtained using the Oxford scanning proton microprobe.

Both species are found on tidal rocks in South-Western Australia. The
spectra serve to illustrate the marked differences in elemental composition between chiton and limpet teeth. These differences include both
major and minor elements. While Fe is a major component of both teeth,
Ca and P are present at much higher levels in the chiton tooth but Si is
higher in the limpet tooth. The spectra show further that Zn but not Cu
occurs at low levels in the chiton tooth but the reverse is the case for
the limpet.

2.1 Elemental Maps - Clavarizona hirtosa

The power of the SPM analysis, however, lies in its ability to scan
the sample, yielding colour-coded elemental maps. These are shown in
Figure 3 for six elements present in a mature chiton radula tooth.
Distinct boundaries between regions of different elemental composition
are well defined. For example, Fe is particularly localized at the top
(or cusp) of the tooth, where Fe_3O_4 and perhaps other phases of Fe bio-
minerals occur. Both Ca and P are distributed throughout the tooth,
suggesting that this is the distribution of the mineralized form of
apatite reported in studies of other species (4). The SPM offers
analytical sensitivity to complement this spatial resolution. Thus
trace amounts of zinc are found localized near the base of the tooth.

2.2 Elemental maps - Patella vulgata

In the case of the limpet P. vulgata, lateral teeth were dissected out
at several positions along the radula corresponding to different stages
of mineralization. Using the SPM, analysis of an early white immature
tooth from row 10 showed that Fe, Si, S and Cl were present at low levels
throughout the tooth but little spatial organization of these elements
was apparent. At the next stage of maturation (e.g. row 28) a brown
colouration was apparent in the base of the tooth, which contained Fe,
Si, P, S, Ca and, at a very low level, Cu. Analysis of the other zones
of the tooth indicated that Fe, P and Ca showed preferential localization in the tooth base. Superposition of the Fe, Ca and Si maps showed
that Si and Ca were localized towards the anterior side but Fe to the
posterior. Clearly, spatial differentiation of many elements is already
established at this early stage of mineralization.

As mineralization progresses (e.g. row 35), all elements have been
deposited in the base and cusp and by row 120, the fully mature tooth
has been established. Distinct boundaries between regions of different
elemental composition (e.g. high Fe, low Si compared to low Fe, high Si)

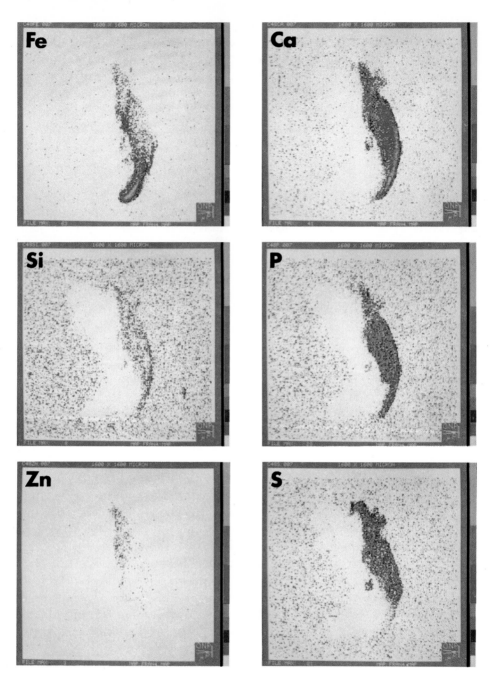

Fig. 3. Scanning proton microprobe maps (1600 x 1600 µm) of Fe, Ca, Si, P, Zn and S in mature lateral tooth of <u>Clavarizona hirtosa</u>. The number of counts (X-rays) is colour coded from green (lowest) to yellow (highest). Absorption corrections have not been applied. Maximum counts range from 63000 for Fe to 16000 for Si and Zn. The white region to the left of the tooth is shadowed by the tooth from the Si(Li) detector.

can be seen. These elemental distributions (11,12) illustrate the
complex compositional changes that occur during the biomineralization of
the limpet tooth. In a more limited study, the same basic pattern of
element distributions was observed in the radula of another limpet species,
Patelloida alticostata from South-Western Australia.

The PIXE data provide insights into possible mechanisms of biomineralization of Fe and Si by identifying the developments of the Fe and Si
deposits and the presence of other elements which may be of significance
in the regulation of biomineralization. For example, P is highly
localized with Fe in the tooth base in the early stages of mineralization
and phosphate has been shown to markedly influence the crystallization of
goethite (13). Intriguingly, the Cu concentration shows dramatic changes
localizing in the fully mature tooth cusp, as shown in Figure 4. In this
comparatively rigid structure, this Cu may be present as Cu oxidases that
catalyse oxidative cross-linking of the organic matter.

 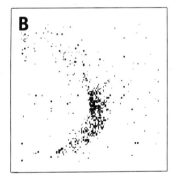

Fig. 4.   Scanning proton microprobe maps of Cu in lateral tooth of
Patella vulgata from (a) row 28 (area shown is 220 μm x 200 μm) and
(b) row 120 (area: 500 μm x 500 μm).

3 MÖSSBAUER SPECTROSCOPY

Further interpretation of these SPM results for P. vulgata has been
greatly assisted by the use of Fe-57 Mössbauer spectroscopy to determine
the chemical form, stoichiometry and crystallinity of iron present in
the teeth. Electron microscopic studies (to be published elsewhere)
have provided complementary data on the shape, size and crystallinity of
the iron-containing components. Mössbauer spectra were recorded over a
wide range of temperatures (420K to 1.3K) using a conventional constant

acceleration spectrometer and a [57]Co in rhodium source.

3.1 Patella vulgata

The spectrum at 1.3K of the mature limpet teeth (row 70 and beyond) consists of two magnetically split sextets which differ only slightly in their hyperfine fields. With increasing temperature, the minor sextet collapses and a doublet appears until it saturates at 16% of the total spectral area at 40K. This spectral behaviour of the minor component is indicative of the superparamagnetism of small particles (14). The major sextet component also shows temperature dependent behaviour, collapsing at ca. 400K to a central doublet due to increasing paramagnetic relaxation. As discussed in detail elsewhere (15), these data indicate the presence of two distinct iron-containing species, the major form being crystals of goethite and the minor being small particles that may well be poorly ordered. Most interestingly, these small particles are more prominent in the early maturing limpet teeth (rows 20-32), accounting for 65% of the total spectral intensity.

Separation of the cusp from the base regions of the teeth leads to a spectrum of the cusps alone. This spectrum (Figure 5) shows an appreciable reduction in the contribution of the minor component, which then appears to be localized in the base of the tooth. Quantitative spectral analysis indicates that 70% of this minor but superparamagnetic component is localized in the tooth base and 30% in the cusp region. In contrast only 5% of the crystalline goethite is present in the base, and 95% is in the cusp.

The mature teeth, after treatment with NaOH, yielded Mössbauer spectra that illustrate clearly (Figure 6) that the intensity of the central superparamagnetic doublet has been reduced. This minor component has clearly been substantially affected by this chemical treatment. The identify of this component is of particular interest because of its rather unusual low temperature Mössbauer behaviour. In this regard it differs from the ferrihydrite core of ferritin, a protein which is known to occur in high concentrations in the hemolymph of molluscs that show extensive biomineralization of iron (16,17).

The Mössbauer spectrum of ferrihydrite in the core of ferritin isolated from the hemolymph of P. vulgata consists at 4.2K of a well-established sextet (18) rather than the doublet seen in the spectra of Figure 5. This ferrihydrite has a mean core diameter of 65-75Å and is poorly crystalline (18). Hence, on Mössbauer spectral criteria alone,

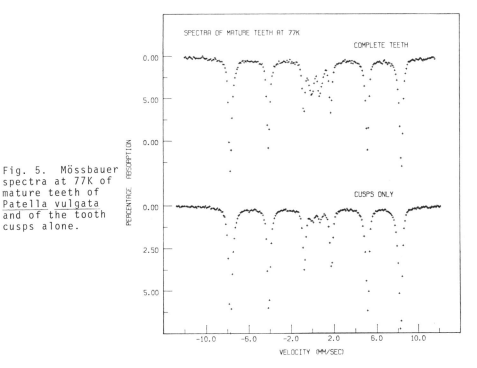

Fig. 5. Mössbauer spectra at 77K of mature teeth of _Patella vulgata_ and of the tooth cusps alone.

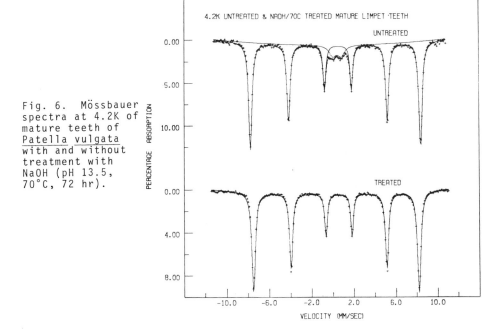

Fig. 6. Mössbauer spectra at 4.2K of mature teeth of _Patella vulgata_ with and without treatment with NaOH (pH 13.5, 70°C, 72 hr).

ferritin is not present in significant amounts in the limpet radula teeth. It is possible that this minor component is composed of micro-crystalline defect α-FeOOH, poorly crystalline ferrihydrite-like material, or a mixture of both of these. In this region of the tooth, the phosphorus and silicon present may inhibit the formation of well crystalline α-FeOOH. Such inhibition has been observed in vitro (13).

The Mössbauer data show definite spatial differentiation between two distinct forms of iron, thus providing a more detailed chemical identification of the species responsible for the spatial differentiation observed in the SPM study. Biosynthetic turnover data are not available for these components but it seems highly unlikely that the minor component is the precursor of the biogenic α-FeOOH. Electron microscopic data (unpublished) indicate that crystalline α-FeOOH is formed directly in the cusp of the tooth from the cellular matrix in which the maturing teeth develop.

We would emphasise that in order to understand biomineralization in these tissues, the PIXE data need to be complemented by a comparably detailed analysis of the organic components present in the radula. Organic materials are intimately involved in the construction of composite biominerals (19) including limpet teeth, but most attention has been directed to the role of cells and macromolecules in deposition of calcium carbonates (20) and calcium phosphates (21). Earlier histochemical studies (22) of Patella vulgata have shown that, prior to the onset of major mineralization, the radula teeth become impregnated with extra proteinaceous, polyphenolic and aminophenolic material. Their role is unclear but possibly the polyphenolics are involved in quinone "tanning". Of particular interest is the localization of Cu in the mineralizing teeth as shown by the SPM data (Figure 4), for polyphenol oxidase is a Cu-dependent enzyme. Although the amount of the polysaccharide chitin appears to decrease at this early stage of mineralization, it is possible that the -OH and $-NH_2$ groups of chitin become less available to the histological stain as mineralization develops in the teeth.

These data do suggest, however, that there are changes in the organic components that are concomitant with changes in the inorganics. The SPM and Mössbauer techniques are powerful probes of the nature and transformations of the inorganic components of the radula teeth. But the chemical and physical nature of the organic matrix, particularly its polymeric and oriented components that appear to exert a strong influence on biomineralization, remain to be investigated.

4 REFERENCES

(1) H.A. Lowenstam. Minerals formed by organisms. _Science_ 171 (1981) 487-490.

(2) S. Mann. Mineralization in biological systems. _Struct. Bonding_ 54 (1983) 125-174.

(3) J. Webb in P. Westbroek and E.W. De Jong (Eds.), Biomineralization and Biological Metal Accumulation. Reidel, Dordrecht (1983) pp.413-422.

(4) H.A. Lowenstam. Lepidocrocite, an apatite mineral, and magnetite in teeth of chitons (Polyplacophora). _Science_ 156 (1967) 1373-1375.

(5) H.A. Lowenstam. Opal precipitation by marine gastropods (Mollusca). _Science_ 171 (1971) 487-490.

(6) R.S. Steneck and L. Watling. Feeding capabilities and limitation of herbivorous molluscs: A functional group approach. _Mar. Biol_ 68 (1982) 299-319.

(7) H.A. Lowenstam. Goethite in radular teeth of recent marine gastropods (Mollusca). Science 137 (1962) 279-280.

(8) N.W. Runham and P.R. Thornton. Mechanical wear of the gastropod radula: a scanning electron microscope study. _J. Zool. Lond_. 153 (1967) 445-452.

(9) N.W. Runham, P.R. Thornton, D.A. Shaw and R.C. Wayte. The mineralization and hardness of the radula teeth of the limpet _Patella_ _vulgata_ L. _Z. Zellforsch_ 99 (1969) 608-626.

(10) J.L. Kirschvink and H.A. Lowenstam. Mineralization and magnetization of chiton teeth: Paleomagnetic, sedimentologic and biologic implications of organic magnetite. _Earth Planet. Sci. Lett_. 44 (1979) 193-204.

(11) G.W. Grime, F. Watt, S. Mann, C.C. Perry, J. Webb and R.J.P. Williams. Biological applications of the Oxford scanning proton microprobe. _Trends Biochem. Sci. January_ (1985) 6-10.

(12) C. Sutton. How protons trace the elements that matter. New Scientist 4 October (1984) 35-39.

(13) U. Schwertmann. Der einfluss einfacher organischer anionen auf die bildung von goethite und hamatit aus amorphem Fe(III)-hydroxid. Geoderma 3 (1970) 207-213.

(14) J. Webb in C.A. McAuliffe (Ed.), Techniques and Topics in Bioinorganic Chemistry. MacMillan, London (1975) pp.270-304.

(15) T.G. St Pierre, D.P.E. Dickson, S. Mann and J. Webb. A study of biomineralization in the teeth of limpets using Mössbauer spectroscopy and electron microscopy. In preparation.

(16) J. Webb and D.J. Macey in P. Westbroek and E.W. De Jong (Eds.), Biomineralization and Biological Metal Accumulation. Reidel, Dordrecht (1983) pp.423-427.

(17) M. Burford, D.J. Macey and J. Webb in Z. Urushizaki, P. Aisen, I. Listowsky and J.W. Drysdale (Eds.), Structure and Function of Iron Storage and Transport Proteins. Elsevier, Amsterdam (1983) pp.219-220.

(18) J. Webb, K.S. Kim, V. Talbot, D.J. Macey, S. Mann, J.V. Bannister, R.J.P. Williams, T.G. St Pierre, D.P.E. Dickson and R. Frankel (1985). See this Volume.

(19) R.J.P. Williams. An introduction to biominerals and the role of organic molecules in their formation. Phil. Trans. Roy. Soc. Lond. B. 304 (1984) 411-424.

(20) S. Weiner and W. Traub. Macromolecules in mollusc shells and their function in biomineralization. Phil. Trans. Roy. Soc. Lond. B. 304 (1984) 425-433.

(21) M.J. Glimcher. Recent studies of the mineral phase in bone and its possible linkage to the organic matrix by protein-bound phosphate bonds. Phil. Trans. Roy. Soc. Lond. B. 304 (1984) 479-508.

(22) N.W. Runham. The histochemistry of the radula of Patella vulgata. Quart. J. Micros. Sci. 102 (1961) 371-380.

Structural and Mechanistic Studies of Metalloproteins and Bioinorganic Complexes

The Domain Structure of Calmodulin: Some Recent Biophysical Studies

Sture Forsen

Physical Chemistry 2, Chemical Centre, POB 124, Lund University
S-221 00 Lund, Sweden

1 INTRODUCTION

Calmodulin (CaM) is an important Ca^{2+} dependent regulatory protein ($M_1 = 16,700$) that is present in seemingly all eucaryotic cells (1). The primary sequence of CaM from a number of sources has been determined and these studies show: (i) that the amino acid sequence of CaM is highly conserved throughout evolution; (ii) the presence of four homologous regions predicted to have the secondary structure "helix-loop-helix" with the loop constituting a potential Ca^{2+} binding site of the "EF-hand" type (fig. 1)

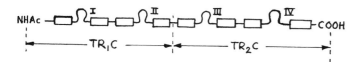

Fig. 1. Schematic structure and tryptic cleave sites of CaM

At the time of writing the X-ray structure of CaM is not yet known although considerable progress has been reported. The molecular properties of CaM have over the last few years or so been subject to study by biochemical and biophysical - primarily spectroscopic - techniques. A recent line of research that has proved to be particularly fruitful is the study of different proteolytic fragments of CaM. One of the most striking results of these studies has been that many of the physical properties of CaM can be closely represented by a superposition of the properties of the two tryptic fragments, TR_1C and TR_2C - essentially comprising the N-terminal and C-terminal half of the native molecule (cf. fig. 1) (2-6). In this lecture we will discuss some recent biophysical studies of CaM and its tryptic fragment - studies that illustrate to what extent CaM indeed can be considered as consisting of two largely independent domains. We will also address the question of co-operative binding of Ca^{2+}.

2 NMR STUDIES

NMR studies of CaM and its proteolytic fragments illustrate well the versatility of the NMR method and the complementary information that can be obtained through studies of different magnetic nuclei. ^{1}H NMR can be used to detect conformation changes in the protein induced by metal ion binding. ^{43}Ca NMR has provided data on the kinetics of ion binding - data that has only recently been supplemented by stopped-flow measurements. ^{113}Cd NMR is uniquely suited to determine metal ion populations at individual ion binding sites and has given convincing evidence for cooperative ion binding in CaM and TR_2C. In addition ^{113}Cd NMR is useful for moni-toring conformation changes in the protein as a result of drug binding etc.

^{1}H NMR

In ^{1}H spectra of CaM two distinct phases are observed as Ca^{2+} is successively added to the Ca^{2+} free protein. The first two Ca^{2+} ions to bind cause conformation changes that are in slow exchange ($k_{exch} < 10\ s^{-1}$). The spectrum during this phase is a superposition of two spectra with varying relative intensities - one increasing as the other decreases (4-10). The obvious interpretation is that only CaM and $(Ca)_2$CaM coexist to a measurable degree. A completely analogous behaviour is shown by the fragment TR_2C indicating that here only TR_2C and $(Ca)_2TR_2C$ coexist in solu-tion. By contrast ^{1}H spectral changes of CaM upon addition of the third or fourth Ca^{2+} or of TR_1C upon addition of two Ca^{2+} are continuous indicating conformation changes in fast exchange ($k_{exch} > 500\ s^{-1}$). Thus ^{1}H NMR indicates (i) the strong (slowly dissociating) Ca^{2+} sites are III and IV; (ii) Ca^{2+} binding to sites III and IV is positively cooperative in both CaM and TR_2C.

^{113}Cd NMR

^{1}H NMR spectra of CaM, TR_1C and TR_2C are almost identical whether Ca^{2+} or Cd^{2+} is added thus justifying the use of Cd^{2+} as a probe for Ca^{2+}. When $^{113}Cd^{2+}$ is added to either CaM or TR_2C two well resolved NMR signals at about -100 ppm are observed (3,4,9). These signals increase in intensity in parallel up to a Cd/CaM (or TR_2C) ratio of 2:1. This behaviour is observed both at low ionic strength (I = 0.030) and at high ionic strength (0.15 KCl). We consider this very convincing evidence for cooperative metal ion binding to the pair of sites III and IV. The chemical shifts of the two ^{113}Cd signals are virtually the same in CaM and TR_2C providing evidence for the structural autonomy of the C-terminal half of CaM (3).

^{43}Ca NMR

From the temperature dependence of the ^{43}Ca NMR signals in the presence of either CaM or TR_1C values of k_{off} for the two weakly bonded Ca^{2+} ions have in both cases been determined to 10^3 s^{-1} at 25 $^{\circ}$C (3,11).

3   STOPPED-FLOW KINETIC STUDIES

Through the use of the newly developed fluorescent Ca^{2+} chelator "Quin 2" (12) it has recently been possible to determine directly the rates of dissociation of Ca^{2+} from CaM, TR_1C and TR_2C (13,14). Two exponential rate processes can clearly be resolved. For CaM at 19 $^{\circ}$C and low ionic strength (20 mM pipes) the fast rate was $k_{off}^f = 550$ s^{-1} and the slow rate $k_{off}^s = 5$ s^{-1}. The amplitude factors obtained convincingly show that both processes correspond to the release of two Ca^{2+} ions. Since the off rates differ by two orders of magnitude it is reasonable to attribute the two processes to dissociation of Ca^{2+} from the two strong (III and IV) and two weak binding (I and II) sites respectively. The picture does not qualitatively change in the presence of 100 mM KCl. Studies of the fragments TR_1C and TR_2C revealed several interesting facts. Under similar experimental conditions the rates of Ca^{2+} dissociation from TR_1C ($k_{off}^{TR_1C} = 400$ s^{-1}) and TR_2C ($k_{off}^{TR_1C} = 10$ s^{-1}) are nearly equal to those for the fast and slow processes in CaM!

4   THERMOCHEMICAL STUDIES

A comparative study of the enthalpy change associated with the binding of Ca^{2+} to CaM, TR_1C and TR_2C has recently been made by Sellers et al. (15,16). The enthalpy change is negative at ambient temperatures in line with results for homologous Ca^{2+} binding proteins. ΔH^{CaM} and ΔH^{TR_2C} are closely linear with the Ca^{2+}/CaM ratio in the range 0 to 2 - a behaviour compatible with cooperative Ca^{2+} binding. At 25 $^{\circ}$C the total enthalpy change for the binding of 4 Ca^{2+} to CaM is $\Delta H^{CaM} = -33$ kJ/mol. At the same temperature the enthalpy changes accompanying the binding of 2 Ca^{2+} to tryptic fragments are: $\Delta H^{TR_1C} = -16$ kJ/mol and $\Delta H^{TR_2C} = -14.5$ kJ/mol. The sum $\Delta H^{TR_1C} + \Delta H^{TR_1C} = -30.5$ kJ/mol, is strikingly close to ΔH^{CaM}. The entropy change associated with Ca^{2+} binding to CaM, TR_1C and TR_2C is positive in all cases.

5   CONCLUSION

The data briefly outlined above convincingly show that the binding of Ca^{2+} ions to sites III and IV is a cooperative process in both CaM and TR_2C - of sites I and II we still know too little to say. Within a small margin CaM may in many respects be considered to be constructed from two domains comprising the N-terminal and C-terminal half of the molecule. This should however not lead one to think that the sum of the two halves equals the whole under all circumstances. In particular the interplay between CaM and other molecules, drugs and/or target proteins, will be dependent on the presence of the unbroken protein allowing for joint interaction of different regions as clearly demonstrated by the unability of fragments to activate target proteins (17).

6   ACKNOWLEDGEMENTS

This article summarizes the work of a large number of collegues and coworkers at or outside Lund University, their names are found in the list of references below.

7   REFERENCES

(1) C.E. Klee, T.C. Vanaman, Adv. Prot. Chem., 35, 213 (1982).

(2) W. Drabikowski, H. Brzeska, S.Y. Venyaminov, J. Biol. Chem. 257, 11582 (1982).

(3) S. Forsen, A. Anderson, I. Drakenberg, O. Teleman, E. Thulin, H.J. Vogel, in B. de Bernard et al. (eds.), "Calcium Binding Proteins", Elsevier, Amsterdam, 1983, pp. 121-131.

(4) E. Thulin, A Andersson, T. Drakenberg, S. Forsen, H.J. Vogel, Biochemistry, 23, 1862 (1984).

(5) A. Aulabaugh, W.P. Niemezura, W.A. Gibbons, Biochem. Biophys. Res. Commun., 118 225 (1984).

(6) D.C. Dalgarno, R.E. Klevit, B.A. Levine, R.J.P. Williams, Z. Dobrowolski, W. Drabikowski, Eur. J. Biochem., 138, 281 (1984).

(7) K.B. Seamon, Biochemistry, 19, 207 (1980).

(8) M. Ikura, T. Hiraoki, K. Hikichi, O. Minowa, H. Yamaguchi, M. Yazawa, K. Yagi, Biochemistry, 23, 3124 (1984).

(9) A. Andersson, S. Forsen, E. Thulin, H.J. Vogel, Biochemistry, 22, 2309 (1983).

(10) R.E. Klevit, B.A. Levine, R.J.P. Williams, FEBS Lett., 123, 25 (1981).

(11) A. Andersson, T. Drakenberg, E. Thulin, S. Forsen, manuscript in preparation.

(12) R.Y. Tsieu, Biochemistry, 19, 2396 (1980).

(13) P. Bayley, P. Ahlström, S.R. Martin, S. Forsen, Biochem. Biophys. Res. Commun., 118, 225 (1984).

(14) A. Andersson, S.R. Martin, P. Bayley, S. Forsen, submitted (1984).

(15) J. Laynez, P. Sellers, E. Thulin, Int. Symp. Thermodyn. Proteins & Bio. Membr., Granada, Spain, May 23-27 (1983).

(16) P. Sellers, J. Laynez, E. Thulin, S. Forsen, manuscript in preparation.

(17) D.L. Newton, M.D. Oldewurtel, M.H. Krinks, J. Shiloach, C.B. Klee, J. Biol. Chem., 259, 4419 (1984).

Syncatalytic Cryospectroscopy and Cryokinetics in The Mechanism of Enzyme Action

Bert L. Vallee

Center for Biochemical and Biophysical Sciences and Medicine, Harvard
Medical School, Boston, MA 02115

SUMMARY

At room temperature the time interval for catalytic and
structural studies of enzymes differs widely, and the delineation of
the characteristics of short-lived enzymatic intermediates in the
course of the action of enzymes has been difficult. Subzero
temperatures, which decrease their rates of reaction, combined with
rapid mixing and rapid scanning instrumentation, allow acquisition of
the spectra of transients in metalloenzyme catalysis. Thus,
contraction of the time frame required for spectral analysis of a
metalloenzyme intermediate and expansion of its lifetime can be
combined to observe kinetics and spectra simultaneously. Toward this
end we have designed a low temperature, stopped flow/rapid scanning
spectrometer. Radiationless energy transfer (RET) monitors the
kinetics of transients, while electronic and EPR spectra identify
substrate induced alteration of the metal coordination sphere at the
time of catalysis. Recent studies of the mechanism of action of
carboxypeptidase A are presented to illustrate the principle.

1 METALS AS STRUCTURAL AND CONFORMATIONAL PROBES IN THE STUDY OF ENZYME MECHANISMS

The three-dimensional structure and conformation of enzymes are
critical to catalytic potential. Numerous experimental approaches can
elucidate structure-function relationships, but few of them can detect
subtle conformational changes that might identify both substrate
binding and catalytic groups and particularly their changes during

catalytic reactions. Such changes when visualized at rates as least
as fast as catalysis, would allow the direct observation of these
important dynamic events essential to the verification of enzyme
mechanisms.

X-ray structure analysis of enzyme-substrate and/or
enzyme-inhibitor complexes has been critical to an understanding of
the mode of interaction of substrates or their analogues with the
active sites of enzymes. Unfortunately, the time-averaging nature of
the approach precludes the direct observation of transient
intermediates; there is good evidence that in solution multiple
conformations of enzymes can interconvert rapidly (1,2), as predicted
by Linderstrøm-Lang (3). The three-dimensional structures of enzymes
in crystals and solutions need not necessarily be identical, and
crystallization can produce interactions, e.g. crystal packing forces,
with energetics comparable to those necessary to maintain particular
conformations. Thus, different crystal forms could well comprise
different populations of enzyme conformers as has been shown, e.g. for
hexokinase whose catalytic properties can vary in different crystal
forms, and at least one of them is completely inactive (4).

If structural and functional data are to define a mechanism of
action, ideally, structure, conformation and activity should be
determined on the same material, in the same physical state and during
identical time intervals. It is perhaps obvious that it is not easy
to meet these objectives. In actuality, catalytic activity must
generally be determined with enzyme solutions in fractions of seconds,
and structure analysis has to be performed on crystals, in days or
weeks. The k_{cat} of enzymes, the major index of their activity, is
markedly decreased in many enzyme crystals e.g. carboxypeptidase A
carboxypeptidase B and glycogen phosphorylase, though in other enzyme
systems crystallization does not affect activity at all (see (5) and
references therein). Hence, at this point in time the effects of
crystallization on enzyme function cannot be generalized. Such
uncertainties render the translation and interpretations of crystal
structures into mechanistic terms quite tenuous.

Thus, while the ultimate verification of reaction mechanisms of
enzymes demands the determination of both their functional and
structural characteristics when acting on the same substrates under
identical experimental conditions and in the same time interval, such
circumstances cannot be achieved readily either in standard kinetic
experiments on the one hand or in thermodynamic experiments on the
other: kinetics call for excellent substrates hydrolyzed as rapidly
as possible, and thermodynamic studies often demand inhibitors or

pseudosubstrates which result in slow reaction or no reaction.
Consequently, views of the characteristics of a given enzyme·substrate
or inhibitor complex derived from either one of the two approaches can
diverge widely. It then comes as no surprise that, at present, the
structural basis of enzymatic activity is generally deduced from
time-averaged procedures at thermodynamic equilibrium, whereas
functional conclusions often depend on pre-steady-state or
steady-state conditions at "kinetic equilibrium". The delineation of
the structure and function of the enzyme·substrate complex at the
moment of catalysis has proven difficult because of the vastly
different time frames when structure and function are both studied at
conventional temperatures.

Theoretically, subzero temperatures can reduce or eliminate this
disparity by detecting transient species of enzyme reactions in
aqueous-organic cryosolvents. Water-in-oil emulsions (a reversed
micellar system), for instance, can provide a medium with a
temperature range from at least +38° to -38°C by supercooling water
without freezing and without requiring changes in its composition.
Such supercooled water-in-oil emulsions are suitable for studies of
both function and structure under identical reaction conditions (6).
Experiments either under equilibrium or kinetic conditions at low
temperatures should allow mechanistic conclusions which are more
realistic than those that are feasible at room temperature for either
modality. Unfortunately, viscosity of these emulsions makes them
unsuitable for stopped-flow or other rapid kinetic techniques.
Conformational changes that might accompany binding of substrate to an
enzyme, occur in picosecond to second intervals. The subsequent
catalytic and product release steps cannot be detected since they take
place in just that time-frame. If both the physical-chemical and
kinetic characteristics of such intermediate states are to be measured
concurrently, their very short lifetimes must be lengthened by
reducing the rates of their breakdown, achieved most readily by
lowering the temperature. Importantly, the contraction of the time
frame required for characterization of an intermediate accompanied by
an extension of its lifetime allows the simultaneous acquisition of
information about its structure and the kinetics of its formation and
breakdown, thus supplying elements of the critical information
required for the delineation of an enzyme mechanism.

We have performed cryospectrokinetic studies utilizing a new
stopped-flow instrument built for such purposes (7,8).

2. CARBOXYPEPTIDASE A

Bovine pancreatic zinc carboxypeptidase A, (9) is now one of the best studied of all enzymes. Having virtually become the classic example of a metalloenzyme, its properties illustrate the potential of a metal atom for the correlation of its function with the structure and conformation of its active center. Carboxypeptidase A has long since served us as a model and as a specific example for the study of enzyme mechanisms in general.

The investigation of enzymatic catalysis of carboxypeptidase A and its structural basis has generated and defined a great variety of experimental approaches to study such relationships between structure and function, thereby making this metalloenzyme our obvious choice to explore an enzyme mechanism through the subzero temperature approach. It seems appropriate both to recall briefly some of the relevant facts regarding this enzyme and some of the questions concerning its mechanism which require further study and experimentation.

2.1 GENERAL PROPERTIES

Both mammalian and fish pancreas contain two zinc carboxypeptidases which catalyse the hydrolysis of amino acid residues from the carboxyl terminus of peptides and proteins, one, named "A", prefers aromatic residues and the other, called "B", is specific for basic residues (10). Both are synthesized in the pancreas as zymogens and their activation involves limited tryptic proteolysis.

Three different forms of the bovine A enzyme have been identified as A_α, A_β and A_γ, and consist of 307, 305 and 300 amino acid residues, respectively (10). The additional residues occur at the amino terminal region of the molecule.

Neurath and his collaborators have determined the amino acid sequence of carboxypeptidase A_α (10). It consists of 307 residues with a molecular weight of 35,268.

X-ray diffraction crystal analysis while confirming the amino acid sequence, identifies the α-carbon and side chain positions in carboxypeptidase A, and in conjunction with the results of chemical modifications, the active site residues (11). Arginine 145 is postulated to be the site of interaction of the free α-carboxyl group of the substrate with the enzyme and Glutamate 270 is thought to be the principal nucleophilic moiety. Other active site residues include Tyrosine 198 and Tyrosine 248. Glutamate 72 and Histidines 69 and 196 are the binding site of the zinc atom which—together with a water molecule—complete a distorted tetrahedral geometry around it. Two half-cysteinyl residues, 138 and 161, are joined by a disulfide linkage.

The zinc atom is essential to the catalytic activity of native carboxypeptidase A, which contains 1 gm-atom of the metal per molecular weight of 34,600 (9). When zinc is removed, the enzyme is completely inactive, whereas its readdition or that of a number of other divalent metal ions restores the dual activities of carboxypeptidase towards peptides and esters.

2.2   INORGANIC MODIFICATIONS AS PROBES OF ENZYMATIC ACTIVITY

The dual substrate specificity of carboxypeptidase is very responsive to the particular metal ion which is substituted for zinc (Table I).

Table I: Activities of Metallocarboxypeptidases.

Metal	% Activity (v/v_{zinc} x 100)	
	Peptidase[a]	Esterase[b]
Apo	0	0
Zinc	100	100
Cobalt	200	110
Nickel	50	40
Manganese	30	160
Cadmium	5	140
Mercury	0	90
Rhodium	0	70
Lead	0	60
Copper[c]	0	0

[a] 0.02 M-benzyloxycarbonylglycyl-L-phenylalanine, pH 7.5, 0°C.
[b] 0.01 M-benzoylglycyl-DL-phenyllactate, pH 7.5, 25°C.
[c] See the text for recent, unpublished data.

Dependent on the particular peptide substrate cobalt-substituted carboxypeptidase is from 2 to 10 times as active as the native zinc enzyme toward peptides, but the activities of these two enzymes towards esters are virtually the same. The esterase and peptidase activities of the Ni(II) and Mn(II) substituted enzymes are also typical, the Cd(II) enzyme shows much less activity towards peptides and the Hg(II), Rh(II), and Pb(II) enzymes are significantly active only towards esters. Extending earlier studies we have found the Cu(II) enzyme to exhibit some activity towards peptide and ester substrates synthesized more recently (Schaeffer and Auld, unpublished observations). The apoenzyme substituted with alkaline-metals and alkaline earths and the remaining transition metal ions are completely inactive both toward peptides and esters (12). Electron density difference maps show that-with the exception of HgII - the metal ion occupies the same site as Zn(II) in all catalytically active metal derivatives of carboxypeptidase A (11).

The spectroscopic properties of some substituent metal ions, particularly Co(II), render them excellent active site probes of carboxypeptidase A with which to study the interaction of the enzyme with substrates and inhibitors and concomitant conformational changes in the course of catalysis (13-15).

2.3 COBALT CARBOXYPEPTIDASE A

Cobalt carboxypeptidase A is both an active peptidase and esterase. At room temperature and -20°C the visible absorption spectrum has a shoulder near 500 nm and maxima at 555 and 572 nm, both with molar absorptivities of about 150, its infrared spectrum has bands at 940 and 1510 nM ($\epsilon \sim 20$) (Fig. 1).

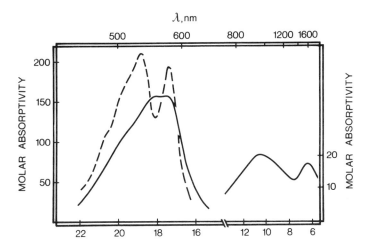

Fig. 1. Visible and near infrared spectra of cobalt carboxypeptidase at 20°C (——) and 4.2°K (---), see 15 for other conditions.

Lowering the temperature to 4°K increases resolution of the visible bands but does not reduce absorptivity. Overall, the spectrum indicates an irregular, tetrahedral or pentacoordinate - like coordination geometry and tight bonding (14,15) all of which may reflect an entatic metal environment (16). Denaturing agents abolish the spectrum; hence, its detection depends on maintenance of the three-dimensional structure of the protein.

In the circular dichroic spectrum there is a negative ellipticity band at 538 nm and a shoulder at about 500 nm. A magnetic field only renders the absorption band at 572 nm optically active. Many inhibitors and pseudosubstrates perturb the circular dichroic spectrum suggesting concomitant rearrangements of the electron distribution about the cobalt atom in accord with the direct role of the metal in peptide hydrolysis. The metal is thought to destabilize the peptide bond that is to be cleaved by coordinating with its carbonyl oxygen atom (17).

The inner-sphere nature of the enzyme-substrate complex has been recognized by oxidation studies in which the substitution-labile Co(II) is converted in situ to the substitution-inert Co(III) atom. Co(III) carboxypeptidase A is entirely inactive toward both peptide and ester substrates (18).

A large number of chemical modifications with organic reagents modify various amino acid residues with concomitant changes in activity of either peptidase or esterase activity or both. Table II here summarizes this important body of experimental data for the convenience of the reader.

Table II. Changes in Peptidase and Esterase Activities on Modification of Functional Residues in Carboxypeptidase A.

| | Control Activity (%) | | Functional residue modified |
Reagent	Peptidase[a]	Esterase[b]	
Acetylimidazole	<2	700	Tyr
Acetic anhydride	<2	600	Tyr
Iodine	<2	500	Tyr
Tetranitromethane	15	200	Tyr
5-Diazo-1H-tetrazole (45X)	<2	100	His,Tyr
2,3-Butanedione/Borate	15	300	Arg
Cyclohexyl-3-(2-morpholino-ethyl) carbodiimide	0	0	Carboxyl

[a]0.02 M benzyloxycarbonylglycyl-L-phenylalanine, pH 7.5, 0°C
[b]0.01 M benzylglycyl-D,L-phenyllactate, pH 7.5, 25°C

Despite extensive studies many features of the mechanism of carboxypeptidase remain in question. Controversy still surrounds the role of the metal and other catalytic residues in the various steps of the catalytic pathway of peptide and ester hydrolysis. A wealth of kinetic, chemical modification and x-ray crystallographic data have strongly implicated the zinc atom, glutamic acid 270 and tyrosine 248 as the key catalytic groups, but their exact <u>function</u> in the active site chemistry is still unknown (19). Thus, Glu 270 has been viewed variously as a general base promoting attack of water at the scissile carbonyl <u>or</u> as a nucleophile forming a covalent anhydride with the acyl segment of a substrate. Neither role has been satisfactorily established. For ester - but not peptide - hydrolysis an anhydride intermediate has been suggested, based on the accumulation of a U.V. absorbing species at -60°C in an organic cryosolvent (20). However, it has not been possible to trap this species and resonance Raman studies indicate that an anhydride does not occur (21). This suggests that the intermediate formed by this unique substrate may be a non-covalent complex, analogous to the metallointermediates we have identified with rapidly turned over substrates at subzero temperatures (22,27,28) (See below).

In view of the many modifications of Tyr-248 that actually increase esterase activity (19) (Table II), the functional significance of this residue also remains in question. This is true even though it has been thought to participate directly in catalysis serving as a general acid (11) and changing conformation during the reaction (2,11).

The status of the metal and its participation in catalysis has proved even more resistant to definition. In the resting enzyme the metal is probably 4-coordinate-like (13). Highly active, metal substituted forms of the enzyme appear to have even more diverse coordination geometries: distorted tetrahedral or five-coordinate-like for Co(II) (13,23) and octahedral for Ni(II) (23).

Ambiguities regarding the environment of the resting metal also extend to its participation in catalysis. The traditional Lewis acid mechanism has the metal interacting directly with the scissile carbonyl activating the carbon for nucleophilic or general base catalysis. Either a true anhydride or a metal-hydroxide acyl intermediate is expected. Alternatively a water or hydroxide bound to the metal might serve as a nucleophile. Though data and intellectual rationales have been put forth supporting each of the various mechanisms, current knowledge is insufficient to define even the most basic bond making or breaking steps in the reaction.

3. CRYOKINETICS AND CRYOSPECTROSCOPY

Definitive advances in understanding the mechanism would require truly innovative experimental approaches to define both the kinetic and static features of the catalytic process and the different states of the reaction and the preceding clearly points to the low temperature approach as the obvious means for the direct detection and characterization of intermediates. We believe that the use of low temperature techniques are the most reasonable and realistic means to extend the lifetimes of such intermediates. Toward this end we have built a stopped-flow instrument operating at temperatures as low as -55°C (7,8) which, combined with Resonance Energy Transfer (RET) kinetics (24-26), provides such a potent, novel approach to enzyme mechanisms. A wide variety of substrates and cryosolvents can be screened rapidly, and the kinetic and associated thermodynamic parameters can be determined readily. A unique feature of this instrument is that it is designed to function also as a rapid scanning cryospectrometer now permitting concurrent characterization of intermediates by both kinetic and spectral means (7). The acquisition of such structural information on pre-steady-state intermediates has remained just as difficult as their kinetic characterization. We have therefore developed stopped-flow equipment that also incorporates a high speed spectrophotometric detector and can operate at temperatures down to -60°C (7,8) thereby enabling the spectral and kinetic identification of new catalytic intermediates (22,27,28) in carboxypeptidase hydrolysis (Fig. 2). The dynamics of the formation and composition of such intermediates formed with fluorescent substrates have been monitored directly by radiationless energy transfer (RET).

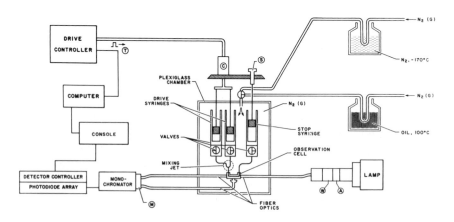

Fig 2: Schematic diagram of the low-temperature, stopped-flow, rapid-scanning spectrometer. Thermostated gaseous nitrogen is passed into the plexiglass environmental chamber that contains the quartz-flow throw cell. The description of the light supply and detector systems for measurement of fluorescence, single wavelength transmittance or rapid scanning fluorescence or absorption modes has been reported (7,8,22).

3.1 SUITABILITY OF CARBOXYPEPTIDASE A FOR THE PROPOSED STUDIES

Cryospectrokinetic investigations of enzymes aim to detect and characterize reaction intermediates at subzero temperatures without altering reaction pathways. These objectives require that structural changes and activity of an enzyme can be measured rapidly and concurrently in a suitable cryosolvent.

For carboxypeptidase A the spectra of a chromophoric, enzymatically functional cobalt atom at the active site signal the structure of the coordination complex in the course of catalysis, while the fluorescence of a dansyl group of rapidly hydrolyzed peptide and ester substrates is the basis of radiationless energy transfer (RET) which serves to measure activity.

Carboxypeptidase A is particularly soluble in salt (29). The depression of the freezing point in salt solutions makes this intrinsic property ideal for studies at subzero temperatures. Thus 4.5 M NaCl lowers the freezing point of water to $-23\,°C$ without altering the reaction pathway or the cobalt spectra (22,26,27), so that both kinetics and spectra can be obtained readily at $-20\,°C$ in this homogeneous, low-viscosity cryosolvent.

The spectra of chromophoric metal atoms at the active sites of metalloenzymes are known to be especially effective probes of structure/function relationships (13-15). The chromophoric and paramagnetic cobalt ion, Co(II), substitutes for the colorless, diamagnetic zinc of carboxypeptidase resulting in a spectrally distinctive and catalytically active derivative (30,31). Its absorption, CD, MCD and EPR spectra indicate an environment of low symmetry of the cobalt atom which is responsive to pH, denaturation, inhibitors and substrates (15,19,31). In fact, the entatic nature of these spectra exemplifies those of other chromophoric metalloenzymes (14-16). The characteristics of RET are also admirably suited for the explotation of structure/function relationships (24-26). They provide a basis for a rapid and sensitive assay of the rates of formation and breakdown of enzyme intermediates by stopped-flow fluorescence. One and the same experiment can disclose both the pre-steady-state and steady-state kinetic features of an enzyme. Analyses at steady-state precisely determine k_{cat} and K_m values (25,26); analyses at pre-steady state demonstrate the number of intermediates, the type of reaction scheme and the individual binding and rate constants (24,26).

3.2 CRYOKINETICS OF CARBOXYPEPTIDASE A

The N-dansylated peptides and analogous depsipeptides have proven to be excellent substrates for both zinc and cobalt carboxypeptidase

A. When assayed under standard conditions, the k_{cat} values of the
zinc enzyme range from 4 to 190 s^{-1} and those of K_m from 2 to 500 µM.
The cryosolvent, 4.5 M NaCl, does not significantly affect the values
of k_{cat} and K_m, which deviate by less than 2-fold from those obtained
in 1 M NaCl, a normal component of assay mixtures added to solubilize
the enzyme. At substrate concentrations ranging from 0.1 to 100 µM,
excellent RET signals are obtained so that assays are convenient at
$[S] > [E] < K_m$ (25,26).

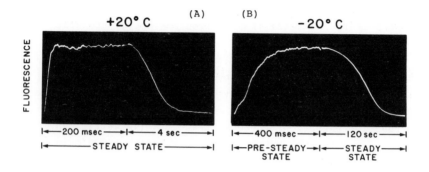

Fig. 3. Stopped-flow RET measurement of the binding and hydrolysis of
50 µM Dns-(Ala)$_2$-Phe by 1 µM carboxypeptidase A in 10 mM Hepes, 4.5 M
NaCl, pH 7.5, at (A) +20 °C and (B) -20 °C (27).

Fig. 3 is a typical example of reactions in which Dns-(Ala)$_2$-Phe is
the substrate. At +20 °C the initial, rapid increase in dansyl
fluorescence to its maximum value coincides with rapid attainment of
the steady-state concentration of ES complexes within the dead-time of
the stopped-flow instrument (Fig. 3A). At the same time, fluorescence
of the enzyme tryptophan decreases. A slow decay in fluorescence is
characteristic of the steady-state time interval and reflects
reduction in the concentration of ES accompanying the conversion of
substrate to products. Instead, at -20 °C a pre-steady-state time
interval persists for 400 ms (Fig. 3B), and two intermediates are
observed readily (see below).

     All substrates exhibit Michaelis-Menten kinetics between -20 to
+20 °C (27). Their kinetic parameters can be determined from the RET
traces both by estimating the turnover number at various initial
substrate concentrations and by analyzing the curves at a single
substrate concentration (25).

     For both the zinc and cobalt enzymes (27), Arrhenius plots for
the substrates are linear over this 40 °C temperature range, indicating
that under these conditions the rate-limiting step does not change.

For all substrates the dependence of K_m on temperature is slight, but that of k_{cat} is strong.

3.3 RELEVANCE OF THE CRYOKINETIC DATA TO THE MECHANISM OF CARBOXYPEPTIDASE

At subzero temperatures the pre-steady-state time interval for all substrates is biphasic, indicating the presence of multiple ES and/or EP complexes, as shown at -20 °C for Dns-(Ala)$_2$-Phe. When substrate is mixed with enzyme, an inital, very rapid rise (<15 ms) in dansyl fluorescence is within the dead time of the instrument (Fig. 3B), corresponding to formation of the Michaelis complex (ES$_1$). A slower exponential rise thereafter is due to formation of a second intermediate (ES$_2$), with a first-order rate constant, k_{obsd}. The rates of formation and breakdown of the intermediates have been determined as a function of substrate concentration to quantitate all the individual rate and equilibrium constants of Scheme I.

Scheme I

$$E + S \underset{}{\overset{K_s}{\rightleftharpoons}} ES_1 \underset{k_{-2}}{\overset{k_2}{\rightleftharpoons}} ES_2 \xrightarrow{k_3} E + P$$

Table III shows the rate and equilibrium constants for the individual steps in the reaction for several substrates. In every case, K_m calculated from these constants is in close agreement with that determined from Lineweaver-Burk plots.

Table III:[a] Michaelis-Menten Parameters and Rate and Equilibrium Constants for the Hydrolysis of Dansylated Substrates by Carboxypeptidase A.

Substrate	K_m (μM)	k_{cat} (s^{-1})	k_2 (s^{-1})	k_{-2} (s^{-1})	k_3 (s^{-1})	K_s (μM)	K_m'[b] (μM)
Peptides							
Dns-Ala-Ala-Phe	13.5	1.18	40.0	3.48	1.32	102	10.9
Dns-Gly-Ala-Phe	12.9	3.72	228.0	6.12	3.88	418	17.6
Esters							
Dns-Ala-Ala-OPhe[c]	1.6	0.062	53.3	0.50	0.062	129	1.3
Dns-Gly-Ala-OPhe	5.6	0.14	15.6	0.66	0.15	75	3.7
Dns-(Gly)$_3$-OPhe	22.3	3.13	32.6	1.41	3.61	164	21.9

[a]Conditions of assay were -20 °C in 10 mM Hepes-4.5 M NaCl, pH 7.5 (27). The Michaelis-Menten parameters and the rate and equilibrium constants were calculated as described in references 24-27. [b]$K_m' = K_s (k_{-2} + k_3)/(k_{-2} + k_2 + k_3)$. [c]At -10 °C.

The interconversion of ES_1 and ES_2 reflected by two first-order constants, k_2 and k_{-2}, indicates that ES_2 does <u>not</u> represent an acyl intermediate. In an acyl enzyme intermediate mechanism, reversal of the acyl complex would occur in a second-order rate process $(k'_{-2} = k_{-2} [P_1])$ and, hence k'_{-2} would essentially be <u>zero</u> in the absence of added product. Furthermore, product P_1 would be a <u>mixed</u> inhibitor and its addition would <u>increase</u> the pre-steady state rate constant, k_{obsd}, for such a mechanism (24,32).

$$k_{obsd} = k_1 + k_{-2} [P_1] + k_2/(K_2/[S] + 1)$$

However, carboxypeptidase A fulfills none of these expectations. For all substrates studied k_{-2} is <u>greater than zero</u>, in fact usually larger than k_3 (Table III). The P_1 products, Phe and OPhe, are <u>competitive</u> inhibitors, in accord with previous studies (19), and k_{obsd} <u>decreases</u> upon addition of P_1. Minimally, these results demonstrate that the C-terminal product is not liberated prior to the rate-limiting step and hence, by inference, that deacylation cannot be rate limiting.

Furthermore, in enzyme mechanisms known to operate through acyl intermediates addition of nucleophiles traps the acyl moiety, regardless of whether or not deacylation is rate limiting (32). In this regard, it is of special relevance that yeast seryl carboxypeptidase behaves in accord with predictions based on the acyl mechanism of chymotrypsin (27): when hydrolysis is carried out in the presence of methanol, the substrate Dns-(Gly)$_3$-OPhe is readily converted to Dns-(Gly)$_3$-OMe. However, when carboxypeptidase A acts on this same substrate, there is no evidence that the product is trapped under any of the conditions investigated, in complete accord with previous studies of other substrates (33), (Klyosov and Vallee, unpublished observations). Methanol, in particular, has proven to be a very effective nucleophile in reactions of other proteases (34), since its intrinsic nucleophilicity is much greater than that of water. Yet, methanol concentrations of up to 50% (v/v) fail to trap any intermediate during hydrolysis by carboxypeptidase A.

The kinetics characterizing the hydrolysis of a series of N-dansylated peptides and depsipeptides by zinc and cobalt carboxypeptidase over the temperature range +2 to -20°C in 4.5 M NaCl are closely similar. Importantly, for the exact matched peptide and ester pair, Dns-Ala-Ala-Phe and Dns-Ala-Ala-OPhe, Arrhenius plots of k_{cat} decrease linearly with decreasing temperature while K_m remains unchanged (28). Hence, over the total range of 40°C the rate determining steps have not changed.

3.4 CRYOSPECTROSCOPY OF COBALT CARBOXYPEPTIDASE A

The decreased rates at subzero temperatures lengthen the
lifetimes of intermediates sufficiently to permit both their
structural and kinetic characterization (22,27,28). Thus, at $-17^{\circ}C$,
the spectra of the cobalt enzyme during catalysis allow direct
visualization of the formation and breakdown of the intermediates for
Dns-Ala-Ala-Phe and Dns-Ala-Ala-OPhe (Fig. 4 and 5). The figure
inserts show the time course of the changes in cobalt absorbance at
510 and 575 nm for the peptide and ester intermediates respectively.

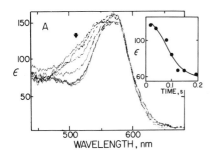
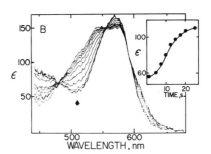

Fig 4. Absorption spectra of the formation (A) and breakdown (B) of
the ES_2 intermediate formed in the reaction of cobalt
carboxypeptidase, 0.1 mM, with Dns-Ala-Ala-Phe, 0.2 mM, at $-17°C$ (28).
Individual spectra were recorded in 16.48 ms. (Insets) Absorbance
change at 510 nm, indicated by the arrows, as a function of time after
mixing.

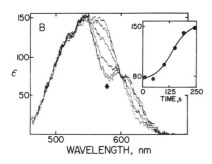
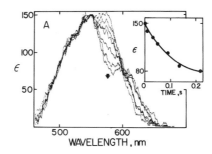

Fig. 5.   Absorption spectra of the formation (A) and breakdown (B) of
the ES_2 intermediate formed in the reaction of cobalt carboxypeptidase
A, 0.1 mM, with Dns-Ala-Ala-OPhe, 0.1 mM, at $-16°C$ (28).   (Insets)
Absorbance change at 575 nm, indicated by the arrows, as a function of
the time after mixing.

The decrease in absorbance at these wavelengths over the first 200 ms interval reflects the rapid formation of these intermediates (Fig. 4A and 5A). At this point in the reaction, the cobalt spectrum of the ester intermediate clearly differs from that of the peptide intermediate, and both differ from that of the enzyme alone. Thus, both peptides and esters markedly disturb the cobalt coordination sphere in a fashion characteristic of the type of substrate (see below). The increase in absorbance in the course of the next several seconds (inserts Fig. 4B, and 5B) signals the reduction in the concentration of these intermediates due to their conversion to enzyme plus products, Dns-Ala-Ala and Phe or OPhe.

The cryospectroscopic and concurrent cryokinetic studies of the cobalt enzyme result in the same reaction scheme as that established for the zinc enzyme (see above). The constants for the zinc and cobalt enzymes are closely similar and characteristic of the two substrate types (Tables III and IV).

Table IV. Cobalt Carboxypeptidase Catalyzed Hydrolysis of a Matched Peptide-Ester Pair: Michaelis-Menten Parameters, and Rate and Equilibrium Constants for Elementary Steps[†].

Substrate	K_m (μM)	k_{cat} (s^{-1})	k_2 (s^{-1})	k_{-2} (s^{-1})	k_3 (s^{-1})	K_s (μM)	K'_m (μM)
Dns-Ala-Ala-Phe	2.77	0.57	36.1	0.17	0.59	154	3.17
Dns-Ala-Ala-OPhe	0.23	0.040	58.6	0.13	0.040	61.3	0.18

[†] Conditions of assay were -20 °C for the peptides and -10°C for the esters in 4.5 NaCl, 10 mM Hepes, pH 7.5 (28). See Table III for definition of K'_m and methods of calculating kinetic parameters.

In the first step of the reaction, both the peptide and ester substrates bind relatively weakly to the metalloenzymes to form their respective ES_1 intermediates. In the next step ES_1 is converted rapidly into a second intermediate, ES_2. The products of the reaction are then released in the slow step of the reaction. The extent to which the cobalt enzyme is converted into the ES_2 intermediate for the peptide or ester at steady-state, as well as the rates of formation and breakdown of ES_2 can be calculated. Accordingly, at the concentrations of Dns-Ala-Ala-Phe and Dns-Ala-Ala-OPhe employed for subzero spectroscopy (Fig. 4 and 5), the peptide and ester ES_2 intermediates form maximally within 200 ms (Fig. 4A and 5A), and at this time they constitute 99 and 95%, respectively, of the total

enzyme present (28). The subsequent breakdown of the intermediate to
free enzyme is much slower, and is complete at 25 s for
Dns-Ala-Ala-Phe (Fig. 4B) and 250 s for Dns-Ala-Ala-OPhe (Fig. 5B).

The ES_2 intermediates generated with a large number of matched
peptide and ester pairs have been examined in this manner. Since the
rates at which these substrates are hydrolyzed vary considerably, the
concentrations of enzyme, 10^{-4}M, and substrate, 10^{-4}M to 10^{-2}M, and
the temperature, 0 to -20°C, have been chosen to optimize conditions
so that both formation, $\leq$250 ms, and breakdown, 10 to 250 s, of the
intermediates may be observed. Further, a substrate concentration
10-fold or more above K_m maximizes the steady-state concentration of
the intermediates.

The cobalt spectra of both peptide and ester intermediates
identify catalysis-related changes in the active site metal
coordination sphere characteristic of each (22,28). The spectra of
the ES_2 intermediates generated with all peptides and analogous esters
examined so far fall into two distinct categories clearly
representative of the two substrate types (Fig. 6).

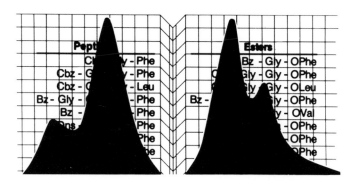

Fig. 6. Schematic representation of the cobalt absorption spectra of
the ES_2 intermediates generated with peptides (left) and esters
(right) of differing lengths, amino acid sequence, COOH-terminal
residue, and NH_2-terminal blocking group.

The ES_2 intermediates of peptides display an absorption maximum at 570
$\pm$3 nm and a band of low intensity at 473 $\pm$6 nm, while those of the
ester analogs exhibit two maxima of unequal intensity at 598 $\pm$3 nm and
551 $\pm$2 as well as a prominent shoulder at 523 $\pm$3 nm. These two classes
of spectra correlate directly and solely with the substrate type i.e.
peptide versus ester. Thus, the spectral features of the peptide ES_2
intermediates (Figure 6) which differ in length (di, tri, tetra),
internal amino acids and their sequences (Gly, Ala, Val, or Glu),
blocking group (Dns, Cbz, Bz) and C-terminal residue (Phe or Leu) are
all the same and exemplify those of a large number of peptides.

Similarly, the spectral features of the ES_2 intermediates for the esters Bz-Gly-OPhe, Cbz-Gly-Gly-OPhe, Cbz-Gly-Gly-OLeu, Cbz-Gly-Gly-OVal, Dns-Gly-Ala-OPhe and Dns-Ala-Ala-OPhe are identical.

Remarkably - and in marked contrast to all other peptides or esters studied - the absorption of the cobalt enzyme in the presence of the dipeptide Gly-Tyr has a maximum at 548 nm and a shoulder at 514 nm (15). Gly-Tyr is known, however, to be hydrolyzed very slowly and to bind in an unproductive mode. The present data reinforce earlier evidence (19) and references therein) that this peptide cannot be considered a "model" (11) for rapidly hydrolyzed substrates.

The corresponding EPR spectra both support and further amplify the deductions drawn from the electronic spectra of the intermediates. Immediately prior to the rate determining step, both peptides and esters disturb the coordination sphere and the symmetry of the metal in a manner characteristic for each substrate (22,28). The frozen solution spectrum of the cobalt enzyme exhibits three resonances with effective g values, g_1 = 5.65, g_2 = 2.98, g_3 = 2.03, but hyperfine structure cannot be resolved in any of these.

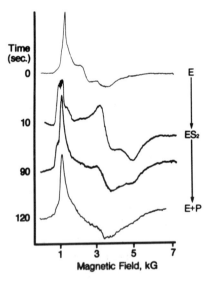

Fig. 7. EPR spectra during breakdown of the ES_2 intermediate formed with Dns-Glu-Ala-Phe, 2 mM, and cobalt carboxypeptidase A, 0.5 mM, at -20°C. The bottom spectrum is that of enzyme plus products after completion of hydrolysis.

Mixing the enzyme with the peptide substrate Dns-Glu-Ala-Phe (27) transforms this spectrum into that of an ES_2 peptide intermediate with effective g values, g_1 = 6.80, g_2 = 2.00, g_3 = 1.40 (Fig. 7, t=10 seconds); importantly, hyperfine structure is now resolved distinctly in g_1, with an effective coupling constant $A_1 = 143 \times 10^{-4} cm^{-1}$.

Hyperfine structure is also resolved on the low field resonance in the EPR spectra of the ES_2 ester intermediates, but that induced by any given peptide and its matching ester differ significantly. The effective hyperfine coupling in g_1 for the ester intermediates is larger by $20 - 40 \times 10^{-4} cm^{-1}$ than that for the corresponding peptide. This confirms that the respective coordination complexes differ structurally. Thus, both the absorption and EPR spectra of the reaction intermediates consistently demonstrate (i) formation of transient metal complexes; (ii) differences between the effects induced by peptide and by ester substrates; and (iii) identities between those induced by all peptides on one hand and by all esters on the other.

The absorption, MCD and EPR spectra of the cobalt enzyme at subzero temperatures are virtually the same as those at 20°C. In contrast, those typical of the peptide and ester intermediates differ remarkably from one another and from that of the resting enzyme or its complexes with products (22,28). The absorption spectra of all peptide intermediates are similar to each other as, in turn, are all ester intermediates (Fig. 4-6).

The EPR, MCD and visible absorption spectra of cobalt carboxypeptidase reflect the low symmetry and irregular metal geometry characteristic of the coordination environment of catalytically essential, entatic active site metal atoms of metalloenzymes (30). They signal the enzyme's readiness for the catalytic process including ligand exchange and/or addition at the metal atom (15,30) and identify characteristic catalysis-related changes in the active site metal coordination sphere.

The intermediates of electron transfer reactions involving metal complex ions have been generally considered to require a compromised geometry between those normally assumed by the initial and final valence states; consequently the transition state would then be thought to be a distorted complex (28). Reasoning by analogy, similar considerations may pertain for the intermediates of metalloenzymes. Metal geometry could be altered markedly and characteristically if different types of substrate molecules such as peptides and esters were to supply a different donor atom transiently during catalysis. Both the spectral shifts and enhanced splitting of the absorption bands and the hyperfine coupling induced in g_1 during catalysis (Fig 7) are both consistent with and suggestive, albeit not diagnostic, of such an underlying event (22). Yet better resolution of such spectra and their interpretation should reveal additional structural details of the underlying chemistry.

These cryokinetic and cryospectroscopic results bear importantly on the mechanism of carboxypeptidase A catalysis. The marked alterations of the cobalt spectra correlate with the formation of intermediates in which a substrate carbonyl and/or carboxyl group is likely coordinated to the metal at a critical step in the course of catalysis. The marked difference of the cobalt spectra for peptides and esters is consistent with previous results of organic and inorganic chemical modifications and of initial rate and RET kinetics which showed that the metal plays critical but different roles in the mechanisms of peptide and ester hydrolysis (19). The metal was considered to be the recognition and binding site of esters through coordination of their carboxyl group while it was envisioned to aid peptide hydrolysis by coordination of the amide carbonyl once Arg 145 has recognized the terminal carboxyl group.

4.   IMPLICATIONS OF CRYOSPECTROKINETIC STUDIES

This cryospectrokinetic approach greatly expands the range of mechanistic questions which can be answered experimentally. Future studies of metallointermediates such as those observed here will be able to examine directly a number of important issues regarding the detailed structure of transients of this and other metalloenzymes, e.g. the exact step at which bond breaking occurs and the role of specific active site residues in catalysis.

Beyond this, however, we wish to stress the pertinence of this approach to widely different experimental systems. Cryospectrokinetic techniques would seem feasible for many enzyme systems with suitable probe characteristics due either to intrinsic inorganic or organic constituents or to the introduction of extrinsic ones by chemical modification of the protein and/or substrate. In all instances such probes should not interfere with catalysis, be highly sensitive and give distinctive signals that respond to perturbations in a time interval shorter than that required for catalysis itself. The search for "ideal" solvents and/or correction for solvent effects is also essential; salt solutions (7) represent an important alternative to aqueous-organic solvent mixtures that have generally been used.

This approach is not limited to the study of enzyme mechanisms. Given suitable spectral readout and solvent characteristics analogous to those described above, it should prove feasible to resolve rapid events in interactions of macromolecules e.g. protein-nucleic acid, antigen-antibody, etc., as well as those that occur when small molecules bind to the recognition sites of macromolecules e.g.

drug-nucleic acid, hormone-receptor etc. Adaptation of the approach
described herein to these systems should provide direct structural,
kinetic and chemical data on short-lived species whose nature or even
existence could previously be evaluated largely by conjecture and
intuition.

5. REFERENCES

1. G. Weber, Adv. Protein Chem. 29, (1975), pp. 1-83.

2. L.W. Harrison, D.S. Auld, B.L. Vallee, Proc. Natl. Acad.
    Sci. USA 72 (1975) pp. 4356-4360.

3. K. Linderstrom Lang, J.A. Schellman in P.D. Boyer (ed), The
    Enzymes (2nd Ed) Vol. I, Academic Press, New York, (1959),
    pp. 443-510.

4. W.F. Anderson, R.J. Fletterick, T.A. Steitz, J. Mol. Biol.
    86, (1974), pp. 261-269.

5. B.L. Vallee and J.R. Riordan in T.K. Li (ed), Versatility of
    Enzymes, (1978), pp. 203-208.

6. J.S. Thompson, H. Gehring, B.L. Vallee, Proc. Natl. Acad.
    Sci. USA 77, (1980), pp. 132-136.

7. D.S. Auld, Methods In Enzymology, Vol. 61, (1979), pp.
    318-335.

8. D. Hanahan, D.S. Auld, Analytical Biochemistry 108, (1980),
    pp. 86-95.

9. B.L. Vallee, H. Neurath, J. Amer. Chem. Soc. 76, (1954), p.
    5006.

10. H. Neurath, R.A. Bradshaw, P.H. Petra, K.A. Walsh, Phil.
    Trans. Roy. Soc. London, Ser. B 257, (1970), pp. 159-176.

11. J.A. Hartsuck, W.N. Lipscomb in P.D. Boyer (ed.), The
    Enzymes, Vol. III, (3rd Ed), Academic Press, New York,
    (1971), pp. 1-56.

12. J.E. Coleman, B.L. Vallee, J. Biol. Chem. 235, (1960), pp.
    390-395.

13. B. Holmquist, T.A. Kaden, B.L. Vallee, Biochemistry 14,
    (1975), pp. 1454-1461.

14. B.L. Vallee, B. Holmquist in D.W. Darnall & R.G. Wilkins
    (ed.), Methods for Determining Metal Ion Environments in
    Proteins: Structure and Function of Metalloproteins,
    Elsevier/North Holland, New York (1980) pp.27-74.

15. S.A. Latt, B.L. Vallee, Biochemistry 10, (1971), pp.
    4263-4270.

16. B.L. Vallee, R.J.P. Williams, Proc. Natl. Acad. Sci. USA 59,
    (1968), pp. 498-505.

17. B.L. Vallee, J.F. Riordan, J.E. Coleman, Proc. Natl. Acad. Sci. USA 49, (1963), pp. 109-116.

18. H.E. Van Wart, B.L. Vallee, Biochemistry 17, (1978), pp. 3385-3394.

19. B.L. Vallee, A. Galdes, D.S. Auld, J.F. Riordan in T.G. Spiro (ed.) Metal Ions in Biology: Zinc Enzymes, Wiley, New York, Vol. 5, (1984), pp. 25-75.

20. M.W. Makinen, L.C. Kuo, J.J. Dymowski, S. Jaffer, J. Biol. Chem. 254, (1979), pp. 356-366.

21. S.J.Hoffman, S.S.-T. Chu, H. Li, E.T. Kaiser, P.R. Corey, J. Amer. Chem. Soc. 105, (1983), pp. 105-107.

22. K.F. Geoghegan, A. Galdes, R.A. Martinelli, D.S. Auld, B.L. Vallee, Biochemistry 22, (1983), pp. 2255-2262.

23. R.G. Rosenberg, C.A. Root, H.B. Gray, J. Am. Chem. Soc. 97, (1975), pp. 21-26.

24. R.R. Lobb, D.S. Auld, Proc. Natl. Acad. Sci. USA 76, (1979), pp. 2684-2688.

25. R.R. Lobb, D.S. Auld, Biochemistry 19, (1980), pp. 5297-5302.

26. R.R. Lobb, D.S. Auld, Experentia 40, (1984), pp. 1197-1206.

27. A. Galdes, D.S. Auld, B.L. Vallee, Biochemistry 22, (1983), pp. 1888-1893.

28. D.S. Auld, A. Galdes, K.F. Geoghegan, B. Holmquist, R.A. Martinelli, B.L. Vallee, Proc. Natl. Acad. Sci. USA 82, (1984), pp. 5041-5045.

29. F.W. Putnam, H. Neurath, J. Biol. Chem. 166, (1946), pp. 603-619.

30. B.L. Vallee in H. Eggerer & R. Huber (ed.), Structural and Functional Aspects of Enzyme Catalysis, Mosbach, Springer, Verlag, Heidelberg (1981), pp. 75-95.

31. B.L. Vallee, S.A. Latt in P. Desnuelle, H. Neurath & M. Otteson (ed.), Structure-Function Relationships of Proteolytic Enzymes, Munksgaard, Copenhagen, (1970), pp. 144-159.

32. A. Fersht, in Enzyme Structure and Mechanism, W.H. Freeman and Co., San Francisco, CA, (1977) pp. 180-185.

33. R. Breslow, D.L. Wernick, Proc. Natl. Acad. Sci. USA 74, (1977), pp. 1303-1307.

34. M. L. Bender, G.E. Clement, C.R. Gunter, F.J. Kezdy, J. Amer. Chem. Soc. 86, (1964), pp. 3697-3703.

The Binuclear Iron Center of Uteroferrin

Bradley C. Antanaitis* and Philip Aisen#

*Department of Physics, Lafayette College, Easton, Pennsylvania 18042 and #Departments of Physiology & Biophysics and Medicine, Albert Einstein College of Medicine, Bronx, New York 10461, U.S.A.

SUMMARY

Uteroferrin is a single-chain basic glycoprotein of MW close to 35,000 found in the uterine secretions of pregnant or hormone-treated pseudopregnant sows and other mammals with similar placental structures. The protein bears two exchangeable iron atoms per molecule and has been postulated to function in transplacental iron transport. Once considered a member of the transferrin class of proteins, and named accordingly, uteroferrin is now known to belong to the newly emerging class of iron-tyrosinate proteins having acid phosphatase activity. Whether the protein's enzymatic activity or reversible iron-binding activity is actually involved in its physiological function remains to be seen. Uteroferrin's most striking feature may well be its capacity to exist in either of two interconvertible forms: purple (oxidized), which is enzymatically inactive and EPR-silent, or pink (reduced), which is enzymatically active and exhibits a novel rhombic $g' = 1.74$ EPR signal. The purple-to-pink conversion is effected by mild reductants such as mercaptoethanol or ascorbate, while oxidants such as ferricyanide or hydrogen peroxide restore the protein's purple color. Remarkably, the oxidative and reductive manipulations producing these color changes have little effect on the integrated intensiy of the protein's visible absorption. Resonance Raman spectra showing characteristic tyrosyl vibrational modes indicate that uteroferrin, like the transferrins, intradiol dioxygenases, and violet Mn-containing acid phosphatases, is a metal-tyrosinate protein. Proton NMR studies corroborate iron coordination by tyrosine and further suggest histidine coordination to each iron of the reduced center, a result in accord with electron spin-echo studies. Little change in the secondary structure of uteroferrin as it undergoes conversion between pink and purple forms can be discerned from circular dichroism spectra.

Quantitative EPR, magnetic susceptibility and proton NMR studies indicate that uteroferrin's two iron atoms are sequestered in a spin-coupled binu-clear center, a property it shares with the structurally similar acid phosphatase from bovine spleen. Mossbauer studies of ^{57}Fe-enriched protein unequivocally establish the existence of the exchange-coupled binuclear center and further indicate that the reducing electron of the pink form is localized mainly on one of the center's two iron atoms.

Several lines of evidence (optical absorption, resonance Raman, proton-NMR and general chemical considerations) suggest that only one of uteroferrin's two irons is chromophoric, namely the one that remains ferric following reduction. Presumably, then, the iron that cycles between the ferric and ferrous states during reversible one-electron redox reactions binds no tyrosines while its intensely colored partner binds two tyrosines.

The spin-coupled binuclear center of uteroferrin is sensitive to a variety of perturbants. Orthophosphate, even in the absence of detectable oxygen, forces the pink protein to its purple, oxidized, EPR-silent state. Molybdate, in contrast, quantitatively converts pink uteroferrin's EPR signal, which is initially rhombic, into an axial form that remains invariant to subsequent addition of phosphate. Vanadate, like phosphate, drives the pink protein to an oxidized EPR-silent state, but itself serves as a one-electron acceptor yielding the vanadyl cation. Remarkably, however, the oxidized protein remains pink, demonstrating a dissociation between color and oxidation state. Guanidine causes a sizable red shift in the pink protein's visible absorption maximum without any loss in the intensity of the protein's $g' = 1.74$ EPR signal, thus demonstrating dissociation of color and oxidation state in a complementary way.

A possible structure of uteroferrin's iron center, rationalizing much of the data presented herein, is given below (Fig. 2).

1 INTRODUCTION

In recent years intensive interdisciplinary efforts to understand such fundamental life processes as iron metabolism and enzyme catalysis have uncovered a new class of purple metalloproteins with acid phosphatase activity (1,2). Of these, porcine uteroferrin, the focal point of this review, and bovine spleen acid phosphatase, a close relative of uteroferrin, are the best characterized (1-8). Both of these vividly colored glycoproteins with MW's close to 35,000 reversibly bind two iron atoms per molecule, exhibit tartrate-insensitive phosphatase activity which peaks at pH 4.9, and undergo reversible one-electron reduction with reagents as diverse as mercaptoethanol, ascorbate and the ferrous ion (2,3,6,8-10). The striking color of both enzymes as well as their phosphatase activity are determined by the redox state of the enzyme, with oxidized protein having a purple color and negligible activity and the reduced protein a pink hue and vigorous phosphatase activity (5,11-15). The earmark of these enzymes is a distinctive rhombic $g' = 1.74$ EPR signal the expression of which is controlled by the binding of phosphate, molybdate and other anionic inhibitors (6,15-17). This signal, observable with the protein in its pink form and then only at temperatures below 35 K, arises from a spin-coupled binuclear iron center.

Isolation in relatively low yields from spleen, presumably from an intracellular locus, and activity comparable to that of prostatic acid phosphatase both point to a role in the regulation of phosphorus metabolism for the beef spleen enzyme (5,12). Furthermore, its effectiveness as a phosphoprotein phosphatase raises the possibility that the spleen enzyme, in concert with protein kinase, may modulate events in intermediary metabolism or protein synthesis (2,18). In contrast, the abundance and extracellular disposition of porcine uteroferrin seem more in line with a transport function (1-2,8). Indeed, recent work by Roberts et al (19-21), suggests that uteroferrin's complement of two iron atoms may be delivered to sites of hematopoiesis in the fetal pig either directly, by uteroferrin itself, or indirectly, with fetal transferrin serving as the vehicle of delivery. While the former hypothesis is still reasonable and attractive, the latter conflicts with more recent iron-exchange studies (Kei Doi et al, unpublished observations). Specifically, iron-exchange experiments performed under conditions matching those of Roberts' group indicate that transfer of iron between native porcine uteroferrin and porcine transferrin is too low to be physiologically significant. Uteroferrin bears N-linked oligosaccharide chains containing 6-phosphomannose units, a structure thought to target acid hydrolases for lysosomal consignment (22). Evidence that N-acetyglucosamine covers the putative recognition marker in the native protein would allow uteroferrin still to be secreted and participate in iron transport (22).

A protein virtually identical to porcine uteroferrin has been isolated from the uterine flushings of progesterone-treated, pseudopregnant mares (1,23). It is possible, therefore, that uteroferrin-like proteins will also be found in other mammals possessing placental structures similar to those of the mare and sow.

Acid phosphatases more or less resembling uteroferrin have been isolated from sources altogether different from mammalian placenta. Specifically such proteins have been found in mouse liver lysosomes (24,25), rat bone and the enamel organ of rat molars (26,27), the sera and spleen of patients with Gaucher's disease (28), intracellular vacuoles of leukemic hairy cells (29), the red kidney bean, Phaseolus vulgaris (30) and the yeast Saccharomyces rouxii (31). Unfortunately, most of these enzymes have been isolated only in catalytic amounts and therefore have yet to be subjected to molecular characterization. Perhaps the class of purple iron-containing phosphatases will enjoy rapid growth once purification procedures improve and interest in these intriguing metalloenzymes is piqued.

2. PHYSICOCHEMICAL PROPERTIES

2.1 Absorption Spectra

When treated with oxidants such as ferricyanide or hydrogen peroxide, uteroferrin, free of phosphate or other strongly interacting anionic inhibitors, is driven to its purple form having a broad intense absorption maximum between 570-575 nm and a prominent near-UV shoulder at 320 nm (2,10). The pink form, generated by mild reductants such as B-mercaptoethanol or ascorbate has its absorption maximum shifted to 510 nm and its near-UV shoulder, now less conspicuous, shifted to 310 nm. Both forms of uteroferrin have a sharp protein-dominated peak at 280 nm flanked by several more or less well-defined shoulders. The intensity of the 280 nm peak is

sensitive to anionic inhibitors, decreasing by 12%-13% upon binding of orthophosphate. Even more remarkable, however, is the near preservation of the integrated
intensity of the primary visible absorption band of the pink and purple forms of the
protein, a result suggesting that only one of uteroferrin's two irons is chromophoric. Studies of mixed-metal forms of the protein, i.e. those bearing Fe-Zn, Fe-
Cu or Fe-Hg, instead of Fe-Fe, and showing little loss of visible absorption per
molecule, confirm this suggestion (32). Although short exposure to dithionite in
the presence of suitable iron chelators allows selective removal of one of uteroferrin's two irons and preparation of mixed metal derivatives of the protein, prolonged exposure to the same reductant causes complete loss of iron, concomitant
bleaching of vivid purple color and loss of phosphatase activity (11,12). Evidently, then, iron is essential for enzymatic activity and an integral constituent
of the protein's redox-sensitive chromophore.

2.2 Resonance Raman Spectra

The detection of resonance-enhanced tyrosyl modes by laser Raman spectroscopy
indicates that uteroferrin's rich purple color arises primarily from tyrosine-to-Fe
(III) charge-transfer transitions (33,34). Such transitions identify uteroferrin as
a member of the rapidly expanding class of metal-tyrosinate proteins, a class which
presently includes the transferrins (2,3), intradiol dioxygenases (2,3) and Mn-
containing violet acid phosphatases (2,35). Pink uteroferrin yields a similar
pattern of resonance-enhanced bands indicating that tyrosine coordination to the
protein's chromophoric iron is maintained following reduction. This observation
suggests that one or more tyrosyl residues are coordinated to an iron that remains
ferric after reduction of the protein, since Fe(II)-phenolate complexes are not
expected to give ligand-to-metal charge-transfer transition in the visible region
(36). Thus, laser Raman studies and optical studies of both native and mixed-metal
hybrids together indicate that uteroferrin binds two types of iron, a chromophoric
tyrosine-rich species that remains ferric and a colorless species that cycles
between the ferric and ferrous states during redox-induced color changes (2,8).
Conspicuous broadening in two of the four high-frequency tyrosyl modes (those centered at 1293 and 1604 cm^{-1}) as well as the intense polarized band at 575 cm^{-1}
suggest coordination by more than one tyrosine. Furthermore, shifts in the positions of the dominant tyrosine C-O stretching band and the 571 cm^{-1} band accompanying reduction signal a redox-induced perturbation of the Fe(III)-tyrosine coordination environment (2,34).

2.3 Circular Dichroism Spectra

CD studies of pink and purple forms of uteroferrin, showing that all absorption
bands in the visible and near-UV regions have low optical activity, are consistent
with assignment of these bands as tyrosine-to-Fe(III) charge-transfer transitions

(2,7,8). CD spectra of synthetic phenolate-ferric complexes typically reveal two widely separated transitions attributable to phenolate-to-Fe(III) charge-transfer transitions, one of which falls in the visible and the other in the near-UV region (37). Conceivably, therefore, the splitting of uteroferrin's primary visible absorption band and prominent shoulder each into two optically active transitions reflects iron coordination by two inequivalent tyrosyl residues (7,8). Then the pair of lower energy transitions (i.e., those at 530 and 345 nm) would be assigned to one tyrosine on the basis of shifts induced by the purple-to-pink conversion while the remaining pair (at 475 and 305 nm) which appear more sensitive to phosphate binding would be assigned to the second tyrosine. The high extinction coefficient of the protein's visible absorption band (4000 M^{-1},cm^{-1} at 550 nm) is consistent with two tyrosines bound to the protein's paramagnetic center (7).

The overall similarity between the CD spectra of pink and purple forms of uteroferrin, buttresses the conclusion drawn from resonance Raman studies that mercaptoethanol reduction fails to disrupt the purple protein's tyrosine coordination. Shifts in peak positions and intensities observed in both CD and Raman spectra, however, are consistent with a rearrangment of these residues. In contrast, preservation of a prominent shoulder at 255 nm in the aromatic region of the protein's CD spectra suggests that disulfide bonds are little affected by the purple-to-pink conversion (2,7). Furthermore, little change in the protein's secondary structure as it undergoes conversion between its purple and pink forms can be discerned from CD spectra (7). Treatment with phosphate, on the other hand, apparently increases the protein's unordered structure at the expense of both its α-helical and β-pleated structure (7). Phosphate also induces a negative Cotton effect at 380 nm which has no obvious counterpart in either the pink or purple form of uteroferrin. The identity of this new band is unknown, but its position in the near-UV suggests, as is the case with hemerythin, that it represents a μ-oxo oxygen-to-Fe(III) charge-transfer transition (38).

2.4 EPR and Magnetic Susceptibility

Like the acid phosphatase from beef spleen, with which it has much in common, fully oxidized purple uteroferrin is very nearly diamagnetic and EPR-silent (7). In its pink form, however, the protein exhibits a striking EPR signal of rhombic symmetry with principal g-values of 1.93, 1.74 and 1.59 (2,3,7-9). Detection of a virtually identical signal in the splenic acid phosphatase indicates that this distinctive signal, much like the g⁻ = 1.94 signal of reduced iron-sulfur proteins (39), may be the spectral signature of a new class of iron-binding proteins. Uteroferrin's g_{av} = 1.74 signal, observable only at temperatures below 35 K, accounts for only one unpaired spin per two irons, a result suggesting that the protein's irons reside in a binuclear spin-coupled S = 1/2 paramagnetic center (2,7). This suggestion is substantiated both by magnetic susceptibility measurements (7) and, most convincingly, by recent [57]Fe-Mossbauer studies (see Section 2.5). Similar centers

have been identified in other iron-binding proteins, viz, hemerythrin (40), ribonucleotide reductase (41) and two-iron ferrodoxins (39). Semimethemerythrin, in
particular, yields EPR signals and LEFE remarkably similar to those of uteroferrin,
indicating an underlying similarity between the paramagnetic centers of these proteins (41). Estimation of the strength of exchange coupling between the irons of
pink uteroferrin by EPR spectral intensity measurements gives a value of only 14
cm^{-1} (2,7). This low value for J has been corroborated by ^{1}H-NMR studies at room
temperature (36).

Mixed-metal, Fe-Zn forms of uteroferrin and the bovine splenic enzyme have been
prepared with nearly full phosphatase activity. Susceptibility and EPR measurements
of the splenic enzyme indicate that its single iron is high-spin ferric in a site of
rhombic symmetry (6). Its g_{av} = 4.3 EPR signal, which accounts for all of the iron
in the protein, exhibits unusual relaxation properties that are sensitive to the
presence of phosphate (6). While it is not known to what extent, if any, the ligand
environment of the iron in the Fe-Zn hybrid has changed from its native configuration, the results of this study leave little doubt that both irons of the native
purple enzyme are high-spin ferric.

2.5 Mossbauer

Mossbauer spectroscopy of [57]Fe-enriched uteroferrin demonstrates unequivocally
that the protein's two irons are juxtaposed in a spin-coupled binuclear center (9).
In the oxidized purple protein both irons are high-spin ferric with their spins
coupled antiferromagnetically to produce an S = 0 ground state. One-electron reduction to the pink form produces an Fe(II) - Fe(III) pair whose spins are now coupled
to give an S = 1/2 ground state (9). The quadrupole splittings of the ferric sites
of the purple protein, though unusually large for a nominal S-state ion, are comparable to those found in oxidized hemerythin, and probably, as is the case with
that protein, reflect a highly asymmetric ligand structure about each iron (9). It
is even tempting to speculate that uteroferrin's reducible ferric ion is penta-
coordinate, like the oxygen-binding iron of hemerythrin. Then the protein's binuclear center, which is known to be essential for catalysis, would have a site
available for coordination by phosphate containing substrates and other tetrahedral
anionic species known to strongly interact with the protein. Equally noteworthy is
the observation that the ferric sites of purple uteroferrin are inequivalent, again
lending credence to the idea that the coordination spheres of the two iron atoms are
different. Furthermore, the large isomer shift of the ferrous ion in pink uteroferrin and the large intrinsic saturation field of the ferric site ($H_{sat} \cong -55T$) are
both consistent with oxygen and nitrogen ligation of each iron (9). Sulfur, if
present at all in the protein's active site, must not be bound to either iron.

2.6 LEFE and Electron-Spin Echo

Pink uteroferrin exhibits a large linear electric field effect (LEFE), demonstrating that its paramagnetic center is non-centrosymmetric and, in accord with
Mossbauer data, suggesting that the reducing electron of the protein's binuclear
center resides primarily on only one of its iron atoms (42). The large deviation
from centrosymmetry also squares well with evidence indicating that tyrosyl residues
coordinated to the pink protein's paramagnetic center are asymmetrically partitioned
between its two iron atoms (42). The magnetic field dependence of the LEFE singles
out the g_{min} (g = 1.59) axis as the direction of most facile electron polarization.
It is tempting therefore, to argue, as for the two-iron ferredoxins, that the g_{min}
axis points away from the ferrous iron and toward an electron-accepting center,
possibly the other iron atom.

Electron spin-echo studies indicate that pink uteroferrin's magnetic electron
interacts with one and possibly two classes of nitrogen nuclei, one of which is the
imidazole nitrogen of an iron-coordinated histidine (42).

2.7 ^{1}H-NMR

In its purple form uteroferrin has no detectable isotropically shifted proton
resonances (36). In contrast, the pink protein exhibits paramagnetically shifted
proton-NMR rich in structure, with well-defined resonances spanning the range from
90 ppm downfield to 70 ppm upfield (36). By comparison with synthetic Fe(II) and
Fe(III) complexes, resonances attributable to the 3,5-H's, 2,6-H's and beta CH's of
ferric-coordinated tyrosine have been assigned (36). No evidence for tyrosine
coordination to Fe(II) was found. Saturation transfer and temperature dependence
studies of the 2,6-H's suggest that the ferric-coordinated tyrosine undergoes 180°
flipping, an interesting result for metal-coordinated tyrosine (36). Solvent-
exchangeable resonances with appropriate chemical shifts further suggest that histidine is coordinated to each iron of the reduced center. Both the reduced values
and temperature dependence of the pink protein's isotropic shifts can be explained
by weak (J $\leq$ 20 cm^{-1}) antiferromagnetic coupling between its pair of iron atoms.
This value agrees with that deduced from EPR spectral intensity measurements (36).
Evans susceptibility measurements of pink and purple uteroferrin show that the
coupling between irons of the oxidized center is much stronger than for the reduced
center. The data give J $\gtrsim$ 80cm^{-1}, a value that is consistent with a μ-oxo bridge
structure for the purple protein.

2.8 Effects of Perturbants

The unusual spin-coupled binuclear iron center of uteroferrin is sensitive to a
variety of perturbants (8,13,15). Orthophosphate, even in the absence of detectable
oxygen, forces the pink protein to its purple (oxidized) EPR-silent state (15), a

finding that implicates an endogenous ligand or group as an electron acceptor. Pyrophosphate and arsenate, under aerobic conditions, produce similar effects, suggesting that all of these tetrahedral anions share a common inhibitory mechanism promoting reoxidation of the pink protein's ferrous iron.   In contrast, molybdate (Fig. 1), another potent competitive inhibitor, quantitatively converts pink utero-ferrin's initially rhombic signal into an axial one that remains invariant to subsequent additions of phosphate.   The substantial decrease in average g-value of the axial signal (cf. 1.74 to 1.68) and a sizable reduction in the value of the exchange coupling constant (J decreases from 14 to 9 cm^{-1}) point to a change in the ligand structure of at least one of the protein's two iron atoms.   Furthermore, the extinguishing of phosphatase activity by molybdate would seem to indicate that molybolate blocks access to the protein's phosphate binding site(s).   Vanadate, like phosphate, compels the pink protein to its oxidized EPR-silent state, but itself accepts an electron from the ferrous ion yielding the vanadyl (VO^{2+}) cation.   Remarkably, however, the protein retains its pink color (λ_{max} = 520 nm) demonstrating a clear dissociation between color and oxidation state.   Guanidine causes a sizeable red shift in the pink protein's absorption maximum without any loss in the intensity of the g˙ = 1.74 EPR signal, which does, however, broaden considerably.   This demonstrates dissociation of color and oxidation state in a way complementary to that of vanadate.

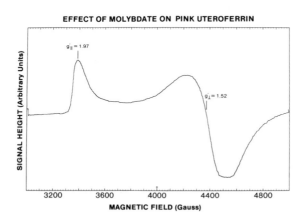

EFFECT OF MOLYBDATE ON PINK UTEROFERRIN

$g_{\parallel}$ = 1.97

$g_{\perp}$ = 1.52

SIGNAL HEIGHT (Arbitrary Units)

MAGNETIC FIELD (Gauss)

3200   3600   4000   4400   4800

Fig. 1.   X-band EPR spectrum of molybdate-treated pink uteroferrin at 9 K.

3.   Proposed Model of the Metal-Binding Site

A possible structure of uteroferrin's binuclear iron center, rationalizing all available observations, may be adduced (Fig. 2).   Highlights of the model are presented below with the main sources of relevant evidence in parentheses.

Uteroferrin's pair of specifically bound iron atoms is sequestered in a spin-coupled binuclear iron center (EPR, susceptibility,[1] H–NMR and Mossbauer). Both irons of the fully oxidized purple protein are high-spin ferric, with their spins antiferromagnetically coupled to yield an S = 0 ground state (Mossbauer, EPR, susceptibility, ^{1}H–NMR). Reversible one-electron reduction produces the pink active form of the enzyme with the spins of its irons, now present as an Fe(II) – Fe(III) pair, coupled to form an S = 1/2 EPR-active ground state (EPR, susceptibility, Mossbauer, ^{1}H–NMR). By analogy to methemerythrins (8,38) and model compounds (43–45), one presumes that the strong coupling between the ferric ions of purple utero-ferrin proceeds via a superexchange pathway through a μ-oxo bridge (^{1}H–NMR and CD). It is likely that two tyrosines are coordinated to a single iron, namely the one that remains ferric following reduction (Raman, CD, optical ^{1}H–NMR, perturbant studies, optical absorption of Fe–Zn hybrids). Thus, only one of uteroferrin's two irons is chromophoric. During redox-induced color changes the chromophoric iron's colorless partner cycles between its ferrous and ferric oxidation states (Mossbauer, optical absorption, Raman). At least one nitrogen-containing ligand, most likely histidine, is coordinated to each iron (^{1}H–NMR, electron spin-echo). The identity of any other iron ligand is unknown. However, covalent coordination by sulfur, as is proposed to occur in the manganese-containing violet acid phosphatases (35), can be ruled out by Mossbauer data. Preliminary EXAFS data for purple uteroferrin also argue against sulfur coordination (46).

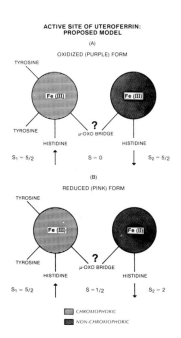

Fig. 2. Possible model of the metal-binding site in uteroferrin.

4. Speculations and Conjectures

Uteroferrin´s phosphatase and reversible iron-binding activities, both of which appear to be modulated by the redox and iron-exchange capabilities of its environmental constituents, raise the intriguing possibility that this unusual protein may serve the fetal pig in more than one way. Thus, as a redox-sensitive phosphoprotein phosphatase, uteroferrin could regulate protein synthesis and metabolism within the cell. On the other hand, as a bearer of a redox-sensitive two-iron center, in which the stability of the iron-protein bond depends on its redox state, uteroferrin could supply iron to the fetal liver or other sites of active hematopoiesis in response to changes in metabolic activity. However, in light of the lack of conclusive evidence for either of these possibilities, a definitive statement of uteroferrin´s function must await further study.

ACKNOWLEDGMENT

This work was supported, in part, by Grant AM 15056 from the National Institutes of Health.

5. REFERENCES

(1) R. M. Roberts and F. W. Bazer (1980) in Steroid Induced Uterine Proteins (W. Beato, ed) pp. 133-149, Elsevier Scientific Publishing Co., Amsterdam.

(2) B. C. Antanaitis and P. Aisen (1983) Adv. Inorg. Biochem. 5, 111-136.

(3) L. Que Jr. (1983) Coord. Chem. Rev. 50, 73-108.

(4) H. D. Campbell, D. A. Dionysus, D. T. Keough, B. W. Wilson, J. deJersey and B. Zerner (1978) Biochem. Biophys. Res. Commun. 82, 615-620.

(5) J. C. Davis, S. S. Lin and B. A. Averill (1981) Biochemistry 20, 4062-4067.

(6) J. C. Davis and B. A. Averill (1982) Proc. Natl. Acad. Sci. U.S.A. 79, 4623-4627.

(7) B. C. Antanaitis , P. Aisen and H. R. Lilienthal (1983) J. Biol. Chem. 258, 3166-3172.

(8) B. C. Antanaitis and P. Aisen (1983) in <u>Structure</u> <u>and</u> <u>Function</u> <u>of</u> <u>Iron</u> <u>Storage</u> <u>and</u> <u>Transport</u> <u>Proteins</u> (I. Urushzaki, P. Aisen, I. Listowsky and J. Drysdale, eds) pp. 503-511, Elsevier Scientific Publishing Co., Amsterdam.

(9) P. Debrunner, M. P. Hendrich, J. deJersey, D. T. Keough, J. T. Sage and B. Zerner (1983) Biochim. Biophys. Acta 745, 103-106.

(10) B. C. Antanaitis and P. Aisen (1984) J. Biol. Chem. 259, 2066-2069.

(11) D. C. Schlosnagle, E. G. Sander, F. W. Bazer and R. M. Roberts (1976) J. Biol. Chem. 251, 4680-4685.

(12) D. T. Keough, D. A. Dionysus, J. deJersey and B. Zerner (1980) Biochem. Biophys. Res. Commun. 94, 600-605.

(13) D. T. Keough, J. L. Beck, J. deJersey and B. Zerner (1982) Biochem. Biophys. Res. Commun. 108, 1643-1648.

(14) D. C. Schlosnagle, F. W. Bazer, J. C. M. Tsibris and R. M. Roberts (1974) J. Biol. Chem. 249, 7574-7579.

(15) B. C. Antanaitis and P. Aisen (1985) J. Biol. Chem. 260, 751-756.

(16) B. C. Antanaitis, P. Aisen, H. R. Lilienthal, R. M. Roberts and F. W. Bazer (1980) J. Biol. Chem. 255, 11204-11209.

(17) B. C. Antanaitis and P. Aisen (1982) J. Biol. Chem. 257, 5330-5332.

(18) E. G. Krebs and J. A. Beavo (1979) Ann. Rev. Biochem. 48, 925-959.

(19) W. C. Buhi, C. A. Ducsay, F. W. Bazer and R. M. Roberts (1982) J. Biol. Chem. 257, 1712-1723.

(20) R. H. Renegar, F. W. Bazer and R. M. Roberts (1982) Biol. Reprod. 27, 1247-1260.

(21) C. A. Ducsay, W. C. Buhi, F. W. Bazer and R. M. Roberts (1982) Biol. Reprod. 26, 729-743.

(22) G. A. Baumbach, P. T. K. Saunders, F. W. Bazer and R. M. Roberts (1984) Proc. Natl. Acad. Sci. U.S.A. 81, 2985-2989.

(23) M. T. Zavy, F. W. Bazer, D. C. Sharp and C. J. Wilcox, (1979) Biol.
Reprod. 20, 689-698.

(24) K. Paigen (1958) J. Biol. Chem. 233, 388-394.

(25) K. Paigen and S. K. Griffiths (1959) J. Biol. Chem. 234, 299-303.

(26) T. R. Anderson and S. U. Toverud (1982) Calcif. Tissue Int. 34, 54-58.

(27) T. R. Anderson, S. U. Toverud, J. B. Price, D. Hamrick, D. Hogan and
L. Braswell (1982) Archs. Oral Biol. 27, 255-259.

(28) D. B. Robinson and R. H. Glew (1980) J. Biol. Chem. 255, 5864-5870.

(29) K.-W. Lam and L. T. Yam (1977) Clin. Chem. 23, 89-94.

(30) S. Nochumson, J. J. O'Rangers and N. V. Dimitrov (1974) Fed. Proc.,
Fed. Amer. Soc. Exp. Biol. 33, p. 1378.

(31) W. N. Arnold and R. G. Garrison (1979) J. Biol. Chem. 254, 4919-4924.

(32) J. L. Beck, D. T. Keough, J. deJersey and B. Zerner (1984) Biochim.
Biophys. Acta 791, 357-363.

(33) B. P. Gaber, J. P. Sheridan, F. W. Bazer and R. M. Roberts (1979) J.
Biol. Chem. 254, 8340-8342.

(34) B. C. Antanaitis, T. Strekas and P. Aisen (1982) J. Biol. Chem. 257,
3766-3770.

(35) Y. Sugiura, H. Kawabe, H. Tanaka, S. Fujimoto and A. Ohara (1981)
J. Biol. Chem. 256, 10664-10670.

(36) R. B. Lauffer, B. C. Antanaitis, P. Aisen and L. Que Jr. (1983) J.
Biol. 258, 14212-14218.

(37) B. P. Gaber, V. Minkowski and T. G. Spiro (1974) J. Am. Chem. Soc. 96,
6868-6873.

(38) B. M. Sjoberg, T. M. Loehr and J. Sanders-Loehr (1982) Biochem. 21, 96-
102.

(39) R. H. Sands and W. R. Dunham (1975) Q. Rev. Biophys. 7, 443-504.

(40) R. G. Wilkins and P. C. Harrington (1983) Adv. Inorg. Chem. 5, 51-85.

(41) B. M. Sjoberg and A. Graslund (1983) Adv. Inorg. Chem. 5, 87-110.

(42) B. C. Antanaitis, J. Peisach, W. B. Mims and P. Aisen (1985) J. Biol. Chem. 260, 4572-4574.

(43) G. M. Mockler, J. deJersey, C. J. O'Connor and E. Sinn (1983) J. Am. Chem. Soc. 105, 1891-1893.

(44) W. H. Armstrong, A. Spool, G. C. Papaefthymiou, R. B. Frankel and S. J. Lippard (1984) J. Amer. Chem. Soc. 106, 3653-3667.

(45) R. G. Wollmann and D. N. Hendrickson (1977) Inorg. Chem. 16, 723-733.

(46) L. Que Jr., personal communication.

The Importance of Electrostatic Interactions Involving Buried Groups in Determining The Structure and Properties of Metalloproteins

Geoffrey R. Moore[1,2], Fiona A. Leitch[3], Graham W. Pettigrew[3], Neil K. Rogers[2] and Glyn Williams[1,2]

1. The Inorganic Chemistry Laboratory, South Parks Road, Oxford OX1 3QR, U.K.

2. The Laboratory of Molecular Biophysics, The Rex Richards Building, South Parks Road, Oxford OX1 3QU, U.K.

3. Department of Biochemistry, Royal Dick School of Veterinary Studies, Summerhall, Edinburgh EH9 1QH, U.K.

SUMMARY

Long-range electrostatic interactions involving buried charges have been shown to influence the redox potentials of Class I cytochromes c and probably to be involved in coupling the redox state of the iron to the conformational state of the protein. Buried charges may also modulate the protein stability. The strength of these interactions has been shown to be strongly influenced by the solvent, even though the charges are buried. Based on these studies and on a review of published work for copper proteins and non-haem iron proteins, it is concluded that the reactivity of metalloproteins is not controlled solely by events occurring at the metal centre; in some cases long-range electrostatic interactions are also important.

1 INTRODUCTION

In many metalloproteins the metal ions and its immediate ligands are buried and are not accessible to the solvent. Often such proteins are redox proteins and as a result of the burial of their redox centres they carry a buried charge in at least one of their oxidation states. The electrostatic interactions of such charges are of central importance in determining the structure and properties of the protein.

Fig. 1. Electrostatic interactions involving buried charges. A metalloprotein surrounded by water is represented. Electrostatic interactions between the buried metal ion (M^+) and other buried charges ($\leftrightarrow$), buried protein dipoles ($\leftrightarrow$) and surface charges ($\leftrightarrow$) are shown. The pervasive influence of the solvent on the stability of the buried charge and the strength of the various interactions is indicated by $\Longleftrightarrow$. Interactions involving ions in solution may also be important.

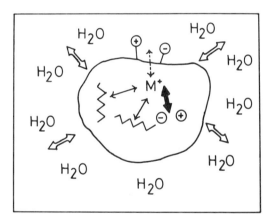

Fig. 1 illustrates some of the types of electrostatic interactions that may help stabilise a buried charge. Though each of these types may be important in a given system they are not all equally easy to detect experimentally. Nor is their theoretical description straightforward. Nevertheless, some progress has been made in characterising electrostatic interactions involving buried charges and in the present paper we report the results of a theoretical and experimental study of such interactions in certain cytochromes c and consider some of their implications for metalloproteins in general. Our approach complements the work of Perutz (1) who described the general importance of electrostatic interactions in proteins.

2 CLASS I CYTOCHROMES c

Class I cytochromes c contain covalently bound haem close to the N-terminus of the protein with histidine and methionine axial ligands (2,3). Various sub-classes are recognisable but most of the Class I cytochromes c have the characteristic fold illustrated in Fig. 2.

Fig. 2. Stereoscopic view of the main-chain and selected side chains of Rhodospirillum rubrum ferricytochrome c_2. The haem is covalently attached to the polypeptide chain by thioether bonds to Cys 14 and Cys 17, and the axial ligands are His 18 and Met 91. The molecule is oriented with the haem propionic acid substituents at the top. Both of these substituents are completely shielded from solvent. The right-hand substituent (HP-7) interacts with the side chains of His 42, Tyr 48 and Trp 62 and the peptide NH's of Ala 41 and His 42. The diagram was constructed from X-ray coordinates (4).

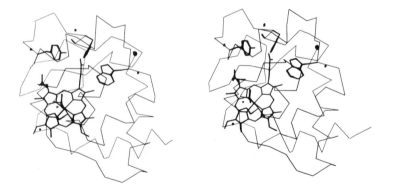

The polypeptide chain is wrapped around the haem so that it is almost entirely buried; in cytochrome c_2 only a hydrophobic edge of the haem is exposed at the surface and the two propionic acid substituents are buried. Mitochondrial cytochrome c has the same general structure with both haem propionates buried (5) but in Chlorobium limicola (f. thiosulfatophilum) cytochrome c_{555} (6) and Pseudomonas aeruginosa cytochrome c_{551} (7) only one of the haem propionates (HP-7) is completely buried. The haem propionates interact with various amino acids including, for the common buried propionate (HP-7) in the proteins listed above, an interaction with a buried positively charged residue. We emphasise this structural feature because buried ion-pairs are not commonly found in globular proteins; for example, in recent surveys (8,9) of 36 proteins it was found that there were only six completely buried ion-pairs and all of these had specific functional roles.

3 REDOX POTENTIALS

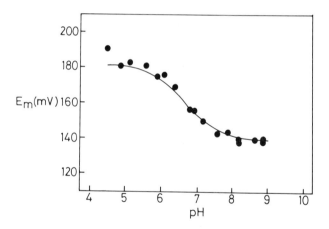

Fig. 3. pH dependence of E_M for C.limicola cytochrome c_{555}
The points are experimental data and the solid line is a theoretical curve calculated assuming there are two pK_a's; one in the oxidised protein (pK_o) of 6.3 and one in the reduced protein (pK_r) of 7.0. These data and analysis were obtained by procedures described elsewhere (12,13).

The redox potentials of the class I cytochromes c vary from ~60mV to 450mV (2, 10 and references therein). Many explanations have been advanced to account for this variation but it is now clear that no single mechanism is responsible (see 10 and references therein). Inorganic chemists have often emphasised bonding interactions at the redox centre (such as hydrogen-bonding and steric interactions affecting metal ligand donor/acceptor properties) but, as Kassner (11) first pointed out, the nature of the haem environment is also important. The main environmental effects are the electrostatic interactions described in Fig. 1. An illustration of the role of electrostatic interactions in determining the level of a redox potential is the pH dependence of the midpoint redox potential (E_M) exhibited by cytochrome $\underline{c}_{555}$(Fig. 3).

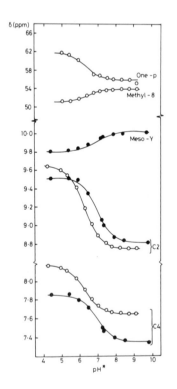

Fig. 4. NMR chemical shifts of selected resonances of C.limicola cytochrome $\underline{c}_{555}$ ● and O are experimental data for the reduced and oxidized proteins respectively. The solid lines are theoretical curves for pK_r=7.0 and pK_o=6.3 respectively. The resonance assignments were obtained from this work or from reference 14, and the experimental procedure has been described elsewhere (13,15). The correspondence in pK_a's for His 37 (C-2 & C-4) and HP-7 (the latter identified from the shifts of haem resonances) together with the E_M analysis showing that the pK_a's are one proton ionisations, identifies them as being of the type (13):

NMR measurements (Fig. 4) identify the ionisations to be composite ionisations involving HP-7 and the interacting His 37. The redox state dependence of the pK_a, and concomitant pH dependence of E_M, results from an electrostatic interaction in the ferric protein between the buried positive charge on the ferrihaem macrocycle and the buried negative charge on the propionate. This interaction is not present in the reduced protein when the ferrohaem macrocycle is uncharged; therefore the propionate is destabilised by reduction of the haem and its pK_a is raised correspondingly.

The redox-state dependent ionisation of HP-7 has also been observed in other cytochromes where the buried propionate interacts with a histidine – e.g. P.stutzeri cytochrome c_{551} (13) and R.rubrum cytochrome c_2 (12 and Fig. 2) – an arginine – e.g. P.aeruginosa cytochrome $c551$ (13) – and in one case where the propionate apparently does not interact with a buried positively charged side chain, Rhodomicrobium vannielii cytochrome c_2 (15).

4 MODELLING ELECTROSTATIC INTERACTIONS

The energy of interaction is given by Coulomb's law,

$$E = \frac{N(q_1 \cdot q_2)}{4\pi\varepsilon_0 \varepsilon_{eff} \cdot r} \quad Jmol^{-1}$$

where $(q_1 \cdot q_2)$ is the charge product, r is the distance between the charges, N is Avogadro's number, ε_{eff} is the effective dielectric constant and ε_0 is the permittivity of free space.

The major difficulty in applying this equation is assigning a value to ε_{eff}. Indeed, the use of a macroscopic concept, such as a dielectric constant, on the molecular level is questionable and various attempts have been made to overcome this problem (see 16, 17 and references therein). The approach we have used to calculate the energy of interaction between the Fe(III) and HP-7 of P.aeruginosa cytochrome $c551$ assigns a uniform dielectric constant of 3.5 to the protein interior and a uniform dielectric constant of 80 to the surrounding solvent (18). If the solvent is ignored, and with the charge location given by the X-ray structure, an interaction potential of 500mV is calculated; much larger than the observed potential of 65mV. If the solvent dielectric response and structure of the protein determined by X-ray crystallography are taken into account then a calculation using the procedure of Warwicker and Watson (19) gives an interaction potential of 90mV (18); in reasonable agreement with the observed potential. 90mV corresponds to an effective dielectric of 19.5 (eqn.1). The main reason for the difference between the calculations is that the charges experience a reaction field from the solvent (18). This is an induced field of the solvent dipoles that opposes the protein field and reduces the observed interaction energy. Thus although the charges are buried they still experience a significant interaction with the solvent. The calculation given above is relatively straightforward because the strength of the charge-charge interaction can be obtained from the pH dependence of E_M assuming that there are negligibly small conformational changes accompanying the ionisations (13). The remaining interactions of Fig. 1 will then be constant over the pH range of interest.

5 ISOENERGETIC ELECTRON TRANSFER

The observations of the previous sections suggest the burial of charged groups may play a role in the attainment of rapid electron transfer. Classical considerations indicate that electron transfer takes place in an activated complex in which the donor and acceptor centres have the same redox potential (20). The formation of complexes of cytochrome c involves complementary charge interactions between the two protein surfaces; mitochondrial cytochrome c is highly positively charged and its natural reaction partners are negatively charged (21 and references therein). In a modelling study, Salemme (22) proposed the structure of the cytochrome c: cytochrome b_5 complex, some of the features of which are illustrated in Fig. 5.

The positively charged surface of cytochrome c was matched with the negatively charged surface of cytochrome b_5 and the proteins docked together so that their redox centres were relatively close. In the model, H_2O is excluded from the protein interface so that the interprotein charge pairs have restricted solvent accessibility. In such a case the redox potentials of the redox centres may be altered by the newly created electrostatic interaction, so facilitating their attainment of the isoenergetic state.   The redox potentials may also be altered by conformational

changes and by other electrostatic interactions, such as those accompanying changes

in solvent accessibility and degree of burial of the redox centres.

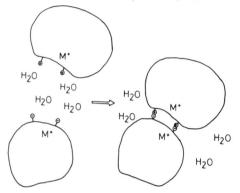

Fig. 5.   Electrostatic interactions between proteins in a complex

6 CONFORMATIONAL CHANGES

The change in oxidation state of mitochondrial cytochrome c is accompanied by a

conformational change.   X-ray analyses (5) show that the iron coordination sphere is

little affected by the redox state change although many regions of the structure are

perturbed.   Figure 6 summarises the sensitive regions detected by solution state NMR

(23) and X-ray studies (5).   Although a precise atomic model is not yet available,

it is clear that one of the most sensitive regions is around the haem propionates.

This, together with data for bacterial cytochromes (Table 1), has led to the

proposal (24) that the removal of the electrostatic interaction Fe(III)---HP-7 in

the reduced protein is partly responsible for triggering the conformation change.

Table 1.   Redox-state conformational changes of Class I cytochromes c.

Protein	Crystal evidence of conformation change	Crystal pH	Haem propionate pKa's	
			HP-6	HP-7
Mitochondrial c	Yes	7.5	>9	<4.5
R.rubrum c2	No	6.0	>9	6.2(ox),7.0(red)
P.aeruginosa c551	No	5.7	<4.5	6.2(ox),7.3(red)

(see 10, 24 and references therein)

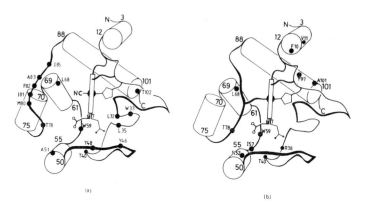

Fig. 6. Redox-state conformational change of tuna cytochrome c (b) and conformational differences between ferricytochrome c and cyanoferricytochrome c (a). The cylinders represent α-helices and ● indicate groups which are conformationally sensitive.

In this model, in order to stabilise the buried negative charge on HP-7 in the reduced protein, a small structural rearrangement occurs around it. This is then transmitted to other parts of the protein, perhaps via movement of the protein α-helices. X-ray analyses of the bacterial proteins in Table 1 do not reveal such a conformation change and this may be because the analyses were carried out at a pH where the HP-7 groups were largely unionised. Small differences in helical packing, especially for the small cytochrome c_{551}, may also be important.

As a test of the hypothesis we are engaged in an NMR study of derivatives of cytochrome c with which we hope to separate the electrostatic contributions to the conformation change from the steric effects resulting from changes at the metal centre itself. Preliminary results for tuna cyanoferricytochrome c (in which the Met ligand is displaced by CN^-) are summarised in Fig. 6. The derivative has the general cytochrome fold in most regions of the structure although the loop of residues from 75–85 is displaced. Regions of the structure sensitive to the redox-state change are also sensitive to the modification although it appears that the latter changes do not exactly mirror the redox-state changes, even though the haem macrocycle is uncharged in cyanoferricytochrome c. This may be because the charge-relay system is less important than suggested here or because the displacement of Met 80 and Thr 78 (which is hydrogen bonded to HP-6 in the native protein) affects the nature of the conformation change. An indication that the latter may be the case is obtained from the observation that displacement of the Met ligand of Pseudomonas ferricytochrome c_{551} by CN^- lowers the pK_a of HP-7 to below 5.7, in contrast to the effect of reduction which raises the pK_a to 7.3. In this case HP-7 is more susceptible to structural changes than to the removal of the interaction with the Fe(III) charge, probably because the helix bearing Arg 47 which interacts with HP-7, is moved by the displacement of the Met ligand.

7. PROTEIN STABILITY

Mitochondrial ferrocytochrome c is more stable than ferricytochrome c (25 and references therein) but, as with conformational changes, there is great difficulty in partitioning the observed stability difference between its electrostatic and non-electrostatic components. The Fe-S bond of ferrocytochrome c is stronger than the Fe-S bond of ferricytochrome c (26), and this is an important factor, but conformational changes away from the redox centre do not appear to be influential in determining the stability difference. Calculations suggest that the charge difference between ferricytochrome c and ferrocytochrome c may be important.

Calculations of the contribution to the stability of a protein arising from the energy of a buried charge are complicated by the need to determine the corresponding energy term in the denatured state. We have considered only the effect of the solvent reaction field on the self-energy of the charge and estimated its contribution to the protein stabilisation energy by comparing a buried charge within a sphere of 15Å radius (with the charge 7Å from the sphere centre - an approximate model of cytochrome c in H_2O) with a charge in the centre of a sphere of 5Å radius (a model for a hypothetical denatured state). The method of images was used for these calculations (see 16 and references therein). The calculated energy of 20 kJ mol^{-1} is appreciably higher than the observed 4-5 kJ mol^{-1} difference between the stabilities of ferri and ferrocytochrome c (25), a reflection of the approximations in the calculations, but it does indicate that the presence of a buried charge may have a significant destabilising effect on the ferricytochrome c.

8. GENERAL IMPLICATIONS FOR METALLOPROTEINS

It has been demonstrated experimentally that buried charges are a common feature of Class I cytochromes c and that electrostatic interactions involving these charges help control the level of the redox potential, couple proton transfer to electron transfer in some cases and, may, for some cytochromes, couple the protein conformational state to its redox state. They may also be important in modulating the protein stability and in determining properties of the activated electron transfer complex. It has also been shown that electrostatic interaction with the solvent may reduce the energy of interaction between buried charges, giving rise to a relatively high effective dielectric within the protein.

Amongst redox proteins there are a number of examples of structures which contain buried charges, including the blue copper proteins, such as azurin in which the copper is buried (27), some Fe/S proteins, such as HIPIP in which the metal cluster is buried (28), and bovine superoxide dismutase in which there are two buried carboxylates close to the buried metal ions (9,29). None of these examples is as well-characterised as the cytochromes considered above, but it is known that the redox potentials of azurin (30,31) and HIPIP (32) are pH dependent over the range 5-9 in an analogous way to that shown in Fig.3 with, in the latter case (33), NMR evidence showing that electrostatic interaction with a parly buried histidine is a contributing factor. The azurin case is less clear and both electrostatic interactions and conformation changes may be important (31,34).

As other types of metalloproteins are characterised we expect more such examples to be discovered. However, it is already clear that the reactivity of metalloproteins is not controlled solely by events occuring at the metal centre, and that long-range electrostatic interactions are also important.

9. REFERENCES

1.   M.F. Perutz, Science __201__ (1978) 1187-1191.

2.   R.P. Ambler in A.B. Robinson & N.O. Kaplan (ed.). From Cyclotrons to Cytochromes, Academic Press, New York (1980) 263-279.

3. T.E. Meyer & M.D. Kamen, Adv. Prot. Chem. 35 (1982) 105-212.

4. G.E. Bhatia, B.C. Finzel & J. Kraut, Coordinates deposited with the protein data bank, Brookhaven USA (1984).

5. T. Takano & R.E. Dickerson, J. Mol. Biol. 153 (1981) 79-115.

6. F.R. Salemme, Ann. Rev. Biochem. 46 (1977) 299-329.

7. Y. Matsuura, T. Takano & R.E. Dickerson, J. Mol. Biol. 156 (1982) 389-409.

8. D.J. Barlow & J.M. Thornton, J. Mol. Biol. 168 (1983) 867-885.

9. A.A. Rashin & B. Honig, J. Mol. Biol. 173 (1984) 515-521

10. G.R. Moore & G.W. Pettigrew, The Structures and Functions of Cytochromes c, Springer Verlag, New York (1985) in preparation.

11. R.J. Kasssner, J. Am. Chem. Soc. 95 (1973) 2674-2677

12. G.W. Pettigrew, T.E. Meyer, R.G. Bartsch & M.D. Kamen, Biochim. Biophys. Acta, 430 (1975) 197-208.

13. F.A. Leitch, G.R. Moore & G.W. Pettigrew, Biochem. 23 (1984) 1831-1838

14. H. Senn, M.A. Cusanovich & K. Wuthrich, Biochim. Biophys. Acta, 785 (1984) 46-53.

15. G.R. Moore, D.E. Harris, F.A. Leitch & G.W. Pettigrew, Biochim. Biophys. Acta, 764 (1984) 331-342

16. N.K. Rogers & M.J.E. Sternberg, J. Mol. Biol. 174 (1984) 527-742

17. A. Warshel & S.T. Russell, Quart. Rev. Biophysics, 17 (1984) 283-422

18. N.K. Rogers, G.R. Moore & M.J.E Sternberg, J. Mol. Biol. 182 (1985) 613-616

19. J. Warwicker & H.C. Watson, J. Mol. Biol. 157 (1982) 671-679

20. R.A. Marcus, Ann. Rev. Phys. Chem. 15 (1964) 155-196.

21. E. Margoliash & H.R. Bosshard, TIBS 8 (1983) 316-320

22. F.R. Salemme, J. Mol. Biol. 102 (1976) 563-568

23. G. Williams, N.J. Clayden, G.R. Moore & R.J.P. Williams J. Mol. Biol. (1985) in press.

24. G.R. Moore, FEBS Letters 161 (1983) 171-175

25. G. McLendon & M. Smith, J. Biol. Chem. 253 (1978) 4004-4008

26. H.A. Harbury et.al. Proc. Natl. Acad. Sci. USA 54 (1965) 1658-1664

27. E.T. Adman & L.H. Jensen, Isr. J. Chem. 21 (1981) 8-12

28. C.W. Carter Jr. et.al, J. Biol. Chem. 249 (1974) 4212-4225

29. J.A. Tainer, E.D. Getzoff, K.M. Beem, J.S. Richardson & D.C. Richardson, J. Mol. Biol. 160 (1982) 181-217.

30. M.C. Silvestrini, M. Brunori, M.T. Wilson & V.M. Darley-Usmar, J. Inorg. Biochem. 14 (1981) 327-338

31. G.W. Pettigrew, F.A. Leitch & G.R. Moore, Biochim. Biophys. Acta. 725 (1983) 409-416

32. I.A. Mizrahi, F.E. Wood & M.A. Cusanovich, Biochem. 15 (1976) 343-348.

33. D.G. Nettesheim, T.E. Meyer, B.A. Feinberg & J.D. Otvos, J. Biol. Chem. 258 (1983) 8235-8239

34. E.T. Adman, G.W. Canters, H.A.O. Hill & N.A. Kitchen, FEBS Letters 143 (1982) 287-292

ACKNOWLEDGEMENTS

We thank the SERC and MRC for financial support, Prof. Sir D.C. Phillips F.R.S. and Prof. R.J.P. Williams F.R.S. for their encouragement and advice, and Mr. P. McLaughlin for help with the computer-graphics.

New Aspects of Mössbauer Spectroscopy

E. Bill, A.X. Trautwein, H. Winkler

Physik, Medizinische Universität, 2400 Lübeck 1, W-Germany

H. Toftlund

Chemistry, University, 4230 Odense M, Denmark

SUMMARY

From the variety of new aspects of Mössbauer spectroscopy, such as field strength dependent spin-Hamiltonian analysis, study of dynamical processes, Rayleigh scattering using Mössbauer radiation, development of Synchrotron radiation as Mössbauer source, Mössbauer scattering, and theoretical studies of Mössbauer parameters using molecular orbital theory, we describe the first two items in more detail.

1 INTRODUCTION

Mössbauer spectroscopy has become a well established tool in biosciences. Most of the biochemical, bioinorganic and biophysical applications deal with ^{57}Fe Mössbauer absorption experiments. The purpose of such experiments is to derive via the interpretation of isomer shifts, quadrupole splittings and magnetic hyperfine interactions an understanding of the electronic structure and the chemical structure-function relation of the compounds under study. During the recent years many methodical aspects of Mössbauer spectroscopy have been further developed and provide us with new applications, such as:

(i)   Determination of metal coordination from spin-Hamiltonian analysis.

(ii) Study of dynamical processes.

(iii) Rayleigh scattering using Mössbauer radiation. This method makes it possible to investigate gross molecular dynamics even in systems which do not contain any Mössbauer isotope (1,2)

(iv) Development of Synchrotron radiation as Mössbauer source. Most recently experiments were successful in discriminating the ^{57}Fe 14.4 KeV Mössbauer resonance line ($\Gamma = 10^{-8}$ eV) from the "white" Synchrotron radiation beam (3). Thus it might soon be possible to perform novel dynamical Mössbauer studies of chemical reactions.

(v)   Mössbauer scattering for complete three-dimensional structure analysis of iron proteins. This is a competitive tool with X-ray structure analysis. It avoids the method of multiple isomorphous replacement by applying the ^{57}Fe nucleus as heavy reference scatterer. Experiments on MbCO crystals have already been performed and described (4,5).

(vi) Combined Mössbauer and molecular orbital investigations. Applications dealing with iron sulfur clusters are presented in this book (6).

In the present paper we describe in more detail our own contributions concerning (i) and (ii).

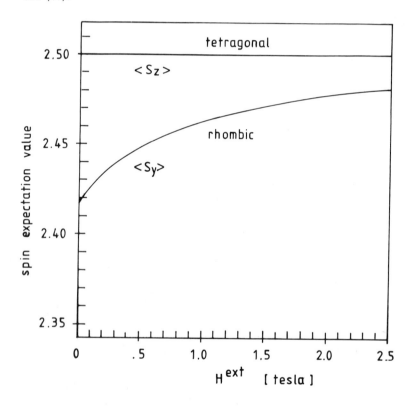

Fig. 1. Spin expectation values in the easy direction of magnetization for the lowest Kramers doublets of tetragonal (D=-1.2 cm^{-1}, E/D=0.05) and rhombic (D=0.9 cm^{-1}, E/D=0.33) iron (S=5/2) as a function of field strength.

2 ANALYSIS OF FERRIC HIGH-SPIN IRON IN SITES WITH RHOMBIC AND TETRAGONAL POINT SYMMETRY

Ferric high-spin iron in sites with tetragonal (E/D = 0, D<0) and rhombic (E/D = 0.33, D>0) point-symmetry provides low-lying Kramers doublets with highly anisotropic g-tensors. The electronic ground states of both sites yield Mössbauer spectra, which are magnetically well resolved, but which do not depend on the orientation of applied magnetic fields. If in addition the identification of excited Kramers doublets is prevented because of relaxation effects it is practically impossible to distinguish rhombic and tetragonal sites in the low-field limit. We therefore tested a method to identify these sites via the field strength dependency of their low-temperature Mössbauer spectra. For the easy direction of magnetization the spin-Hamiltonian of the electronic ground state can be written in the tetragonal case (D<0) as $H = D[S_z^2 - 1/3\ S(S+1)] + g\ \beta\ H^{ext}\ S_z$ and in the rhombic case (D>0) as $H = D\ 2/3(S_z^2 - S_y^2) + g\ \beta\ H^{ext}\ S_y$. The spin expectation value in the tetragonal case will be $\langle S_z \rangle = -5/2$, independent of the strength of the external field H^{ext}. In the

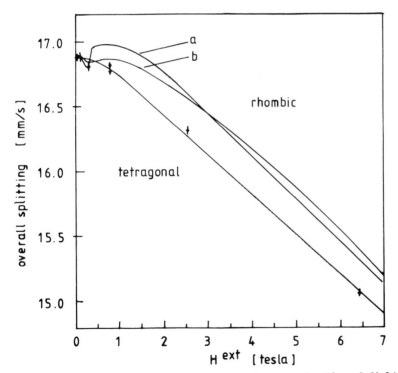

Fig. 2. Overall splitting of Mössbauer spectra as a function of field strength.
Tetragonal case: D=-1.2 cm^{-1}, E/D=0.05, ΔE_Q=-0.8 mm s^{-1}, η=0.4, $V_{\hat{z}\hat{z}} \perp z$, $A/g_n\beta_n$=(-21.5, -21.5, -21.1) Tesla.
Rhombic case: E/D=0.33, ΔE_Q=-0.8 mm s^{-1}, η=0.4, $A/g_n\beta_n$=(-21.0, -21.9, -21.0) Tesla, (a) D=0.6 cm^{-1}, (b) D=1.2 cm^{-1}.

rhombic case within the low-field limit ($g\beta H \ll D$) the expectation value $<S_y>$ will be less than 5/2 because of spin-mixing: $\vec{<S>} = (0.22, 2.42, 0.15)$. Increasing H^{ext} leads to a "strengthening of the quantization axis" and to saturation behavior of $<S_y>$ (Fig. 1). The overall splitting of the relevant low-temperature Mössbauer spectra (which is proportional to the hyperfine field, $\vec{H}^{hf} = \vec{H}^{ext} - \bar{\bar{A}} \vec{<S>}/g_n\beta_n$ is correspondingly affected by $\vec{<S>}$.

We have applied this method to investigate the oxidized cofactor iron of Putidamonooxin (7,8). Plotting the measured overall splitting (at 4.2 K) versus H^{ext} and comparing these experimental data with the calculated $H^{hf} - H^{ext}$ dependency clearly indicates that we are dealing with a tetragonal ferric high-spin species (Fig. 2).

3 STUDIES OF DYNAMICAL PROCESSES

By far the most intensely studied dynamical process is the superparamagnetism of small magnetically ordered particles. Its observation rests on the magnetic hyperfine coupling between nucleus and electrons. Rearrangements of ligands or parts of a molecule, however, are usually accompanied by alterations of the electric quadrupole interaction.

While superparamagnetism can be modelled by letting a magnetic field flip from positive to negative, a process which maintains the axis of quantization, variations of the electric field gradient (efg) tensor as mediator of the electric quadrupole coupling generally affect not only the magnitude including the sign but more importantly also the orientation of the efg. This makes the description in terms of a relaxation model more complicated. On the other hand more information is buried in the spectroscopic data.

In order to avoid the introduction of too many free parameters in a simulation procedure one has to try a reasonable guess about the behavior of the efg tensor and then to demonstrate its consistency with the experimental findings. We will discuss this on hand of an example, which exhibits spin-crossover dynamics, and which may serve also as model compound for heme proteins. (Additional examples, dealing with low-temperature molecular dynamics, have been described by us recently elsewhere (9,10).

Besides oxygenation and carboxylation of myoglobin and hemoglobin also electron transfer reactions of heme proteins are often associated with a change of the spin state of iron from high-spin to low-spin and vice versa. Investigating this transition may yield information about how the spin-crossover mechanism determines the reaction rate. Fe(II) complexes with hexadentate ligands of the type given in Fig. 3 may serve as appropriate models, because they exhibit spin-crossover beha-

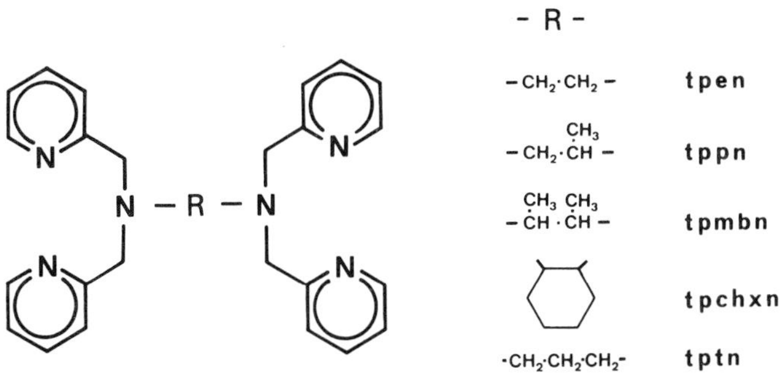

Fig. 3. The tetrakis (2-pyridyl-methyl)-R ligand type and some examples for R.

vior in the temperature range $100K \leq T \leq 400K$ as identified by magnetic susceptibility measurements (11). We have performed experimental Mössbauer studies on
$Fe_{0.1}Zn_{0.9}(tpchxn)(ClO_4)_2 \cdot nH_2O$ (tpchxn = tetrakis(2-pyridyl-methyl)-trans-1,2-cy-
clohexadiamine), where the transition rates are expected to fall into the time
window of ^{57}Fe Mössbauer spectroscopy because according to Gütlich (12) dilution
of ferrous spin-crossover systems with Zn causes in general an enhancement by
weakening the cooperative interaction strength.

In Fig. 4 some representative Mössbauer spectra are displayed. At 100K clearly two
doublets can be distinguished:
(1) with $\Delta E_Q = 0.47$ mms^{-1} and $\delta^* = 0.46$ mms^{-1} from low-spin Fe(II),
(2) with $\Delta E_Q = 3.63$ mms^{-1} and $\delta^* = 1.00$ mms^{-1} from high-spin Fe(II).
At 200K an additional line is discernible which may be attributed to a third doublet
(3) with $\Delta E_Q = 1.53$ mms^{-1} and $\delta^* = 0.93$ mms^{-1}. (*=rel. to α-Fe).

It is tempting to assume that the $S=2 \rightleftarrows S=0$ transition might proceed via an intermediate triplet state. However, doublet 3 does not qualify for this intermediate because of its rather large isomer shift.

At elevated temperatures the lines broaden and tend to merge which is characteristic for relaxation processes. For a quantitative analysis in terms of an appropriate model it is necessary to know the relative orientations of the efg's involved since this information cannot be extracted uniquely from the experimental
data. We have performed therefore molecular orbital calculations for the known
geometry of the low-spin species and for assumed geometries of the two high-spin
species to get independent information about the Euler angles between the efg's.
It turned out that the principal-axes systems coincide in all three cases, but
that the major component $V_{\tilde{z}\tilde{z}}$ of the efg tensor is positive in the low-spin species,

negative in the high-spin species represented by doublet 2, and again positive but rotated by 90° in the species corresponding to doublet 3. Furtheron there is considerable axial asymmetry in all three cases.

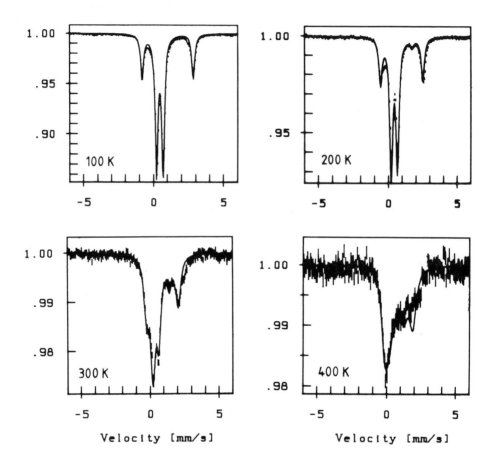

Fig. 4. Mössbauer spectra of $Fe_{0.1}Zn_{0.9}(tpchxn)(ClO_4)_2$ at four different temperatures. The solid lines are simulations with the parameters given in Table I.

The high-temperature spectra have been analysed in terms of the generalized stochastic theory of lineshape commonly referred to Blume (13,14). The solid lines in Fig. 4 correspond to the optimal simulations. The resulting values for the relevant parameters are given in Table I.

Table I: Relaxation parameters used for the simulations in Fig. 4 (uncertainty is of the order of 10%). p_{LS} and p_{HS} denote occupation probabilities of the low-spin and high-spin states, respectively, and W represents transition probabilities.

T[K]	p_{LS}	p_{HSI}	p_{HSII}	W(LS⇄HSI) [MHz]	W(LS⇄HSII) [MHz]	W(HSI⇄HSII) [MHz]
100	0.75	0.25	0	0	0	0
200	0.69	0.26	0.05	0.2	.2	0
300	0.50	0.35	0.15	1.4	0.5	0.2
400	0.18	0.50	0.32	3.2	1.8	1.8

The compound studied here is one of the rare if not the only case up till now where the rates for spin-crossover have been shifted successfully into the Mössbauer time window so that the underlying mechanism can be investigated in detail.

4 ACKNOWLEDGEMENTS

We want to thank Deutsche Forschungsgemeinschaft and Stiftung Volkswagenwerk for their support of this work.

5 REFERENCES

(1) Y.F. Krupyanskii, F. Parak, V.I. Goldanskij, R.L. Mössbauer, E. Gombman, H. Engelmann, I.P. Suzdalev, Z. Naturforsch., 37c, 57 (1982).

(2) F. Parak, A.X. Trautwein, in A.G. Schneck, C. Paul (Eds.), Brussels Hemoglobin Symposium, Edition de L'Université de Bruxelles, 1984, p. 299.

(3) E. Gerdau, R. Rüffer, H. Winkler, W. Tolksdorf, C.P. Klages, J.P. Hannon, Phys. Rev. Lett. 54, 835 (1985)

(4) F. Parak, R.L. Mössbauer, W. Hoppe, U.F. Thomanek, D. Bade, J. de Physique Colloq. C6, 37, C6-703 (1976).

(5) R.L. Mössbauer, F. Parak, W. Hoppe, in U. Gonser (Ed.), Topics in Current Physics, Vol. 25, Springer-Verlag, Heidelberg, 1981, p. 5.

(6) R. Bläs, E. Bill, S. Lauer, A.X. Trautwein, H. Winkler, M. Grodzicki, A. Kostikas (this volume).

(7) E. Bill, F.-H. Bernhardt, A.X. Trautwein, H. Winkler, Eur. J. Biochem. 147, 177 (1985).

(8) E. Bill, PhD-thesis, Universität des Saarlandes, Saarbrücken (1985).

(9) E. Bill, N. Blaes, K.F. Fischer, U. Gonser, K.H. Pauly, R. Preston, F. Seel, R. Staab, A.X. Trautwein, Z. Naturforsch., 39b, 333 (1984).

(10) R. Montiel-Montoya, E. Bill, A.X. Trautwein, H. Winkler, L. Ricard, M. Schappacher, R. Weiss, Rev. Port. Quim. 27, 278 (1985).

(11) H. Toftlund, S. Yde-Andersen, Acta Chem. Scand. A35, 575 (1981).

(12) P. Gütlich, in J.G. Stevens, G.K. Shenoy (Eds.), Mössbauer Spectroscopy and Its Chemical Applications, ACS, Washington, 1981, p. 405.

(13) M. Blume, Phys. Rev. 174, 351 (1968).

(14) H. Winkler, Habilitationsschrift, Hamburg (1983).

Molecular Orbital Theory and Mössbauer Spectroscopy: Electronic Structure Studies of Bioinorganic Iron Sulfur Clusters

R. Bläs, E. Bill, S. Lauer, A.X. Trautwein, H. Winkler

Physik, Medizinische Universität , 2400 Lübeck 1, W-Germany

M. Grodzicki

Theoretische Physik, Universität, 2000 Hamburg 36, W-Germany

A. Kostikas

Nuclear Research Center "Demokritos", Aghia Paraskevi, Greece

SUMMARY

The electronic structure of mononuclear, binuclear, and cubane iron sulfur clusters is derived from Iterative Extended Hückel and from Self Consistent Charge $X\alpha$ Molecular Orbital Calculations. Spin-coupling constants are estimated applying Noodleman's "broken spin-symmetry" concept. From the electronic structure molecular properties have been evaluated, such as electron density and electric field gradient at the iron nucleus, fine structure parameters D, E and the g-tensor, and the magnetic hyperfine coupling tensor. The calculated data are compared with parameters which were obtained from single-crystal Mössbauer experiments or from the spin-Hamiltonian analysis of magnetic Mössbauer measurements. From our investigation we conclude that the study of structural, spectroscopic and electronic properties of biomolecules (in the present case iron sulfur proteins) benefits by the combined theoretical and experimental investigation of corresponding bioinorganic model clusters.

1 INTRODUCTION

The structure and electronic properties of active centers in the
iron-sulfur redox proteins have been investigated extensively by
numerous spectroscopic methods (1). A great deal of information about
active centers in iron-sulfur proteins has also been obtained by
parallel studies of synthetic analogs (where the cysteinyl residues
are simulated by thiolate ligands (2-9)). These studies have provided
a large amount of experimental data, which motivated us to start
theoretical investigations of the electronic structure of these
complexes in order to derive a consistent picture of structural,
spectroscopic, and electronic properties.

Our molecular orbital (MO) calculations on mononuclear Fe-S complexes
with a $Fe^{II}S_4$ core and on binuclear Fe-Mo-S complexes containing the
$Fe^{II}S_2Mo$ core are based on the semiempirical Iterative Extended Hückel
theory (10,11) (IEHT), followed by a procedure which includes spin-
orbit coupling (12) among the highest occupied iron-like molecular
orbitals. FeS_2Fe clusters, with the two irons being spin-coupled, we
have additionally investigated with a more sophisticated MO-Xα
version, which allows spin-unresticted calculations (13), and which is
based on Noodleman's "broken spin-symmetry" concept (14). From the MO
electronic structure we have derived fine and hyperfine structure
parameters (15-17); they include g-factors, zero-field splittings D
and E, ligand field splitting 10Dq, electron charge density $\rho(o)$,
quadrupole splitting ΔE_Q, sign and orientation of the main component
V_{ZZ} of the electric field gradient (efg) tensor, asymmetry parameter
η, and magnetic hyperfine tensor A.

2 MONONUCLEAR Fe-S CLUSTERS

It has been suggested (18) that the strong similarity between the
electronic ground state of $[Fe(SPh)_4]^{2-}$ and that of the FeS_4 core of
reduced rubredoxin (Rd_{red}) may be due to apparently similar distortions in the Fe-S clusters of the two compounds. In pursuance of this
notion and to obtain information about the effect of different
geometries, we have included in our calculations also (i) the
synthetic complex (18) $[Fe(dts)_2]^{2-}$, although on the basis of the type
of ligands it can not be considered as an analog for the active site
in Rd_{red}, and (ii) the cluster $[Fe(SH)_4]^{2-}$, which has been used by
other workers as a model for rubredoxin (19-21).

The energy sequence of the highest occupied molecular orbitals (HOMO's) of $[Fe(SPh)_4]^{2-}$, $[Fe(dts)_2]^{2-}$ and $[Fe(SH)_4]^{2-}$ is such, that five MO's of mainly iron character lie above the doubly occupied MO's with mainly ligand character. The relatively narrow energy spacings between the five "iron-like orbitals" favour a spin of 2 according to Hund's first rule. This result is in qualitative agreement with experimental data, which show definitively that the iron in $[Fe(SPh)_4]^{2-}$, in $[Fe(dts)_2]^{2-}$, and in Rd_{red} is in a ferrous high-spin state (18,22) with relatively small energy spacing 10Dq; this requires the consideration of spin-orbit coupling among the five HOMO's. Working out the Boltzmann average of the resulting 25 spin states leads to good agreement between calculated and measured temperature dependences of quadrupole splitting within the temperature range 4.2 K $\leq T \leq$ 300 K for $[Fe(SPh)_4]^{2-}$ and for $[Fe(dts)_2]^{2-}$, respectively (Fig. 1). From inspection of Fig. 1 it is obvious that $[Fe(dts)_2]^{2-}$ exhibits considerable temperature dependence in ΔE_Q; this situation is due to the fact that the energetically low-lying orbital doublet e_g is split by ca. 200 cm^{-1} only, a very rare case for quasi-tetrahedrally

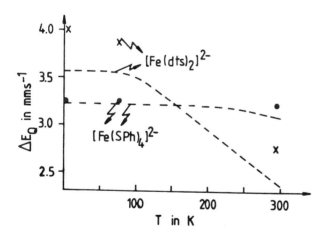

Fig. 1. Quadrupole splitting $\Delta E_Q(T)$ for $[Fe(SPh)_4]^{2-}$ and $[Fe(dts)_2]^{2-}$. The experimental values are indicated by ($\bullet$) for $[Fe(SPh)_4]^{2-}$ and by (X) for $[Fe(dts)_2]^{2-}$, respectively.

coordinated ferrous high-spin iron. The "normal" situation would be that the orbital doublet e_g is split by $\sim$ 1000 cm^{-1} like in the other FeX_4 compounds (X either Cl or S) under study here. This specific feature of $[Fe(dts)_2]^{2-}$ is most likely the reason why our calculated

Table I. Quadrupole splitting ΔE_Q, asymmetry parameter η, electron density $\rho(o)$, isomer shift δ, zero-field splittings D and E, averaged crystal field splitting 10Dq, gyromagnetic factors $g_{\hat{x}}$, $g_{\hat{y}}$, $g_{\hat{z}}$, and magnetic hyperfine coupling components $A_{\hat{x}}$, $A_{\hat{y}}$, $A_{\hat{z}}$ for reduced rubredoxin (4) and its model compounds (1: $[Fe(SH)_4]^{2-}$; 2: $[Fe(SPh)_4]^{2-}$; 3: $[Fe(dts)_2]^{2-}$). All values correspond to 4.2 K.

Method	IEHT	IEHT	spin-Hamil. analysis	IEHT	spin-Hamil. analysis	spin-Hamil. analysis
Material	1	2	2	3	3	4
Ref.	20	present work[e,f]	18	present work	18	22
ΔE_Q(mm s^{-1})[a]		±3.24		-3.58		
ΔE_Q(mm s^{-1})[b]	±3.6	±3.22	-3.24	-3.54	-4.00	-3.25
η	1	0.93	0.67	0.1	0.5±0.2	0.65
$\rho(o)(a_0^{-3})$[c]		15066.96		15067.0		
δ(mm s^{-1})[d]			0.66		0.67	0.70
D(cm^{-1})	4.40	-6.42[6.98]	5.98^g	6.64	6.57	7.8
E(cm^{-1})	1.40	2.38[2.22]	1.42^g	0.53	1.78	2.2
10Dq(cm^{-1})	3200	3000[3000]		2700		
$g_{\hat{x}}$		2.11[2.11]	2.12	2.12	2.1	2.11
$g_{\hat{y}}$		2.01[2.19]	2.19	2.14	2.14	2.19
$g_{\hat{z}}$		2.19[2.01]	2.01	2.00	2.00	2.00
$A_{\hat{x}}$(mm s^{-1})	1.32	0.65[0.65]	1.16	1.12	1.05	1.36
$A_{\hat{y}}$(mm s^{-1})	1.79	1.26[0.63]	0.63	1.12	0.4	0.56
$A_{\hat{z}}$(mm s^{-1})	0.84	0.63[1.26]	2.09	2.3	1.60	2.03

(a) Value for ground state configuration (see Fig. 2) without spin-orbit coupling.

(b) Value for 4.2 K, including spin-orbit coupling.

(c) Calculated charge density $\rho(o)$ at the iron nucleus.

(d) Relative to α-Fe at room temperature.

(e) In the spin-Hamiltonian analysis and in the present calculation, D, g, and A tensors are given in the main axes system of the efg ($|V_{\hat{x}\hat{x}}| \leq |V_{\hat{y}\hat{y}}| \leq |V_{\hat{z}\hat{z}}|$). In our calculation $V_{\hat{z}\hat{z}}$ is positive and $V_{\hat{y}\hat{y}}$ is negative, with nearly identical absolute values ($\eta \sim 1$). Therefore we can interchange our $\hat{z}$ and $\hat{y}$ axes without affecting our results, this makes our calculated data of column 3 (with square brackets) fully consistent with those listed in column 4.

(f) Values without and in square brackets were evaluated with Δ_1 = 800 cm^{-1}, Δ_2 = 3100 cm^{-1}, Δ_3 = 3250 cm^{-1}, Δ_4 = 3400 cm^{-1}.

(g) The fine structure parameters D and E are taken from P.M. Champion et al., JACS 66, 1819 (1977) for the spin-Hamiltonian analysis.

magnetic hyperfine coupling parameters do not compare well with the corresponding spin-Hamiltonian parameters (especially A_g; see Table I and discussion below), because the spin-Hamiltonian formalism is applicable only for cases with relatively well isolated orbital singlet as ground state.

For a complete account and intercomparison of calculated and experimental fine structure and hyperfine parameters we summarized our results, together with literature values in Table I. An important point that must be taken into account, when comparing results from MO calculations and spin-Hamiltonian analysis of experimental data, is the correct assignment of reference axes systems. In the spin-Hamiltonian analysis the various fine structure and hyperfine tensors (D, g, A, V) are assumed to be given in their principal axes system (PAS), and very often, to reduce the number of parameters, the various PAS are assumed to coincide (22). In the case of polycrystalline samples it is not possible to relate the PAS to the molecular geometry. The MO calculation, on the other hand, is carried out in a reference axes system fixed on the molecule. Thus, for a meaningful comparison, the axes assignment must be based on physical considerations, for example on the direction of the $\hat{z}$ axes of the efg-PAS. This point is clearly illustrated in the case of $[Fe(SPh)_4]^{2-}$ from our MO calculations in Table I (column 3).

3 BINUCLEAR FeS$_2$Mo CLUSTERS

A prominent representative of thiometalates is the MoS^{2-} ion, which originally was used as ligand in transition metal coordination compounds (23) and from which later a series of compounds with FeMoS moieties were synthesized (6,7,24-29). In the present contribution we describe electronic and magnetic structure studies of three iron and MoS^{2-} containing clusters for which the synthesis and structure determination by X-ray diffraction have been reported previously: $[(SPh)_2FeS_2MoS_2]^{2-}$ [I] (9), $[S_5FeS_2MoS_2]^{2-}$ [II] (9), and $[Cl_2FeS_2MoS_2]^{2-}$ [III] (7,29).

Applying the IEHT procedure to these clusters, subsequently working out spin-orbit coupling among the five HOMO's of each cluster and finally evaluating molecular expectation values yields fine structure and hyperfine structure data, as summarized in Table II together with spin-Hamiltonian results, which have been derived from experimental Mössbauer spectra (30,31).

Table II. Quadrupole splitting ΔE_Q, orientation of the main component $V_{\hat{z}\hat{z}}$ of the efg in PAS, asymmetry parameter η, electron density $\rho(o)$, isomer shift δ, zero-field splittings D and E, averaged crystal field splitting 10Dq, gyromagnetic factors $g_{\hat{x}}$, $g_{\hat{y}}$, $g_{\hat{z}}$, and magnetic hyperfine coupling components $A_{\hat{x}}$, $A_{\hat{y}}$, $A_{\hat{z}}$ for FeMoS compounds. All values correspond to 4.2 K.

Method	IEHT	spin-Hamil. analysis	IEHT	spin Hamil. analysis	IEHT	spin Hamil. analysis
Material	$I: [(SPh)_2FeS_2MoS_2]^{2-}$		$II: [S_5FeS_2MoS_2]^{2-}$		$III: [Cl_2FeS_2MoS_2]^{2-}$	
Ref.	present work	9,31	present work	9,31	present work	30
$\Delta E_Q(mm\ s^{-1})^a$	+2.36		+1.86		+2.00	
$\Delta E_Q(mm\ s^{-1})^b$	$+2.24^{e,f}$	$+1.96^f$	$+1.69^{g,f}$	$+1.44^f$	$+1.99^{h,i}$	$+2.15^j$
$V_{\hat{z}\hat{z}}$	⊥Fe-Mo		⊥Fe-Mo		⊥Fe-Mo	
η	0.1	0.1	0.4	0.3	0.15	0.2±0.2
$\rho(o)(a_0^{-3})^c$	15067.91		15067.58		15067.36	
$\delta(mm\ s^{-1})^d$		0.45		0.49		0.59
$D(cm^{-1})$	-7.5	-4.3	-9.6	-3.6	-6.1	-5.7^{+3}_{-2}
$E(cm^{-1})$	0.58	1.3	0.6	0.57	1.5	$0.57^{+0.60}_{-0.30}$
$10Dq(cm^{-1})$	2400		2150		1900	
$g_{\hat{x}}$	2.04		2.04		2.02	
$g_{\hat{y}}$	2.06		2.06		2.08	
$g_{\hat{z}}$	2.19		2.23		2.17	
$A_{\hat{x}}(mm\ s^{-1})$	1.96	≳1.2	1.88	≳1.20	1.94	≳1.2
$A_{\hat{y}}(mm\ s^{-1})$	1.81	1.1	1.81	1.00	1.83	1.2
$A_{\hat{z}}(mm\ s^{-1})$	0.81	0.78	0.74	0.73	0.79	0.82±0.02

(a) Value for ground state without spin-orbit coupling.

(b) Value for 4.2 K, including spin-orbit coupling.

(c) Calculated charge density $\rho(o)$ at the iron nucleus.

(d) Relative to α-Fe at room temperature.

(e) D, g, efg, and A tensors are collinear, the efg-principal axis
    $V_{\hat{z}\hat{z}}$ is in the molecular xy plane between the -x and +y axis;
    i.e., $V_{\hat{z}\hat{z}}$ is perpendicular to the Fe-Mo direction.

(f) Calculated and measured ΔE_Q is temperature independent between
    4.2 and 300 K.

(g) D, g, efg, and A tensors are collinear, the efg-principal axis
    $V_{\hat{z}\hat{z}}$ is in the molecular xy plane between the +x and +y axis; i.e.,
    $V_{\hat{z}\hat{z}}$ is perpendicular to the Fe-Mo direction.

(h) D, g, efg, and A tensors are collinear, the efg-principal axis
    $V_{\hat{z}\hat{z}}$ is along the molecular x axis; i.e. perpendicular to the Fe-Mo
    direction.

(i) Calculated ΔE_Q slightly temperature dependent: 1.99 mm s^{-1} at
    4.2 K and 1.88 mm s^{-1} at 300 K.

(j) Measured ΔE_Q slightly temperature dependent: 2.15 mm s^{-1} at
    4.2 K and 2.10 mm s^{-1} at 293 K.

A specific feature of the FeMoS model compounds studied here is the
orientation of the main component of the efg, $V_{\hat{z}\hat{z}}$, with respect to the
molecular frame. In all three compounds the theoretical efg component
$V_{\hat{z}\hat{z}}$ is oriented perpendicular to the Fe-Mo axis. Since the experimental determination of the orientation of the efg tensor with respect to
the molecular axes is a prerequisite for a decisive check of MO
calculations on the binuclear bioinorganic systems under study here,
we carried out orientation and magnetic field dependent Mössbauer
measurements with single crystals of III (30). From a whole series of
experimental results (one of them is shown in Fig. 2) it is clear,
that $V_{\hat{z}\hat{z}}$ is positive and indeed oriented perpendicular to the Fe-Mo
axis, in full agreement with our calculated results.

Further support for the reliability of our calculated electronic
structure of the five compounds investigated by IEHT is derived from
the correlation between isomer shift δ and electron charge density at
the iron nucleus $\rho(o)$. Plotting the δ and $\rho(o)$ values summarized in
Tables I and II, yields the diagram shown in Fig. 3. In addition to
the iron-sulfur compounds we have investigated $[FeCl_4]^{2-}$, in order to
extend the range of δ and $\rho(o)$ values. The isomer shift calibration
constant α, which relates δ and $\rho(o)$ values via $\Delta\delta = \alpha\Delta\rho(o)$, turns out
to be $\alpha = -0.25$ mm s$^{-1}a_o^3$ in the present case, close to the values
which we have obtained from MO studies of several other iron-compounds
(15,32,33). We want to point out that our calculated results indicate

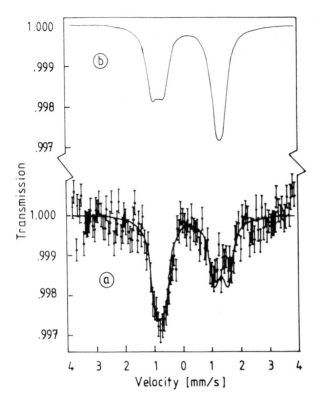

Fig. 2: Experimental Mössbauer spectrum of a single crystal of
$[Cl_2FeS_2MoS_2]^{2-}$ at RT with an external field of 1.8T,
parallel to the Fe-Mo direction of one of the two anions within the unit cell. (Taken from ref. 30).
(a) Simulation assuming that $V_{\hat{z}\hat{z}}$ is directed perpendicular
to the Fe-Mo axis;
(b) for comparison the theoretical spectrum if $V_{\hat{z}\hat{z}}$ would
point parallel to the Fe-Mo axis.

a relatively large charge concentration in the overlap region of the
Mo-S bonds, approximately twice the corresponding value in the
terminal Fe-Cl or Fe-S bonds. This is the reason why the compounds I,
II, and III exhibit smaller isomer shifts than compounds 1, 2, and 3
(Fig. 3), because charge delocalisation from Fe 3d AO's into the
overlap region of Mo-S bonds results in decreased shielding of Fe core

s AO's, and thus in an increase of ρ (o) at the iron nucleus (34). This finding confirms the function of MoS_4^{2-} as a charge-withdrawing ligand, which was found also in previous studies of FeMoS complexes (9,25,35,36).

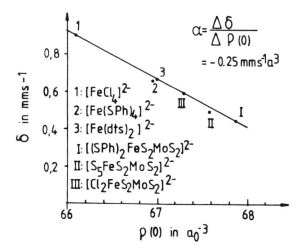

Fig. 3: Correlation between measured isomer shifts δ (measured at 4.2
        K rel. to α-Fe at RT) and calculated electron charge densities
        at the iron nucleus ρ(o) for iron-sulfur compounds and for
        $[FeCl_4]^{2-}$.

4 SPIN-COUPLED 2Fe-2S CLUSTERS

Spin-coupled metal clusters are a challenge for electronic structure theories in predicting coupling constants J (at least qualitatively) correctly. Beyond the level of approximations of standard MO
techniques theoretical models have been developped (37-40) to evaluate
J. The procedure which was applied to $[Fe_2S_2(SR)_4]^{2-}$ by Noodleman et
al. (14,41) is based on the Landé-rule, which relates the energy
separation between two states, having spin S and S-1, respectively,
with J:

$$E(S) - E(S-1) = -2JS.$$

Applying this concept to the above mentioned cluster, with the two
paramagnetic irons ($|S_{1/2}| = 5/2$) being antiparallel spin-coupled (S =
$S_1 + S_2 = 0$), yields E(S = 5) - E(S = 0) = -30J. In order to predict J

(its absolute value is of the order 100 cm^{-1}) with the correct sign
and the right order of magnitude the energies $E(S = 5)$ and $E(S = 0)$
have to be evaluated with relatively high precision, for example by
ab initio SCF-CI calculations. To avoid this costly procedure
Noodleman has developped the "broken spin-symmetry" concept (42) and
applied it to $[Fe_2S_2(SR)_4]^{2-}$; his estimate yields

$$E(S = 5) - E(\text{"broken spin-symmetry"}) = -25J.$$

Since IEHT calculations are by far not accurate enough to predict
total energies $E(S_{max} = 5)$ and $E(\text{"broken spin-symmetry"})$ of the
cluster under study we have developped a spin-unrestricted MO
procedure (13) which includes local exchange in Stoner-approximation (43) and neighbour contributions in the $X\alpha$-approximation (44,45).

The J-value of -337 cm^{-1} which we find for $[Fe_2S_2(SH)_4]^{2-}$ is in
reasonable agreement with Noodleman's et al. calculated scattered
Wave-$X\alpha$ value (14) of -303 cm^{-1}, and in qualitative agreement with the
experimental values of -183 cm^{-1} (for oxidized spinach-ferredoxin
(46)) and of -149 cm^{-1} (for the dianion $[Fe_2S_2(C_6H_4(CH_2S)_2)_2]^{2-}$ (47)).
Thus the theoretical models which are based on the "broken spin-
symmetry" concept and which avoid explicit CI calculations predict
qualitatively correct the spin-coupling of $|S_1| = 5/2$ and $|S_2| = 5/2$ to
$S = S_1 + S_2 = 0$ within the above mentioned clusters. We want to
mention, however, that this method is not adequately correct when
spin-coupling of $|S_1| = 5/2$ and $|S_2| = 2$ to $S = S_1 + S_2 = 1/2$ occurs
(13,14,41).

We have used our spin-unrestricted MO results also to calculate fine
and hyperfine structure parameters. Table III summarizes these results
for various cluster-geometries (Fig. 4) and sizes of $[Fe_2S_2(SR)_4]^{2-}$
together with experimental results for the synthetic cluster
$[Fe_2S_2(C_6H_4(CH_2S)_2)_2]^{2-}$ and for 2Fe-2S ferredoxins. Inspection of
these data indicates that charge- and spin-density distributions are
more sensitive on changes in cluster-geometry than on changes in
cluster-size.

Because of the symmetry of the spin-coupled $[Fe_2S_2(SH)_4]^{2-}$ cluster
(C_2-axis $\hat{=}$ molecular x-axis in Fig. 4) the lowest unoccupied molecular
orbital (LUMO) of α-spin at site $Fe_{(1)}$ is energetically degenerate
with the LUMO of β-spin at site $Fe_{(2)}$ (Fig. 5). Hence, the reduction
of $[Fe_2S_2(SH)_4]^{2-}$ would result in an equal distribution of the addi-

tional electron over these two MO's. This, however, is in contradiction with the well-known fact that reduced 2Fe-2S ferredoxins exhibit
a Mössbauer spectrum which consists of a 1:1 superposition of ferric
high-spin and ferrous high-spin subspectra (51). As model for this si-

Table III. Effective Fe AO occupancies $N_{nl}(Fe)$, spin-density
$\rho^{spin}(Fe)$, quadrupole splitting ΔE_Q and asymmetrypara-
meter η for $[Fe_2S_2(SR)_4]^{2-}$ as derived from spin-unrestricted MO calculations and corresponding experimental
data.

	$[Fe_2S_2(SH)_4]^{2-}$ position of hydrogen[a]			$[Fe_2S_2(SCH_3)_4]^{2-}$	$[Fe_2S_2(C_6H_4(CH_2S)_2)_2]^{2-}$
	1	2	3		
$N_{3d}(Fe)$[b]	5.73	5.97	5.72	5.93	6.12
$N_{4s}(Fe)$[b]	0.66	0.24	0.71	0.70	0.60
$N_{4p}(Fe)$[b]	0.71	0.52	0.72	0.62	0.54
$\rho^{spin}_{3d}(Fe)$[b]	4.33	4.09	4.33	4.13	3.93
ΔE_Q^{calc} (mm s^{-1})	0.49	-1.84	1.09	0.71	0.50
ΔE_Q^{exp} (mm s^{-1})	0.36[c], 0.60[d], 0.61-0.73[e]				
η^{calc}	0.90	0.90	0.13	0.45	0.68
η^{exp}	0.42[d], 0.5±0.3[e]				

(a) See Fig. 4.
(b) Calculated from a bond-order weighted population analysis (ref.13)
(c) Ref. 48.
(d) Ref. 49.
(e) Ref. 50.

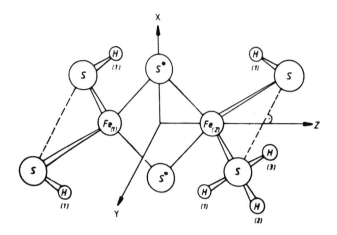

Fig. 4: Structure of $[Fe_2S_2(SH)_4]^{2-}$ which mainly is based on the structure of $[Fe_2S_2(C_6H_4(CH_2S)_2)_2]^{2-}$ (ref. 48). The three different hydrogen positions are in the plane of Fe and the terminal S.

tuation we studied a hypothetical (reduced) spin-coupled $[Fe_2S_2(SH)_4]^{3-}$ cluster, the geometry of which differs from the oxidized $[Fe_2S_2(SH)_4]^{2-}$ cluster

(i) by increasing the Fe-Fe distance by 0.05 Å (this change is consistent with data derived from EXAFS measurements on oxidized and reduced 2Fe-2S ferredoxin (52)), and

(ii) by increasing the Fe-S distances by 0.035 Å (leaving the $Fe_{(1)}$-S distances unchanged).

These structural changes lift the degeneracy of the two LUMO's with α-spin on $Fe_{(1)}$ and β-spin on $Fe_{(2)}$ ($12a_1$ in Fig. 5). with the result that the additional electron upon reduction of $[Fe_2S_2(SH)_4]^{2-}$ will be mainly located at site $Fe_{(2)}$ (Fig. 6), yielding a ferrous high-spin iron.

In Table IV we compare our calculated fine and hyperfine structure data with values which have been derived from the spin-Hamiltonian analysis of Mössbauer measurements of reduced 2Fe-2S ferredoxins. The increase of cluster size by replacing the terminal hydrogens by CH_3 groups in $[Fe_2S_2(SH)_4]^{3-}$ changes the calculated values to a minor

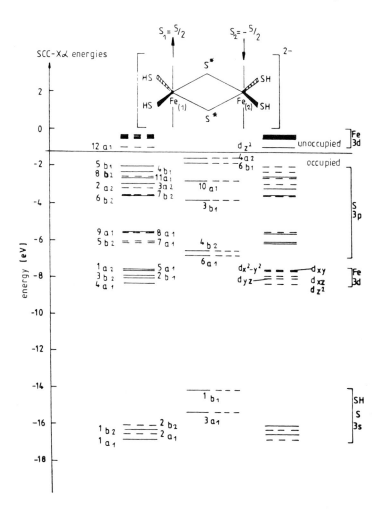

Fig. 5: One-electron valence MO energies of $[Fe_2S_2(SH)_4]^{2-}$. Solid
lines correspond to α-spin ("spin up") and dashed lines to
β-spin ("spin-down").

extend. The only significant disagreement between theoretical and
experimental data occurs in the efg; especially the sign of $V_{\hat{z}\hat{z}}$ on the
ferric as well as on the ferrous site does not match with experiment.
From the extensive experimental test of the ferrous site in
$[Cl_2FeS_2MoS_2]^{2-}$ we have, however, confidence that the similar
situation in $[Fe_2S_2(SH)_4]^{3-}$ will yield similar results. Mössbauer
measurements with single-crystals of reduced 2Fe-2S ferrodoxin
certainly would elucidate this ambiguity.

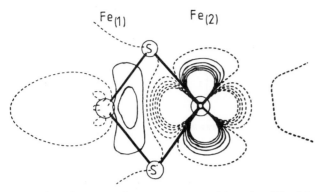

Fig. 6: Electron density map within the 2Fe-2S plane of the HOMO in
$[Fe_2S_2(SH)_4]^{3-}$. The lines represent electron densities
0, ±0.02, ±0.04, ±0.06, ±0.08, ±0.10, ea_0^{-3}.

Table IV. Spin-unrestricted MO results for $[Fe_2S_2(SH)_4]^{3-}$ and
$[Fe_2S_2(SCH_3)_4]^{3-}$ together with experimental data from
reduced 2Fe-2S ferredoxins at 4.2 K.

		$[Fe_2S_2(SH)_4]^{3-}$	$[Fe_2S_2(SCH_3)_4]^{3-}$	exp.
$\Delta E_Q (mm\ s^{-1})$	ferric	-1.38	-1.56	0.60^a, 0.68^b
	ferrous	3.09	3.16	-3.00^a, -3.20^b
	ferric	0.75	0.73	0.6 ± 0.3^a
	ferrous	0.55	0.59	$0.0 + 0.20^a$
$\Delta\delta (mm\ s^{-1})$		-0.43	-0.41	-0.29^a, -0.41^d
$g_{\tilde{x},eff}^{\ e}$		1.87	1.86	1.89^a, 1.94^f
$g_{\tilde{y},eff}^{\ e}$		1.90	1.88	1.96^a, 1.94^f
$g_{\tilde{z},eff}^{\ e}$		1.99	1.98	2.05^a, 2.01^f
$A_{\tilde{x},eff}(MHz)^e$	ferric	-49.0	-48.4	-51 ± 1^a, -56 ± 3^f
	ferrous	8.6	6.4	11.1 ± 5.5^a, 14 ± 3^f
$A_{\tilde{y},eff}(MHz)^e$	ferric	-49.0	-48.4	-49 ± 1.5^a, -50 ± 1.5^f
	ferrous	26.7	24.1	16.8 ± 5.5^a, 21 ± 4^f
$A_{\tilde{z},eff}(MHz)^e$	ferric	-49.0	-48.4	-42 ± 1.5^a, -43 ± 3^f
	ferrous	46.7	44.2	35.3 ± 2^a, 35 ± 1.5^f

(a) Ref. 50.

(b) Ref. 53.

(c) Difference of isomer shifts of ferric and ferrous site at 4.2 K.

(d) Ref. 54.

(e) Calculated according to Gibson's vector coupling model; see ref.53.

(f) Ref. 49.

5 SPIN-COUPLED 4Fe-4S CLUSTERS

We have extended the application of our spin-unrestricted MO calculations to $[Fe_4S_4(SH)_4]^{2-}$, the structure (55) of which we have taken from $[Fe_4S_4(SCH_2Ph)_4]^{2-}$ (Fig. 7). The average formal oxidation state of each iron is +2.5, in agreement with the experimental observation that only one Mössbauer doublet is obtained for this cluster (55,56). Correspondingly we derive the same quadrupole splitting, asymmetry parameter and spin density for the four iron sites (Table V). The average spin-density on each iron (calculated from a bond-order weighted population analysis (13)) is 3.3, i.e. considerable amount of spin-density is located on neighbouring sulfur atoms. This, however, does not imply that any paramagnetism can be observed experimentally, because antiparallel spin-coupling is such that α- and β-spin-densities cancel each other, yielding in total a diamagnetic groundstate for the $[Fe_4S_4(SH)_4]^{2-}$.

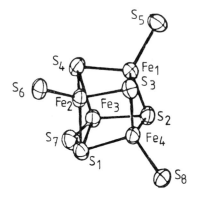

Fig. 7: Structure of $[Fe_4S_4(SH)_4]^{2-}$ (ref. 55).

Table V. Effective Fe AO occupancies $N_{nl}(Fe)$, spin-density $\rho_{3d}^{spin}(Fe)$, quadrupole splitting ΔE_Q, and asymmetry parameter η for $[Fe_4S_4(SH)_4]^{2-}$ as derived from spin-unrestricted MO calculations, and corresponding experimental data.

	$[Fe_4S_4(SH)_4]^{2-}$	exp[a]
$N_{3d}(Fe)$[b]	6.70	
$N_{4s}(Fe)$[b]	0.68	
$N_{4p}(Fe)$[b]	0.39	
$\rho_{3d}^{spin}(Fe)$[b]	3.30	
$\Delta E_Q(mm\ s^{-1})$	1.45	1.26
η	0.02	<0.4

(a) Ref.s 55,56.
(b) Calculated from a bond-order weighted population analysis (ref.13)

6 CONCLUSION

On the basis of MO calculations we have investigated the electronic structure of mononuclear, binuclear, and cubane iron sulfur clusters. Particularly we have evaluated the electron density and the electric field gradient tensor at the iron nucleus, fine structure parameters such as D, E, and the g tensor, and the hyperfine coupling tensor. The specific procedure which we have applied for evaluating these molecular observables includes (i) the MO charge distribution via the first order density matrix, and (ii) atomic expectation values, which we have derived from atomic calculations.

Our study of mononuclear Fe-S compounds deals with the application of the IEHT MO method to $[Fe(SH)_4]^{2-}$, $[Fe(SPh)_4]^{2-}$, and $[Fe(dts)_2]^{2-}$. We conclude from our work that the complex anion $[Fe(SPh)_4]^{2-}$ seems to be a reasonable model for the ground state electronic structure of reduced rubredoxin, because the electronic and magnetic structure parameters, which are obtained from our calculations as well as from the spin-Hamiltonian analysis of experimental Mössbauer spectra, exhibit the same characteristics of charge and spin distribution as reduced rubredoxin does. The other anion, $[Fe(dts)_2]^{2-}$, displays considerably less anisotropy within its charge and spin distribution, exemplified by the very rare situation under fourfold coordinated ferrous high-spin complexes, i.e., that the energy splitting of the HOMO e_g is only of the order of 300 cm^{-1}. In addition this small splitting most likely is the reason for the mismatch of spin-Hamiltonian and calculated MO results.

We have also investigated the binuclear Fe-Mo-S systems $[(SPh)_2FeS_2MoS_2]^{2-}$, $[S_5FeS_2MoS_2]^{2-}$, and $[Cl_2FeS_2MoS_2]^{2-}$ with the IEHT MO method. A specific feature of these systems is their negative D value, while the mononuclear Fe-S systems under study here are characterized by a positive D value. This has to do with the fact that among the expectation values of the orbital angular momentum the component $\langle l_{\hat{z}} \rangle$ is the leading term for the binuclear systems, while for the mononuclear systems it is the $\langle l_{\hat{y}} \rangle$ component. This situation is correspondingly reflected in the g and A tensors of binuclear and mononuclear systems, i.e., $g_{\hat{z}}$ is largest among $g_{\hat{p}}$, and $A_{\hat{z}}$ is smallest among $A_{\hat{p}}$ components for the Fe-Mo-S clusters, while for the Fe-S clusters it is the $g_{\hat{y}}$ and the $A_{\hat{y}}$ terms which are mainly affected.

Another characteristic feature of our IEHT MO calculations on Fe-Mo-S systems is the orientation of the main component of the efg, $V_{\hat{z}\hat{z}}$, with respect to the molecular frame. In all three compounds under study here $V_{\hat{z}\hat{z}}$ is oriented perpendicular to the Fe-Mo axis, irrespective of changes within reasonable limits for the structure of the used model compounds or for the molybdenum parameters in the semiempirical MO calculation. The calculated orientation of $V_{\hat{z}\hat{z}}$ is in agreement with our experimental single crystal work on $[Cl_2FeS_2MoS_2]^{2-}$.

From the correlation between measured isomer shift δ and calculated charge density $\rho(o)$ at the iron nucleus we derive for the compounds studied here an isomer shift calibration constant α = -0.25 mm s^{-1}, which is close to our values found for other iron-containing compounds ($\alpha \simeq$ -0.2 mm s^{-1}). From the trend of δ and $\rho(o)$ values of the binuclear Fe-Mo-S systems with respect to the mononuclear Fe-S systems we conclude, that MoS_4^{2-} is a charge-withdrawing ligand, which partially delocalizes charge from Fe 3d AO's into the overlap region of Mo-S bonds.

Studying the electronic structure of spin-coupled 2Fe-2S and 4Fe-4S clusters we have used a more sophisticated MO method than IEHT. This method includes local exchange in the Stoner-approximation and neighbour contributions in the Xα-approximation and allows spin-unrestricted calculations. Applying further the "broken spin-symmetry" concept yields accurate enough total energies which at least make qualitative predictions of spin-coupling constants possible. Further use of our spin-unrestricted MO results was made by calculating fine and hyperfine structure parameters for $[Fe_2S_2(SR)_4]^{2-,3-}$ and for $[Fe_4S_4(SR)_4]^{2-}$ clusters. Comparing these parameters with experimental data clearly indicates (i) the presence of two ferric high-spin sites in $[Fe_2S_2(SR)_4]^{2-}$, one ferric high-spin site and one ferrous high-spin site in $[Fe_2S_2(SR)_4]^{3-}$, and four mixed-valence sites in $[Fe_4S_4(SR)_4]^{2-}$, (ii) antiparallel spin-coupling of these paramagnetic sites, (iii) considerable spin delocalisation from Fe 3d AO's into ligand AO's, (iv) considerable backdonation of electron charge from ligand AO's to Fe 3d,4s,4p AO's, (v) the necessity of (structural) inequivalent Fe sites in $[Fe_2S_2(SH)_4]^{2-}$ in order to localize the additonal electron at one of the two sites upon reduction of this cluster, and (vi) the insignificance of direct metal-metal bonding.

In conclusion we want to emphasize that the study of structural, spectroscopic, and electronic properties of biomolecules can be strongly supported by the combined theoretical and experimental investigation of corresponding bioinorganic model clusters.

7 ACKNOWLEDGEMENTS

    We want to thank Deutsche Forschungsgemeinschaft and Stiftung Volkswagenwerk for their support of this work.

8 REFERENCES

(1)   W. Lovenberg (Ed.), Iron Sulfur Proteins, Academic Press, New York 1973.

(2)   R.H. Holm, A. Ibers in W. Lovenberg (Ed.), Iron Sulfur Proteins, Academic Press, New York 1977, p. 205

(3)   D. Coucouvanis, D.G. Holah, F.J. Hollander, Inorg. Chem. 14, 2657 (1975).

(4)   D.G. Holah, D. Coucouvanis, J. Am. Chem. Soc. 97, 6927 (1975).

(5) A. Kostikas, V. Petrouleas, A., Simopoulos, D. Coucouvanis,
     D.G. Holah, Chem. Phys. Lett. 38, 582 (1976).

(6) D. Coucouvanis, Acc. Chem. Res. 14, 201 (1981).

(7) A. Müller, R. Jostes, H.J. Tölle, A.X. Trautwein, E. Bill,
     Inorg. Chim. Acta 46, L121 (1980).

(8) A. Müller and E. Diemann, in A. Müller, E. Diemann (Ed.s)
     Transition Metal Chemistry, Verlag Chemie, Weinheim 1981, p. 221.

(9) D. Coucouvanis, P. Stremple, E.D. Simhon, D. Swenson, N.C. Baen-
     ziger, M. Draganjac, L.T. Chan, A. Simopoulos, V. Papaefthymiou,
     A. Kostikas, V. Petrouleas, Inorg. Chem. 22, 293 (1983).

(10) R. Rein, N. Fukuda, H. Win, G.A. Clarke, F.E. Harris, J. Chem.
     Phys. 45, 4743 (1966).

(11) R. Rein, G.A. Clarke, F.E. Harris in Quantum aspects of heterocy-
     clic compounds in chemistry and biochemitry II, Israel Academy of
     Sciences and Humanities, Jerusalem 1970.

(12) A.X. Trautwein in Structure and Bonding, Springer, Heidelberg
     1976, Vol. 20, p. 101.

(13) R. Bläs, PhD-work, University of Saarbrücken (1985).

(14) L.L. Noodleman, E.J. Baerends, J. Am. Chem. Soc. 106, 2316
     (1984).

(15) V.R. Marathe, A.X. Trautwein in B.V. Thosar, P.K. Iyengar (Ed.s),
     Advances in Mössbauer Spectroscopy, Elsevier, New York 1983,
     p. 398

(16) A.X. Trautwein, E. Bill, R. Bläs, S. Lauer, H. Winkler, A.
     Kostikas, J. Chem. Phys. 82, 3584 (1985).

(17) A.X. Trautwein, E. Bill, R. Bläs, S. Lauer, H. Winkler, A.
     Kostikas, Rev. Port. Quim. 27, 186 (1985).

(18) D. Coucouvanis, D. Swenson, N.C. Baenziger, C. Murphy, D.G. Holah, N. Sfarnas, A. Simopoulos, A. Kostikas, J. Am. Chem. Soc. 103, 3350 (1981).

(19) G.H. Loew, D.Y. Lo, Theor. Chim. Acta (Berlin) 32, 217 (1974).

(20) L. Eisenstein, D.R. Franceschetti, Chem. Phys. Lett 50, 167 (1977).

(21) R.A. Bair, W.A. Goddard III, J. Am. Chem. Soc. 100, 5669 (1978)

(22) C. Schulz, P.G. Debrunner, J. Phys. (Paris) 37, Colloq. C6-153 (1976).

(23) A. Müller, E. Ahlborn, H.H. Heinsen, Z. Anorg. Allg. Chem. 386, 102 (1971).

(24) A. Müller, E. Diemann, R. Jostes, H. Bögge, Angew. Chem. 93, 957 (1981); Int. Ed. 20, 934 (1981).

(25) A. Müller, W. Hellmann, J. Schneider, U. Schimanski, U. Demmer, A.X. Trautwein, U. Bender, Inorg. Chim. Acta 65, L41 (1982).

(26) A. Müller, S. Sarkar, H. Bögge, R. Jostes, A.X. Trautwein, U. Lauer, Angew. Chem. 22, 561 (1983).

(27) D. Coucouvanis, E.D. Simhon, N.C. Baenzinger, J. Am. Chem. Soc. 102, 6644 (1980).

(28) D. Coucouvanis, N.C. Baenzinger, E.D. Simhon, P. Stremple, D. Swenson, A. Simopoulos, A. Kostikas, V. Petrouleas, V. Papaefthymiou, J. Am. Chem. Soc. 102, 1732 (1980),

(29) R.H. Tieckelmann, H.C. Silvis, T.A. Kent, B.H. Huynh, J.V. Waszczak, B.-K. Teo, B.A. Averill, J. Am. Chem. Soc. 102, 5550 (1980).

(30) H. Winkler, E. Bill, S. Lauer, A.X. Trautwein, A. Kostikas, V. Papaefthymiou, H. Bögge, A. Müller, E. Gerdau, U. Gonser, J. Chem. Phys. 82, 3594 (1985).

(31) V. Papaefthymiou, PhD thesis, Ioannina, Greece, 1983.

(32) J.P. Sanchez, J.M. Friedt, A.X. Trautwein, R. Reschke, Phys. Rev. B 19, 365 (1979).

(33) R. Reschke, A.X. Trautwein, J.P. Desclaux, J. Phys. Chem. Solids 38, 837 (1977).

(34) P. Gütlich, R. Link, A.X. Trautwein, in Mössbauer Spectrocopy and Transition Metal Chemistry, Inorg. Chem. Concepts (Springer, Heidelberg, 1978), Vol. 3.

(35) A. Simopoulos, V. Papaefthymiou, A. Kostikas, V. Petrouleas, D. Coucouvanis, E.D. Simhon, P. Stremple, Chem. Phys. Lett. 81, 261 (1981).

(36) A. Müller, S. Sarkar, Angew. Chem. Int. Ed. 16, 705 (1977).

(37) R.K. Nesbet, Phys. Rev. 122, 1497 (1961).

(38) P.O. Löwdin, Rev. Mod. Phys. 34, 80 (1962).

(39) P.W. Anderson, in F. Seitz, D. Turnball (Ed.s), Solid State Physics, Vol. 14, Academic Press, New York 1963.

(40) P.J. Hay, J.C. Thibeault, R. Hoffmann, J. Am. Chem. Soc. 97, 4883 (1975).

(41) L. Noodleman, J. Chem. Phys. 74, 5737 (1981).

(42) "broken spin-symmetry" in this context means that the "spin-up" density at one paramagnetic site has as mirror image the corresponding "spin-down" density at the other paramagnetic site, with the mirror plane intersecting the two sulfur-bridges and being perpendicular to the FeS_2Fe plane.

(43) O.K. Andersen, J. Madsen, U.K. Paulsen, O. Jepsen, J. Kollar, Physica 86-88B, 249 (1977).

(44) M. Grodzicki, J. Phys. B13, 2683 (1980).

(45) R. Bläs, M. Grodzicki, V.R. Marathe, A.X. Trautwein, J. Phys. B13, 2693 (1980).

(46) G. Palmer, W.R. Dunham, J.A. Fee, R.H. Sands, T. Iizuka, T. Yonetani, Biochim. Biophys. Acta 245, 201 (1971).

(47) W.O. Gillum, R.B. Frankel, S. Foner, R.H. Holm, Inorg. Chem. 15, 1995 (1976).

(48) J.J. Mayerle, S.E. Denmark, B.V., Pamphilis, J.A. Ibers, R.H. Holm, J. Am. Chem. Soc. 97, 1032 (1975).

(49) E. Münck, P. Debrunner, J.C.M. Tsibris, I.C. Gunsalus, Biochem. 11, 855 (1972).

(50) W.R. Dunham, A.J. Bearden, I.T. Salmeen, G. Palmer, R.H. Sands, W.H. Orme-Johnson, H. Beinert, Biochim. Biophys. Acta 253, 134 (1971).

(51) C.E. Johnson, in U. Gonser (Ed.) Mössbauer Spectroscopy in Biology, Topics in Applied Physics, Vol. 5, Springer Verlag, Heidelberg 1975, p. 139.

(52) B.K. Teo, R.G. Shulnian, G.S. Brown, A.E. Meixner, J. Am. Chem. Soc. 101, 5624 (1979).

(53) R.H. Sands, W.R. Dunham, Quart. Rev. Biophys. 11, 443 (1975).

(54) P.K. Mascharak, G.C. Papaefthymiou, R.B. Frankel, P.H. Holm, J. Am. Chem. Soc. 103, 6110 (1981).

(55) B.A. Averill, T. Herskovitz, R.H. Holm, J.A. Ibers, J. Am. Chem. Soc. 95, 3523 (1973).

(56) R.B. Frankel, B.A. Averill, R.H. Holm, J. Phys. (Paris) 35, Colloq. C6-107 (1974).

Resonance Raman Spectroscopy of Iron-Sulfur Proteins

Jacques MEYER, Jean-Marc MOULIS, Marc LUTZ

DRF-Biochimie Microbienne (INSERM U.191), Centre d'Etudes Nucléaires,
85 X, 38041 Grenoble, France (J.M. and J.M.M.) and DB-Biophysique,
Centre d'Etudes Nucléaires de Saclay, 91191 Gif-sur-Yvette, France
(M.L.)

SUMMARY

The application of resonance Raman (RR) spectroscopy to iron-sulfur
proteins has made significant progress in the past few years.
Characteristic spectra are now available for |1Fe|, |2Fe-2S|, |3Fe-xS|
and |4Fe-4S| sites in rubredoxins and ferredoxins, and band
assignments have been carried out for all of these active sites. RR
spectroscopy can now be used for the characterization of slight
structural differences among various Fe-S sites, and of conformational
changes of these prosthetic groups upon redox transitions.

1 INTRODUCTION

Our knowledge of the structure and function of the various types of
iron-sulfur (Fe-S) clusters present in proteins has been expanding
considerably over the last few years (18). Some of the unsolved
problems, to be mentionned below, would require high resolution structural data which are accessible to X-ray crystallography of proteins
in only a very few cases. Thus, additional structural data, in particular on proteins in solution, are highly desirable. Resonance Raman
(RR) spectroscopy, in which laser excitation within an electronic

---

Abbreviations : Av : Azotobacter vinelandii, Cp : Clostridium
pasteurianum, EPR : electron paramagnetic resonance, Fd : Ferredoxin,
Rd : Rubredoxin, RR : resonance Raman.

absorption band produces selective enhancement of Raman lines arising from vibrations of the chromophore, can potentially provide such information. This technique has indeed proved to be a very selective and sensitive probe of chromophores in biological systems, whatever their physical state (3). In the case of Fe-S proteins, the quality of early RR spectra was limited by experimental difficulties, but significant progress has been achieved recently (12, 19), allowing the collection of a substantial set of experimental data and of structural information (8, 15, 23, 24). Some of the most significant of these results are summarized below.

2 CLUSTER TYPE DETERMINATION

One of the first problems met upon isolation of a new Fe-S protein is the identification of its prosthetic group(s). For ferredoxins and rubredoxins, this is in most cases readily carried out with widely used techniques such as optical or EPR spectroscopy. For complex Fe-S proteins, serious difficulties often arise, which have led to the elaboration of a number of elegant chemical and spectroscopic methods of cluster identification (16).

Fe-S chromophores differ from each other by their numbers of atoms and by their point group symmetry : as the numbers of Raman-active bands depend on both of these properties, RR spectroscopy may be expected to provide fingerprints for the various types of Fe-S prosthetic groups. Various technical improvements, in particular the use of low temperature (ca. 20K), and the avoidance of glass cells which yield a troublesome Raman scattering in the 300-500 cm^{-1} range (11), have allowed the obtention of RR spectra displaying high signal-to-noise ratios over wide frequency ranges for several ferredoxins and rubredoxins.

The 488 nm-excited low temperature RR spectrum of Clostridium pasteurianum rubredoxin (Cp Rd) exhibits four bands, including the very strong 319 cm^{-1} line, in the 300-400 cm^{-1} range (Figure 1) where Fe-S stretching modes are expected. Overtones and combinations of the fundamental bands are observed, as well as low frequency components in the 100-300 cm^{-1} range, which most probably arise from FeS_4 bending modes (Figure 1). Similar spectra have been obtained for various Rd (23).

|2Fe-2S| ferredoxins, as typified by spinach Fd, display six bands in the 280-430 cm^{-1} range (Figure 2), with three prominent ones at ca. 285, 330 and 395 cm^{-1} (13, 24). In addition, the low temperature spectra (13, see also Figure 2) show several low frequency bands assignable to |2Fe-2S| bending modes, and high frequency bands (500-900 cm^{-1})

arising from overtones and combinations of the fundamental stretching modes.

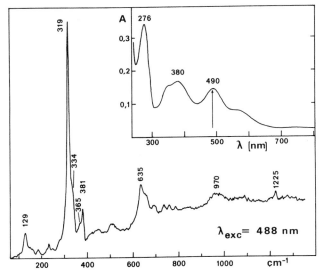

Figure 1 - RR spectrum of C. pasteurianum rubredoxin, excited at 488 nm. T = 24 K, scanning speed 50 cm^{-1}/min, 2 scans ; time constant 1.8 s ; slitwidth 500 µm. Insert : UV-visible absorption spectrum of rubredoxin, 0.42 mg/ml in Tris-Cl 0.1 M, pH8 ; pathlength 2 mm.

RR spectra of |4Fe-4S| ferredoxins display ten bands in the 250-400 cm^{-1} range (12, 14, 15), including a very strong one at 340 cm^{-1}. Unlike in the spectra of proteins containing mono- and binuclear active sites, no high frequency band is detected, and only one low frequency band is observed at 145 cm^{-1}.

Three-iron clusters have been discovered more recently, but are found in a rapidly increasing number of proteins (2, 5, 6). However, the only X-ray structure available to date is that of ferredoxin I from Azotobacter vinelandii (Av FdI), which also contains a |4Fe-4S| cluster (20). The contribution of the three-iron cluster in RR spectra of Av FdI has been determined either by subtracting a |4Fe-4S| RR spectrum from the 457.9 nm-excited spectrum (12), or by using a 488 nm excitation, which minimizes the contribution of the tetranuclear center. The former method yields low temperature RR spectra of the three-iron cluster characterized by two strong bands at 350 and 397 cm^{-1} and a medium band at 268 cm^{-1} (Figure 3). Altogether six to eight lines are observed in the Fe-S stretching frequency range.

Hence, detailed and characteristic RR spectra of mono-, bi-, tri- and tetranuclear Fe-S clusters in rubredoxins and ferredoxins are now available, and provide a sound basis for the identification of such clusters in larger and more complex proteins. Indeed, RR spectroscopy has already been used to confirm the |3Fe| → |4Fe| conversion in aconitase upon activation of the enzyme, and to demonstrate the presence of a 3Fe cluster in the membrane-bound hydrogenase from Desulfovibrio desulfuricans (9).

3 MONITORING OF STRUCTURAL VARIATIONS AND BAND ASSIGNMENTS

Thanks to its high sensitivity to slight structural changes, RR spectroscopy can be used to detect structural variations among the active sites of different proteins containing the same type of Fe-S cluster, or conformational changes likely to occur in a protein upon redox transitions or substrate binding. However, the translation of spectral differences into well defined structural variations is not a straightforward process, since it requires assignments of the observed bands to normal modes of the chromophore. Conversely, the comparison of RR spectra obtained from structurally related molecules may provide useful indications for band assignments (14, 15, 24).

3.1 Rubredoxins

The RR spectra of Rd from various origins are very similar (23). Four widely spaced Fe-S stretching bands are observed in the 300-400 cm^{-1} region, instead of the only two expected for a tetrahedral FeS$_4$ structure. Normal mode calculations have shown that the splitting of the Raman-active stretching modes cannot be accounted for by the S-Fe-S angle distortions observed in the X-ray structures, and that coupling of Fe-S stretching with S-C-C bending and with other ligand modes had to be included in the calculations (23). Thus, in the case of Rd, RR spectroscopy affords data not only on the structure of the chromophore, but also on the kinematic coupling of the latter to its close polypeptidic environment.

3.2 |2Fe-2S| ferredoxins

Ferredoxins containing |2Fe-2S| clusters are found mainly in oxygen-evolving photosynthetic organisms, where they display considerable structural homology (22). Accordingly, the RR spectra of several such proteins are nearly identical (17). On the other hand, |2Fe-2S| proteins from various sources differ from plant-type Fd in many respects. Discrepancies in EPR and UV-visible spectra, and in amino acid sequence are matched by differences in RR spectra in the cases of adrenodoxin (19, 24) and of the |2Fe-2S| Fd from C. pasteurianum (13).

Although all |2Fe-2S| proteins display roughly similar RR patterns, frequency differences of up to 20 cm^{-1} between homologous bands indi-

cate structural variations. The RR spectra of spinach Fd and of adrenodoxin differ mainly in the 310-360 cm^{-1} region (19, 24), whereas the
RR spectra of spinach Fd and of |2Fe-2S| CpFd display discrepancies
over the whole Fe-S stretching frequency range (13).

Synthetic analogs of |2Fe-2S| prosthetic groups assume a nearly
ideal D_{2h} symmetry, as shown by X-ray crystallography and by the mutual exclusion of four IR-active and four Raman-active Fe-S stretching
modes (24). The presence of six or seven bands in the Fe-S stretching
region of protein RR spectra (13, 24) shows that the active sites of
the latter are more distorted than the synthetic analogs. Normal mode
calculations have been performed on the basis of a number of experimental data (24). Although the $^{34}S^* \rightarrow {}^{32}S^*$ isotopic shifts indicated
some coupling between Fe-S* and Fe-Scys stretching modes, these latter
modes have been assigned to bands occurring in the 310-360 cm^{-1} region
where the spectra of spinach Fd and adrenodoxin differ most (24).
Bands attributed to Fe-S* stretching modes in spectra of adrenodoxin
undergo shifts of ca. 20 cm^{-1} to lower frequency upon reduction, which
indicates a weakening of the Fe-S* bonds (24). We have recently measu-
sured $^{34}S^* \rightarrow {}^{32}S^*$ isotopic shifts on low temperature RR spectra of

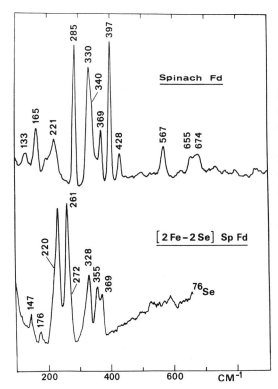

Figure 2 - RR spectra of
native (T = 25 K, 6 scans)
and of ^{76}Se-substituted
(T = 30 K, 7 scans) spinach
Fd, excited at 457.9 nm.
Other conditions as in Figure
1. The strong 231 cm^{-1} band
(unlabelled) in the spectrum
of Se-substituted Fd arises
at least in part from Raman
scattering of ice.

spinach Fd and found nearly uniform relative frequency shifts of 0.7 to 1.0 % for all of the bands in the 280-430 cm^{-1} range. Hence, the coupling between Fe-S* and Fe-Scys stretching modes is more extensive than previously reported (24), and to such a point as to forbid any discrimination between the two types of modes on the basis of isotopic shifts alone. The coupling between terminal and bridging modes may be expected to decrease upon Se* → S* substitution (14, 15). We have therefore recorded low temperature RR spectra of |2Fe-2Se| spinach Fd (Figure 2) : they show considerable improvement over previously publi- shed spectra of Se-substituted adrenodoxin (21), and compare favorably with recently reported spectra of |2Fe-2Se| synthetic analogs (1). Measurements of ^{82}Se* → ^{76}Se* isotopic shifts have allowed the assign- ment of the 355 and 369 cm^{-1} bands to Fe-Scys stretching modes, while those at 220 cm^{-1} and 261 cm^{-1} are attributed to Fe-Se* stretching modes (Meyer et al., in preparation). The intermediate isotopic shifts of the 272 cm^{-1} and 328 cm^{-1} bands indicate that mixing of terminal and bridging modes is occurring, although to a much lesser extent than in native spinach Fd : this is most probably due to the large mass difference, in the former protein, between the bridging Se and the terminal S atoms. It is tempting to derive assignments for the Fe-Scys modes of native spinach Fd from those given above for Se-substituted spinach Fd. However, this would not be realistic since the coupling of bridging and terminal modes occurring in spinach Fd may significantly shift the Fe-Scys stretching modes from the positions where they would be expected in the absence of coupling. We are presently collecting additional experimental data which are expected to allow refinements of the proposed band assignments for the |2Fe-2S| chromophores, as well as more accurate estimations of structural differences between various proteins of this type.

3.3 Three-iron proteins

Much controversy has been raised about the structure of three-iron centers in various proteins (2). The X-ray crystal structure of Av FdI shows a nearly planar |3Fe-3S| ring, whereas chemical analysis and X- ray absorption spectroscopy of aconitase and of Desulfovibrio gigas FdII are incompatible with the former structure and rather suggest the presence, in these proteins, of a |3Fe-4S| cluster derived from a |4Fe-4S| center by removal of an iron atom (2). The occurrence of two very different structures is inconsistent with the observation that all three-iron proteins investigated to date have very similar magne- tic properties (2).

A thorough RR investigation of several 3Fe proteins, including Av

FdI in solution and in a crystalline state, has confirmed the similary
of all trinuclear iron-sulfur prosthetic groups (8). Furthermore, normal mode calculations have led to the conclusion that the RR spectra
are not compatible with the nearly planar |3Fe-3S| structure (8).
According to these calculations, the frequency of the strong 350 cm^{-1}
band (in low temperature spectra), which has been attributed to a
totally symmetric stretching mode of the inorganic core, is critical
for the derivation of structural information : for a planar or a chair
Fe$_3$S$_3$ structure, even if the latter displays acute Fe-S-Fe angles, the
totally symmetric stretching mode of the inorganic core is expected in
the 200-300 cm^{-1} range. The occurrence of the latter mode near to
350 cm^{-1} can be explained by the presence of a fourth bridging sulfide
atom, resulting in a cubane-like structure missing one iron atom (8).

   The low temperature 457.9 nm-excited RR spectra of Av FdI, after
subtraction of the contribution of the |4Fe-4S| cluster, and of ferri-
cyanide oxidized CpFd display similar features, in particular the
strong 350 cm^{-1} band (Figure 3). They are thus consistent with the

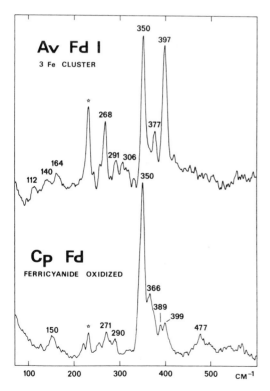

Figure 3 - RR spectra of Av
FdI (T = 25 K, 12 scans) and
of ferricyanide oxidized Cp Fd
(T = 28 K, 11 scans), excited
at 457.9 nm. Other conditions
as in Figure 1. The contribu-
tion of the |4Fe-4S| cluster
was subtracted from the spectrum of Av FdI as described in
(12). The starred bands at
231 cm^{-1} arise from Raman
scattering of ice.

main conclusion of Johnson et al. (8), namely the occurrence of a common architecture for the three-iron clusters. Nevertheless, conspicuous differences in the numbers of bands and in the frequencies of various bands are observed between the two spectra, particularly in the 100-170 cm^{-1}, 260-310 cm^{-1}, 360-400 cm^{-1} and 470-480 cm^{-1} regions (Figure 3). These discrepancies involve spectral components of both the inorganic core and the terminal bonds (8) : therefore, the three-iron clusters of the two proteins are expected to assume structures differing slightly in both of these parts.

3.4 |4Fe-4S| ferredoxins

RR spectra of |4Fe-4S| ferredoxins have first been assigned in T_d symmetry, as only six bands were observed in the Fe-S stretching frequency range (7). Recent improvements have allowed the detection of nine (8) or ten (12, 14, 15) Fe-S stretching bands, which indicates that the chromophore assumes a symmetry lower than T_d. We have recently collected an extensive set of RR data on native and Se-substituted Cp Fd, as well as on synthetic analogs of their active sites. Our results are consistent with the occurrence, in all $|4Fe-4X|^{2+}$ clusters investigated so far (15), of a mainly tetragonal distortion lowering the symmetry from the T_d to the D_{2d} point group.

RR spectra of only a few proteins containing $|4Fe-4S|^{2+}$ clusters are available (6, 12, 19). The low temperature spectra of CpFd and of Bacillus stearothermophilus Fd are nearly identical (12), despite significant differences in the primary structures of the two proteins, and the presence of only one |4Fe-4S| cluster in the latter. Spectra of reduced HiPIP, which also contains a $|4Fe-4S|^{2+}$ cluster, differ from the preceding ones mainly by their displaying less numerous Fe-S stretching bands (8, 19). Upon oxidation to the $|4Fe-4S|^{3+}$ state, the 362 cm^{-1} band of reduced HiPIP shifts to 370 cm^{-1}, suggesting a strengthening of the Fe-Scys bonds (19). On the other hand, reduction of Cp Fd to the $|4Fe-4S|^{+}$ state did not result in detectable spectral changes (19). In the latter case, however, most of the Fd bands in the 250-320 cm^{-1} region were obscured by the Raman scattering of dithionite.

4 CONCLUSIONS AND PROSPECTS

The active development of RR spectroscopy of Fe-S proteins in the last four years has led to the emergence of a comprehensive set of normal mode assignments for the now classical mono-, bi-, tri- and tetranuclear iron-sulfur clusters in their most stable oxidation state. Some problems, mainly involving a few conflicting experimental data (see above), should be resolved in the near future. Listed below are a few significant questions concerning the structure of Fe-S prosthetic groups, the elucidation of which might greatly benefit from the use of RR spectroscopy.

By analogy with the observed properties of synthetic Fe-S clusters (10), the active sites of Fe-S proteins may be expected upon redox processes to undergo conformational changes that can potentially be characterized by RR spectroscopy. Successful studies along these lines will require the availability of good quality RR spectra of various proteins in two or more of their redox states. Furthermore, it may be anticipated that RR spectroscopy will be effective in characterizing Fe-S clusters in proteins more complicated than ferredoxins (9), Fe-S prosthetic groups bound to ligands other than cysteine (4), or associated with or containing other metals, such as Mo or Ni (i.e. nitrogenases or certain hydrogenases).

ACKNOWLEDGEMENTS

We thank J. Roux for typing the manuscript. This research has been supported in part by funds from the CNRS (APP PIRSEM 1105, 1107 and 3075).

REFERENCES

1. BEARDWOOD, P. and GIBSON, J.F. (1984).
   J. Chem. Soc., Dalton Trans. 1507-1516.

2. BEINERT, H. and THOMSON, A.J. (1983).
   Arch. Biochem. Biophys. 222, 333-361.

3. CAREY, P.R. (1982).
   Biochemical Applications of Raman and Resonance Raman
   Spectroscopies, Academic Press, New York.

4. FEE, J.A., FINDLING, K.L., YOSHIDA, T., HILLE, R., TARR, G.E.,
   HEARSHEN, D.O., DUNHAM, W.R., DAY, E.P., KENT, T.A. and MUNCK, E.
   (1984).
   J. Biol. Chem. 259, 124-133.

5. IMAI, T., SAITO, H., TOBARI, J., OHMORI, D. and SUZUKI, K. (1984).
   FEBS Lett. 165, 227-230.

6. JOHNSON, M.K., HARE, J.W., SPIRO, T.G., MOURA, J.J.G., XAVIER,
   A.V. and LEGALL, J. (1981).
   J. Biol. Chem. 256, 9806-9808.

7. JOHNSON, M.K., SPIRO, T.G. and MORTENSON, L.E. (1982).
   J. Biol. Chem. 257, 2447-2452.

8. JOHNSON, M.K., CZERNUSZEWICZ, R.S., SPIRO, T.G., FEE, J.A. and
   SWEENEY, W.V. (1983).
   J. Am. Chem. Soc. 105, 6671-6678.

9. JOHNSON, M.K., CZERNUSZEWICZ, R.S., SPIRO, T.G., RAMSAY, R.R. and
   SINGER, T.P. (1983).
   J. Biol. Chem. 258, 12771-12774.

10. LASKOWSKI, E.J., FRANKEL, R.B., GILLUM, W.O., PAPAEFTHYMIOU, G.C.,
    RENAUD, J., IBERS, J.A. and HOLM, R.H. (1978).
    J. Am. Chem. Soc. 100, 5322-5337.

11. LUTZ, M. (1977).
    Biochim. Biophys. Acta 460, 408-430.

12. LUTZ, M., MOULIS, J.-M. and MEYER, J. (1983).
    FEBS Lett. 163, 212-216.

13. MEYER, J., MOULIS, J.-M. and LUTZ, M. (1984).
    Biochem. Biophys. Res. Commun. 119, 828-835.

14. MOULIS, J.-M., MEYER, J. and LUTZ, M. (1984).
    Biochem. J. 219, 829-832.

15. MOULIS, J.-M., MEYER, J. and LUTZ, M. (1984).
    Biochemistry 23, 6605-6613.

16. ORME-JOHNSON, W.H. and ORME-JOHNSON, N.R. (1982).
    Chapter 2 of reference 18.

17. OZAKI, Y., NAGAYAMA, K., KYOGOKU, Y., HASE, T. and MATSUBARA, H.
    (1983).
    FEBS Lett. 152, 236-240.

18. SPIRO, T.G. (1982).
    Editor of "IRON-SULFUR PROTEINS", Wiley Interscience, New-York.

19. SPIRO, T.G., HARE, J., YACHANDRA, V., GEWIRTH, A., JOHNSON, M.K.
    and REMSEN, E. (1982).
    Chapter 11 of reference 18.

20. STOUT, C.D. (1982).
    Chapter 3 of reference 18.

21. TANG, S.P.W., SPIRO, T.G., MUKAI, K. and KIMURA, T. (1973).
    Biochem. Biophys. Res. Commun. 53, 869-874.

22. TSUKIHARA, T., KOBAYASHI, M., NAKAMURA, M., KATSUBE, Y., FUKUYAMA,
    K., HASE, T., WADA, K. and MATSUBARA, H. (1982).
    Biosystems 15, 243-257.

23. YACHANDRA, V.K., HARE, J., MOURA, I. and SPIRO, T.G. (1983).
    J. Am. Chem. Soc. 105, 6455-6461.

24. YACHANDRA, V.K., HARE, J., GEWIRTH, A., CZERNUSZEWICZ, R.S.,
    KIMURA, T., HOLM, R.H. and SPIRO, T.G. (1983).
    J. Am. Chem. Soc. 105, 6462-6468.

Alkaline Phosphatase: An Enzyme with Multiple Catalytic Metal Ions at Each Active Center: ^{31}P and ^{113}Cd NMR in Solution Correlated with The Crystal Structure

Joseph E. Coleman and Peter Gettins

Department of Molecular Biophysics and Biochemistry, Yale University, New Haven, CT 06510

SUMMARY

The crystal structure of E. coli alkaline phosphatase and ^{113}Cd and ^{31}P NMR of the enzyme have been correlated. Each active center contains 3 metal binding sites (A, B and C) in a triad of 3.9 x 4.9 x 7 Å. For a ^{113}Cd$_6$ enzyme, 3 ^{113}Cd NMR signals are present at 150, 70 and 2 ppm, each integrating to 2 Cd nuclei whose chemical shifts can be assigned to the speific ligand environment revealed by the electron density map; N, N, N at A; N, O, O at B; and O, O, O, O at C. Ser 102 which forms a phosphoseryl intermediate lies adjacent to and between sites A and B. The Cd enzyme turns over slowly such that the formation of the noncovalent (E·P) and covalent (E-P) phosphoenzymes can be followed by ^{31}P and ^{113}Cd NMR. ^{31}P-^{113}Cd coupling shows the phosphate of E·P to be coordinated to the A site metal ion. Despite its lack of coordination to phosphate, B site metal has a profound effect on the chemical shift of E·P. On formation of E-P the ^{31}P resonance becomes a singlet suggesting that phosphate moves out of the coordination sphere of both metal ions. Shifts in the E-P $\rightleftharpoons$ E·P equilibrium as a function of pH and the Zn $\rightarrow$ Cd substitution suggest that a Zn-$^-$OH (Cd-$^-$OH) at A site is the nucleophile in the dephosphorylation of serylphosphate 102.

Abbreviations: AP, alkaline phosphatase; E-P, the covalent phosphoseryl residue; E·P, the noncovalent phosphate complex; (Zn$_A$Cd$_B^{--}$C)$_2$AP, alkaline phosphatase dimer with metal ions or no metal ion (--) in sites A, B and C.

1 INTRODUCTION

Alkaline phosphatases are Zn(II) metalloenzymes of great importance to mammalian physiology. These membrane-attached proteins participate in Ca(II) and HPO_4^{2-} uptake at the intestinal brush border, are essential for the formation of hydroxyapatite, and have less well determined functions in kidney and placenta. Although the molecular events that insert these enzymes (whose currently known function is the nonspecific hydrolysis of phosphate monoesters) into these complex processes are unknown, the periplasmic alkaline phosphatase from E. coli has proved to be a valid prototype for the catalytic domains of the more complex mammalian enzymes. These prototypic features include the Zn(II) ions and the formation of a phosphoserine intermediate. The properties of the E. coli enzyme are summarized in Table I.

TABLE I

MOLECULAR PROPERTIES OF THE ALKALINE PHOSPHATASE FROM E. COLI

1. MW=94,000

2. TWO IDENTICAL SUBUNITS (MW=47,000)

3. 449 AA RESIDUES

4. SER 102 IS PHOSPHORYLATED TO FORM THE COVALENT PHOSPHOENZYME INTERMEDIATE, E-P

5. DEPHOSPHORYLATION OF E-P IS RATE LIMITING AT LOW pH

6. DISSOCIATION OF PRODUCT, P_i, FROM THE NONCOVALENT COMPLEX, E·P, IS RATE LIMITING AT ALKALINE pH, $k_{cat} \cong 10^2 sec^{-1}$

7. FROM THE CRYSTAL STRUCTURE THERE ARE THREE METAL BINDING SITES, A, B AND C AT EACH ACTIVE CENTER

      LIGANDS TO A: HIS 331, HIS 372, HIS 412, AND 1 OR 2 H_2O
                                 MOLECULES

      LIGANDS TO B: HIS 370, ASP 51, ASP 369

      LIGANDS TO C: ASP 153, GLU 322, THR 155, ASP 51 SHARED
                                 WITH SITE B

8. THE GENERAL STRUCTURE OF EACH MONOMER IS AN α-β-α CORE WITH 10 MAJOR β-RIBBONS (BOTH PARALLEL AND ANTIPARALLEL) RUNNING THROUGH THE CORE OF THE MOLECULE

The dimer of alkaline phosphatase is shown in Fig. 1A and is the α-carbon chain trace taken from the electron density map of the native $Zn(II)_4Mg(II)_2$ protein plus the electron density map of the 6 Cd(II) ions substituted in $Cd(II)_6AP$ determined from the anomalous dispersion of X-rays by Cd (1). The three [113]Cd NMR signals, A, B and C, from [113]$Cd(II)_6AP$ in solution are shown in Fig. 1B. Each signal integrates to 2 Cd nuclei if the small upfield signals are included (see below). Assignments of the

A, B and C resonances to specific metal binding sites in the crystal structure is based on ^{113}Cd chemical shift vs. ligand-type (2,3). The detailed ligand structure is shown in Fig. 2. The 153 ppm signal is assigned to the N,N,N site, the 70 ppm signal to the N,O,O site and the 2 ppm signal to the O,O,O,O site (2).

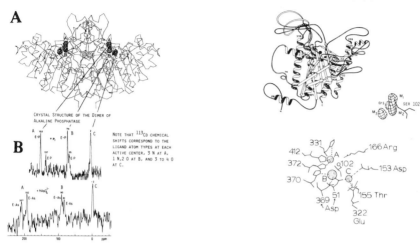

Fig. 1. A. Chain trace (α-carbon) of the dinmer of AP with the Cd anomalous dispersion map superimposed. B. ^{113}Cd NMR signals from the E-P form of Cd$_6$AP (above) and mixed E·As and E-As (below). Fig. 2. (Right) Richardson diagram of the AP monomer. (Rt) Difference map of As superimposed on the Cd map. Ser 102 is behind and between sites A and B, designated M$_1$ and M$_2$ in this diagram. (Below) Detailed ligand structure around sites A, B and C.

The reasons that a simple phosphomonoesterase requres 3 metal ions in a triad 3.9 x 4.9 x 7 Å at each active center have been only partially worked out. The chemical shift of the ^{113}Cd resonances from both A and B sites are changed by the shift from the phosphoserine intermediate (E-P) to the noncovalent phosphate intermediate (E·P). A small amount of E·P present in the Cd(II)$_6$AP accounts for the upfield satellite signals (Fig. 1B). On the other hand, the signal from the C site which does not appear to participate directly in catalysis is not influenced by the E-P ⇌ E·P equilibrium. The arsenate complex gives rise to similar ^{113}Cd signals (Fig. 1B). ^{31}P and ^{113}Cd NMR of the enzyme in solution correlated with the crystal structure of the [Cd(II)]$_6$ enzyme gives enough information about the structure of the active center to propose a mechanism for both the hydrolysis and phosphotransferase reactions catalyzed by alkaline phosphatase. A formulation of the alkaline phosphatase

mechanism (both hydrolysis and phosphotransferase reactions) is
given in Scheme 1.

$$
\text{(1)} \quad E + ROP \underset{k_{-1}}{\overset{k_1}{\rightleftharpoons}} E \cdot ROP \underset{k_{-2}}{\overset{k_2}{\rightleftharpoons}} E\text{-}P
\begin{cases}
\underset{k_{-3}}{\overset{k_3}{\rightleftharpoons}} E \cdot P \underset{k_{-4}}{\overset{k_4}{\rightleftharpoons}} E + P_i \\
\underset{k_{3'}}{\overset{k_{-3'}}{\rightleftharpoons}} E \cdot R'OP \underset{k4'}{\overset{k_{-4'}}{\rightleftharpoons}} E + R'OP
\end{cases}
$$

It is probable that the transferase mechanism is symmetrical about
E-P and involves both formation of an E·R'OP complex and dissociation
of the product phosphoalchohol as separate steps.

The rate-limiting-step for the hydrolysis reaction at low pH
is dephosphorylation of E-P, while at high pH where the enzyme
is maximally active, significant equilibrium concentrations of
E-P disappear and dissociation of product from E·P becomes rate
limiting (4,5). Since the ^{31}P resonances of enzyme-bound E·P
and free P_i are in slow chemical exchange, it is possible to apply
the technique of ^{31}P NMR inversion transfer to determine the rate
constant for phosphate dissociation, k_{off}, when this falls within
the limits of $10s^{-1}$ to $100s^{-1}$. Influences of different metal
ion species, anions, and pH on the rate limiting step can thus
be determined and are summarized later in the paper.

2 METAL ION BINDING TO ALKALINE PHOSPHATASE STUDIED BY ^{113}Cd NMR

2.1 Cd(II)-Substituted Alkaline Phosphatase.

In vitro removal of Zn(II) from the native protein (best done
by ammonium sulfate at pH 9 (4)) and reconstitution of the enzyme
with Cd(II) ions has produced a remarkably versatile enzyme for
both NMR and X-ray studies. Cd(II) appears to have the useful
property for both X-ray and NMR of easily occupying both N-containing
and O-containing ligand sites, and therefore becomes a valuable
probe for all kinds of metal binding sites (3).

While Cd(II) provides a powerful spectroscopic probe for the
active center of alkaline phosphatase, it also maintains an enzymatic
function, i.e. substrate turnover, albeit slow, forms the requisite
phosphoenzyme intermediates. Thus Cd(II) does not distort the
active center enough to prevent the catalytic mechanism from operating. The rate constants for the Cd(II) enzyme are 10^2 to 10^3
times slower than the Zn(II) enzyme which allows the turnover
of the phosphoenzyme intermediates to be followed in the NMR tube
by both ^{113}Cd and ^{31}P NMR (Figure 3). The enzyme is one with
^{113}Cd(II) in the A and B site of one monomer (resonances A' and
B' in Figure 3a). Addition of substrate, phosphate, gives a ^{31}P
resonance at ~13 ppm (Figure 3a) which can be identified as E·P.
This identification can be most easily made with saturation transfer

which shows the species giving the 13 ppm signal to be in fascile exchange with inorganic phosphate, the ^{31}P resonance at 2.5 ppm. The E·P resonance shows a 30 Hz ^{31}P–^{113}Cd coupling which shows the phosphate to be coordinated to one of the two Cd(II) ions. The metal ion to which E·P is coordinated is A as shown by heteronuclear decoupling (4).

After 48 hrs, ~50% of the bound phosphate on the Cd_2 enzyme has phosphorylated ser 102, the ^{31}P signal at 8 ppm. By 72 hrs the phosphate has shifted entirely to ser 102. The resonance of phosphoryl ser 102 is a singlet, hence the phosphate moiety has moved out of the coordination sphere of both the A and the B Cd(II) ions.

2.2 ^{113}Cd NMR as a Probe of the Interconversion of Conformational States at the Active Center.

The change in the chemical shift of the ^{113}Cd resonances from

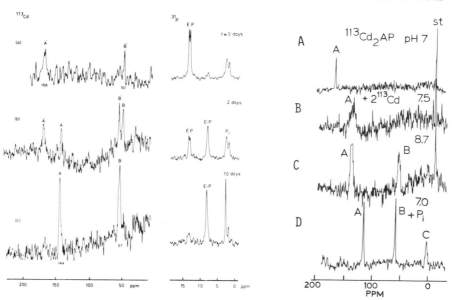

Fig. 3. Time course for the phosphorylation of $(^{113}Cd_A{}^{113}Cd_B)$-$(--_A--_B)AP$ as followed by ^{113}Cd NMR (left) and ^{31}P NMR (right). a, Phosphate first forms E·P (coupled resonance). b, After 2 days the phosphate is equally split between E·P and E–P (singlet at 8 ppm). c, After 10 days the enzyme is mostly present as E–P.

Fig. 4. (Right) ^{113}Cd NMR (44 MHz) of $(^{113}Cd_A--)_2AP$ (A); $(^{113}Cd_A{}^{113}Cd_B)_2AP$, pH 7.5 (B); Sample B at pH 8.7 (C); Sample C + $2P_i$, pH 7 (D).

both A and B site Cd(II) ions as the phosphoenzyme shifts from
E·P to E-P (Figure 3) suggests that a significant change in conformation around the two coordination sites occurs when ser 102 is
phosphorylated. The ^{113}Cd NMR probe also detects a number of
other equilibria between conformational states at the active center
of alkaline phosphatase.

If 2 Cd(II) ions are added to apoalkaline phosphatase at pH
6.5, a single Cd(II) resonance appears at 170 ppm which integrates
to two ^{113}Cd(II) nuclei (Figure 4A), reflecting equal occupancy
of the two A sites with Cd(II) in slow exchange with free Cd(II). When
a second pair of ^{113}Cd(II) ions is added at pH 7.5 which would
be expected to occupy the B sites, not only does a resonance corresponding to B site not appear, but the original A site resonance
is severely broadened as well as being chemically shifted (Figure
4B). The most likely postulate to explain this is that the less
tightly bound B site Cd(II) ions are in relatively fascile exchange
with "free" Cd(II) and that the time rate of this exchange corresponds to intermediate chemical exchange on the ^{113}Cd NMR time
scale which broadens the ^{113}Cd resonances beyond detection. We
have previously presented a detailed analysis of the exchange
rates and chemical shift differences required for intermediate

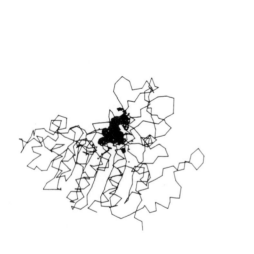

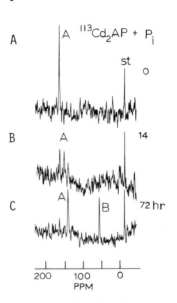

Fig. 5. Difference Fourier map of the native enzyme + 2mM P_i vs
apoenzyme overlaid on the α-carbon trace.

Fig. 6. (Right) ^{113}Cd NMR (44 MHz) of (^{113}Cd$_A$--$_B$)$_2$AP + 2 equivalents
P_i at t=0, t=14h and t=72h; pH 6.5.

chemical exchange at Cd(II) sites in proteins (5). The conformational flux resulting from such an exchange must be transmitted to the adjacent A site through the protein structure, since the A site metal ions are not less tightly bound (in fact more tightly bound) as shown by equilibrium dialysis studies (6).

That there is ample opportunity for conformational changes at the active center involving the metal ion binding is supported by the crystallographic studies. The difference Fourier map of the Zn(II) enzyme minus the apoenzyme is shown in Figure 5 superimposed on the α-carbon chain trace of the monomer. There are very large conformational changes (in addition to the removal of the metal ion electron density) occurring in the vicinity of the active center when the metal ions are removed. The metal ions can in a sense be characterized as organizers of the active center. Fascile exchange of any one of the sites could well be expected to be associated with conformational flux at the frequency of the exchange. A higher pH would be expected to slow down metal ion exchange and by pH 8.5 a B site resonance does appear for the $^{113}Cd(II)_4AP$ (Figure 4C). The A site resonance has narrowed again, but both remain relatively broad suggesting that while the conformational flux has slowed, it is still present.

Addition of the phosphate dianion at pH 7 (forming E-P) radically reduces the conformational modulation of the ^{113}Cd resonances (Figure 4D). Both A and B site resonances become sharp. This is true as well at pH values where E·P is the major species. One must conclude that formation of either phosphoenzyme, E-P or E·P, significantly restricts conformational change at the active center. This is also supported by the X-ray diffraction work which show enhanced resolution in the immediate area of the active center, i.e. the temperature factors in this area of the molecule are significantly reduced on phosphorylation (Wyckoff, unpublished data). If only 4 Cd(II) ions are present, phosphorylation of the enzyme is associated with migration of a small amount of Cd(II) to the unoccupied C site as shown by the ^{113}Cd resonance at 0 ppm (Figure 4D). While we have not been able to show a significant effect of C site metal ion on the activity in the case of the Zn(II) enzyme or on the rate of phosphorylation or dephosphorylation of E-P (7), the binding of the three Cd(II) ions to A,B and C appears to be cooperative in the presence of the phosphate dianion. The migration in Figure 4D is one indication of this, and further proof of this cooperativity will be shown below.

2.3 Cd(II) Migration Induced by Phosphorylation of $(Cd_A)_2(-_B)_2$ Alkaline Phosphatase

A different manifestation of the cooperativity, not only within one active center, but between the two active centers located 30A apart across the monomer-monomer interface, is demonstrated by phosphorylation of the enzyme containing [113]Cd(II) symmetrically in the A sites alone. The typical A site [113]Cd resonance (amplitude = 2 [113]Cd(II) ions) for this species is shown in Figure 6A. When excess phosphate (>2 moles/mol enzyme) is added to Cd_2 AP at pH 6.5, formation of one mole of phosphoenzyme per mole of dimer (equally distributed between E·P and E-P) is observed within one hour. By 4 hours this has all become phosphoserine (E-P), but still only one mole is formed.

By 14 hours (the earliest time after phosphorylation that adequate [113]Cd transients can be collected), the A site [113]Cd resonance is no longer homogeneous, but has split into three (Figure 5B). Thus phosphorylation appears to initially induce at least three separate conformations of the active center. In fact if the ^{31}P signal from E-P is examined carefully it is composed of at least two overlapping resonances (see ref. 4). During the next 48 hours, the Cd(II) continues to rearrange as indicated by changing [113]Cd resonances and finally stabilizes as two separate narrow resonances which can be identified as one A site [113]Cd and one B site [113]Cd (Figure 5C). During this rearrangement the E-P stoichiometry remains constant at 1 mole/mole enzyme (4).

The obvious interpretation is that while A site occupancy alone is sufficient for phosphorylation to occur, there must be some sort of conformational interaction between the monomers which prevents phosphorylation of the second site. At the phosphorylated site the adjacent B site is now able to form a complex with Cd(II) more stable than the A site complex in the unphosphorylated monomer, hence the Cd(II) slowly migrates from the unphosphorylated A site to the B site on the phosphorylated monomer. It is not difficult to visualize that the addition of the phosphate dianion, either as E·P or E-P, could stabilize an active center of $Cd_A-HPO_4^=-Cd_B$. The dashes are not meant to be coordination bonds, since only in E·P is there evidence for a bond to Cd_A. In the case of E-P, the phosphate does not appear from the ^{31}P NMR criteria to be coordinated to either metal, but certainly is within the outer sphere, since Cd_A, Cd_B and ser 102 are all within a 4 A radius (Figure 2) and thus $HPO_4^=$ could stabilize the 2 metal configuration.

What is difficult to explain is the initial failure to phosphorylate the second active center of $(Cd(II))_2AP$ and restore symmetrical stability of the two A site Cd(II) complexes. The only reasonable conclusion would appear to be that phosphorylation of one site causes a conformational change at the second which prevents phosphorylation. How could this happen? A detailed crystallographic view of the monomer-monomer interface between the two 3-metal active centers is shown in Figure 7. The section of polypeptide chain contributing the ligands Asp 369 and His 370 to the B site and His 372 to the A site then extends across the monomer-monomer interface, penetrates the other monomer and makes a turn which places Asp 380 within a few angstroms of the opposite active center (Figure 6). It is possible that this forms a pathway for conformational change leading to negative cooperativity.

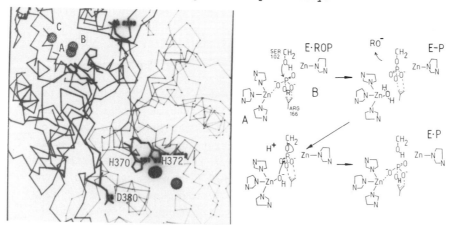

Fig. 7. Detailed polypeptide stretching in the monomer-monomer region opposite the two active centers of the dimer. His 370 and His 372 are ligands to B and A site metal ions respectively. D380 is Asp 380 from the left hand monomer.

Fig. 8. (Right) Proposed mechanism of action of AP based on NMR finding. The nucleophile in the first step is Ser 102 and in the second step a Zn-$^-$OH.

   The Cd(II) migration as described above appears to be an artifact of starting with an enzyme with only the two A sites filled. The phenomenon was originally believed to be part of an "artifactual" explanation for negative cooperativity (4). Normally of course no such migration would operate in enzyme turnover and the sequential ^{31}P and ^{113}Cd NMR studies show that the migration of the Cd(II) is not required for phosphorylation, but is a consequence of the phosphorylation. While it is indeed possible with Zn_4 and Cd_6 enzymes to form two moles of phosphoenzyme per mole dimer at low pH, it is also clear from ^{31}P NMR that at pH 8, the Zn_4 or Zn_6 enzymes will bind only one mole of phosphate per mole of dimer (4). This confirms numerous ^{32}P-labelling studies made during the early history of this enzyme. What was controversial and has been clarified by the NMR studies is the fact that two moles of phosphoserine can be made to form at low pH. This is easy to do with the Cd(II) enzyme, but difficult with Zn(II), since even at pH 5 E·P=E-P, although NMR shows the sum of the two intermediates to be 2 at pH 5. It is worth emphasizing, however, that the evidence suggests that at alkaline pH where the enzyme is active, negative cooperativity may be a real phenomenon. A pH dependence for phosphate binding to Zn(II)$_4$AP at pH 8.0 appears to be negatively cooperative (4), a phenomenon also detected by the effect of phosphate on Cl$^-$ binding as measured by ^{35}Cl NMR (7).

2.4 Mg(II) Effects on E. coli Alkaline Phosphatase.

Mg(II) has classically been described as an activator of the E. coli enzyme (6), although Mg(II) activation of the mammalian membrane-attached alkaline phosphatases is much more dramatic. In the case of $(Zn(II)_A Zn(II)_B)_2$ AP where addition of Mg(II) results only in occupancy of C sites, Mg(II) has very little effect on the k_{off} of P_i as measured by inversion transfer (8), and hence little effect on the steady state turnover number, since k_{off} is rate limiting (Table II). On the other hand addition of Mg(II) to the Zn(II)$_2$ alkaline phosphatase where B sites can be occupied has dramatic effects on turnover, although not a simple activation when examined in detail. The ^{31}P chemical shifts of E·P and E-P will be discussed further below, but Mg(II) in B site does have significant effects on the chemical shift of E·P, shifting the ^{31}P resonance upfield of that for free inorganic phosphate (Table II). At the same time in the absence of Tris, the k_{off} for phosphate slows from 35 sec^{-1} to ~1 sec^{-1} (Table II). Hence Mg(II) in B is actually an inhibitor of hydrolysis! The unexpected finding that correlates with the "activation effects" previously observed is that Mg(II) in B greatly enhances the phosphotransferase reaction as well as greatly potentiating the well-known ionic strength activation of the enzyme which is an effect of Cl$^-$ ion (8). Hence when a "normal" alkaline phosphatase assay of the $(Zn_A Mg_B)_2$ enzyme is done in 1 M Tris HCl, a significant activation is observed because of the greatly enhanced formation of Tris-phosphate and an enhanced Cl$^-$ activation (see ref. 8).

3 MECHANISM OF PHOSPHATE HYDROLYSIS BY ALKALINE PHOSPHATASE AS SYNTHESIZED FROM THE ^{31}P NMR, THE CRYSTAL STRUCTURE AND KINETICS (INCLUDING ^{31}P INVERSION TRANSFER).

3.1 Functional Consequences of Metal Ion Substitutions at A and B Sites

Native alkaline phosphatase can be isolated containing 2-4 Zn(II) ions and 1-2 Mg(II) ions (6) and shows a sigmoid pH-rate profile with an apparent pK_a from 7.5-8 with maximum activity above pH 9 (2). By systematically replacing the metal ions at each pair of sites, A, B and C, with pairs of metal ions of different species, it has been possible to differentiate some of the functions of the individual metal binding sites (9). Functional character- istics of the alkaline phosphatases with various metal ions at each of the three pairs of binding sites at each active center

Table II

Effect of Metal Ions on the E-P $\rightleftharpoons$ E·P Equilibrium and on the Rate of Dissociation of Phosphate from E·P.[a]

Metal Site Occupancy at the Active Center	pH at which E-P = E·P pH	Chemical Shift		k_{off}(pH) s^{-1}
		E-P	E·P	
		ppm		
$[Zn_A Zn_B]_2 AP$	5	8.6	4.3	~35(8)[b]
$[Zn_A Zn_B Mg_C]_2 AP$	5	8.6	3.4	~35(8)
$[Zn_A Mg_B]_2 AP$	4.5	8.5	1.8	~1(8)[c]
$[Zn_A Mg_B]_2 AP + 1 M Cl^-$	4.5	8.5	1.8	~15(9)
$[Zn_A Cd_B]_2 AP$	6	8.0	12.6	~2(9)
$[Cd_A Cd_B][--_A--_B]AP$	10	8.4	13.4	<1(9)[d]
$[Cd_A Cd_B Cd_C]_2 AP$	8.7	8.7	13.0	<1(9)[d]
$[Cd_A Cd_B Cd_C]_2 AP + 1 M Cl^-$	8.7	8.7	13.0	~6(9)

a. All measurements were made in 0.01 M Tris-0.01 M acetate unless otherwise indicated.

b. k_{off} is the rate-limiting step for the Zn(II) enzyme, hence is = to the steady-state hydrolysis rate.

c. This is a very slow enzyme until Cl^- is added. Tris, 1M, causes an additional enhancement due to the additive phosphotransferase reaction.

d. k_{off} is not the steady-state rate for the Cd(II) enzyme, since phosphorylation of the enzyme is even slower.

are summarized in Table II by listing the ^{31}P chemical shifts
of E·P and E-P, the pH where [E·P]=[E-P] and the dissociation
rate of product, P_i, as determined by ^{31}P inversion transfer (8).

The apparent pK_a of activity is a major reflection of the proton
dissociation behavior of one or more groups involved in the catalytic
mechanism. Arguments based on the minimal mechanism for this
enzyme suggest that this pK_a directly controls the equilibrium
between E·P and E-P, i. e. k_3/k_{-3} (8,9). For the native enzyme
at low pH, $k_{-3} >> k_3$, hence E-P is the major equilibrium species,
while at alkaline pH, $k_3 >> k_{-3}$ and E·P is the major equilibrium
species, even though the reaction is still proceeding through
E-P (8).   We propose that the pH dependency of the E-P/E·P ratio
is a direct reflection of the pK_a of a water molecule coordinated
to the A site metal ion. The best way of following the pH-dependency
of the ratio of phosphointermediates is to follow the ^{31}P NMR
signals of the two intermediates as a function of pH (Table II).
From the data in Table II, the metal ion at A site appears to
have the major influence on the pK_a of the group controlling this
equilibrium. Zn(II) in A must induce a relatively low pK_a such
that the midpoint of the E-P $\rightleftharpoons$ E·P equilibrium is near pH 5 (Table
II). In contrast Cd(II) must result in a pK_a at least 3 pH units
higher, between 8 and 10 (Table II). The midpoint of the E-P
$\rightleftharpoons$ E·P equilibrium is several pH units lower than the actual pK_a
because of the ratio of kinetic constants, $k_{phosphorylation}/k_{dephos^-}$
$_{phorylation}$. The most plausible explanation for this phenomenon
associated with the Zn(II) to Cd(II) substitution is that the
activity-linked pK_a represents that of a coordinated solvent on
the A site metal ion (4,8,9). This pK_a would be expected to be
much higher for solvent coordinated to Cd(II), a softer metal
with less polarizing power making the coordinated solvent a poorer
acid. Within the dramatic changes in pH profile induced by changing
Zn(II) to Cd(II) in A site, the nature of the B site metal ion
has a secondary and much smaller effect on the pK_a, e.g. Mg(II)
in B lowers the pK_a while Cd(II) in B raises the pK_a (Table II).

^{31}P NMR data suggest that A site metal ion, initially coordinating phosphate in the E·P complex, develops an open coordination
site after formation of E-P, since phosphate appears to move out
of the first coordination sphere of the A site metal ion on phosphorylation of serine 102 (Figure 3). This would allow a solvent
molecule to coordinate the A site metal ion generating an ^-OH
in the correct position to be the nucleophile attacking the phosphorous
of E-P.

3.2   Influence of the B site metal ion on the Conformations of the E·P and E-P Intermediates.

The chemical shifts of the E·P complexes of the three enzyme species containing Zn(II) in A sites and either Mg(II), Zn(II) or Cd(II) in B sites, show large variation; E·P resonates at 1.8 ppm, 4.3 ppm and 12.6 ppm for species containing Mg(II), Zn(II) or Cd(II) respectively (Table II). Phosphate of E·P is anchored by coordination to the A site metal ion and possibly also by inter-action with Arg 166 which swings down toward the A site metal ion (4) (Figure 2).   Thus one may picture E·P as a complex in which phosphate is relatively fixed, possibly allowing small conforma-tional changes induced by the adjacent B site metal ion to cause significant distortion of phosphate bond angles, a feature known to induce large downfield ^{31}P shifts (5).   On the other hand the noncoordinated phosphate group of the phosphoserine may not be rigidly held. Compatible with this postulate is the observation that the ^{31}P shift of E-P is relatively insensitive to the nature of the metal ion at either A or B sites being 8.0, 8.6, 8.4 and 8.5 ppm for $(Zn(II)_A Cd(II)_B)_2 AP$, $(Zn(II)_A - Zn(II)_B)_2 AP$, $(Cd(II)_A - Cd(II)_B)_2 AP$ and $(Zn(II)_A Mg(II)_B)_2 AP$ respectively.

3.3   Influence of B site Metal Ion on Dissociation of Inorganic Phosphate.

The substitution of Cd(II) for Zn(II) at both A and B sites not only shiftsthe midpoint of the E-P ⇌ E·P equilibrium to alkaline pH, but also dramatically lowers the phosphate dissociation rate (Table II), while enzyme turnover is reduced by 2 to 3 orders of magnitude (2,9). At pH 9 the dissociation rate of P_i from the Cd(II) enzyme is ~1 s^{-1} (8), which is still too fast for disso-ciation to be rate limiting and suggests that dephosphorylation is also extremely slow and remains rate limiting for Cd(II)$_6$AP even at pH 9. If B site Zn(II) in Zn(II)$_4$AP is replaced by Cd(II) to form the $(Zn(II)_A Cd(II)_B)_2 AP$ hybrid, P_i dissociation falls dramatically, from a value of 35 sec^{-1} for Zn(II)$_4$ Mg(II)$_2$AP at alkaline pH to 2 s^{-1} (Table II). Slowing of product dissociation is accompanied by the unusual downfield shift in the E·P resonance, from the near-free value of 3.4 ppm for Zn(II)$_4$Mg(II)$_2$AP to values between 12 and 13.4 ppm when cadmium occupies B site (Table II) (8). An altered phosphate conformation and a reduced phosphate dissociation rate may both be manifestations of small changes in the active site brought about by replacement of the native

B site Zn(II) or Mg(II) with the larger Cd(II) ion.

3.4   Mechanism of Action Incorporating Conclusions from the NMR Data.

A diagram of the mechanism which it is possible to synthesize from the current data is shown in Figure 8. The characteristics of the hybrid metal phosphatases provide a much clearer picture of the functions of the separate metal ions (9). A site metal, which is occupied by zinc in the native enzyme, serves to coordinate the phosphate group in the non-covalent complex.

^{31}P NMR spectrum of the $(Zn(II)_A Cd(II)_B)_2$ AP is a good illustration of these conclusions. In the ^{31}P spectrum of the phospho form of this hybrid at low pH, there is a major resonance at 8.0 ppm which is assignable to E-P of the hybrid. As the pH is raised this resonance disappears to be replaced by a prominent singlet at 12.66 ppm, assignable to E·P of the hybrid (Figure 9). Thus

12.6 ppm

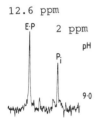

Fig. 9. ^{31}P NMR (88MHz) of the $(Zn_A Cd_B)$ AP at pH 9.0 plus excess phosphate.

replacement of $^{113}Cd(II)$ at A site by Zn(II) removes the 30Hz coupling on E·P, as expected if the phosphate of E·P is coordinated to the A site metal, Zn(II), but not to the B site metal ion which remains $^{113}Cd(II)$ in the hybrid. The unusual downfieldshift of the E·P resonance (12.66 ppm) remains and confirms that the Cd(II) in B site is primarily responsible for the lowfield shift.

As the phosphate is transferred to serine 102, its coordination site on A site metal ion would become available to solvent. Phosphorylation of serine 102 can proceed slowly in the absence of B site metal ion, but is accelerated by its presence (6). This is probably due to additional charge neutralization of the negative phosphate group as it moves toward serine 102 and therefore closer to the B site metal ion. The metal ion at B site could be close enough to the seryl oxygen to potentiate the formation of seryl-O⁻,

though there is no evidence as yet for direct coordination. Presumably
the non-covalent complex with a phosphomonoester as substrate,
E·ROP, would be analogous. Dephosphorylation of the phosphoserine
is inefficient and rate limiting at low pH where the concentration
of $Zn-OH^-$, formed by ionization of a water molecule bound to A
site zinc would be small. At alkaline pH dephosphorylation is
greatly accelerated, paralleled by a shift in the E-P $\rightleftharpoons$ E·P equilibrium to the right and accompanied by a large increase in the
concentration of the nucleophile. Charge neutralization at the
phosphoserine by the metal ion at B site would also potentiate
the nucleophilic attack of ^-OH at the second stage of the mechanism.
Dissociation of product phosphate from the highly positively charged
active center then apparently becomes rate limiting. The pK_a
of the bound water is primarily determined by the A site metal
ion and thus differs most between $Zn(II)_4AP$ and $Cd(II)_6AP$ (Table
II). This work was supported by Grant AM09070-21 from the NIH.

4 REFERENCES

(1) H.W.Wyckoff, M. Handschumacher, H.M. Krishna Murthy, J.M. Sowadski,
Adv. Enzymol. and Related Areas of Mol. Biol. <u>55</u> (1983) 453-480.

(2) J.E. Coleman, P. Gettins, Adv. Enzymol. and Related Areas
of Mol. Biol. <u>55</u> (1983) 381-452.

(3) I.M. Armitage, J.E. Otvos, in Berliner, Rubin (eds), Biological
Mag. Res., Plenum Press (1982) pp. 79-144.

(4) P. Gettins, J.E. Coleman, J. Biol. Chem. <u>258</u> (1983) 396-407.-
P.Gettins, J.E. Coleman, J. Biol. Chem. <u>258</u> (1983) 408-416.

(5) J.E. Coleman, I.M. Armitage, J.F. Chlebowski, J.D. Otvos,
A.J.M. Schoot Uiterkamp, in Shulman (ed.) Biological Applications
of Mag. Res., Academic Press (1979) pp. 345-389.

(6) J.E. Coleman, K.-I. Nakamura, J.F. Chlebowski, J. JBiol. Chem. <u>258</u>
(1983) 386-395.

(7) P. Gettins, J.E. Coleman, J. Biol. Chem. <u>259</u> (1984) 11036-11040.

(8) P. Gettins, M. Metzler, J.E. Coleman, J. Biol. Chem. <u>260</u> (1985)
2875-2883.

(9) P. Gettins, J.E. Coleman, J. Biol. Chem. <u>259</u> (1984) 4991-4997.

Magnetic Resonance Spectroscopy of Oxygen-17 To Probe The Action of Metalloenzymes: Liver Alcohol Dehydrogenase

Moon B. Yim, Gregg B. Wells, Lawrence C. Kuo, Marvin W. Makinen*

Department of Biochemistry and Molecular Biology, The University of Chicago, Cummings Life Science Center, 920 East 58th Street, Chicago, Illinois 60637 U.S.A.

SUMMARY

The use of oxygen-17 as a spectroscopic probe of Co^{2+}-substituted metalloenzymes is discussed. Continuous wave, microwave power saturation studies of a variety of metalloprotein and small molecule complexes of paramagnetic metal ions show that the value of the saturation parameter $P_{1/2}$ [microwave power at which the saturation factor $(1 + \gamma^2 H_1^2 T_1 T_2)^{-1}$ equals 0.5] is affected by the presence of oxygen-donor ligands enriched with oxygen-17 while no change is observed with ligands enriched with oxygen-18. The influence of oxygen-17 on the microwave saturation properties can be accounted for by a change in the extent of spectral diffusion among the spin packets of an inhomogeneously broadened EPR absorption line and arises through contact hyperfine interactions of oxygen-17 with the paramagnetic metal ion. This spectroscopic probe is applied to a variety of binary and ternary complexes of active site specific Co^{2+}-reconstituted liver alcohol dehydrogenase (CoLADH) to assign the coordination number of the active site metal ion. No influence of oxygen-17 enriched water is observed for the binary $CoLADH-CF_3CH_2OH$ complex, in general agreement with expectations based on X-ray crystallographic studies, while a shift in $P_{1/2}$ is observed for the ternary $CoLADH-NAD^+-CF_3CH_2OH$ complex prepared in the presence of $H_2^{17}O$. These results, together with those of earlier spectroscopic and kinetic investigations, confirm our suggestion [M. W. Makinen, W. Maret, M. B. Yim, Proc. Natl. Acad. Sci. (USA) 80 (1983) 2584-2588] that the oxidation of alcohol catalyzed by LADH requires the participation of a neutral metal-bound water molecule in a penta-coordinate complex of the active site metal ion.

---

*To whom to address correspondence.

1   INTRODUCTION

In the catalytic action of a variety of metalloenzymes, a solvent molecule or oxygen-donor atom of the substrate is bound to the active site metal ion. Well known examples of such metalloenzymes are carboxypeptidase A (1), thermolysin (2), carbonic anhydrase (3), alcohol dehydrogenase (4), and alkaline phosphatase (5). In a series of chemical, kinetic, and spectroscopic studies of carboxypeptidase A (CPA[†]) and liver alcohol dehydrogenase (LADH[†]), we have shown that the coordination environment of the active site metal ion is expanded to accommodate a fifth ligand in catalytically competent reaction intermediates, and we have pointed out (6-9) how the metal-bound water molecule may have an integral chemical role in the catalytic cycle. The presence of a metal-bound oxygen donor ligand in the active site was detected with use of ligands enriched with oxygen-17 and an enzyme derivative that was site-specifically reconstituted with Co^{2+} for the catalytically active Zn^{2+}. We monitored the EPR absorption of the active site specific Co^{2+}-substituted enzyme and observed that the strength of the microwave magnetic field that was needed to achieve a value of the saturation factor $(1 + \gamma^2 H_1^2 T_1 T_2)^{-1}$ of 0.5 was affected by the (I=5/2) nucleus of oxygen-17 when enriched into an oxygen-donor ligand. In this communication, we discuss how this effect, associated with the incorporation of oxygen-17 into the inner coordination shell of a paramagnetic metal ion, can be accounted for by a change in the extent of spectral diffusion between the spin packets of the EPR absorption line. We apply this effect to LADH to confirm our earlier suggestions (7-10) that the catalytically competent active site metal ion requires the participation of a metal-bound water molecule in alcohol oxidation.

2   RESULTS

In Figure 1 we present the (first-derivative) EPR absorption spectrum of CoLADH and data illustrating the influence of $H_2^{17}O$ on the c.w. microwave power saturation properties of the prominent low-field resonance absorption near g~6.67. The intersection point of the asymptotes of the c.w. saturation curve defines the parameter $P_{1/2}$ where the saturation factor $(1 + \gamma^2 H_1^2 T_1 T_2)^{-1}$ has a value of 0.5 (11-13). It is seen that increasing the concentration of $H_2^{17}O$ results in a decrease in the value of $P_{1/2}$ with no change in slope at high microwave power. The presence of $H_2^{18}O$ in contrast has no influence on the value of $P_{1/2}$, demonstrating that the shift observed with $H_2^{17}O$ is magnetic in origin.

In parallel experiments we have observed that the presence of $H_2^{17}O$ does not influence the c.w. microwave power saturation properties of the Co^{2+} ion when CF_3CH_2OH is added to CoLADH to form the binary enzyme-inhibitor complex. Since solvent molecules are sequestered near the active site metal ion upon inhibitor binding (14) and the metal-bound water molecule is displaced in binary enzyme-inhibitor complexes(15), this observation indicates that the shift in $P_{1/2}$ requires an oxygen-17 enriched oxygen donor-ligand within the inner coordination shell of the metal ion. It also indicates that the influence of oxygen-17 is not mediated by distant

---

[†]Abrreviations: CPA, carboxypeptidase A; Ches, 2-(N-cyclohexylamino)ethanesulfonic acid; c.w., continuous wave; EPR, electron paramagnetic resonance; LADH, liver alcohol dehydrogenase; metHb, (aquo)methemoglobin; metMb, (aquo)metmyoglobin; Tes, N-<u>tris</u>-(hydroxymethyl)methyl-2-aminoethanesulfonic acid.

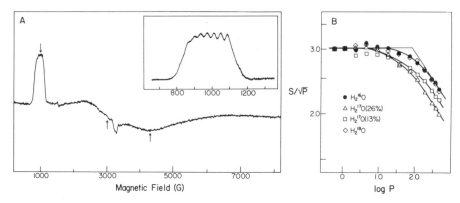

Fig. 1. First derivative EPR absorption spectrum of active site specific CoLADH. The inset in Panel A shows the expanded spectrum of the low-field resonance absorption with hyperfine structure due to the ^{59}Co ($I = 7/2$) nucleus. In Panel B are compared the c.w. saturation curves of the low field absorption for CoLADH in media of different isotopic oxygen content. The equivalence of the saturation curves of natural abundance and oxygen-18 enriched solvent shows that the shift in $P_{1/2}$ with introduction of oxygen-17 is magnetic in origin. The log $P_{1/2}$ values for these saturation curves are($\bullet$,$\diamond$) 2.00, natural abundance or $\geq 45\%$ $H_2{}^{18}O$; ($\square$)1.75, 13 g-atoms % $H_2{}^{17}O$; ($\triangle$) 1.53, 26 g-atoms % $H_2{}^{17}O$. Only the slope for the enzyme in natural abundance solvent is drawn for purposes of clarity in data presentation. CoLADH was dissolved to 1.2 mM in active sites in 0.05 M Tes buffered to pH 7 at 0^oC. EPR samples were prepared directly in quartz sample tubes by addition of appropriate aliquots of natural abundance, oxygen-17 enriched, or oxygen-18 enriched water. The final concentrations of CoLADH and Tes were 0.6 mM in active sites and 0.025 M, respectively. The sample temperature was 8 K. Typical conditions of spectral data collection have been published (7,8).

water molecules near the paramagnetic site that may have magnetic interactions with the bulk solvent. We have reported similar observations for CoCPA and its glycyl-L-tyrosine inhibitor complex (6).

In Figure 2 we compare c.w. power saturation curves of metHb and metMb for the g~2 resonance absorption line that is characteristic of the high-spin Fe^{3+} ion of the heme group. Although the difference in the value of $P_{1/2}$ for natural abundance and $H_2{}^{17}O$ enriched samples decreases with increasing temperature, there is no change in the slope of the asymptote at high microwave power. It is important to note, however, that the direction of the change in $P_{1/2}$ upon addition of $H_2{}^{17}O$ differs for the two proteins despite their similar tertiary structures and heme environments. For metMb, $P_{1/2}$ is shifted to higher values upon addition of $H_2{}^{17}O$ while for metHb this parameter is shifted to lower values. As in the case of CoLADH, we observed that $H_2{}^{18}O$ did not influence the c.w. power saturation properties of the EPR absorption of the Fe^{3+} ion; furthermore, no effect was observed for these proteins in solutions containing $\geq 95\%$ D_2O.

We have also investigated the influence of oxygen-17 on the saturation properties of paramagnetic metal ions in structurally defined, magnetically dilute, polycrystalline matrices. In addition to detection of a shift in $P_{1/2}$ induced by the presence of oxygen-17 enriched acetate in $Co_{0.001}Zn_{0.999}(CH_3COO)_2(imidazole)_2$ (6), we have also observed for the compounds $Co_{0.001}Zn_{0.999}(Ph_3PO)_2Cl_2$ (16), $Co_{0.0005}Mg_{0.9995}(CH_3COO)_2 \cdot 4H_2O$ (17), and $Cr_{0.0005}Al_{0.9995}K(SO_4)_2 \cdot 12H_2O$ (18) a corresponding influence of oxygen-17.

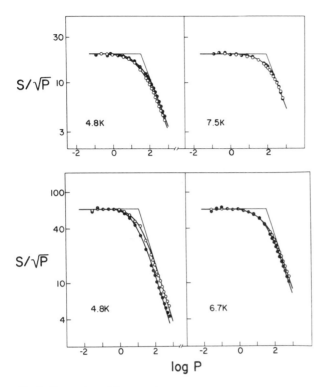

Fig. 2. Comparison of the c.w. microwave power saturation behavior of metHb (upper panel) and metMb (lower panel) in natural abundance(●) and oxygen-17 enriched [26 g-atoms % (○)water]. It is important to note that introduction of $H_2^{17}O$ results in faster relaxation (increased $P_{1/2}$) for metMb but slower relaxation (decreased $P_{1/2}$) for metHb. Sperm whale metMb (Sigma Chemical Company) was dissolved to a concentration of 4.8 mM in 0.02 M phosphate buffered to pH 6.5. Human metHb was prepared by oxidation of human oxyhemoglobin with potassium ferricyanide and was dialyzed and concentrated to 4.0 mM (in heme) in 0.10 M phosphate buffered to pH 6.2. EPR samples were prepared directly in quartz sample tubes by addition of equal volumes of natural abundance or oxygen-17 enriched water. The final concentrations were 2.4 mM metMb in 0.01 M phosphate and 2.0 mM metHb (in heme) in 0.05 M phosphate. Typical conditions of spectral data collection have been published (13).

We have published the results of studies showing that the presence of $H_2^{17}O$ influences the c.w. microwave power saturation behavior of the active site metal ion in the ternary CoLADH-NADH-CF$_3$CH$_2$OH complex (8). No effect is detected for the CoLADH-NADH-(para-N,N'-dimethylaminocinnamaldehyde) complex prepared at pH 9.1. X-ray crystallographic studies of the structurally similar ternary inhibitor complex of CoLADH-tetrahydroNADH-(para-N,N'dimethylaminocinnamaldehyde) show sequestered solvent molecules in the vicinity of the active site metal ion, and only the carbonyl oxygen of the aldehyde group is bound to the metal ion (14). Therefore, our EPR results are compatible with the results of these X-ray crystallographic studies.

In Figure 3 we present the (first-derivative) EPR absorption spectrum of the ternary CoLADH-NAD+-CF$_3$CH$_2$OH complex formed in solution at pH 9.0. This pH corresponds to the region of maximum catalytic activity in alcohol oxidation (8,10). The inset compares the c.w. microwave power saturation curves for the complex prepared with

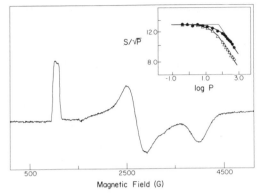

Fig. 3. First-derivative EPR absorption spectrum and c.w. saturation curves of CoLADH-NAD+- CF$_3$CH$_2$OH at pH 9. The inset shows the c.w. saturation curves for the complex prepared in natural abundance (●) and in oxygen-17 enriched water [26 g-atoms % H$_2$^{17}O (Δ)]. Estimates of log P$_{1/2}$ values are correspondingly 1.78 and 1.30. CoLADH was dissolved to 0.17 mM in active sites in 5 mM Tes containing 0.5 M KCl buffered to pH 7 at 0°C. Immediately prior to use, a stock solution of 0.2 M NAD$^+$was prepared in 1 M Ches buffered to pH 9.1. The ternary complexes of CoLADH were prepared directly in EPR sample tubes by addition of appropriate aliquots of NAD+, CF$_3$CH$_2$OH, and natural abundance or oxygen-17 enriched water. The final concentrations were 0.60 mM CoLADH (in active site), 200 mM NAD+, and 0.05 M CF$_3$CH$_2$OH in 0.1 M Ches at pH 9. The sample temperature was 5.1 K.

natural abundance and oxygen-17 enriched H$_2$O. As in Figure 1 and 2, the presence of H$_2$^{17}O induces a shift in the value of P$_{1/2}$ with no change in the slope of the asymptote at high microwave power.

3   DISCUSSION

The characteristic features of the influence of oxygen-17 on the c.w. microwave power saturation properties of the paramagnetic complexes in Figures 1-3 are that (i) the slope of the asymptote of the saturation curve at high microwave power is not altered by introduction of oxygen-17; (ii) the magnitude of the shift in P$_{1/2}$ from its value observed for the complex prepared with natural abundance materials decreases with increasing temperature; and (iii) the shift in P$_{1/2}$ may occur towards either higher or lower value. These characteristics can be interpreted on the basis of the spin-packet model of EPR absorption lines originally introduced by Portis (19), as extended to include the influence of spectral diffusion (20-23). According to this model, an inhomogeneously broadened EPR absorption line consists of an envelope of a continuous distribution of homogeneous resonance lines f(w-w'), each centered at a different separation (w'-w$_0$) from the mean frequency w$_0$. The homogeneous lines characterized by a linewidth 1/T$_2$ correspond to sets of electron spins that interact with different nuclear spin configurations, all of which superimpose to form the overall inhomogeneously broadened line with linewidth 1/T$_2$*. As an EPR transition is saturated by irradiation with increasing levels of microwave power, the spin-packets interact through spectral diffusion to transfer saturation, providing an additional relaxation pathway to achieve internal thermal equilibrium.

Under conditions of spectral diffusion, it can be shown (24,25) that the apparent spin-lattice relaxation time is defined by the relationship $T_1' = T_1T_D/(T_1+T_D)$ where T_D is the characteristic spectral diffusion time and T_1 is the true spin-lattice relaxation time in the absence of spectral diffusion. The limiting conditions that may obtain are $T_1 \gg T_D$ or $T_D \gg T_1$, the latter condition characterizing noninteracting (independent) spin-packets. The limiting values of T_1' are correspondingly $T_1' \sim T_D$ and $T_1' \sim T_1$. We suggest that incorporation of oxygen-17 into the inner coordination sphere of the paramagnetic metal ion alters the extent of the interaction of the spin-packets through spectral diffusion and cross-relaxation. Since the susceptibility is determined by $1/T_1$ under conditions of high microwave power, i.e., $T_1 \gg T_2 \gg 1/\gamma H_1$ (26), $P_{1/2}$ is correspondingly governed predominantly by $1/T_1$ or $1/T_D$. On this basis saturation of an EPR absorption line under conditions of increased spectral diffusion

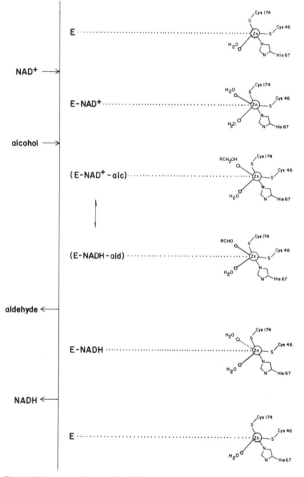

Fig. 4. The compulsory-ordered, ternary complex mechanism of LADH. The diagram illustrates the immediate coordination environment of the active site metal ion determined on the basis of spectroscopic studies. The metal ion is represented as a circle and the donor-ligand atoms of protein amino acid sidechains are those of cysteine-46, cysteine-174, and histidine-67 (4). The basis of assignment of the coordination environment of the active site metal ion is discussed for the ternary LADH-NAD+-alcohol complex in Figure 3 while that for the LADH-NADH-aldehyde complexes has been previously published (8).

requires additional microwave power with a resultant increase in $P_{1/2}$. On the other hand, if the extent of the interaction among the spin-packets is reduced, effectiveness of the transfer of saturation through spectral diffusion is decreased with a resultant shift of $P_{1/2}$ to lower values. Futhermore, the temperature dependence of T_D is expected to be much smaller than that of T_1 in Orbach [$T_1 \sim \exp(\Delta/kT)$] or Raman [$T_1 \sim T^7$ or T^9] processes (27). For this reason the influence of T_D on $P_{1/2}$ and consequently the shift in $P_{1/2}$ will decrease with increasing temperature. SInce the diffusion time $T_D \sim (T_2)^4/(T_2^*)^3$ (22) and both T_2 and T_2^* are influenced by nuclear hyperfine interactions, the shift in $P_{1/2}$ must arise through hyperfine interactions of oxygen-17 with the metal ion, modulated through electron-nuclear dipolar coupling. We discuss the basis of the change in spectral diffusion in greater detail elsewhere (28).

On this basis Figure 3 provides evidence that a water molecule is coordinated to the active site metal ion in the CoLADH-NAD$^+$-CF$_3$CH$_2$OH complex. We have previously demonstrated in a similar manner that a metal-bound water molecule also obtains in the ternary complex CoLADH-NADH-CF$_3$CH$_2$OH (8). Since three amino acid sidechains serve as ligands to the metal ion and it is probable that true alcohol substrates are coordinated to the active site metal ion (29,30), the detection of metal-bound H$_2$^{17}O in these complexes indicates that the active site metal ion is penta-coordinate in catalytically competent reaction intermediates. We have published spectroscopic evidence that the active site metal ion is penta-coordinate in the binary CoLADH-NAD$^+$ complex (7). These combined results lead to the description of the reaction cycle of LADH as illustrated in Figure 4. The binding of coenzyme results in a change in coordination number so that ternary complex interconversion proceeds via the intermediacy of a penta-coordinate active site metal ion. These results stand in marked contradiction to the interpretations of the mechanism on LADH based only on X-ray structural studies of the crystalline enzyme in the "closed" conformation (4, 29-31). We have pointed out on the basis of the pH profiles of k_{cat} and k_{cat}/K_M of ZnLADH and CoLADH that the metal-bound water molecule in ternary complex interconversion must be neutral in the physiologic pH range and that a neutral water molecule may serve a vital catalytic role as a conduit in catalyzing proton abstraction from the alcoholic OH group prior to hydride transfer (8,10). The functional role of the water molecule bound to the active site metal ion in a penta-coordinate configuration is schematically illustrated in FIgure 5. Recent studies with model metal ion complexes showing that a neutral metal-bound water molecule may serve as a conduit in proton transfer (32) support this interpretation of the chemical role of the active site metal-water complex of LADH in alcohol oxidation.

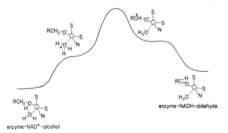

Fig. 5. Catalytic role of the active site metal-bound water molecule of LADH in ternary complex interconversion. The pathway begins with metal-bound alcohol forming a hydrogen bridge to the metal-bound water molecule and proceeding to transfer of the proton with subsequent release to bulk solvent presumably via the proton-transfer system in the active site (4,14). With release of the proton to the bulk solvent, abstraction of the hydride ion can occur by the nearby pyridinium group of NAD$^+$. See earlier discussion in ref. 8.

4 ACKNOWLEDGMENTS

This work has been supported by USPHS grants of the National Institutes of Health (GM 21900 and AA 06374). G.B.W. was supported by an MSTP grant of the National Institutes of Health (GM 07281), and L.C.K. was a predoctoral student supported by a National Institutes of Health training grant (GM 07183).

5 REFERENCES

(1) F. A. Quiocho, W. N. Lipscomb, Adv. Prot. Chem. 25 (1971) 1-78.

(2) B. W. Matthews, L. H. Weaver, W. R. Kester, J. Biol. Chem. 249 (1974) 8030-8044.

(3) K. K. Kannan, A. Liljas, I. Waara, P. C. Bergstén, S. Lovgren, B. Strandberg, N. Bengtsson, U Carlbom, K. Fridborg, L. Jarüp, M. Petef, Cold Spring Harbor Symp. Quant. Biol. 36 (1971) 221-231.

(4) C. I. Brändén, J. Jörnvall, H. Eklund, B. Furugren, in P. D. Boyer (ed.), The Enzymes, 3rd Edn., Vol. XI, Academic, New York, 1975, pp. 103-190.

(5) J. M. Sowadski, B. A. Foster, H. W. Wyckoff, J. Mol. Biol. 150 (1981) 245-272.

(6) L. C. Kuo, M. W. Makinen, J. Biol. Chem. 257 (1982) 24-27.

(7) M. W. Makinen, M. B. Yim, Proc. Natl. Acad. Sci. (U.S.A.) 78 (1981) 6221-6225.

(8) M. W. Makinen, W. Maret, M. B. Yim, Proc. Natl. Acad. Sci. (U.S.A.) 80 (1983) 2584-2588.

(9) M. W. Makinen, L. C. Kuo, M. B. Yim, W. Maret, G. B. Wells, J. Mol. Catalysis 23 (1984) 179-186.

(10) W. Maret, M. W. Makinen, submitted for publication.

(11) H. Beinert, W. H. Orme-Johnson, in A. Ehrenberg, B. Malmström, T. Vänngard (eds.), Magnetic Resonance in Biological Systems, Pergamon, Oxford, 1967, pp. 221-247.

(12) H. Rupp, K. K. Rao, D. O. Hall, R. Cammack, Biochim. Biophys. Acta 537 (1978) 255-269.

(13) M. B. Yim, L. C. Kuo, M. W. Makinen, J. Magn. Resonance 46 (1982) 247-256.

(14) E. Cedergren-Zeppezauer, J. P. Samama, H. Eklund, Biochemistry 21 (1982) 4895-4909.

(15) T. Boiwe, C. I. Brändén, Eur. J. Biochem. 77 (1977) 173-179.

(16) D. Vivien, J. F. Gibson, J. Chem. Soc. (Faraday Trans. II) 71 (1975) 1640-1653.

(17) J. N. van Niekerk, F.R. L. Schoening, Acta Cryst. 6 (1953) 609-612.

(18) A. C. Larson, D. T. Cromer, Acta Cryst. 22 (1967) 793-800.

(19) A. M. Portis, Phys. Rev. 91 (1953) 1071-1078.

(20) T. G. Castner, Jr., Phys. Rev. 115 (1959) 1506-1515.

(21) N. Bleombergen, S. Shapiro, P. Pershan, J. Artman, Phys. Rev. 114 (1959) 445-459.

(22) A. Kiel, Phys. Rev. 125 (1962) 1451-1455.

(23) S. Clough, C. A. Scott, J. Phys. C. (Proc. Phys. Soc. (London), Ser. 2) 1 (1968) 919-931.

(24) L. Kevan, P. A. Narayana, in M. M. Dorio and J. H. Freed (eds.), Multiple Electron Resonance Spectroscopy, Plenum, New York, 1979, pp. 229-259.

(25) H. Yoshida, D. F. Feng, L. Kevan, J. Chem. Phys. 58 (1973) 3411-3419.

(26) J. S. Hyde, Phys. Rev. 119 (1960) 1492-1495.

(27) A. Abragam, B. Bleany, Electron Paramagnetic Resonance of Transition Ions, Oxford University Press, Oxford, 1970.

(28) G. B. Wells, M. B. Yim, M. W. Makinen, manuscript in preparation.

(29) H. Eklund, J. P. Samama, L. Wallén, C. I. Brändén, A. Akeson, T. A. Jones, J. Mol. Biol. 146 (1981) 561-587.

(30) H. Eklund, B. V. Plapp, J. P. Samama, C. I. Brändén, J. Biol. Chem. 257 (1982) 14349-14358.

(31) I. Bertini, M. Gerber, G. Lanani, C. Luchinat, W. Maret, S. Rawer, M. Zeppezauer, J. Am. Chem. Soc. 106 (1984) 1826-1830.

(32) R. Kluger, M. K. Wong, A. K. Dodds, J. Am. Chem. Soc. 106 (1984) 1113-1117.

Progress in the Characterization of *Thermus* Respiratory Proteins

J.A. Fee, T. Yoshida, B. Zimmerman, D. Kuila, W.R. Ranger

Biophysics Research Division, The University of Michigan, Ann Arbor, Michigan 48109, USA and Isotope and Nuclear Chemistry Division. Los Alamos National Laboratory, Los Alamos, New Mexico 87545, USA

We have been purifying and characterizing respiratory proteins from the extremely thermophilic aerobe, <u>Thermus thermophilus</u>.

Cytochrome $c_1 aa_3$

We have used the spectral properties of the tightly bound cytochrome c, as an indicator of the redox state of the components of cytochrome aa_3 in reductive, oxidative and potentiometric titrations. During the latter, we assume all redox components are in equilibrium with the mediators: At pH 7.8 cytochrome c_1 has $E_m =$ 205 mV (n = 1), Cu_A has $E_m = 265$ mV (n = 1), cytochrome a has $E_m = 270$ mV (n = 1 and 60 % spectral contribution at 605 nm), and cytochrome a_3/Cu_B has $E_m \sim 360$ mV (n = 2 and 40 % spectral contribution at 605 nm). Reductive and oxidative titrations are consistent with an equilibration between cytochrome c_1, cytochrome a and Cu_A but not between cytochrome a and the cytochrome a_3/Cu_B pair. These observations are consistent with a conformational change controlling electron transfer between c_1, a, Cu_A redox components and the a_3/Cu_B pair.

When hydrogen peroxide is added to cytochrome $c_1 aa_3$ a difference optical spectrum (oxidized + peroxide minus oxidized) is observed with a trough at 413 nm and a peak at 433 nm ($\Delta E = 27$ mM^{-1} cm^{-1}) and peaks at 606 nm and 580 nm. Others have observed similar changes with bovine cytochrome aa_3 suggesting that the two enzymes form similar complexes. The reaction with peroxide is slow (4.2 hr^{-1} at 50 μM H_2O_2), and appears to be reversed by incubation with catalase (0.35 hr^{-1}). We find no difference between the EPR spectra of oxidized and peroxo enzymes. Drs. T.A. Kent and E. Münck have recorded the Mössbauer spectrum of ^{57}Fe enriched peroxo complex and have found no apparent changes from the "preparation II" type spectrum.

Ethyl peroxide and t-butyl peroxide also form complexes with cytochrome c_1aa_3 having similar spectral properties. The following dissociation constants have been measured at pH 7.8 and 25 $^\circ$C: =0.5 M(HOOH), =30 M(EtOOH), = 4 mM(t-BuOOH). Our results suggest that peroxides react with the cytochrome a_3 to form a complex having electronic properties very similar to those of the resting protein; an end-on complex would be consistent with our data.

Rieske Fe/S Protein

The redox potential has been measured in the pH range 6.7 to 9.2. Below pH 8, E_m is constant and equal to ~ 150 mV while above pH 8 E_m decreases ~ 60 mV/unit pH. A reversible effect of pH on the optical spectrum of oxidized protein was found and shown to be determined by an ionizing group with pK_a ~ 8. These observations are consistent with the following equilibria associated with the [2Fe-2S] clusters of Rieske protein:

$$H \cdot P_{ox} \rightleftarrows P_{ox} + H^+; \; pK_a \sim 8$$

$$HP_{ox} + e^- \rightleftarrows HP_{red}.$$

Previous work suggested that each [2Fe-2S] cluster of Rieske protein was coordinated by only two cysteine residues. Working in collaboration with Drs. John F. Cline and Brian Hoffman it has been found that the cluster is coordinated to ^{14}N containing ligands, and we speculate here that the structure of the Rieske cluster is

with one of the coordinating imidazole rings ionizing with pK_a ~ 8.

Cytochrome o

An additional cytochrome c oxidase has been purified from Thermus membranes. The enzyme consists of two subunits, ~ 18 and ~ 37 KD, in a 1:1 ratio and one B-type heme per molecule; no other metals are present at significant levels. The spectral properties of the enzyme are characteristic of cytochrome o as found previously by others. Thus, the CO compound of the reduced protein difference spectrum (CO + reduced minus reduced) shows a trough at 434 nm and a peak at 419 nm.

Oxygen Binding to The Binuclear Iron Center of Hemerythrin

Joann Sanders-Loehr

Department of Chemical, Biological, and Environmental Sciences,
Oregon Graduate Center, Beaverton, Oregon 97006, USA

SUMMARY

   The structure of the oxygenated complex of the respiratory protein,
hemerythrin, has been investigated by resonance Raman spectroscopy and
x-ray crystallography. From the observed shifts in vibrational frequencies in deuterated solvent it is proposed that the bound dioxygen is in
the form of a hydroperoxide ion. Difference electron density maps
indicate that the hydroperoxide is stabilized by hydrogen bonding to the
oxo bridge of the binuclear iron center.

1 INTRODUCTION

   Hemerythrin is the non-heme iron respiratory protein of several
marine invertebrates. In binding oxygen its binuclear iron center is
oxidized from ferrous to ferric with a concomitant reduction of oxygen
to peroxide (1). Autooxidation to ferric methemerythrin results in a
loss of the ability to bind molecular oxygen and an increased affinity
for small anions such as azide, cyanide, and hydroxide.

$$\text{Deoxyhemerythrin} \; \underset{}{\overset{+ \, O_2}{\rightleftharpoons}} \; \text{Oxyhemerythrin} \; \xrightarrow{+ \, N_3^-} \; \text{Azidomethemerythrin}$$

$$(Fe^{2+}/Fe^{2+}) \qquad\qquad (Fe^{3+}/Fe^{3+}/O_2^{2-}) \qquad\qquad (Fe^{3+}/Fe^{3+}/N_3^-)$$

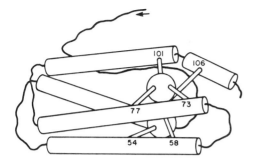

Fig. 1. Subunit structure of methemerythrin from <u>Themiste</u> <u>dyscritum</u>
based on 2.0 Å resolution electron density map (3). Numbers refer to
amino acid residues identified as iron ligands; the ligand from residue
25 is behind the lower iron atom.

Hemerythrin occurs as an octamer in the coelomic fluid (2). The
crystal structure at 2.0 Å resolution shows that each subunit contains
two iron atoms which are located inbetween four approximately parallel
sections of α-helix (Fig. 1). The upper two helices provide 3 histidine
ligands to the upper iron atom and 1 bridging carboxylate, while the
lower two helices provide 2 histidine ligands to the lower iron atom and
another bridging carboxylate (Fig. 2). The third bridging ligand in the
confacial bioctahedron has been assigned to an oxo group derived
from solvent. The sixth ligand on the lower iron atom is an azide in
azidomethemerythrin (Fig. 2), appears to be a peroxide in oxyhemerythrin (6,7), and is absent in methemerythrin (4).

Structures analogous to the binuclear iron complex in hemerythrin
have recently been obtained from mixtures of ferric salts, acetate, and
the tridentate ligand tris(1-pyrazolyl)borate (8) or 1,4,7-triaza-
cyclononane (9). The two iron atoms are in a confacial bioctahedron
with one oxo and two carboxylate bridges in the same configuration as in
hemerythrin (Fig. 3), indicating that this is indeed a favorable
coordination geometry for ferric iron. Both the model compounds (8,9)
and methemerythrin (1,2,4) show the expected characteristics for an
Fe(III)-O-Fe(III) complex: a short Fe-O bond distance of 1.8 Å, strong
antiferromagnetic coupling with a -J of ~100 cm^{-1}, intense absorption
bands near 350 nm with an extinction of ~4,000 M^{-1} cm^{-1} per iron, and
a strongly resonance-enhanced vibrational mode near 500 cm^{-1} in the
Raman spectrum. This vibrational frequency has been identified as the

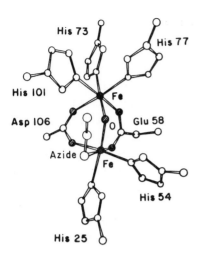

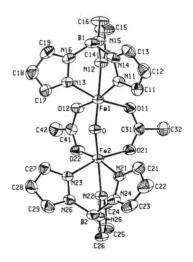

Fig. 2. (Left) Structure of binuclear iron center in azidomethemerythrin
at 2.0 Å resolution (4). A similar structure has been observed
for the azidomet form of the muscle protein, myohemerythrin (5).

Fig. 3 (Right) Structure of the tris(1-pyrazolyl)borate (HBpz$_3$) model
compound, (HBpz$_3$)FeO(CH$_3$COO)$_2$Fe(HBpz$_3$), from reference 8.

symmetric stretch of an Fe-O-Fe moiety on the basis of its ∿15 cm^{-1}
shift to lower energy when the oxo bridge is isotopically substituted
with ^{18}O (8,10).

Although a high resolution crystal structure of oxyhemerythrin is
not yet available, it appears to be structurally similar to the ligated
forms of methemerythrin. The oxidation state of the bound dioxygen has
been unambiguously identified as peroxide (in an end-on configuration)
from the behavior of the O-O stretching vibration at 844 cm^{-1} (10). A
comparison of the extended x-ray absorption fine structure (EXAFS) of
oxyhemerythrin and azidomethemerythrin shows that the two forms contain
the same number and types of ligands including short Fe-O bonds characteristic of the Fe-O-Fe group (11). The presence of an oxo-bridged
binuclear iron center in oxyhemerythrin has also been clearly indicated
from the similarity of the electronic spectral properties and magnetic
susceptibility (-J = 77 cm^{-1}) to those of azidomethemerythrin (1).

2 RESONANCE RAMAN SPECTROSCOPY OF OXYHEMERYTHRIN

Definitive evidence for the presence of an oxo-bridged iron center
in oxyhemerythrin has been obtained by resonance Raman spectroscopy.
When the protein is exposed to near-uv excitation a resonance-enhanced
peak at 486 cm^{-1} is observed (Fig. 4a). The assignment of this vibration as an Fe-O-Fe symmetric stretch is established by its shift to 472
cm^{-1} upon substitution of ^{18}O into the oxo bridge (Fig. 4b). Although
the oxo bridge in oxyhemerythrin does not exchange with solvent, slow
exchange does occur when the protein is reduced to deoxyhemerythrin and
incubated in $H_2^{18}O$ (7). After reoxygenation the protein was transferred
back to $H_2^{16}O$ so that for the experiment shown in Fig. 4b the only ^{18}O
remaining was in the oxo bridge. In an attempt to determine whether the
oxo group is protonated or hydrogen bonded, the protein was exposed
to D_2O. The 4 cm^{-1} shift of the Fe-O-Fe vibration to <u>higher</u> energy
(Fig. 4c) is indicative of hydrogen bonding of the oxo bridge in
oxyhemerythrin.

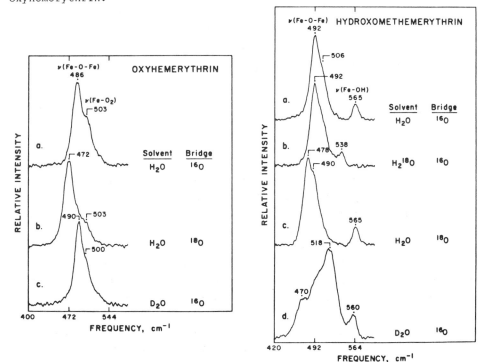

Fig. 4. (Left) Resonance Raman spectrum of oxyhemerythrin obtained with
363.8 nm excitation at 0°C.

Fig. 5. (Right) Resonance Raman spectrum of hydroxomethemerythrin
obtained with 363.8 nm excitation at 0°C.

Table 1.   Fe-O-Fe vibrational frequencies in hemerythrins

Hemerythrin Adduct	(Fe-O-Fe) in cm^{-1}	Shift in D_2O in cm^{-1}
None	512	0
N_3^-	507	0
Cl^-	510	0
$HCOO^-$	513	0
CN^-	512	
SCN^-	514	
Oxy (HO_2^-)	486	+4
OH^-	492	+26

Comparison of the resonance Raman spectra of oxyhemerythrin and a
number of methemerythrins has led to the recognition of two spectral
characteristics which appear to signal hydrogen bonding of the oxo
bridge: (1) location of the Fe-O-Fe vibration near 490 cm^{-1} in H_2O and
(2) an upward shift of the vibrational frequency in D_2O. In most forms
of methemerythrin the Fe-O-Fe vibration occurs in the 507-514 cm^{-1} range
and is totally unaffected by deuteration of the protein (Table 1). This
implies that the conformation of the binuclear iron site is unaltered by
deuterium substitution of various functional groups such as the amide
backbone and the imidazole ligands. The two anomalous forms of the
protein are oxyhemerythrin and hydroxomethemerythrin in which the
Fe-O-Fe vibration is at 486-492 cm^{-1} (15-28 cm^{-1} decrease) and at a
substantially higher frequency after deuteration. The effect in
hydroxomethemerythrin is particularly marked where the primary Fe-O-Fe
vibration at 492 cm^{-1} (Fig. 5a) shifts to 478 cm^{-1} with an ^{18}O-substi-
tuted bridge (Fig. 5c) and to 518 cm^{-1} in D_2O (Fig. 5d). That fact that
only certain adducts exhibit these hydrogen bonding characteristics
implies that the added ligand in these cases is facilitating hydrogen
bond formation. Furthermore, the crystal structure shows that the
ligand binding site in hemerythrin is quite hydrophobic with no possible
protein donor or acceptor groups within hydrogen bonding distance of the
exogenous ligand or the oxo bridge (6).

A model which accounts for the anomalous behavior of oxyhemerythrin
is shown in Figure 6. It predicts that the bound peroxide ion is
protonated and hydrogen bonded to the oxo bridge. The analogous
structure for hydroxomethemerythrin would have the hydroxide ligand

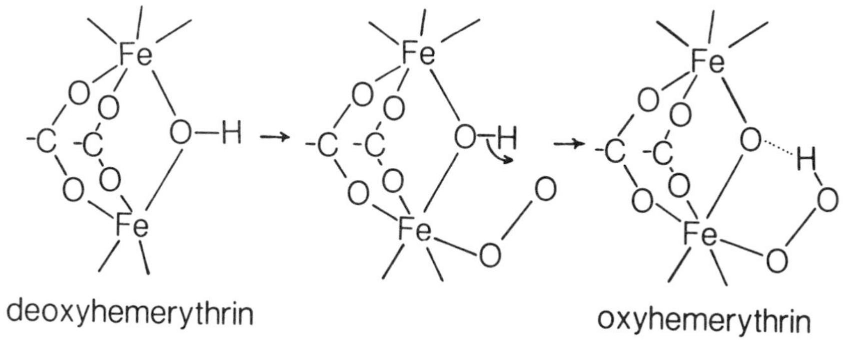

deoxyhemerythrin   oxyhemerythrin

Fig. 6.   Proposed structures for oxyhemerythrin and deoxyhemerythrin and
a possible mechanism for their interconversion (6).

hydrogen bonded to the oxo bridge either directly (requiring a
4-membered ring) or via an intervening water molecule. The hydrogen
bond in hydroxomethemerythrin appears to be weaker than in oxyhemerythrin because an additional non-hydrogen-bonded Fe-O-Fe component
occurs at 506 cm^{-1} (Fig. 5a) and shifts to 490 cm^{-1} in Fe-^{18}O-Fe
(Fig. 5c). The equilibrium between the two conformations is temperature-dependent with the H-bonded component becoming more prevalent at
77 K.

Additional evidence for a hydroperoxide structure in the bound
dioxygen moiety of oxyhemerythrin comes from an analysis of the vibrational modes associated with the peroxide: the O-O stretch at 844 cm^{-1}
and the Fe-O_2 stretch at 503 cm^{-1}. These spectral components can be
separated from the Fe-O-Fe vibration by an appropriate choice of
excitation wavelengths. As shown in Figure 7, the intensity of the
Fe-O-Fe peak is most enhanced by excitation into the absorption band at
360 nm, which can be thus be assigned as an $O^{2-} \rightarrow$ Fe(III) charge transfer
band of the Fe-O-Fe moiety. The peroxide-related peaks are selectively
enhanced with excitation close to 530 nm, suggesting an $O_2^{2-} \rightarrow$ Fe(III)
charge transfer assignment for the visible absorption band.

When oxyhemerythrin is deuterated, the Fe-O_2 frequency shifts down
to 500 cm^{-1} and the O-O frequency shifts up to 847 cm^{-1} (Fig. 8).
These 3 cm^{-1} shifts are most clearly seen in the computer-generated
difference spectra (Fig. 8) and are indicative of peroxide protonation.
Such protonation is expected for a peroxide which is coordinated to iron
in an end-on fashion. Similarly, the Fe-OH vibration of the bound

hydroxide at 565 cm^{-1} in hydroxomethemerythrin shifts 5 cm^{-1} to lower energy in D$_2$O (Fig. 5). Anions such as azide and thiocyanate which are typically unprotonated show no deuterium isotope dependence in the Fe-N vibrations of their respective methemerythrin complexes (7). The shift of the peroxide O-O stretch to higher frequency in D$_2$O indicates that electronic or structural alterations accompanying deuteration are out-weighing the mass effect. In the case of cobalt-substituted myoglobin, in which the bound dioxygen is believed to be hydrogen bonded to the distal histidine, the O-O vibration at 1124 cm^{-1} shifts 12 cm^{-1} to higher energy in the deuterated protein (12).

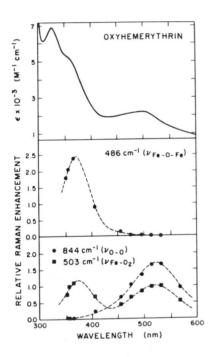

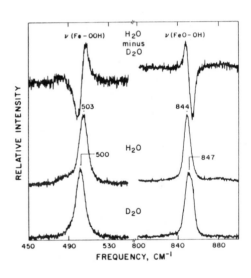

Figure 7. (Left) Absorption spectrum (upper) and enhancement profiles (middle, lower) for oxyhemerythrin. Raman enhancements for peaks at 486, 503, and 844 cm^{-1} measured relative to height of 981 cm^{-1} peak from sulfate internal standard (7).

Figure 8. (Right) Resonance Raman spectrum of oxyhemerythrin obtained with 530.9 nm excitation in H$_2$O and D$_2$O (7). The uppermost traces are computer-generated difference spectra.

3 X-RAY DIFFERENCE DENSITY PROFILES

Further support for the hydroperoxide model (Fig. 6) comes from a comparison of electron density contours at the exogenous ligand site of azidomethemerythrin (Fig. 9) and oxyhemerythrin (Fig. 10). These difference maps are obtained by subtracting the observed structure factors for methemerythrin (which lacks a sixth ligand) from the observed structure factors for azidomethemerythrin or oxyhemerythrin. For azidomethemerythrin the difference map clearly shows a region of electron density corresponding to the bound azide ion. In addition, the peak of negative density to the left of the lower iron atom and the peak of positive density to the right indicates a shift in the location of the iron upon azide binding. The oxyhemerythrin difference map appears to be similar to that of azidomethemerythrin. It shows an analogous movement of the lower iron atom towards the incoming ligand with significant new electron density arising from the bound dioxygen. The dioxygen is coordinated end-on, as expected from spectroscopic studies (1,10) and, hence, most likely to be in the form of a hydro-peroxide. The most notable differences between the maps for oxy and azidomethemerythrin are that the hydroperoxide appears to lie closer to the Fe-Fe axis than does the azide and that the upper half of the Fe-O-Fe moiety (the oxo group and the upper iron atom) has moved toward the hydroperoxide. Both of these observations can be explained by the formation of a hydrogen bond between the bridging oxo group and the iron-bound hydroperoxide.

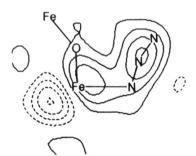 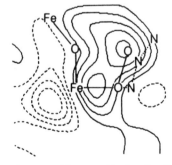

Fig. 9 (Left) Difference map of azidomet minus methemerythrin in the $O_{oxo}-Fe-N_{azide}$ plane at 2.2 Å resolution (6). Solid lines indicate positive electron density, dashed lines indicate negative electron density. Atom positions from the 2.0 Å refinement of azidomethemerythrin projected onto O-Fe-N plane.

Fig. 10 (Right) Difference map of oxy minus methemerythrin at 2.2 Å resolution (6). Conditions as in Fig. 9. Atoms positions for peroxide estimated from this difference map.

If the dioxygen is coordinated as hydroperoxide in oxyhemerythrin, it must become protonated upon reduction. Kinetic studies have indicated that the binding of dioxygen to deoxyhemerythrin is very rapid (close to diffusion-controlled) and has no observable pH dependence (1,2). A mechanism that is consistent with these findings is presented in Figure 6. In this scheme a hydroxo bridge between the two Fe(II) atoms in deoxyhemerythrin is the source of the proton. With the bridging oxygen moiety already in place, the system is ideally poised to react with dioxygen. It can do so rapidly since no major atom rearrangements are required. Although the structure of the binuclear iron center in deoxyhemerythrin is less well characterized than in the other forms of the protein, the hydroxo-bridged formulation is in agreement with the following results: i) low resolution difference density profiles indicate that the iron centers are slightly further apart in deoxyhemerythrin (6); ii) there is much less correlated motion of the iron atoms according to the temperature dependence of the iron-iron peak observed by EXAFS (11); and iii) the weak but detectable magnetic interaction between the iron atoms is that expected for a hydroxo-bridged binuclear Fe(II) complex (13).

4 CONCLUSION

The elucidation of the structure of the binuclear iron center in hemerythrin has led to the question of whether this type of iron complex recurs in other metalloproteins. Presently available information indicates that this is likely to be the case. The existence of an Fe-O-Fe unit with a solvent-exchangeable oxygen has been clearly demonstrated in ribonucleotide reductase (14). For another three proteins, purple acid phosphatase (15), uteroferrin (15) and methane monooxygenase (16), this cluster is strongly suspected although its presence has not yet been observed by vibrational spectroscopy. The latter three proteins share with hemerythrin the tendency to undergo a one electron reduction to form a spin-paired Fe(II)-Fe(III) system which gives rise to a characteristic $S=1/2$ EPR signal. It will be of interest to determine what aspects of the hemerythrin structure are repeated in these proteins and whether their binuclear iron centers are involved in reactions with molecular oxygen.

5 REFERENCES

(1) J. Sanders-Loehr, T. M. Loehr, Adv. Inorg. Biochem. 1 (1979) 235-252.

(2) R. G. Wilkins, P. C. Harrington, Adv. Inorg. Biochem. 5 (1983) 51-85.

(3) L. C. Sieker, R. E. Stenkamp, L. H. Jensen in H. B. Dunford, D. Dolphin, K. N. Raymond, L. C. Sieker (Eds.), The Biological Chemistry of Iron, D. Reidel Publishing Company, Boston 1982, pp. 161-175.

(4) R. E. Stenkamp, L. C. Sieker, L. H. Jensen, J. Am. Chem. Soc. 106 (1984) 618-622.

(5) S. Sheriff, W. A. Hendrickson, J. L. Smith, Life Chem. Rep. Suppl. Ser. 1 (1983) 305-308.

(6) R. E. Stenkamp, L. C. Sieker, L. H. Jensen, J. D. McCallum, J. Sanders-Loehr, Proc. Natl. Acad. Sci. USA 82 (1985) 713-716.

(7) A. K. Shiemke, T. M. Loehr, J. Sanders-Loehr, J. Am. Chem. Soc. 106 (1984) 4951-4956.

(8) W. H. Armstrong, A. Spool, G. C. Papaefthymiou, R. B. Frankel, S. J. Lippard, J. Am. Chem. Soc. 106 (1984) 3653-3667.

(9) K. Wieghardt, K. Pohl, and W. Gebert, Angew. Chem. Int. Ed. Engl. 22 (1983) 727.

(10) D. M. Kurtz, Jr., D. F. Shriver, I. M. Klotz, Coord. Chem. Rev. 24 (1977) 145-178.

(11) W. T. Elam, E. A. Stern, J. D. McCallum, J. Sanders-Loehr, J. Am. Chem. Soc. 104 (1982) 6369-6373.

(12) T. Kitagawa, M. R. Ondrias, D. L. Rousseau, M. Ikeda-Saito, T. Yonetani, Nature (London) 298 (1982) 869-871.

(13) R. C. Reem, E. I. Solomon, J. Am. Chem. Soc. 106 (1984) 8323-8325.

(14) B.-M. Sjoberg, A. Graslund, Adv. Inorg. Biochem. 5 (1983) 87-110.

(15) B. C. Antanaitis, P. Aisen, Adv. Inorg. Biochem. 5 (1983) 111-136.

(16) M. P. Woodland, H. Dalton, J. Biol. Chem. 259 (1984) 53-58.

The Structue of The Copper-Containing Oxygen-Transporting Hemocyanins from Arthropods

Anne Volbeda & Wim G.J. Hol

Laboratory of Chemical Physics, Department of Chemistry, University of Groningen, Nijenborgh 16, 9747 AG Groningen, The Netherlands

SUMMARY

   Hemocyanins make up the class of oxygen-carrying proteins with dinuclear copper sites. The first medium resolution X-ray structure of a member of this class has been determined. It is the structure of hemocyanin from the spiny lobster *Panulirus interruptus*, which is an arthropod. This hemocyanin is a hexamer with a molecular weight of approximately 460,000 dalton. Each subunit is folded into three domains. A qualitative description of their structure is presented. A carbohydrate moiety is attached to an "appendix" of domain 1. Domain 2 contains the oxygen binding dinuclear copper site. The electron density map shows no protein bridging ligand to the coppers. Domain 3 contains a β-barrel which is topologically similar to β-barrels found in several other proteins. Available amino acid sequence data suggest that the polypeptide architecture of spiny lobster hemocyanin is universal to all arthropodan hemocyanins.

1 INTRODUCTION

   Hemocyanins are the large copper containing oxygen transport proteins occurring in a great number of invertebrates. One of their characteristics is an intensely blue colour upon oxygen binding. The two other classes of oxygen transporting proteins found in nature are the hemoglobins and the hemerythrins, containing respectively one and two iron atoms at the oxygen binding site. Hemocyanins are not located inside erythrocytes but occur freely dissolved in the hemolymph. Two types of hemocyanins exist, one belonging to the phylum of the arthropods, the other to the phylum of the molluscs (1-3). Both bind oxygen in a cooperative manner at dinuclear copper sites and many spectroscopic characteristics are very similar. Their molecular architecture, however, is completely different. The molluscan hemocyanins are cylindrical molecules built up from 10 to 20 subunits, each of which consists of 7 to 8 domains. A dinuclear copper site is located in each of these domains, which have a molecular mass of ~50,000 daltons. Arthropodan hemocyanins, on the other hand, are hexamers or oligo-hexamers, consisting of individual subunits with a molecular mass of ~ 75,000 daltons. Each subunit contains one pair of copper atoms. Other proteins containing dinuclear copper sites are ascorbate oxidase, laccase, ceruloplasmin and tyrosinase, which are all enzymes (4). Oxytyrosinase and oxyhemocyanin show remarkably similar spectra. Therefore the determination of the three-dimensional structure of a hemocyanin mole-cule could also be helpful for a better understanding of the active site of several enzymes.

   The first medium resolution X-ray structure of a hemocyanin molecule has been determined in our laboratory (5). It is the structure of the oxygen carrier of the spiny lobster *Panulirus interruptus*, an arthropod. Being a single hexamer it is one of the smallest hemocyanins known, having still a molecular mass of ~ 460.000 daltons. It contains three subunit types, designated a, b and c. The amino acid sequence of subunit a was determined concurrently with the X-ray investigation by the group of Beintema at the biochemical laboratory of the Groningen University and is virtually completed now. Available partial sequence information regarding the b and c subunits (Beintema et al., personal communication) shows that the b subunit differs only a few percent in sequence with the a subunit, but that the a and c subunit types are much less closely related.

   After a short summary of the practical work which went into the X-ray structure determination, a qualitative description of the three-dimensional structure is presen-ted. Special attention is paid to the dinuclear copper site, to structural similari-ties with other proteins and to the structure of arthropodan hemocyanins in general.

2 X-RAY STRUCTURE DETERMINATION

   The monoclinic crystals used for the X-ray studies were grown from native *Panulirus interruptus* hemocyanin (6-7). They were colourless and gave a diffraction pattern to ~ 3.2 Å resolution. Suitable crystals were found at low pH and low salt concentrations. Upon dissolving some of them it appeared that they contained only the subunits a and b, in roughly equal amounts. The entire hexamer was contained in the asymmetric unit. At 5 Å resolution its shape and 32 point group symmetry became apparent (7). The orientation of the molecular symmetry axes could be obtained by rotation function studies. Two isomorphous heavy atom derivatives were prepared, giving useful phase information to ~ 4 Å resolution. The three-dimensional difference Patterson of the platinum derivative could be solved and eventually a large number of heavy atom sites was found: 32 for the platinum derivative and 70 for the Hg-derivative (7). These sites allowed a precise determination of the molecular centre as well as of the direction of the molecular symmetry axes.

An electron density map calculated with the 4 Å multiple isomorphous phases was used to obtain the molecular envelope. Using this envelope a map of much better quality could be calculated by means of density averaging and phase improvement procedures as described by Bricogne (8). In this map the position of the copper ions in each subunit became clear (9). Beyond 4 Å resolution there was no heavy atom information. Therefore the extension of the protein phases to 3.2 Å resolution had to rely entirely on molecular averaging procedures (10). After many cycles this resulted in a 3.2 Å electron density map of remarkably high quality, in which the polypeptide chain could be followed without problems (5). We were quite fortunate that the sixfold molecular averaging worked so well, because it very probably would not have done so if the two subunit types occurring in our crystals had been more different from each other. Apparently the structural differences between subunit a and b are very small, in agreement with the small differences in amino acid sequence reported by Beintema and coworkers recently.

Very recently a complete hemocyanin model, containing more than 32,000 atoms, was built into the electron density distribution at a computer graphics system, using the program GUIDE (11) and the amino acid sequence of subunit a. This model is being refined now on a Cyber 205 super computer.

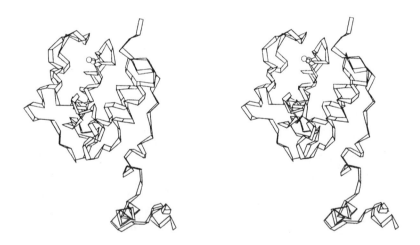

HEMOCYANIN DOMAIN 1   HEMOCYANIN DOMAIN 1

Fig. 1. Stereo ribbon diagram of domain 1 of *Panulirus interruptus* hemocyanin. The blank spheres indicate the disulfide bridge. This picture as well as figures 2, 3, 4 and 5 were produced by a computer program written by A.M. Lesk and K.D. Hardman (12).

3 POLYPEPTIDE FOLDING

Each subunit of the *Panulirus interruptus* hemocyanin hexamer folds its ~ 660 residues into three distinct domains (figures 1-4). The first domain contains ~ 175 amino
acids. It can be subdivided into a larger globular part and a small, but interesting,
appendix which lies close to the molecular twofold. Six α-helices occur in the larger
part, four of them running quite anti-parallel to each other. Also one disulfide bridge
is located here, linking together residues 93 and 98. The appendix consists of one α-
helix and one β-strand, which is part of a β-sheet involving two other β-strands from
domain 3. A special residue of this β-strand is asparagine 167, to which the single
carbohydrate moiety is covalently attached. At least three sugar groups are visible in
the electron density map, indicating a relative immobility. Yet the carbohydrate is
pointing freely into solution and does not make contacts with amino acid side chains,
except for the first sugar group. Its function is not yet known and many other arthropod hemocyanins are known not to contain any carbohydrate group (2-3).

Domain 2 consists of ~ 220 residues and is also mainly helical. It has a more
globular shape then the first domain. Functionally it is the most important domain,
because it contains the oxygen binding dinuclear copper site, which will be described
below in a special section. Seven α-helices are found, four of them surrounding the
two coppers. In addition there are two two-stranded anti-parallel β-sheets. This is

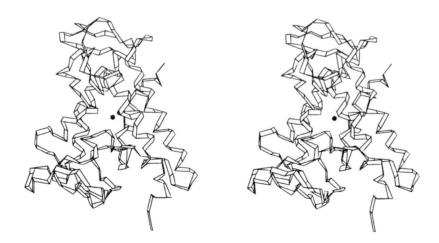

HEMOCYANIN DOMAIN 2   HEMOCYANIN DOMAIN 2

Fig. 2. Stereo ribbon diagram of domain 2, viewed from the same direction as domain
     1. The coppers are depicted by two small black spheres. One of them is partly
     obscured by the first α-helix.

the most central domain in the hexamer, being almost completely surrounded by domain 1
and 3 and by other subunits.

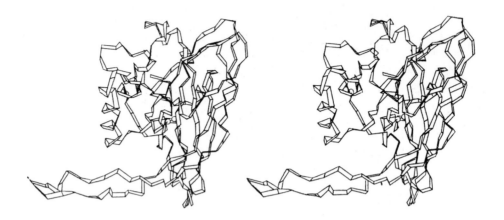

HEMOCYANIN DOMAIN 3   HEMOCYANIN DOMAIN 3

Fig. 3. Stereo ribbon diagram of domain 3, viewed from the same direction as domain 1
and 2. The two disulfide bridges are indicated by blank spheres.

Domain 3 is the largest and most irregularly shaped domain. It contains ~ 260
residues. The core of this domain is a seven-stranded anti-parallel β-barrel, from
which several long loops extend which make extensive contacts with domain 1 and 2.
The first loop contains the two β-strands which form a β-sheet with the β-strand
located in the appendix of domain 1. Six α-helices and two disulfide bridges can be
found in this domain. The first disulfide bridge links together residues 483 and 502,
the second one residues 562 and 609.

4 THE β-BARREL IN DOMAIN 3

A very interesting structural similarity was found between the third domain of
hemocyanin and functionally completely differently proteins as Cu,Zn-superoxide
dismutase (13), the immunoglobulins (14) and actinoxanthine (15). They all happen to
have a β-barrel with the same topology. The β-barrels can be superimposed onto one
another (5), giving for domain 3, Cu,Zn-superoxide dismutase and immunoglobulin REI
~ 60 equivalent Cα-positions, with a root mean square deviation of less than 2.5 Å.
Because there is hardly any or no amino acid sequence homology, this structural

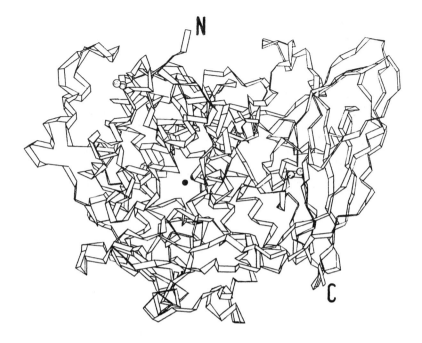

Fig. 4. Ribbon diagram of one subunit, viewed from the same direction as the three
        domains. N and C indicate the N- and C-terminus.

relationship could be the result of convergent evolution. Possibly the anti-parallel
β-barrel is just a case of a stable secondary structure element, allowing a large
variability in amino acids and loops. In any case, the dinuclear copper site of
hemocyanin occurs in an entirely different domain and has thus no evolutionary
relationship with the metal binding site in Cu,Zn-superoxide dismutase.

5 THE DINUCLEAR COPPER SITE

The crystals used for the X-ray structure determination were grown under conditions
of low oxygen affinity. They were colourless and did not show an absorption band at
340 nm (16). This suggests that we have determined the structure of deoxy-hemocyanin,
in which the oxidation state of the coppers is Cu(I). A less likely possibility is
that the crystals contain met-hemocyanin, with a Cu(II) oxidation state. EXAFS studies
have been planned to resolve this question.

The copper to copper distance in the current hemocyanin model is 3.7 ± 0.3 Å. This
agrees reasonably well with the latest EXAFS results (17), where a distance of ~ 3.45 Å

was found for deoxy-hemocyanin, ~ 3.6 Å for oxy-hemocyanin and ~ 3.4 Å for metaquo-
hemocyanin. These EXAFS studies also predicted 2 copper ligands for deoxyhemocyanin
and 4 for oxyhemocyanin, including the bound oxygen and a bridging ligand. Possibly
the more distant ligands were not detectable by this technique. The X-ray structure
shows three histidines per copper ion (figure 5), which is in agreement with the model,
based on older EXAFS measurements, for deoxy-hemocyanin of Brown et al. (18). Also
studies on Cobalt substituted hemocyanins (19-20) pointed to three histidine ligands
per copper. The six ligands are provided by the four α-helices surrounding the dinuclear copper site. Two helices provide two histidine ligands, which are separated
by one helix-turn. The immediate surroundings of the oxygen binding site is very hydrophobic.

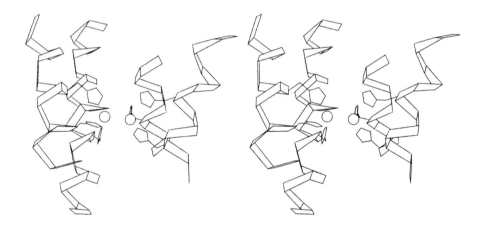

HEMOCYANIN COPPER SITE HEMOCYANIN COPPER SITE

Fig. 5. Stereo ribbon diagram of the dinuclear copper site, showing the four surrounding α-helices and the six histidine ligands. The coppers are indicated by
the small open spheres.

At the present stage of the structure determination the ligand-copper bond lengths
and the ligand-copper-ligand bond angles are not yet very accurate, so only a very
qualitative analysis of the copper coordination can be given. What the electron density map clearly shows is that the coppers do not lie in the same plane as their ligating atoms. For Cu(I) with its filled $3d^{10}$ orbital the most stable three coordination
would be trigonal, while in model compounds also distorted T-shaped coordinations have

been found (21). Accordingly there will be some strain at the hemocyanin oxygen
binding site, presumably making the transition from the deoxy to the oxy state easier.

The electron density map shows no sign (yet) of a bridging ligand, which is believed to facilitate the strong diamagnetic coupling between the unpaired Cu(II)
electron spins in oxyhemocyanin. Often a bridging tyrosine has been suggested (22).
However, the nearest tyrosine hydroxyl group in the *Panulirus interruptus* hemocyanin
X-ray structure is more than 10 Å distant from both coppers. Of the tyrosines which
are invariant in seven arthropodan hemocyanin subunits (23), the distance of the
closest hydroxyl group to the coppers is more than 17 Å (table 1). In deoxy-hemocyanin
there may not be a bridging ligand. For tyrosine to be the bridging ligand in oxy-
hemocyanin, extremely large conformational changes would be necessary. This does not
seem very likely. Although the resolution of our data is only 3.2 Å, crystallographic
refinement of the X-ray structure may show in the future the presence of a small
bridging ligand such as a μ-hydroxo group. After refinement a more detailed analysis
of the geometry of the oxygen binding site will be possible.

Table 1. Distances of the hydroxyl groups of invariant tyrosines (23) to the center
of the dinuclear copper site.

domain	Panulirus interruptus sequence number	distance (Å)
2	183	20,7
2	339	24,5
3	340	22,0
3	401	25,9
3	616	18,4

6 THE STRUCTURE OF ARTHROPODAN HEMOCYANINS

Electron microscopy studies have indicated that the *Panulirus interruptus* hexamer
is a common building block of all multi-hexameric arthropodan hemocyanins (1). Very
recently the amino acid sequences of seven different arthropodan hemocyanin subunits
were compared with each other, three of them complete and the other four, among them
Panulirus interruptus subunit a, far advanced (23). The X-ray structure was used as a
guide. The comparison showed a high degree of homology along the entire sequence,
domain 2 being most similar. The homology was especially large for residues which
appear to be buried in the X-ray structure. A few deletions or insertions were
found, but these all happened to occur in surface regions. Apparently, arthropodan
hemocyanins have not only similar quaternary structures, but also very similar tertiary structures.

Many questions are still to be settled, such as the structure of oxy-hemocyanin,

the path of entrance by oxygen and the mechanism of cooperativity. In this connection
it may be mentioned that the distance between nearest dinuclear copper sites in
Panulirus hemocyanin is ~ 46 Å. Other points to be settled are the binding sites of
allosteric effectors such as H^+ and Ca^{2+}. Some of these questions will be answered
when the structure of an arthropodan oxyhemocyanin, one of which is being determined
(24-25), will be available.

Although these and many other questions remain to be answered, and the polypeptide
folding of the molluscan hemocyanins remains to be established, it is interesting to
see that the three classes of oxygen transport proteins with known three-dimensional
structure - the hemoglobins, hemerythrins and arthropod hemocyanins have such vastly
different architectures despite their common function.

7 ACKNOWLEDGEMENT

We like to thank Lies van Schaick, Wilma Schutter and Wil Gaykema for their numerous
contributions to this investigation. All computations were performed at the Computer
Centre of the University of Groningen. This research was supported by the Dutch Foundation for Chemical Research (SON) with financial aid from the Dutch Organisation for
the Advancement of Pure Research (ZWO).

8 REFERENCES

(1) E.F.J. van Bruggen, W.G. Schutter, J.F.L. van Breemen, M.M.C. Bijlholt & T.
    Wichertjes in M. Harris (ed.), Electron Microscopy of Proteins, Academic Press,
    New York (1981), pp. 1-37.
(2) K.E. van Holde & K.I. Miller, Q. Rev. Biophys. 15 (1982) 1-129.
(3) H.D. Ellerton, N.F. Ellerton & H.A. Robinson, Progr. Biophys. Mol. Biol. 41
    (1983) 143-248.
(4) F.L. Urbach in H. Sigel (ed.), Metal ions in biological systems, volume 13,
    copper proteins, Marcel Dekker, Inc., New York (1981), pp. 73-115.
(5) W.P.J. Gaykema, W.G.J. Hol, J.M. Vereijken, N.M. Soeter, H.J. Bak & J.J. Beintema,
    Nature 309 (1984) 23-29.
(6) H.A. Kuiper, W. Gaastra, J.J. Beintema, E.F.J. van Bruggen, A.M.H. Schepman & J.
    Drenth, J. Mol. Biol. (1975) 619-629.
(7) E.J.M. van Schaick, W.G. Schutter, W.P.J. Gaykema, A.M.H. Schepman & W.G.J. Hol,
    J. Mol. Biol. 158 (1982) 457-485.
(8) G. Bricogne, Acta Crystallogr. A32 (1976) 832-847.
(9) W.P.J. Gaykema, E.J.M. van Schaick, W.G. Schutter & W.G.J. Hol, Chemica Scripta
    21 (1983) 19-23.
(10) W.P.J. Gaykema, A. Volbeda, W.G.J. Hol, submitted for publication.
(11) N.P. Brandenburg, S. Dempsey, B.W. Dijkstra, L.J. Lijk & W.G.J. Hol, J. Appl.

Cryst. 14 (1981) 274-279.

(12) A.M. Lesk & K.D. Hardman, Science 216 (1982) 539-540.

(13) J.A. Tainer, E.D. Getzoff, K.M. Beem, J.S. Richardson & D.C. Richardson, J. Mol. Biol. 160 (1982) 181-217.

(14) O. Epp, P. Colman, H. Fehlhammer, W. Bode, M. Schiffer, R. Huber & W. Palm, Eur. J. Biochem. 45 (1974) 513-524.

(15) V.Z. Pletner, A.P. Kuzin, S.D. Trakhanor & P.V. Kostetsky, Biopolymers 21 (1982) 287-300.

(16) M. Vincent & W.G.J. Hol, unpublished results.

(17) G.L. Woolery, L. Powers, M. Winkler, E.I. Solomon & T.G. Spiro, J. Am. Chem. Soc. 106 81984) 86-92.

(18) J.M. Brown, L. Powers, B. Kincaid, J.A. Larrabee & T.G. Spiro, J. Am. Chem. Soc. 102 (1980) 4210-4216.

(19) S. Suzuki, J. Kino, M. Kimura, W. Mori & A. Nakahara, Inorg. Chim. Acta 66 (1982) 41-47.

(20) S. Suzuki, J. Kino & A. Nakahara, Bull. Chem. Soc. Jpn. 55 (1982) 212-217.

(21) C.A. Reed in K.D. Martin & J. Zubieta (eds.), Biochemical and Inorganic Aspects of Copper Coordination Chemistry, Adenine, New York (1985), in press.

(22) Compare pp. 163-166 in (3).

(23) B. Linzen et al., (1985), accepted by Science.

(24) K.A. Magnus & W.F. Love, J. Mol. Biol. 116 (1977) 171-173.

(25) K.A. Magnus & W.F. Love, Life Chem. Rep. 1, Suppl. 1 (1983) 61-64.

Optical Detection of Paramagnetic Resonance by Magnetic Circular Dichroism. Applications to Metalloproteins

Andrew J. Thomson, Christopher P. Barrett, Jim Peterson and Colin Greenwood*

Schools of Chemical and Biological Sciences*,
University of East Anglia, Norwich NR4 7TJ, United Kingdom.

SUMMARY

   The intensity of the magnetic circular dichroism (MCD) spectrum of a paramagnetic molecule is inversely proportional to the spin temperature, T_s, at liquid helium temperature. Irradiation of the sample with a microwave field of constant frequency will, if resonance occurs, raise the spin temperature. This is detected by a change in the intensity of the MCD signal. Thus it is possible to measure paramagnetic resonance by optical detection using MCD spectroscopy. This is a form of optical double magnetic resonance (ODMR) which appears not to have been carried out on proteins before. We have constructed a microwave cavity with optical access to enable the MCD spectrum of a frozen, aqueous metalloprotein solution to be measured in a microwave field in the Q-band (35 GHz) frequency range. The ODMR spectra of some simple copper(II) complexes are discussed. Results have also been obtained for the copper(II) ion in the blue protein azurin. The MCD-ODMR spectrum enables the relative orientations of the ground state g-tensor and the optical transition-moment tensors to be determined. In this way useful information about the angular distribution of ligands about a central metal ion in an isotropic solution of a metalloprotein appears to be available.

1 INTRODUCTION

   The intensity of the magnetic circular dichroism (MCD) spectrum of a paramagnetic molecule is inversely proportioned to the spin temperature, T_s, at liquid helium temperature (1). Irradiation of the sample with a microwave field of constant frequency will, if resonance occurs, raise the spin temperature. This can be detected

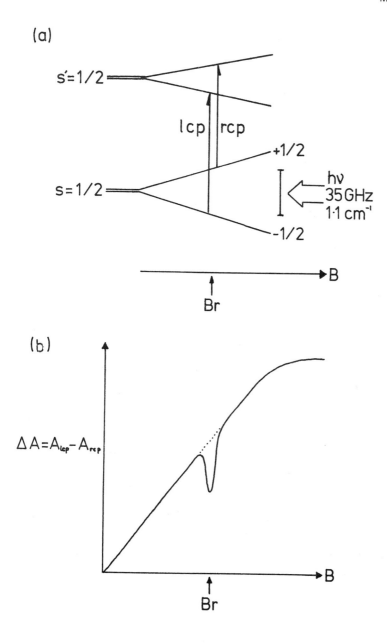

Fig.1   The MCD-ODMR experiment.

by a change in the intensity of the MCD signal. Thus it is in principle possible to measure paramagnetic resonance by optical detection using MCD spectroscopy. This is a form of optical double microwave resonance (ODMR) which appears not to have been carried out on frozen aqueous solutions of proteins before.

The possibility of using a combined MCD microwave resonance experiment to study the paramagnetic centres in metalloproteins is an attractive one. It would enable each optical band in the electronic spectrum to be associated with a given g-value observed in the EPR spectrum. Furthermore, by measuring the MCD spectrum at a magnetic field at which microwave resonance occurs both in the presence and absence of an applied microwave field the optical spectrum arising from a species with a given g-value could be determined. Therefore we have designed and constructed an apparatus to investigate the optical detection of paramagnetic resonance by magnetic circular dichroism. We report the successful detection of such resonance from frozen aqueous solutions of cupric EDTA, and from the blue copper protein azurin. Further we show how the analysis of the band shape of the ODMR spectrum of a paramagnetic species with an anisotropic ground state g-tensor can allow determination of the relative orientations of the principle axes of that tensor and those of the optical transition moment tensor. Thus it becomes possible to measure the relative polarisations of the optical transitions of an isotropic solution of a metalloprotein.

2   PRINCIPLES OF MEASUREMENT

The principles involved in an MCD-ODMR experiment are shown in figure 1a, illustrated with a system with ground and excited states having effective spins of 1/2 and placed in a static magnetic field B, parallel to the laboratory Z axis. Optical transitions between the ground and excited states are induced by right and left circularly polarised photons propagated along the magnetic field axis according to the selection rules $\Delta M_S = 0$ and $\Delta M_L = +1$ or -1 respectively. The intensity of the MCD signal is given by $\Delta A (= A_L - A_R)$ where A_L and A_R are the absorbances for left and right circularly polarised light. At a temperature of 1.5K the MCD intensity is almost wholly due to the Boltzmann population difference between the ± 1/2 Zeeman sublevels of the ground state. A plot of ΔA against applied magnetic field B will vary as shown in figure 1b. For a temperature of 1.5K and a Zeeman splitting, $g\beta B$, of less than ~4cm^{-1} the variation of ΔA with B is linear, Curie law behaviour. Magnetic saturation occurs at higher B values. Application of a microwave field of frequency hν with its oscillatory magnetic field linearly polarised perpendicular to B will induce magnetic dipole transitions from $M_S = -1/2$ to $+1/2$ when the resonance condition $h\nu = g\beta B_r$ holds. The spin temperature of the system will be raised by an amount depending upon the microwave power level and the spin lattice relaxation time. Thus the MCD signal is partially quenched and the microwave induced resonance will be observed on a plot of ΔA against B as indicated in figure 1b.

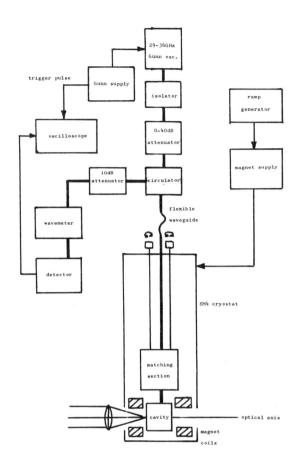

Fig.2.   Microwave and field scan circuit.

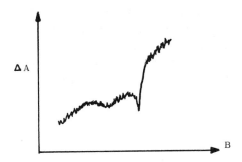

Fig. 3.   Cu(EDTA) in glycerol/water.   MCD intensity
           as the field passes through resonance.

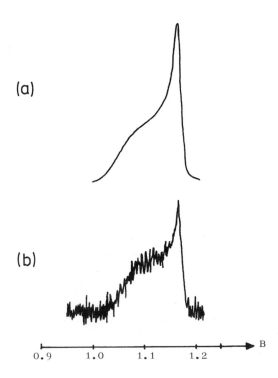

Fig. 4a.   Absorption mode Q-band EPR of Cu(EDTA).
            Frequency = 34.02GHz, power = 7mW,
            temperature = 139K.
     4b.   MCD-ODMR of Cu(EDTA), monitored at 750nm.
            Frequency = 32.22GHz, power = 0.1mW,
            temperature = 1.7K.

In order to carry out such an experiment a frozen aqueous solution must be held at cryogenic temperature in a high Q microwave cavity which has optical access along the direction of the static field. A split-coil, re-entrant top-loading super-conducting magnet, such as the SM-4 built by Oxford Instrument Company, is ideal for this type of experiment. A microwave guide terminating in a cavity, with optical access, can be lowered into the sample space. The cavity is immersed in liquid helium and can be pumped to ~1.5K.

MCD measurements are carried out in our laboratory using a JASCO J-500D spectro-polarimeter fitted with a superconducting magnet, type SM4 (Oxford Instruments PLC, Osney Mead, Oxford). The magnet contains a Helmholtz pair of solenoids capable of generating a maximum field of 5 Tesla along the axis midway between the coils. The sample space between the split-pair is rectangular in cross-section with strain-free optical windows normal to the field axis. This space can be filled with liquid helium from the main helium bath and pumped, independently of the bath, to a tempera-ture of ~1.5K. Access is from the top of the magnet cryostat via a long cylindrical tube of diameter 40 nm.

A rectangular cavity resonating in the TE_{102} mode at the Q-band frequency has been built. The sample is placed at the centre of the cavity in a cylinder of teflon, internal diameter 2 mm and length 1 mm, with ends sealed by silica windows made from quartz cover slips. Optical access through the cavity is via two holes of diameter 2.0 mm drilled in opposite walls of the cavity. The cavity can be matched from out-side of the cryostat. The microwave circuit is shown in figure 2.

3 RESULTS AND DISCUSSION

(a) Copper(II) EDTA in aqueous solution and 50% (v:v) glycerol gives a convenient test of the equipment. The MCD spectrum between 500-800 nm is temperature dependent arising from the excited d-states of the copper(II) ion. Figure 3 shows a plot of the intensity dependence of the MCD spectrum at 740 nm as a function of magnetic field at 1.7K both in the absence and presence of microwave radiation of frequency 32.221 GHz. The MCD intensity is partially quenched on application of the magnetic field. The MCD-ODMR spectrum can be obtained by differencing the intensity variation of the MCD signal with and without microwaves. The shape of this spectrum is compared with that of the Q-band EPR spectrum recorded in the absorption mode, figure 4. There is good agreement between the two line shapes.

(b) Azurin (Pseudomonas aeruginosa) is a blue copper protein with a known struc-ture determined by X-ray crystallography (2). The co-ordination site consists of one methionine, one cysteine and two histidine ligands. Figure 5 shows the MCD of azurin from Pseudomonas aeruginosa at 1.05 Tesla field and 1.7K. The spectrum is shown with and without microwave irradiation at 32.68 GHz and 30 mW. The MCD spectrum is

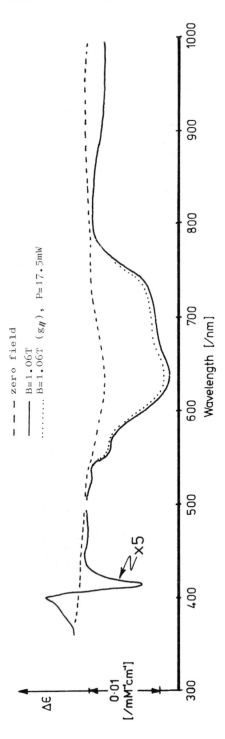

Fig. 5 MCD of azurin ($\underline{\text{P. aeruginosa}}$) with cytochrome c_{551} at 1.06T and 1.7K. 1.17mM in 50% (v/v) H_2O/glycerol. Microwave frquency was 31.68GHz.

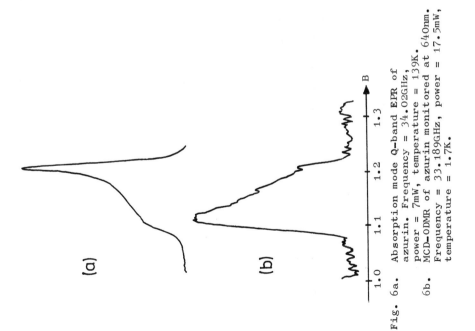

Fig. 7.   Computer simulation of MCD–ODMR
lineshapes for $g_\parallel$ =2.29, $g_\perp$ =2.06
Lorentzian lineshape = 3mT.
Optical polarisations are;
(i) 99% z polarised
(ii) 50% z, 50% xy polarised
(iii) 99% xy polarised.

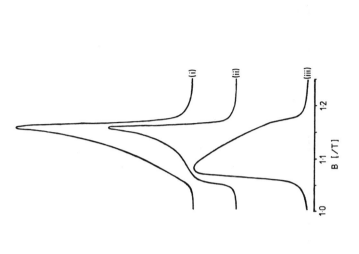

Fig. 6a.   Absorption mode Q-band EPR of
azurin. Frequency = 34.02GHz,
power = 7mW, temperature = 139K.
6b.   MCD–ODMR of azurin monitored at 640nm.
Frequency = 33.189GHz, power = 17.5mW,
temperature = 1.7K.

partially quenched. By contrast the optical bands between 400 and 410 nm, due to a trace of impurity cytochrome c_{551}, are unaffected by microwave irradiation. The ODMR spectrum detected at 640 nm is shown in figure 6(a) and should be compared with the Q-band EPR spectrum, recorded in the first absorption mode, figure 6(b). It is clear that the ODMR band shape is quite different and that only the $g_{//}$ component of the g-tensor is being detected optically.

This contrasts with the results for Cu EDTA, figure 4. The ODMR detected via the Cu^{2+} d-d bands at 750 nm has the same shape as that of the Q-band EPR. The ODMR line shape depends upon the polarisation of the optical transition being used to detect the magnetic resonance. Figure 7 shows a computer simulation of ODMR line shapes for three cases of optical polarisation, namely, isotropic z = x = y, axial with a transition mainly z polarised (z = 0.9, xy = 0.1) and axial with a transition mainly xy polarised (z = 0.01, xy = 0.99). This dependence upon the polarisation of the optical transition arises because for MCD signals to be detected the optical transition must be polarised perpendicular to the magnetic field. Clearly the azurin band at 640 nm is primarily xy polarsied. This result had already been deduced from single crystal EPR and polarised optical crystal spectra of plastocyanin, a protein with the same coordination geometry as azurin (3). The pronounced optical polarisation arises because the optical transitions are charge-transfer transitions from cysteine, RS^-, to Cu^{2+}, and the cysteine group is perpendicular to the direction in which $g_{//}$ lies.

Hence the ODMR experiment relates the directions of the ground-state g-tensor and the optical transition-moment tensor. If the assignment of the optical transitions are understood then the ligand orientations may be deduced. Furthermore, the technique promises to allow the optical bands due to a given paramagnet to be deconvoluted by partial quenching of the MCD signal with resonant microwaves. In this way the optical features of transition-metal ions in multi-centred proteins can be disentangled.

Acknowledgements.   Thanks are due to the S.E.R.C., and the Royal Society for grants in aid of this work.

4   REFERENCES

(1) A.J. Thomson and M.K. Johnson, Biochem. J. **191** (1980) 411-420.

(2) E.T. Adman, R.E. Stenkamp, L. Sieker and L.H. Jensen, J.Mol.Biol.
     123 (1978) 35-47.

(3) K.W. Penfield, R.R. Gay, R.S. Himmelwright, N.C. Eickman, V.A. Norris,
     H.C. Freeman and E.I. Solomon, J.Amer.Chem.Soc. 103 (1981) 4382-4388.

Redox Titration and Reversible Removal of Copper from Cu-Amine Oxidase

Bruno Mondovì, Alessandro Finazzi Agrò, Giuseppe Rotilio and Stefania Sabatini

Institute of Applied Biochemistry and Biological Chemistry, University of Rome and C.N.R. Center of Molecular Biology, Rome, Italy.

SUMMARY

Beef plasma amine oxidase contains two cupric copper per 180,000 daltons, which can not be reduced by ferrocyanide or ascorbate, but only by dithionite or NADH in the presence of a redox mediator.

Copper can be reversibly removed from the protein by treatment with dithionite and cyanide. The reconstituted protein recovers the spectroscopic properties of the native enzyme and the enzymic activity almost completely.

The esr parameters of the enzyme treated with phenylhydrazine, an inhibitor reacting with the organic cofactor of the amine oxidases, are changed as to suggest that only one of the two copper atoms is affected by the reaction with the inhibitor.

It is proposed that the association (not necessarily implying structural proximity) between the copper atom and the organic cofactor determines the spectroscopic and catalytic properties of amine oxidases.

Abbreviations: PQQ = pyrrolquinoline quinone; PH = phenylhydrazine;
EDTA: ethylenediaminetetracetic acid (disodium salt);
esr = electron spin resonance; AO = amine oxidase.

INTRODUCTION

Copper-dependent amine oxidases are enzymes that catalyze oxidative deamination of primary amines, according to the reaction:

$$RCH_2NH_2 + O_2 + H_2O \longrightarrow RCHO + NH_3 + H_2O_2$$

They are present in plants and in many animal tissues. The mechanism of action of these enzymes is still obscure. The most controversial point being the postulated presence of a second cofactor beside copper and its identity. Recently Ameyama et al. (1) found spectral similarity of pyrrolquinoline quinone (PQQ) and the chromophores isolated from copper containing amine oxidases and Lobstein-Verbeck et al. (2) suggested that in bovine serum amine oxidase PQQ is the second prosthetic group, covalently bound to the enzyme.

Cu-amine oxidases react with carbonyl reagents, like phenylhydrazine (PH), forming chromophoric adducts absorbing around 400 nm and inactivates the enzymes.

Although the copper is essential for the enzymatic activity, its role is not clear. In fact it neither binds the substrate (3) nor undergoes valence change upon anaerobic addition of substrate (3, 4). Its redox behaviour has not been systematically studied, leaving open the question concerning its role in the electron transfer between the substrate and oxygen. The amine-oxidizing site seems to be identical with the carbonyl-like site, mainly on the basis of inhibition studies (5,6). This site has been located either in close proximity of the copper (7), or far apart from it (8, 9), both claims resting on rather indirect evidence.

In view of the controversial picture arising from the existing knowledge of Cu- amine oxidases, a more rigorous approach was undertaken, and beef plasma amine oxidase was subjected to a reinvestigation covering some intriguing points related to the prosthetic group(s). Redox reactions of the copper were studied to provide at least approximate values of its redox potential.

MATERIALS AND METHODS

All chemicals were purchased from commercial source and used without further purification.

Bovine plasma amine oxidase was purified according to Mondovì et al. (10). The activity of the enzyme was determined according to Tabor and Tabor (11) by monitoring the production of benzaldehyde at 250 nm ($\varepsilon = 12,500$ M^{-1} cm^{-1}). One unit of enzyme was defined as the amount causing an O.D. change of 0.001/min in a 3 ml assay. Protein was deter-

mined by a biuret method (12) and by the absorbancy at 280 nm,
$E_{1cm}^{1\%} = 13$, was calculated on the basis of dry weight determinations.

The copper-free enzyme was prepared according to the following
procedure: i) reduction by excess dithionite in air; ii) addition of 3
mM KCN for 1-3 mM copper-enzyme; iii) overnight dialysis against 50 mM
KCN in 0.1 M phosphate buffer pH 7.2; iv) exhaustive dialysis against
0.1 M phosphate buffer. Reconstitution was obtained by adding 1 mM
$CuCl_2$. The mixture was left standing for 12 h and then dialyzed against
0.1 M phosphate buffer containing 2 mM EDTA. The reconstituted enzyme
was dialyzed against the same buffer containing 0.1 M $NaClO_4$ and finally against buffer alone. This procedure always left 10-15% residual
copper in the apoenzyme. A similar method was recently published by
Suzuchi et al. (13).

Optical spectra were obtained with a Beckman Acta III spectrophotometer. Esr spectra were recorded at approximately 9 GHz with a Varian
E 9 spectrometer equipped with the Varian variable temperature apparatus. Copper analyses were made with the spectrophotometric procedure
of Brumby and Massey (14) using acid hydroxylamine-biquinoline as the
copper reagents. Anaerobic dithionite solutions were prepared by dissol
ving an appropriate weight of dry, fresh powder deposited in a lateral
arm of a Thunberg device into deoxygenated buffer solutions.

RESULTS

Redox reactions of the copper

In buffered solutions at pH 7.2, NADH slowly reduced the enzyme
copper anaerobically, but only in the presence of phenazine methosul-
phate as mediator. Neither ferrocyanide nor ascorbate was able to reduce the copper, even in high excess and in the presence of suitable mediators such as methylene blue and toluidine blue. Reacting the enzyme
with PH or substrate - both of which change the esr line shape (see
below) without affecting the signal intensity - had no influence on the
apparent redox behaviour of the enzyme.

Under anaerobic conditions dithionite reduced the enzyme-copper
with half-time in the range of several minutes. The visible absorption
of the enzyme was bleached as well. Reoxidation, as monitored by reappearance of both esr and optical spectra, was practically immediate.
Experiments with dithionite are reported in fig. 1.

The visible and esr spectra lost in the apoenzyme were almost
fully recovered in the reconstituted protein (fig. 2). Table I shows
the copper content and specific activity of native, copper-free and reconstituted protein.

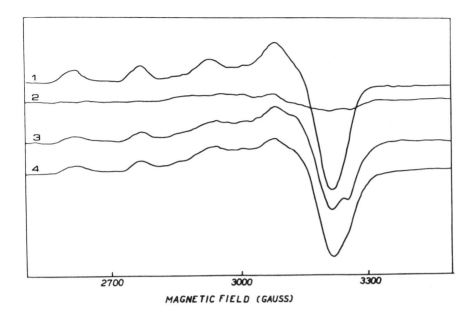

MAGNETIC FIELD (GAUSS)

Figure 1. Low temperature, x-band esr spectra of the reaction between plasma amine oxidase and $Na_2S_2O_4$.

1: 20 mg protein dissolved in 0.1 M phosphate buffer pH 7.2 (2.4×10^{-4}M copper);
2: after anaerobic addition of 3 equivalents of $Na_2S_2O_4$, frozen 3 min after mixing;
3: as in 2, after readmission of air and 10 min standing at room temperature;
4: as 3, after 30 min. standing at room temperature.
Esr conditions: microwave frequency, 9.14 GHz; microwave power, 20 mwatts; field modulation amplitude, 10 gauss; temperature, $-160°C$.

Table I - Properties of copper-free and reconstituted bovine plasma amine oxidase. The data are the average of three preparations.

	% Copper content	% Specific activity (per copper)
Native enzyme	100	100
Dithionite-cyanide-treated enzyme	6	0
Reconstituted enzyme	63	80

Copper can be also reversibly removed with the same procedure also from samples previously treated with PH.

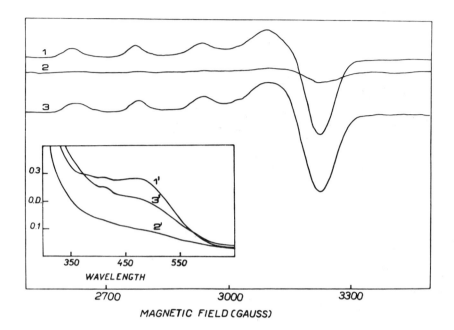

Figure 2. Esr and optical spectra of copper-free and reconstituted plasma amine oxidase.

1: 22 mg/ml protein dissolved in 0.1 M phosphate buffer, pH 7.2 (2.4 x 10^{-4}M copper);
2: after the treatment described in the text in order to remove copper;
3: protein reconstituted with the proper copper complement from the sample as in 2 according to the procedure described in the text. Gain x 2 with respect to spectra 1 & 2 to account for dilution. Esr conditions as in Fig. 1. The insert shows the corresponding optical spectra.

<u>Effect of the reaction with PH on the esr spectrum of the copper</u>

The esr spectra of native, PH-treated and reconstituted PH-treated AO samples were significantly different each other (fig. 3), although the substantial identity of g and A values of the reconstituted enzyme (see curves 3 of fig. 2 and 5 of fig. 3) indicates that the native copper ligands were maintained in the presence of PH. In this context it is also interesting to note that, on repeated experiments, the amount of copper which could be removed by the standard procedure out-lined above was always significantly less from the PH-treated enzyme than from the untreated protein, as 20-25% residual copper was repro-ducibly found in the former one. It is also evident from fig. 3 that the esr parameters measured in the presence of PH are very similar to those obtained upon anaerobic addition of substrate to the enzyme.

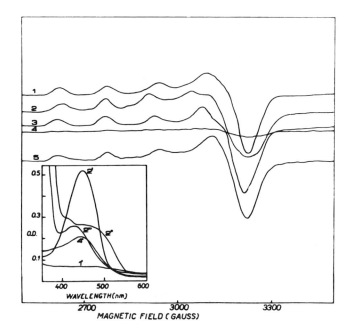

Figure 3. Esr and optical spectra of plasma amine oxidase in various conditions.

1: 18 mg/ml protein $(2 \times 10^{-4}M$ copper) in 0.1 M phosphate buffer pH 7.2;

2: as 1 after treatment with $1 \times 10^{-4}M$ PH and 6 hours incubation at room temperature (same spectrum was obtained with $5 \times 10^{-3}M$ PH);

3: as 1 after anaerobic addition of $1 \times 10^{-2}M$ benzylamine;

4: as 2 after copper removal according to the procedure used for the native enzyme;

5: as 4 after readdition of copper following the procedure described in the text.   The insert shows the corresponding optical spectra.

2" Immediately and 2''' after 60 min on addition of $Na_2S_2O_4$.

DISCUSSION

    The copper of beef plasma amine oxidase has been shown to have a rather low redox potential as compared, for instance, to that of other non-blue copper-containing oxidases or related enzymes, such as superoxide dismutase (15) and dopamine-β-hydroxylase (16). Even excess ascorbate at pH 7.2 (E $\simeq$ 50 mV) is not able to reduce the amine oxidase copper. NADH can reduce it, but even in the presence of mediators the equilibrium is reached very slowly, so that an estimate of the copper redox potential by this method would be an inaccurate one. The enzyme reduced by nearly stoichiometric dithionite is reoxidized by oxygen in a rather short time. This result, though not apparently related to the role of copper in the enzymic catalysis, where its reduction by substrate is not established (17), supports a possible function of the metal in the catalytic oxygen activation by this enzyme. In fact, fast reoxidation by oxygen is not observed in reduced superoxide dismutase nor in reduced azurin and plastocyanin, which are functionally reoxidized by other molecules.

The reduced amine oxidase lost a great part of its copper if dialyzed against CN⁻ at neutral pH, while the oxidized enzyme (data not reported) was practically unaffected by much higher CN⁻ concentrations. This procedure allowed a study of spectral properties of the apo- and reconstituted protein in greater detail than in previous reports (13,18, 19). The optical and esr spectra of the reconstituted enzyme show that the method to obtain the apoprotein is valid, as far as the spectral properties of the metal center are concerned, while some lack of reproducibility was observed as far the amount of copper recombined in the different preparations and the extent of activity recovery.

The esr spectra of AO reacted with PH seem to indicate either a physical proximity or a functional correlation between copper and the organic cofactors. In fact, reaction with the inhibitor modifies the copper esr spectrum of the native enzyme ($g_\parallel$ = 2.29; $A_\parallel$ = 168 gauss) in a rather specific way (see fig. 3) even though the esr spectrum of the protein after reaction with PH (fig. 3,2) is evidently heterogeneous. In particular, it appears as if only part (approximately half) of the copper were modified by the reaction with PH. The new species has smaller $A_\parallel$ (134 gauss) and greater $g_\parallel$ (2.31) and this change is indicative of changes of symmetry (more distorted) and/or ligands upon binding of PH (20). However the analogous changes ($A_\parallel$ = 152 gauss, $g_\parallel$ = 2.30) observed with substrate (fig. 3) and the fact, established with another enzyme of the same class (3), that the substrate nitrogens do not coordinate the copper, favour the conclusion that the copper is "indirectly" affected by the reaction of the protein with PH, as through conformational rearrangement of the protein region possibly including both the metal and the organic cofactor. In fact the type of change is compatible with a close proximity of the substrate (and PH)-binding site to the copper, while the extent of the change observed with PH is not against the stoichiometry of two copper atom per PH-reacting group.

Acknowledgement. This work has been in part supported by"Ministero della Pubblica Istruzione". The authors wish to thank Mr. A. Ballini for skilful technical assistance.

REFERENCES

1) M. Ameyama, M. Hayashi, K. Matsushita, E. Shinagawa and O. Adachi, Agr. Biol. Chem. 48 (1984) 561-565.

2) C.L. Lobstein-Verbeek, J.A. Jongejan, J. Frank and J.A. Duine, FEBS Letters, 170 (1984) 305-309.

3) B. Mondovì, G. Rotilio, M.T. Costa, A. Finazzi-Agrò, E. Chiancone, R.E. Hansen and H. Beinert, J. Biol. Chem. 242 (1967) 1160-1167.

4) R. Barker, N. Boden, G. Nayley, S.C. Charlton, E. Henson, M.C. Holmes, I.D. Kelly, and P.F. Knowles, Biochem. J. 177 (1979) 289-302.

5) F. Buffoni, Pharmacol. Rev. 18 (1966) 1163-1199.

6) E.A. Zeller in The Enzymes (P.D. Boyer, H. Lardy and K. Myrbäck eds.) 2nd Edn. Vol. 8, Academic Press Publishers, New York, London (1963), pp. 314-335.

7) A. Finazzi-Agrò, P. Guerrieri, M.T. Costa, and B. Mondovì, Eur. J. Biochem. 74 (1977) 435-440.

8) M.D. Kluetz, and P.G. Schmidt, Biochemistry 16 (1977) 5191-5199.

9) H. Zeidan, K. Watanabe, L.H. Piette and K.T. Yasunobu, J. Biol. Chem. 255 (1980) 7621-7626.

10) B. Mondovì, P. Turini, O. Befani and S. Sabatini, Methods in Enzymoloty 94 (1983) 314-318.

11) C.W. Tabor, H. Tabor and S.M. Rosenthal, J. Biol. Chem. 208 (1954) 645-661.

12) J. Goa, Scand J. Clin. Lab. Invest. 5 (1953) 218-222.

13) S. Suzuchi, T. Sakurai, A. Nakahara, T. Manabe and T. Okuyama, Biochemistry 22 (1983) 1630-1635.

14) P.E. Brumby and V. Massey, Methods in Enzymology 10 (1967) 473-474.

15) G. Rotilio, L. Morpurgo, L. Calabrese and B. Mondovì, Biochim. Biophys. Acta, 302 (1973) 229-235.

16) T. Skotland, and T. Ljones, Inorg. Persp. Biol. Med. 2 (1979) 151-180.

17) K.T. Yasunobu, E. Ishizaki and N. Minamiura, Mol. Cell Biochem. 13 (1976) 3-29.

18) H. Yamada and K.T. Yasunobu, J. Biol. Chem. 237 (1962) 3077-3080.

19) J.M. Hill and P.J.G. Mann, Biochem. J. 91 (1964) 171-182.

20) A. Desideri, L. Morpurgo, G. Rotilio and B. Mondovì, FEBS Lett. 98 (1979) 339-341.

Electronic Absorption Spectroscopy
of Cobalt Angiotensin Converting Enzyme

James F. Riordan, Frank Lee, Michael W. Pantoliano, Barton Holmquist

Center for Biochemical and Biophysical Sciences and Medicine, Harvard
Medical School, Boston, MA 02115 U.S.A.

SUMMARY

Angiotensin converting enzyme (ACE) is a metalloenzyme containing
one g-atom of zinc per mole. Binding of zinc to ACE is much weaker
than to other zinc metalloproteases and detailed kinetic analyses
indicate that this is due to more facile zinc dissociation. The
binding of active-site directed inhibitors has been examined using
cobalt(II) ACE. In order to obtain the milligram quantities of enzyme
needed for this purpose, a new high-capacity affinity chromatography
procedure was developed based on the specific ligand
N-carboxyalkyl-Phe-Gly. The spectra of Co(II)-ACE complexes with
inhibitors display absorption maxima at higher wavelengths and greater
absortivities than Co(II)-ACE alone. The presence of a Co$\longrightarrow$S charge
transfer band in the near UV spectrum of the Co(II)-ACE-Captopril
complex indicates direct binding of the thiol group of the inhibitor
to the active site metal.

1 INTRODUCTION

Angiotensin converting enzyme (ACE, dipeptidyl carboxypeptidase,
E.C. 3.4.15.1), a zinc metalloenzyme, is a broad specificity
carboxypeptidase that catalyzes the hydrolysis of the penultimate
peptide bond at the carboxy terminal of many peptides. Its principal
known physiological function is to catalyze the hydrolysis of

angiotensin I, releasing the carboxy terminal dipeptide His-Leu and the potent vasoconstricting octapeptide, angiotensin II. ACE thereby plays a role in the regulation of blood pressure and ACE inhibitors have been found clinically useful as antihypertensive agents. Such inhibitors have been designed to interact with the zinc atom in ACE.

Kinetic studies (1) have helped to understand the role of zinc in ACE catalysis and inhibition. Two advances have now made it possible to study the metal binding site of ACE directly and in greater detail: an affinity chromatographic system allows isolation of homogeneous ACE from rabbit lung tissue in large quantities (2), and replacement of zinc at the active site of ACE with cobalt generates a spectral probe responsive to the binding of inhibitors (3).

2 Methods

Metal-free ACE (apo-ACE) was prepared from enzyme obtained originally from rabbit lung tissue and purified to homogeneity by affinity chromatography (vide supra) (2). A solution of purified enzyme in 50 mM Hepes, pH 7.5, 0.3 M NaCl, 1 μM zinc acetate was concentrated first by ultrafiltration and further to 1.11×10^{-4}M using a collodion bag apparatus. Zinc was removed from the concentrated enzyme by dialysis over a period of 40 hr. against four changes of a 150-fold volume excess of 1,10-phenanthroline (OP) (Aldrich Chemical Co.) 1 mM, in 50 mM Hepes, pH 7.5, 0.3 M NaCl. The chelating agent was then removed by dialysis against five changes of a 150-fold volume excess of metal-free 50 mM Hepes, pH 7.5, 0.3 M NaCl.

Cobalt ACE was prepared by adding aliquots of 5 mM $CoSO_4$ ("Specpure" grade, Johnson Matthey Co.) to the apo-ACE solution. The Co-ACE-Enalaprilat complex was formed by adding 1 equiv. cobalt to apo-ACE, then the inhibitor, and then additional cobalt as described above. Other Co-ACE-inhibitor complexes were obtained by first adding inhibitor (1 equiv. aliquots from a 5 mM solution) and then $CoSO_4$. Precautions were taken throughout to avoid contamination with adventitious metal ions (4).

Assays and absorption spectra were measured on a Varian 219 spectrophotometer. ACE activity was routinely assayed by using

---

Abbreviations: ACE: angiotensin converting enzyme; Hepes: hydroxyethylpiperazine sulfate; Tris: Tris(hydroxymethyl) aminomethane; Sepharose-28-CA-Phe-Gly: N-[1(S)-carboxy-5-aminopentyl]-L-phenylalanylglycine immobilized on Sepharose with a 28A spacer; Fa: N-furanacryloyl; OP: 1,10-phenanthroline; EDTA: ethylenediamine tetraacetic acid; Enalaprilat: N-[1(S)-carboxy-3-phenylpropyl]-L-Ala-L-Pro; Captopril: (D-3-mercapto-2-methylpropanoyl)-L-Pro.

Furanacryloyl-Phe-Gly-Gly as a substrate and monitoring the decrease
in absorbance at 334 nm (5). Near UV spectra were obtained by
diluting apo-ACE 10-fold to reduce the absorbance contributed by the
protein. Metal-free Hepes buffer was used as a reference. The
spectra were stored on an Apple IIe computer system using a Varian
Master Scan program and the final spectra were obtained with a
Spectrum Calculations program.

2.1 Isolation of ACE

ACE was purified from frozen young rabbit lungs (Pel-Freez
Biologicals, Inc.) Briefly, crude homogenates were prepared in a
Waring Blendor with 5 mM Tris-HCl buffer, pH 7.4, and centrifuged at
20000g for 30 min. The pellet was resuspended in cold 50 mM Tris-HCl,
pH 8.5, containing 1.0% (v/v) Nonidet-P40 (BRL Inc.), centrifuged at
50000g for 75 min.

The solubilized membrane fraction supernatant was concentrated by
ammonium sulfate precipitation and finally purified by affinity
chromatography on Sepharose-28-CA-L-Phe-Gly, (Figure 1) an affinity
resin designed and prepared in this laboratory (2). This resin uses
the specific ligand N-carboxylalkyl-L-Phe-Gly and a 28A spacer.

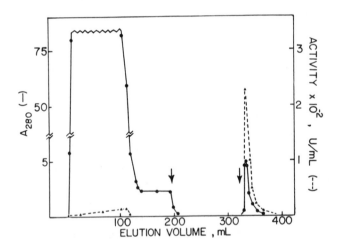

Figure 1. Affinity chromatography of solubilized pulmonary ACE on
Sepharose-28-CA-L-Phe-Gly. The column was washed with 12 column
volumes of starting buffer (20 mM Mes, pH 6.0, 0.50 M NaCl, 0.10 mM
zinc acetate, 0.1% Nonidet-P40) followed by 24 column volumes of the
same buffer but without detergent (first arrow). Elution was
initiated with 50 mM sodium borate, pH 8.9 (second arrow). The A_{280}
that remains in fractions collected after the column was washed with
starting buffer is due to the 0.1% Nonidet.

2.2 Determination of Stability and Rate Constants

The Zn-ACE stability constant, K_c, was determined by dialyzing fully active solutions of the enzyme (initially containing 7 μM $ZnCl_2$ to ensure optimal activity at pH 7.5) against metal-free Hepes, pH 7.5, 0.3 M NaCl at 25°C. After reaching equilibrium these enzyme solutions were diluted 100-fold into either A) a metal-free solution of the same buffer or B) the same buffer adjusted to 7μM $ZnCl_2$. K_c was determined knowing the total zinc content of the dialyzed enzyme solution and the zinc-free and zinc-bound concentrations of ACE determined by enzymatic assay of A and B.

Rates of zinc dissociation from Zn-ACE were determined in the presence of added OP or EDTA by measuring enzymatic activity using 0.5 mM Fa-Phe-Gly-Gly as substrate. Under these conditions deviations from linearity in plots of absorbance vs. time reflect metal dissociation and can be converted to rate constants by published methods (6).

3 Results

3.1 Rates of Dissociation

The interaction of zinc with carboxypeptidase A, thermolysin, and carbonic anhydrase has been studied (7-11) by following the rates of metal dissociation from these enzymes in the presence of different concentrations of chelating agents and as a function of pH. The observed rate differences have been interpreted in terms of the known metal binding groups of these enzymes. Similar studies with ACE and various chelators have been undertaken in this laboratory (1).

The chelator 1,10-phenanthroline (OP) interacts with Zn-ACE to form an OP-Zn-ACE ternary complex which dissociates to Zn-OP and apoenzyme. EDTA, on the other hand, acts only as a metal scavenger, and hence it is possible to obtain a dissociation rate constant by following the time course for loss of enzymatic activity. At pH 7.0, in the presence of 5×10^{-5} M EDTA, the rate of dissociation is $7.5 \times 10^{-3} sec^{-1}$ corresponding to a half-life for zinc dissociation of 92.4 sec. This is significantly shorter than that for carboxypeptidase, and, in particular carbonic anhydrase. Dissociation rates and half lives for these metalloenzymes are shown in Table 1.

Table 1

Dissociation Rates of Various Zinc Metalloenzymes

Complex	$k_d{}'$ (sec^{-1})	$t_{1/2}$	
Zn-ACE[a]	7.5×10^{-3}	92.4	sec
Zn-Carboxypeptidase A[b]	4×10^{-4}	28.3	min
Zn-Carbonic Anhydrase[c]	4×10^{-9}	5.4	yr

a) 25°C, 0.3 M NaCl, 50 mM Hepes, pH 7.0; b) 25°C, 1.0 M NaCl, 0.1 M Tris, pH 7.0; c) 25°C, I=0.1 M, pH 8.0.

The dissociation rate constant was measured as a function of pH. It reaches a minimum at pH 8.2 - 8.3 and increases thereafter suggesting an attack of hydroxide ion on the metal center, either directly or via formation of an HO-Zn-ACE species having more labile metal-enzyme bonds.

The stability constant, K_c, for the metal complex at the active site of ACE was determined by measuring enzyme activity and metal concentration after equilibrium dialysis. Metal concentration was determined by atomic absorption spectrometry rather than through the use of metal ion buffers (12) to avoid any interaction between a chelating agent used for metal buffering and the enzyme. K_c for ACE was found to be 1.66×10^8 M^{-1} in 50 mM Hepes 0.3 M NaCl at 25°C. From the relationship $k_f = k_d K_c$ it can be calculated that at pH 7.5 the rate constant for formation of Zn-ACE is 5.9×10^5 M^{-1}sec^{-1} at 25°C, very similar to that for carboxypeptidase A (7.7×10^5 M^{-1}sec^{-1}). A comparison of the metal-protein stability constants for the zinc metalloenzymes, which range over five orders of magnitude, is shown in Table 2.

Table 2

Metal-Protein Stability Constants of Zinc Metalloenzymes[a]

Zinc Metalloenzyme	$\log K_c$ (M^{-1})
Carbonic Anhydrase	12[b],13[c]
Thermolysin	11.3[d], 12.6[e]
Carboxypeptidase A	9.5[f], 10.5[g]
Angiotensin Converting Enzyme	8.2[h]

a) from ref (13); b) pH 7.0, 01 M Na phosphate, 25°C; c) pH 8.0, I = 0.1, 25°C; d) pH 7.5, I = 0.1, 25°C; e) pH 7.2, I = 0.02, 25°C; f) pH 7.0, 1.0 M NaCl, 0.1 M Tris, 25°C; g) pH 8.0, 1.0 M NaCl, 0.05 M Tris, 4 C; h) pH 7.5, 0.3 M NaCl, 0.05 M Hepes, 25°C.

3.2 Absorption Spectroscopy of Cobalt ACE

The activities of Zn-ACE and cobalt-substituted-ACE were measured with N-furanacryloyl-Gly-Leu-Ala and N-furanacryloyl-Gly-Leu-Gly. Relative to the zinc enzyme, Co-ACE has 120% activity with the former and 70% with the latter. It has already been shown to have 55% activity with N-furanacryloyl-Phe-Gly-Gly [14] while the metal free-enzyme is essentially devoid of activity.

The difference absorption spectrum for Co-ACE minus apo-ACE (Fig. 2) exhibits a broad band of low absorptivity with a maximum at 525 nm (ε= 75 M^{-1} cm^{-1}). It is similar in band position to the visible spectrum of cobalt thermolysin and has approximately half the absorbance of cobalt carboxypeptidase A (Fig. 2).

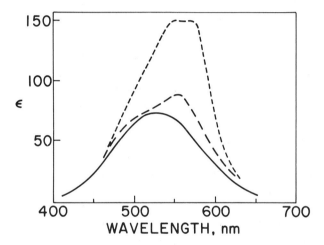

Figure 2. Co-ACE (———), Co-thermolysin (— — —), and Co-carboxypeptidase A (-- -- --) absorption spectra. All spectra were recorded in 50 mM Hepes, pH 7.5 in either 0.3 M (for ACE) or 1 M NaCl.

Aliquots of Co(II) were added to 100 μl samples of 1.1×10^{-4}M apoenzyme and the change in absorbance measured at 520 nm. A stoichiometric titration was unobtainable under these conditions indicating weak binding of metal. A calculated K_d for the cobalt enzyme of 1×10^{-4} M gives a reasonable fit to the titration curve. The experimental difficulties arising from weak association between cobalt and free enzyme are reduced when the titrations are performed in the presence of a chelating inhibitor.

Enalaprilat binds tightly only to metal-reconstituted ACE thereby shifting the equilibrium toward EMI in the following reaction:

$$E + M \longrightarrow EM \longrightarrow EMI$$

where E stands for enzyme, M for metal, and I for inhibitor. As expected, titration in the presence of the inhibitor is stoichiometric and agrees with previous findings that 1 g-atom of metal, either zinc or cobalt, is bound per mole of ACE (3,13,14). In addition, the spectrum of the Co-ACE-Enalaprilat complex differs dramatically from that of Co-ACE alone with a maximum at 552 nm and $\varepsilon = 300$ M^{-1} cm^{-1}.

Other inhibitors also induce remarkable changes in the visible absorption spectrum of Co-ACE (Fig. 3). Changes occur in the positions, intensities, and patterns of the cobalt d $\longrightarrow$ d transitions. In general, binding of inhibitor shifts the 525 nm centered absorption band of the Co-ACE to longer wavelengths. At the same time there is an increase in the molar absorptivities of these bands-from 75 M^{-1} cm^{-1} for Co-ACE to values that range from 130 to 560 M^{-1} cm^{-1}. The band patterns themselves show a great deal of variety and resolution; in most cases up to three distinct bands can be discerned.

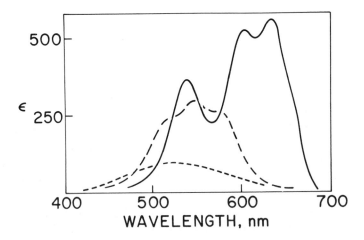

Figure 3. Absorption spectrum of Co-ACE (- - - - -) in the presence of Captopril (- -) or Enalaprilat (————).

In particular, the spectrum of the Co-ACE-Captopril complex shows two intense bands at 618 nm (520 M^{-1} cm^{-1}) and a less intense one at 540 nm (350 M^{-1} cm^{-1}). That of the Co-ACE-Enalaprilat complex shows bands at lower wavelengths. There is a central band at 552 nm (300 M^{-1} cm^{-1}) and 580 nm (130 M^{-1} cm^{-1}).

Because Captopril is a thiol, the near-UV spectra of the
Co-ACE-inhibitor complexes were examined. S--->Co(II) charge transfer
bands usually occur in the 250-350 nm region and have molar
absorptivities around 1000 M^{-1} cm^{-1}. Only the Co-ACE-Captopril
complex produced such an absorption band. The spectrum of the
Co-ACE-Captopril complex exhibits a maximum at 295 nm (ε=2600 M^{-1}
cm^{-1}) which has been assigned as a S--->Co(II) charge transfer band,
indicative of direct ligation of the thiol group of Captropril to the
active site metal ion.

4 Discussion

Exact identification of the metal binding ligands in ACE requires
X-ray crystallography and must await crystallization of the enzyme.
It is possible, however, to gain information about the possible
structure of the enzyme's active site by examining the kinetics of
enzyme inactivation in the presence of a suitable chelating agent.

The ternary complex OP-Zn-ACE is formed eight times faster than
OP-Zn-Carboxypeptidase-A which suggests that the metal binding site of
ACE is more accessible to OP. Moreover, the breakdown of OP-Zn-ACE to
apoenzyme and Zn-OP is faster than that of the equivalent
carboxypeptidase A and carbonic anhydrase complexes indicating that
zinc binding to ACE is weaker than to other zinc metalloenzymes (Table
1). One conclusion that can be drawn from these findings is that
there is an absence of steric constraints at the metal binding site.

The range of formation constants for ACE, carboxypeptidase A,
thermolysin and carbonic anhydrase is small in contrast with the range
of dissociation constants. The dissociation constants show the
following order: Zn-carbonic anhydrase < Zn-carboxypeptidase A <
Zn-ACE and differ by about 6 orders of magnitude. As a consenquence,
the pattern of stability constants follows the reverse order of
dissociation constants (Table 2). Metal binding to Zn-ACE is 100-fold
weaker than to Zn-carboxypeptidase A and 1000-fold weaker than to
Zn-thermolysin.

In general, the strength of metal binding in metalloenzymes
appears to decrease with a decreasing number of nitrogen ligands. In
carboxypeptidase A and thermolysin, the metal ion is bound with two
histidines and the carboxylate of one glutamic acid residue. This
might suggest that metal binding in ACE may involve less than two
nitrogen atoms.

Another approach to defining the position and role of zinc at the
active site in metalloenzymes has been through the use of
cobalt-substituted enzymes. In all zinc enzymes studied, including
carbonic anhydrase, alkaline phosphatase, carboxypeptidase A, and
thermolysin, the cobalt enzyme is active indicating that the Co(II)

ion is bound to the active site of the enzyme and plays a role in catalysis. The spectral properties of the cobalt atom in these enzymes and its reponses to factors like pH, inhibitors, and substrates, not only at equilibrium but also at various stages in the catalytic pathway, have allowed deductions about the metal coordination geometry and its significance to catalysis (15).

Cobalt carboxypeptidase A, cobalt thermolysin and Cobalt-ACE have similar spectra. In the first two enzymes, the active site metal ion is thought to be in an irregular tetrahedral geometry (16,17). The Co-ACE spectrum presents unusual features but strongly suggests that this enzyme too has a distorted coordination geometry.

The spectra of Co-ACE in the presence of inhibitors have maxima at relatively long wavelengths and display very high absorptivities when compared to Co-ACE spectra recorded in the absence of inhibitors. These spectra are also are very structured indicating that the Co(II) ion acquires a more tetrahedral-like geometry when it is coordinated with these inhibitors and implying that significant changes occur in the coordination environment of the metal ion on binding of inhibitor. Similar spectra are obtained with cobalt carboxypeptidase A and cobalt thermolysin in the absence and presence of inhibitors. In these cases, X-ray crystallographic and spectral data indicate distored tetrahedral geometries (16-19). In the case of the two latter enzymes, the active site zinc is coordinated to two histidyl imidazoles, one glutamyl carboxylate, and probably one water molecule. The metal ligands in ACE are thus far unknown but evidence gathered from a comparison of the spectra of CoACE in the presence of either Captopril or Enalprilat, inhibitors whose mechanisms involve metal ligation, indicates that sulfur is not one.

The zinc-containing enzymes ACE, carboxypeptidase A, and thermolysin show the following similarities. Each contains a zinc ion essential for activity; each is inhibited by metal chelating agents; and in each, critical glutamyl, tyrosyl, and, for the first two, arginyl residues at the active site have been implicated by chemical modification studies. Delineation of the nature of the active site has been particularly important in the case of ACE because it has led to the design of highly potent metal-coordinating inhibitors that have proved to be clinically effective in the treatment of hypertension (20). Recent evidence has indicated that a number of functionally-related zinc dipeptidyl carboxypeptidases may also participate in the processing of peptide hormones and in the metabolism of neuropeptides (21). Thus, the potential for selective drug design may be applicable to these systems as well.

5 REFERENCES

(1)   R. Shapiro, J.F. Riordan, Biochemistry 23 (1984) 5225-5230.

(2)   M.W. Pantoliano, B. Holmquist, J.F. Riordan, Biochemistry 23 (1984) 1037-1042.

(3)   F. Lee, B. Holmquist, J.F. Riordan, in preparation.

(4)   R.E. Thiers, in D. Glick, (Ed), Methods of Biochemical Analysis, Wiley-Interscience, New York; Vol. 5.

(5)   P. Bunning, B. Holmqist, J.F. Riordan, Biochemistry 22 (1983) 103-110.

(6)   J.E. Barnes, A.J. Waring, in "Pocket Programmable Calculators in Biochemistry", J. Wiley & Sons (1980).

(7)   R.J. Rogers, E.J. Billo, J. Inorg. Biochem. 12 (1980) 335-341.

(8)   E.J. Billo, J. Inorg. Biochem. 10 (1979) 331-339.

(9)   E.J. Billo, K.K. Brito, R.G. Wilkins, Bioinorg. Chem. 96 (1978) 461-469.

(10) R.G. Wilkins, K.R. Williams, J. Am. Chem. Soc. 96 (1978) 2241-2245.

(11) R.W. Henkens, J.M. Sturtevant, J. Am. Chem. Soc. 90 (1968) 2669-2676.

(12) S.R. Cohen, I.B. Wilson, Biochemistry 5 (1966) 904-909.

(13) S.G. Kleeman, W.M. Keung, J.F. Riordan, J.Inorg. Biochem. submitted.

(14) P. Bunning, J.F. Riordan, J. Inorg. Biochem. in press.

(15) M. Das, R.L. Soffer, J. Biol. Chem. 250 (1975) 6762-2768.

(16) S.A. Latt, B.L. Vallee, Biochemistry 10 (1971) 4263-4269.

(17) B. Holmquist, B.L. Vallee, J. Biol. Chem. 249 (1974) 4601-4606.

(18) W.N. Lipscomb, J.A. Hartsuck, F.A. Quiocho, G.N. Reeke Jr., Proc. Natl. Acad. Sci. U.S.A. 64 (1969) 28-35.

(19) P.M. Colman, J.N. Jansonius, B.W. Matthews, J. Mol. Biol. 70 (1972) 701-717.

(20) M.J. Antonaccio, D.W. Cushman, Federation Proc. 40 (1981) 2275-2284.

(21) Y.P. Loh, Ann. Rev. Neurosci, 7 (1984) 189-222.

Interfacial Properties of c-Type Cytochromes at an Electrolyte/Electrode Interface

K. Niki,[1] Y. Kawasaki,[1] C. Hinnen,[2] Y. Higuchi[3] and N. Yasuoka[3]

[1] Department of Electrochemistry, Yokohama National University, Yokohama 240, Japan
[2] Laboratoire d'Electrochimie Interfaciale du CNRS, 92190 Meudon-Bellevue, France
[3] Institute for Protein Research, Osaka University, Suita, Osaka 565, Japan

SUMMARY

The redox behavior of the adsorbed c - type cytochromes on silver and gold electrodes are investigated by voltammetric and spectroelectrochemical techniques. The redox behavior monitored by an electroreflectance method agrees quite well with the results obtained by voltammetry for both cytochromes c_3 and c. However, the formal potential of the adsorbed cytochrome c_3 monitored by SERS is different from that observed by the voltammetry and corresponds to that of the most positive redox site among the four hemes in the molecule. The SERS results reveal that the cytochrome c_3 molecules are highly oriented at the electrode surface so that Heme - 1 interacts specifically with the electrode. The adsorbed cytochrome c_3 layer on the electrode behaves like an electronic conductor the the heterogeneous electron transfer reaction of cytochrome c_3 in the bulk through the adsorbed layer.

1 INTRODUCTION

Cytochrome c_3 is a tetraheme protein present in the respiratory chain of anaerobic bacteria of the genus *Desulfovibrio*. These bacteria use either organic substrates or molecular hydrogen as electron donors and sulfate ions as terminal electron acceptors. On the external surface of the cytoplasmic membrane of the sulfate reducing bacteria, molecular hydrogen generated from organic substrates is oxidized by the periplasmic hydrogenase which specifically reduces cytochrome c_3, and then the electrons are transferred to sulfate inos through a complex electron transfer chain. Cytochtome c_3 plays an important role as an electron carrier in the respirarory chain. Cytochromes c_3 contain about 110 amino acid residues, and have molecular weights of approximately 14,000. The four hemes are covalently attached to the polypeptide chain by thioether linkage of cysteinyl residues and their axial ligands are histidine residues. The three dimensional structures at high resolution have been determined for cytochromes c_3 from *D. vulgaris*, Miyazaki strain, (1,2) and *D. desulfuricans*, Norway strain, (3,4). Their structures were found to be very similar in spite of their low sequence homology (5). The redox potentials (macroscopic and intrinsic formal potentials)[*] of the four hemes in the cytochrome c_3 molecule have been extensively studied by electrochemical (6-12), ESR (13-15), and NMR(16,17) methods to elucidate the mechanism of the electron transfer in cytochromes c_3. It appears that these four hemes are characterized by four separate but closely spaced formal potentials and that weak intramolecular heme-heme interactions are expected.

PHYSICOCHEMICAL PROPERTIES OF CYTOCHROME C_3 FROM *D. VULGARIS*, MIYAZAKI STRAIN.

Cytochrome c_3 isolated from *D. vulgaris*, Miyazaki F strain, contains 107 amino acid residues with the molecular weight of 13,995 (18). The iron-to-iron distance ranges from 11.0 to 17.8 Å. The four heme groups are closely packed with the adjacent pairs of the heme planes being nearly perpendicular to each other. All heme groups are highly exposed to the solvent. The differences in the heme structures and their environments indicate that the four heme groups are non-equivalent. The cytochromes c_3 show a reversible voltammetric response from which one can calculate the macroscopic formal potentials by the least square fitting to the theoretical equation (10). The potential difference between the most positive one and the most negative one is only 115 mV for cytochrome c_3 from DvM in 0.03 M phosphate buffer at pH 7.0 and 25 °C. Effects of temperature, pH of the solution, supporting electrolytes, and solvents on the redox behavior of the hemes are well correlated with the structure of cytochrome c_3 from DvM. The most negative formal potential could be assigned to Heme-2 and the most positive one to Heme-1, respectively. Heme-1 would be an electron acceptor from hydrogenase and Heme-2 would be an electron outlet of cytochrome c_3. The intermediate formal potentials could be assigned to Heme-3 and Heme-4, which could be an electron storage. Heme-3 and Heme-4 are considered to be equivalent sites or considered to have slightly different formal potentials because the heme binding groups of these hemes are very much alike. A certein intramolecular attractive interaction could be expected between Heme-3 and Heme-4 because the spacing of the formal potentials between these hemes is only 18 mV.

c-Type cytochromes are adsorbed strongly on electrodes from aqueous solutions

---

[*] Formal potential, $E^{\circ\prime}$, is related to Nernst equation with the activity replaced by the concentration of reactants in the fixed composition of the medium.

The macroscopic formal potentials are obtained when the redox sites in the molecule are indistinguishable. If these redox sites are distinguishable, in principle, the intrinsic formal potentials are obtainable (8).

and the heterogeneous electron transfer reactions between electrodes and cytochromes in the solutions are strongly influenced by the nature of the adsorbed layer. Different models have been proposed to explain the electrode process through a monolayer of the adsorbed cytochromes (19, 20). The adsorbed layer of cytochrome c_3 on the electrode does not inhibit the electron transfer from the electrode to cytochrome c_3 in the bulk of the solution. On the other hand, the reduction peak potential in the cyclic voltammogram for cytochrome c is shifted from its formal potential to the formal potential of the adsorbed cytochrome c on the electrode. That is, the reduction peak is about 350 mV more negative than the formal potential.

EXPERIMENTAL SETUP

Horse heart cytochrome c, Type IV, from Sigma Chemical Co. was purified chromatographically. Cytochrome c_3 was isolated from $D.\ vulgaris$, Miyazaki F strain, and purified as previously described (2). The investigations consist on one hand of classical voltammetric and admittance (by superimposing a small ac modulation on the dc potential) measurements and on the other hand of simultanous optical (electroreflectance) and admittance measurements to investigate an overall redox characteristic of the adsorbed cytochrome layer (21). The surface enhanced Raman scattering (SERS) spectroscopy is also applied to investigate the redox behavior of the adsorbed cytochrome layer at the electrode surface.

VOLTAMMETRIC STUDIES

Both cytochrome c_3 and cytochrome c exhibit a well-defined pseudo-capacitance peak at about - 0.5 V ($vs.$ Ag/AgCl.sat. KCl) on both silver and gold electrodes in a neutral solution as shown in Fig. 1. In the case of cytochrome c, however, the peak potential depends on the nature of the electrolyte. These peaks are visible on the voltammogram as shown in Fig. 1 as more or less well-defined redox waves. It is interesting to note that the potential of the pseudo-capacitance peak which is originated from a redox process of the adsorbed species does not vary with the nature of cytochromes because their respective reversible redox potential values are + 0.01 V for the native cytochrome c and - 0.53 V for the native cytochrome c_3. The pseudo-capacitance peak potential of

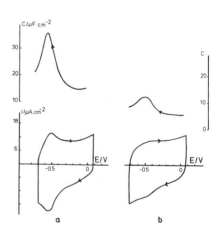

Fig. 1   Capacitive C(E) and voltammetric curves for adsorbed cyt. c_3 (a) and cyt. c (b) on gold electrode in 0.02 M KClO$_4$ at pH 6.

the adsorbed cytochrome c_3 agrees with the formal potential of cytochrome c_3 in the bulk of the solution. On the other hand, the pseudo-capacitance peak potential of the adsorbed cytochrome c is markedly shifted toward negative potential from the formal potential of the bulk species.

ELECTROREFLECTANCE STUDIES

The simultaneous electroreflectance for the adsorbed cytochrome c_3 at $\lambda = 405$ nm and the pseudo-capacitance curves with respect to the electrode potential of the gold electrode reveal that the highest enhancement of the optical signal was observed at the peak potential of the capacity curve. The electroreflectance spectra of the adsorbed cytochrome c on the gold electrode at various electrode potentials are shown in Fig. 2. The typical spectra are displayed at E_p with both cytochrome c_3 and cytochrome c. This

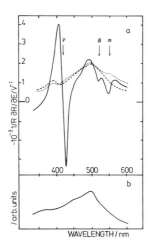

Fig. 2 (a) Electroreflectance at the peak potential (———) in the presence of adsorbed cyt. c on gold electrode in 0.02 M $KClO_4$ at pH 6. (·········) at - 0.7 V and (————) at + 0.1 V. (b) er spectrum of gold electrode at pzc.
α, β and γ represent the peaks in the absorption spectrum of cytochrome c.

structure is gradually attenuated as the potential is shifted in either positive or negative direction from E_p because the adsorbed species are supposed to be completely oxidized or reduced, respectively, under the extereme potentials and both exhibit a closely similar structure which is also very like the metallic electroreflectance effect of the gold electrode as shown in Fig. 2 - b.

A qualitative understanding of the electroreflectance spectra can be obtained in considering the change in absorbance properties of the cytochromes from the ferric form of the hemes in cytochromes to the ferrous form upon the electrochemical reduction. When such a redox conversion occurs in the adsorbed cytochromes on the electrode surface (the redox reaction rate must be fast on the time scale of the ac modulation frequency) by the modulation of the electrode potential by a small ac voltage, an electroreflectance effect will be observable and the highest enhancement would be expected at the formal potential of the adsorbed cytochromes.

The redox processes of the adsorbed cytochrome c_3 and cytochrome c on both gold and silver electrodes monitored by electrochemical methods well accord with those monitored by the electroreflectance method because an overall optical property of the adsorbed cytochromes is measured with the both methods.

SURFACE ENHANCED RAMAN SCATTERING OF ADSORBED C - TYPE CYTOCHROMES.

Raman signals from the molecules adsorbed on silver, copper, gold electrodes and

colloids were enhanced by $10^5 \sim 10^{10}$ greater than what one would expect for a monolayer on these metal substrates and this technique has been named as a surface enhanced Raman scattering (SERS) spectroscopy (22). Although the mechanism of SERS has
not been completely explored, this technique is a powerful tool to investigate the
interfacial and conformational information of biological molecules at an electrolyte/
electrode interface under *in situ* condition (23 - 26).

The SERS spectra of ferric and ferrous cytochromes c_3 on the silver electrode
are compared with the normal solution Raman scattering (NSRS) spectra in Fig. 3. The
dots in Fig. 3 designate the four key bands (Band I to IV, from the left to the
right), which enable us to distinguish the oxidation state of heme proteins (27, 28).
Band I is sensitive to both the oxidation and the spin states of the heme iron. Band
II and IV can be the oxidation and spin state marker of heme proteins.

The shift of Raman bands between NSRS and SERS spectra is small indicating that
the structure of the heme chromophore in cytochrome c_3 is not greatly perturbed when
it is adsorbed on the electrode surface. Figure 4 shows the variation of SERS spectra of the adsorbed cytochrome c_3 with respect to the electrode potential of the
silver electrode. At very positive electrode potentials, Band IV is observed at 1385
cm^{-1} and the band position is indicative of the ferric cytochrome c_3. On shifting
the electrode potential toward negative, Band IV for the ferrous form at 1375 cm^{-1}
starts to appear at - 0.32 V (*vs.* Ag/AgCl·sat. KCl) and Band IV for the ferric form
disappears at - 0.46 V. The formal potential of the adsorbed cytochrome c_3 is estimated to be - 0.40 V. That is, the heme chromophore, which is monitored by SERS, is
reduced completely at the potential much more positive than the formal potential of
the adsorbed cytochrome c_3, at which half of the hemes in the molecule are reduced.
If cytochrome c_3 molecules were randomly oriented at the electrode surface, the formal potential of the adsorbed cytochrome c_3 ob-
served by SERS would be equal to the formal potential determined by voltammery.

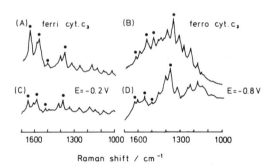

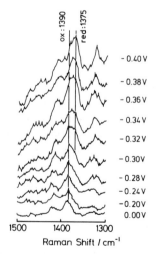

Fig. 3   NSRS(A,B) and SERS(C,D) spectra of cyt. c_3
(0.5 mM for NSRS and 0.6 μM for SERS) on Ag electrode in 0.03 M phosphate buffer at pH 7.0.
An excitation wavelength is 514.5 nm.

Fig. 4   SERS spectra of cyt. c_3 on Ag
electrode as a function of wave number
and potential. Experimental conditions
are given in Fig. 3.

The formal potential of the adsorbed cytochrome c, on the other hand, determined by voltammetry agrees with that determined by SERS because cytochrome c contains only one heme chromophore in the molecule. Figure 5 represents the SERS spectra of cytochrome c adsorbed on the silver electrode. The oxidation state marker Band IV is shifted from 1375 cm^{-1} for the ferric form to 1366 cm^{-1} for the ferrous form at about - 0.25 V, which was mentioned earlier by Cotten et al. (23). That is, the formal potential of the adsorbed cytochrome c is about 0.35 V more negative than that of the bulk species. This is probably because the cytochrome c molecule is unfolded when it is adsorbed on the electrode surface and the interaction between the heme chromophore and the electrode becomes stronger.

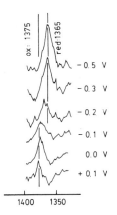

Fig. 5   SERS spectra of cyt. c on Ag electrode at various electrode potentials. Experimental conditions are given in Fig. 3.

The voltammogram of the adsorbed cytochrome c_3 reveals that only one fourth of the hemes in the adsorbed molecule is reduced at - 0.40 V. That is, the fromal potential monitored by SERS would correspond to that of the most positive redox site among the four hemes in the molecule[*] and it would be the intrinsic formal potential.

The question is raised as to which heme in the molecule will perticipate in the redox reaction at the potential more positive than the formal potential of the adsorbed cytochrome c_3 on the electrode.

The exposed edge of Heme - 1 is located in a cavity surrounded by eight lysine and one gultamine residues. It is well known that amines are strongly adsorbed on metal surfaces and that they often act as a corrosion inhibitor to the metals. It is quite conceivable that the amines from lysine and gultamine residues would be anchors of the cytochrome c_3 molecule to the metal surface so that the interacting site would be Heme - 1, which is condidered to have the most positive formal potential from the voltammetric results. The interaction between the cytochrome c_3 molecule and the silver electrode through the lysine and gultamine residues are so strong that the molecules are highly oriented toward the electrode surface. There are few possibilities that the other hemes interact specifically with the silver electrode.

Since the Raman enhancement is limited to the functional groups in the range of

---

*) The macroscopic formal potentials of cytochrome c_3 from DvM in the bulk are - 0.439, - 0.496, - 0.514, and - 0.556 V (vs. Ag/AgCl·sat. KCl). Thus the formal potential of the cytochrome c_3 molecule is given to be - 0.501 V (the average of the four macroscopic formal potentials), which is also determined by voltammetry. If the most positive redox site is noninteracting, its intrinsic formal potential will be very close to the macroscopic formal potential. The intrinsic and macroscopic formal potentials of cytochrome c_3 from D. gigas were calculated from NMR data (16).

5 Å from the electrode surface (25, 26), the enhancement would be attributable to the most positive redox site, namely, Heme - 1. The Raman enhancement by other heme chromophores would be much weaker than that by Heme - 1 because the distances between the electrode and these hemes are greater than 10 Å.

The effect of $[Co(CN)_6]^{3-}$ ion on the electrode reaction of cytochrome c_3 on the silver electrode is examined. Since it is well known that $[Co(CN)_6]^{3-}$ interacts with lysine residues, $[Co(CN)_6]^{3-}$ would interact with the lysine residues, which form a cavity for Heme - 1. Figure 6 shows the cyclic voltammograms of cytochrome c_3 on the silver electrode in the absence and in the presence of $[Co(CN)_6]^{3-}$. The peak currents due to the redox reaction of cytochrome c_3 are almost diminished by the addition of $[Co(CN)_6]^{3-}$ ion. That is, the electrode reaction of cytochrome c_3 is completely inhibited by $[Co(CN)_6]^{3-}$. It has been shown that $[Co(CN)_6]^{3-}$ ion is not specifically adsorbed on the silver electrode but that the cytochrome $c_3 - [Co(CN)_6]^{3-}$ complex is confirmed to be adsorbed on the silver electrode by the differential capacitance measurement of the electrode. The SERS spectra of the cytochrome $c_3 - [Co(CN)_6]^{3-}$ complex reveal that the formal potential of the most positive redox site, Heme - 1, is almost unaffected by $[Co(CN)_6]^{3-}$.

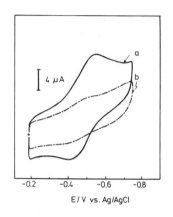

Fig. 6   Cyclic voltammograms of cyt. c_3 on Ag electrode (a) in the absence and (b) in the presence of 10 mM $[Co(CN)_6]^{3-}$ 70 μM cyt. c_3.

It may be concluded that $[Co(CN)_6]^{3-}$ ion interacts with the lysine residues in the vicinity of Heme - 1 and decelerates the electron transfer rate of cytochrome c_3 at the electrode surface. However, it does not affect the formal potential of Heme - 1 because the SERS measurements are carried out under the equilibrium condition.

ELECTRON TRANSFER RATE FROM THE ELECTRODE TO CYTOCHROME c_3 IN THE BULK THROUGH THE ADSORBED CYTOCHROME c_3 LAYER ON THE ELECTRODE.

The intermolecular electron exchange rate constant between cytochrome c_3 molecules is estimated to be 10^4 M^{-1}s^{-1} (5×10^5 M^{-1}s^{-1} for cytochrome c_3 from D. vulgaris, Hildenborough strain (29)) by the NMR pattern. The heterogeneous electron transfer reaction rate at the electrode through the adsorbed cytochrome c_3 layer is determined to be 1 cm s^{-1} by the galvanostatic double pulse method. The heterogeneous electrode transfer rate constant at the electrode can be calculated from the intermolecular electron exchange rate constant and the amount of the adsorbed cytochrome c_3 on the electrode surface provided that the adsorbed layer mediates the electron exchange between the electrode and the bulk species and that the adsorbed cytochrome c_3 behaves as it does in the bulk. Since the amount of the adsorbed cytochrome c_3 on the electrode is determined to be 1×10^{-11} moles/cm^2, the hetrogeneous electron transfer reaction rate constant at the electrode surface is estimated to be 10^{-4} cm/s. These results indicate that the adsorbed cytochrome c_3 layer on the electrode does not behave as an electron mediator in the electrode reaction of the bulk species in the solution but it behaves as an electronic conductor.

ACKNOWLEDGMENT

This work was supported by Grant-in Aid for Scientific Research from the Ministry of Education, Science and Culture of Japan (No. 59550544 for KN) and Asahi Glass Foundation for Industrial Technology (KN) for which the authors would like to express their sincere thanks. The authors wish to acknowledge the support to our research project and kind supply of sulfate reducing bacteria by Ajinomoto Co.

REFERENCES

1) Y. Higuchi, S. Bando, M. Kusunoki, Y. Matsuura, N. Yasuoka, M. Kakudo, T. Yamanaka, T. Yagi, H. Inokuchi, *J. Biochem. (Tokyo)* 89 (1981) 1659 - 1662.

2) Y. Higuchi, M. Kusunoki, Y. Matsuura, N. Yasuoka, M. Kakudo, *J. Mol. Biol.* 172 (1984) 109 - 139.

3) R. Haser, M. Pierrot, M. Frey, F. Payan, J. P. Astier, M. Bruschi, J. LeGall, *Nature (London)* 282 (1979) 806 - 810.

4) M. Pierrot, R. Haser, M. Frey, F. Payan, J. P. Astier, *J. Biol. Chem.* 257 (1982) 14341 - 14348.

5) Y. Higuchi, M. Kusunoki, N. Yasuoka, M. Kakudo, T. Yagi, *J. Biochem. (Tokyo)* 90 (1981) 1715 - 1723.

6) K. Niki, T. Yagi, H. Inokuchi, K. Kimura, *J. Electrochem. Soc.* 124 (1977) 1889 - 1891.

7) K. Niki, T. Yagi, H. Inokuchi, K. Kimura, *J. Am. Chem. Soc.* 101 (1979) 3335 - 3340.

8) W. F. Sokol, D. H. Evans, K. Niki, T. Yagi, *J. Electroanal. Chem.* 108 (1980) 107 - 115.

9) K. Niki, Y. Kawasaki, N. Nishimura, Y. Higuchi, N. Yasuoka, M. Kakudo, *J. Electroanal. Chem.* 168 (1984) 275 - 286.

10) K. Niki, Y. Kobayashi, H. Matsuda, *J. Electroanal. Chem.* 178 (1984) 333 - 341.

11) P. Bianco, J. Haladjian, *Electrochim. Acta* 26 (1981) 1001 - 1004.

12) P. Bianco, J. Haladjian, *J. Electroanal. Chem.* 137 (1982) 367 - 376.

13) D. V. Der Vartanian, A. V. Xavier, J. LeGall, *Biochimie* 60 (1978) 321 - 325.

14) A. V. Xavier, J. J. G. Moura, J. LeGall, D. V. Der Vartanian, *Biochimie* 61 (1979) 689 - 695.

15) R. Cammack, G. Fauque, J. J. G. Moura, J. LeGall, *Biochim. Biophys. Acta* 784 (1984) 68 - 74.

16) H. Santos, J. J. G. Moura, I. Moura, J. LeGall, A. V. Xavier, *Eur. J. Biochem.* 141 (1984) 283 - 296.

17) K. Kimura, S. Nakajima, K. Niki, H. Inokuchi, *Bull. Chem. Soc. Japan* 58 (1985) 1010 - 1012.

18) W. Shinkai, T. Hase, T. Yagi, H. Matsuura, *J. Biochem. (Tokyo)* 87 (1980) 1747 - 1756.

19) F. Scheller, *Bioelectrochem. Bioenerg.* 4 (1977) 490 - 499.

20) B. A. Kuzunetsov, G. P. Shumakovich, N. M. Mestechkina, *Bioelectrochem. Bioenerg.* 4 (1977) 412 - 421.

21) C. Hinnen, R. Parsons, K. Niki, *J. Electroanal. Chem.* 147 (1983) 329 - 337.

22) M. Fleischman, P. J. Hendra, A. J. McQuillan, *Chem. Phys. Lett.* 26 (1974) 163 - 166.

23) T. M. Cotton, S. G. Schultz, R. P. Van Dayne, *J. Am. Chem. Soc.* 102 (1980) 7960 - 7962.

24) R. L. Birke, J. R. Lombardi, L. A. Sanchez, in K. Kadish (ed) *Adv. Chem. Ser.* (*American Chem. Soc.*) No. 201 (1980) 69 - 107, and literatures cited therein.

25) E. Koglin, J. M. Séquaris, *J. Phys. (Paris)* 44 (1983) C 10 - 487 - 480.

26) V. Brabec, K. Niki, *J. Biophys. Chem.* submitted.

27) T. Kitagawa, Y. Kyogoku, T. Iizuka, M. I. Saito, *J. Am. Chem. Soc.* 98 (1976) 5169 - 5173.

28) M. Abe, T. Kitagawa, Y. Kyogoku, *Chem. Letters* (1976) 249 - 252.

29) J. J. G. Moura, H. Santos, I. Moura, J. LeGall, G. R. Moore, R. J. P. Williams, A. V. Xavier, *Eur. J. Biochem.* 127 (1982) 151 - 155.

Structure of a Small Rubredoxin: Tentative Assignment of Amino Acid Sequence and Three Dimensional Structure of The Rubredoxin From *Desulfovibrio Desulfuricans* (Strain 27774)

L.C. SIEKER, R.E. STENKAMP, L.H. JENSEN AND J. LEGALL

Department of Biological Structure, Department of Biochemistry, University of Washington, Seattle, Wash. U.S.A. and Department of Biochemistry, University of Georgia, Athens, Georgia, 30602, U.S.A., Groupe Commun d'Enzymologie, DB/SRA B.P. n 1, 13115 St Paul, les-Durance, France.

SUMMARY

The rubredoxin from the anaerobe <u>Desulfovibrio</u> <u>desulfuricans</u> (strain 27774) has been crystallized with triclinic symmetry, space group P1 with cell parameters: a=24.92 Å, b=17.79 Å, c=19.72 Å, α =101.02°, β =83.37°, γ =104.52°. Amino acid composition studies indicate this rubredoxin is atypical in that it contains histidine and is the smallest rubredoxin isolated thus far. The unit cell volume for this crystalline form is small indicating a short polypeptide chain and limited solvent content. Crystal diffraction data, including both reflections of each Friedel pair, were collected to 1.5 Å resolution. A truncated <u>D</u>. <u>vulgaris</u> molecular model was used with the rotation function to determine the low resolution structure. Solution of the structure is being pursued at high resolution.

1 INTRODUCTION

Rubredoxin (RBDD) from the sulfate and nitrate reducing strain of <u>Desulfovibrio</u> <u>desulfuricans</u> (strain 27774) is being studied by x-ray diffraction methods to determine its three dimensional structure. The amino acid composition indicates a polypeptide chain of approximately 48 residues and the first occurrence of histidine in a rubredoxin from an anaerobic organism (1) . Figure 1

----

* The amino acid composition listed in that report should have 5 Glu residues added to it.

shows the amino acid sequences of five different rubredoxins from three
different types of bacteria. There is considerable homology among the
sequences but distinct differences are also obvious. A comparison of the
three-dimensional structures of the upper three proteins (manuscript in
preparation) shows virtually identical chain folding with the strictly conserved
aromatic groups being in very similar orientations. It seems reasonable to
expect a similar folding of the chain for the smaller RBDD, keeping in mind that
some residues will be deleted.

FIGURE 1

SEQUENCES OF FIVE RUBREDOXINS

```
                    5                 10                 15
RBCP   MET-Lys-Lys-Tyr-Thr-CYS-Thr-Val-CYS-GLY-TYR-Ile-TYR-ASP-PRO-
RBDV                     Val                      Glu
RBDG       Asp Ile     Val                      Glu
RBPE       Asp         Glu     Ser Ile                          Glu
RBPA       Gln     Phe Glu         Leu


                    20                25                 30
RBCP   Glu-Asp-Gly-Asp-Pro-Asp-Asp-Gly-Val-Asn-Pro-GLY-Thr-Asp-PHE-
RBDV   Ala Glu             Thr Asn         Lys             Ser
RBDG       Lys                 Ser     Ile-Lys             Lys
RBPE       Glu         ---     Gly Asn     Ala Ala         Lys
RBPA       Leu Val Gly         Thr Pro Asp Gln Asp     --- Ala


                    35                40                 45
RBCP   Lys-ASP-Ile-Pro-Asp-Asp-TRP-Val-CYS-PRO-Leu-CYS-GLY-Val-Gly-
RBDV   Asp     Leu     Ala                 Val         Ala Pro
RBDG   Glu     Leu                 Ala     Val         Ala Ser
RBPE   Ala     Leu     Ala                 Thr         Ala Asp
RBPA   Glu     Val Ser Glu Asn                         Ala


                    50                55
RBCP   LYS-Asp-Glu-PHE-Glu-Glu-Val-Glu-Glu
RBDV       Ser         Ala Ala --- ---
RBDG       Ala         Lys Gln --- ---
RBPE       Ala         Val Lys Met Asp ---
RBPA       Glu Asp         Val Tyr     Asp
```

RBCP, RBDV, RBDG, RBPE and RBPA designate the rubredoxins from
Clostridium pasteurianum, Desulfovibrio vulgaris, D. gigas,
Peptostreptococcus eldsenii and Peptococcus aerogenes.
The amino acid residues of the other rubredoxins are placed
in the appropriate column where they differ from the rubredoxin
of Clostridium pasteurianum. Deletions are shown as dashes in
the column.

2 EXPERIMENTAL

Crystals of this rubredoxin belong to the triclinic system with one molecule in the unit cell. The cell parameters are: a=24.922(4) Å, b=17.786(3) Å, c=19.715(3) Å, α =101.02(1)$^{\circ}$, β =83.37(1)$^{\circ}$, and γ =104.52(1)$^{\circ}$. The molecules are so tightly packed that the crystal solvent content is smaller than that of any other crystalline protein reported in the literature (2). This fact increases the diffracting power of the crystal but limits access of heavy atoms in soaking experiments and could hinder molecular replacement techniques (3) due to loss of contrast between protein and solvent in the crystal. The decision to attempt the solution of the structure by the use of the rotation function was based on the fact that this method worked well in the determination of the structure of RBDV which also contained a small amount of well ordered water (4).

Reflection data, including both members of each Friedel pair, were measured in resolution shells to 1.5 Å, a total of 11,600 measurements. Crystal deterioration, monitored by remeasuring ten (and later twelve) reflections periodically throughout the data collection period, was about 9% at the end. The data were corrected for deterioration and absorption by the normal procedures. Computational details will be presented elsewhere in a more complete description of this work.

A measure of the quality of the data can be determined by comparing replicates. Of 1540 reflections replicated at the overlapping shells of data, $R = \sum (F_1^2 - F_2^2) / \sum 0.5 \cdot (F_1^2 + F_2^2) = 0.03$. The anomalous scattering from iron and sulfur contributes to a difference between Friedel reflection mates, and this value of R is 0.05 indicating a significant signal above the comparable value of 0.03 for the replicate data.

3 RESULTS

A Patterson synthesis calculated with the Bijvoet differences as coefficients clearly showed a single peak with hints of four closely associated peaks, indicating the expected Fe-4Cys tetrahedral coordination complex. Since the space group is P1, determination of the orientation of the molecule in the cell is sufficient because the translation is arbitrary. Using the Fe-4S cluster, the atoms of the polypeptide backbone and those atoms from most of the strictly homologous residues of the RBDV structure, a rotation function against the 26.0 to 5.0 Å data set with a radius of 15 Å produced a rotation which appeared correct (5). This partial structure was corrected further for interfering or overlapping side chains in the triclinic cell by deleting the offending atoms. Many of the amino acid residues were defined as alanine since the side chains were not obvious at this stage of the analysis. This model was the input for calculating the subsequent electron density (e.d.) maps used for the analysis of the structure. The reliability factor (or residual) R= $\sum \| F_o |-|F_c \| / \sum | F_o |$ was 0.436 (5.0 to 3.5 Å data) for the initial model. Several cycles of refinement by a restrained least squares algorithm (6), designed to fit a proposed model to the observed data, reduced the residual R to 0.337 (5 to 3.5 Å).

A new difference e.d. map was then calculated to see what additional structure could be found, and atoms were added or deleted as indicated. After several cycles of: 1) Refinement, 2) Adding, deleting or shifting atoms and 3) Inspecting appropriate e.d. maps, a 2.1 Å map was calculated by adding higher order reflections (R=0.382, 5 to 2.1 Å).

The 2.1 Å map was inspected for features consistent with the known three-dimensional folding of rubredoxins generally and with the amino acid composition for RBDD (4,7), taking into consideration the juxtaposition of neighboring residues from adjoining molecules in the packing arrangement within the crystal. The e.d. map clearly shows an overlap problem of the chain from residue 20 to 23 with residue 5 of an adjoining molecule. Closer inspection of this region indicated that it was possible to fit the density best by bridging this loop between residues 19 and 24 with a glycine residue, shortening the loop by three residues. This Gly20 not only fits the density but also fulfills the general rule of a Gly being located at a beta bend where chains reverse direction (8).

Extensive refinement and editing of this model has not led to a satisfactory fitting of the electron density. This region is very congested due to close association of chains between neighboring molecules and the region including residues 16 to 28. Inspection of Figure 1 shows that many of the residue changes and all of the internal deletions occur here. The uncertainties in amino acid sequence and the deletions have impeded the interpretation of the map. There is a significant amount of electron density which remains to be fit in connecting the two pieces of polypeptide chain. Extensive refinement using different subsets of the data (based on resolution) has not produced satisfactory models for the e.d. map. We have obtained respectable R values of 0.20 for the 5-1.5 Å data, even with 10 to 15% of the protein main chain omitted! We believe the refinement process has introduced some artifact or bias, and we are continuing attempts to solve this problem. The chemical sequence determination is also in progress to aid in the interpretation of the e.d. map.

The Fe-S distances at the current stage of structure analysis are not significantly different from each other; Fe-Cys 6 = 2.35 Å, Fe-Cys 9 = 2.23 Å, Fe-Cys 39 = 2.25 Å, and Fe-Cys 42 = 2.26 Å. The average distance, 2.27 Å, is similar to the average distances found for RBCP and RBDV. These bond lengths are quite tentative and should be accepted with caution until the structure is completely determined and refined.

Figure 2 shows a tentative amino acid sequence, and Figure 3a shows the alpha carbon chain of RBDD which can be compared to the alpha carbon chain of RBDV in 3b.

FIGURE 2

TENTATIVE SEQUENCE FOR RBDD

(obtained from crystallographic studies)

```
                        5                   10                  15
RBDD    MET-Gly-LYS-TYR-Ala-CYS-Ala-Val-CYS-Gly-TYR-Ala-TYR-Asp-Pro-

                        20                  25                  30
        Ala-Ser --- --- --- --- --- --- --- --- --- --- Gly-Gly-PHE-

                        35                  40                  45
        Asp-Ala-Leu-PRO-Gly-ASP-TRP-Val-CYS-Pro-VAL-CYS-Gly-Val-Ser-

                        50
        LYS-Asp-Glu-PHE-Gly
```

Legend: Those residues that are quite certain are in capital
letters. The unknown part of the molecule including possible
deletions in the sequence is shown as ---.

FIGURE 3

STEREOSCOPIC VIEWS OF (A) RBDD AND (B) RBDV

(A)

(B)

4 References

(1). Sieker,L.C., L.H. Jensen, B.C. Prickril & J. LeGall. J. Mol. Biol. <u>171</u>, (1983). 101-103.
(2). Matthews,B.W. J. Mol. Biol. <u>33</u>, (1968). 491-497.
(3). Rossmann,M.G. The Molecular Replacement Method, International Science Review Series, vol 13, Gordon & Breach, New York. (1972).
(4). Adman,E.T., L.C. Sieker, L.H. Jensen & J. LeGall. J. Mol. Biol. <u>112</u>, (1977). 113-120.
(5). Crowther, R.A. in M.G. Rossmann (ed.) The Molecular Replacement Method, International Science Review Series, vol 13, (1972). pp. 173-183.
(6). Hendrickson,W.A. & J.H. Konnert. in R. Srinivasan (ed.) Biomolecular Structure, Function, Conformation & Evolution, vol 1, Oxford: Pergamon Press. (1980). pp 43-57.
(7). Watenpaugh, K.D., L.C. Sieker & L.H. Jensen. J. Mol. Biol. <u>131</u>, (1979). 509-522.
(8). Richardson, J.S. in C.B. Anfinsen, J.T. Edsall & F.M. Richards (ed.) Advances in Protein Chem., vol 34, Academic Press Inc., New York. (1981). pp. 167-339.

Super-Reduction of 7Fe *Azotobacter Vinelandii* Ferredoxin I and Direct Conversion to the 8Fe-Form

P.J. Stephens*, T.V. Morgan*, C.D. Stout[†], B.K. Burgess[††]

*Department of Chemistry, University of Southern California, Los Angeles, CA 90089-0482, USA.
[†]Department of Crystallography, University of Pittsburgh, Pittsburgh, PA 15260, USA.
[††]Department of Molecular Biology and Biochemistry, University of California at Irvine, Irvine, CA 92717, USA.

ABSTRACT
    Reduction of aerobically isolated 7Fe *Azotobacter* vinelandii ferredoxin I (7Fe)FdI, {[3Fe-3S]$^{3+}$, [4Fe-4S]$^{2+}$}, by excess sodium dithionite (DT) at pH 7.5 leads to time-independent absorption, circular dichroism (CD) and EPR spectra, attributable to reduced (7Fe)FdI, {[3Fe-3S]$^{2+}$, [4Fe-4S]$^{2+}$}. However, at pH $\gtrsim$ 8, reduction by excess DT leads to continuously time-dependent absorption, CD and EPR spectra. Two, distinct "g=1.94" EPR signals develop, one of which appears to be the precursor of the other. The two EPR-active species are assigned respectively to "super-reduced" (7Fe)FdI, {[3Fe-3S]$^{2+}$, [4Fe-4S]$^{1+}$} and reduced (8Fe)FdI, {2[4Fe-4S]$^{1+}$}. [(8Fe)FdI was recently obtained directly by anaerobic reconstitution of apo-FdI]. Addition of Fe^{2+} and S^{2-} to DT-reduced (7Fe)FdI at either pH 7.5 or 9.0 does not appreciably enhance the conversion to (8Fe)FdI. It appears, therefore, that over the pH range 7.5-9.0, significant conversion of (7Fe)FdI to (8Fe)FdI proceeds only via "super-reduction" of (7Fe)FdI.

    X-ray crystallography has shown that aerobically isolated *Azotobacter* vinelandii ferredoxin I contains one [4Fe-4S] and one [3Fe-3S] cluster [1,2]. The former exhibits a stoichiometry, [Fe$_4$S$_4$(S-cys)$_4$], and structure essentially identical to the [4Fe-4S] clusters of *Peptococcus* aerogenes ferredoxin [3] and *Chromatium* vinosum HIPIP [4]. The latter is a novel cluster, of stoichiometry [Fe$_3$S$_3$(S-cys)$_5$X] in which the Fe$_3$S$_3$

core is nearly planar and X is unidentified and may be H_2O (or OH^-).
As isolated, <u>Azotobacter</u> <u>vinelandii</u> ferredoxin I (henceforth (7Fe)FdI)
exhibits nearly isotropic EPR at g $\sim$ 2.01[5]. On reduction, (7Fe)FdI
has been reported to become EPR silent[5]. Mössbauer spectroscopy of
(7Fe)FdI as isolated and after sodium dithionite (DT) reduction found
that: (i) in both states the [4Fe-4S] cluster is diamagnetic,
consistent with a $[4Fe-4S]^{2+}$ oxidation state; (ii) the [3Fe-3S] cluster
is reduced by DT, is paramagnetic in both oxidation levels, being
responsible for the g $\sim$ 2.01 EPR when oxidised, but being EPR silent
when reduced[6]. Since "g=1.94" EPR was not observed on reduction of
(7Fe)FdI and since reaction with $Fe(CN)_6^{3-}$ generates additional EPR
intensity at g $\sim$ 2.0, it has been concluded that the [4Fe-4S] cluster
is a HIPIP-type cluster, expressing the $[4Fe-4S]^{2+/3+}$ redox couple[5].
Thus, immediately subsequent to the recent X-ray crystallography and
Mössbauer spectroscopy, the redox states of (7Fe)FdI were believed to
be:*

$$\{[3Fe-3S]^{2+}, [4Fe-4S]^{2+}\} \xleftarrow{+1e^-} \{[3Fe-3S]^{3+}, [4Fe-4S]^{2+}\} \xrightarrow{-1e^-} \{[3Fe-3S]^{3+}, [4Fe-4S]^{3+}\}$$

as isolated

Detailed studies of the $Fe(CN)_6^{3-}$ oxidation of (7Fe)FdI in our
laboratory[7-9] have recently shown that a) an oxidised HIPIP, $[4Fe-4S]^{3+}$
cluster is not formed and b) that reaction with $Fe(CN)_6^{3-}$ is degradative
and progressive, leading eventually to apoprotein. To date, we have
identified two intermediates <u>en route</u> to apoprotein:

$$\{[3Fe-3S]^{3+}, [4Fe-4S]^{2+}\} \rightarrow \{[3Fe-3S]^{3+}, [4Fe-4S]'\} \rightarrow \{[3Fe-3S]^{3+}, -\} \rightarrow \{-, -\}$$

In the first intermediate the $[4Fe-4S]^{2+}$ cluster is oxidised in a 3-
electron process to a paramagnetic, EPR-active species [4Fe-4S]', whose
structure is discussed in detail elsewhere[7]. Subsequently, the
[4Fe-4S] cluster is completely destroyed, leaving a 3Fe protein
containing only the original [3Fe-3S] cluster[8,9]. Finally, the
[3Fe-3S] cluster is destroyed.

Since the [4Fe-4S] cluster is not, as previously believed, a HIPIP-
type cluster, the possibility exists that it is therefore a low-
potential cluster of the bacterial ferredoxin type, whose redox
potential is extremely low, such that under the reducing conditions
hitherto employed it remains unreduced. We have obtained evidence in

*FOOTNOTE: The 3^+ charge of the oxidised [3Fe-3S] cluster follows from
the Fe^{3+} state of all $3Fe$[6] and the Fe_3S_3 core stoichiometry[1,2].

favor of this view from studies of the reduction of (7Fe)FdI at higher pH than normally employed. We have found, and recently reported briefly [7], that at pH $\overset{>}{\sim}$ 8.0 "g=1.94" EPR is observed on reduction with DT. The simplest interpretation of this result is that the oxidation level $\{[3Fe-3S]^{2+} \cdot [4Fe-4S]^{1+}\}$ is being formed.

However, the possibility exists of a more complex interpretation. The 3Fe clusters of <u>Desulfovibrio gigas</u> ferredoxin II (<u>D. gigas</u> Fd II) and beef heart aconitase are known to be capable of conversion to [4Fe-4S] clusters when Fe and S^{2-} are added under reducing conditions [10,11]. In the case of beef heart aconitase, the reduced 3Fe cluster executes this process even in the absence of externally administered Fe and S^{2-}, presumably by intermolecular cluster cannibalisation[11,12]. It must be considered possible, therefore, that the reduction of (7Fe)FdI at high pH leads to a reduced state of an 8Fe form of ferredoxin I, via conversion of the [3Fe-3S] cluster to a [4Fe-4S] cluster. This latter possibility is made more probable by our recent reconstitution from the apoprotein of ferredoxin I of an 8Fe, $\{2[4Fe-4S]^{1+/2+}\}$ protein, which in its reduced state exhibits "g=1.94" EPR[13].

We have carried out further studies of the reduction of (7Fe)FdI at high pH. The purpose of this communication is to report evidence obtained for <u>both</u> formation of "super-reduced" (7Fe)FdI <u>and</u> conversion to reduced (8Fe)FdI.

MATERIALS AND METHODS
All materials and methods were as described previously[7,13].

RESULTS AND DISCUSSION
(7Fe)FdI as isolated (7Fe)FdI$_{ox}$) exhibits near-IR-visible-near-UV absorption and circular dichroism (CD) attributable to both Fe-S clusters present, and EPR and low temperature magnetic circular dichroism (MCD) due to the $[3Fe-3S]^{3+}$ cluster[7]. On anaerobic addition of excess DT to (7Fe)FdI$_{ox}$ in 0.1M potassium phosphate buffer, pH 7.5, the absorption, CD and MCD change, while the EPR vanishes. The absorption and CD after reduction are shown in Figure 1. The absorption is bleached somewhat, while the CD changes shape substantially. Subsequent to the initial change, the absorption, CD and EPR remain unaltered for at least several hours. The spectroscopic changes are consistent with formation of reduced (7Fe)FdI, (7Fe)FdI$_{red}$, in which the [3Fe-3S] cluster is reduced to the 2+ level and the [4Fe-4S] cluster remains in the EPR-silent 2+ oxidation level.

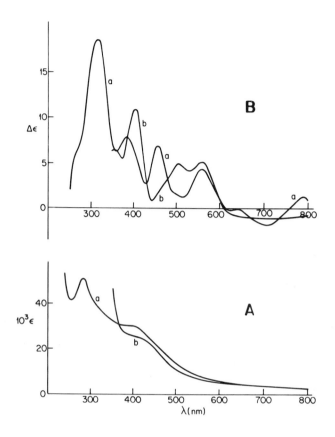

FIGURE 1:   Absorption (A) and CD (B) of (7Fe)FdI$_{ox}$, a, and DT-reduced (7Fe)FdI$_{ox}$, b, in 0.1 M potassium phosphate buffer, pH 7.5. [DT]:[(7Fe)FdI$_{ox}$] ∿ 20,

Increase of pH to values > 9.0 produces no significant change in the absorption and CD of (7Fe)FdI$_{ox}$.   However, DT reduction at pH ∿8.0 leads to continuously time-dependent absorption and CD.   Initially, reduction leads to spectra identical in shape to those obtained at pH 7.5.   However, continued monitoring shows that bleaching of both absorption and CD occurs subsequently, the rate of this process increasing with increasing pH.   Figures 2 and 3 illustrate results obtained at pH 9.0 in 0.1 M Tris-HCl buffer.   No evidence of stabilization of the optical spectra was observed over times as long as 5 hrs.

The EPR after DT reduction of (7Fe)FdI$_{ox}$ at pH > 8.0 also exhibits time dependence, as illustrated in Figure 4 for pH = 9.0.   Initially, the removal of the g ∿ 2.01 signal of (7Fe)FdI$_{ox}$ is observed. Subsequently, "g=1.94" EPR appears.   However, not only is the amplitude of "g=1.94" EPR time-dependent, but the shape changes with time also

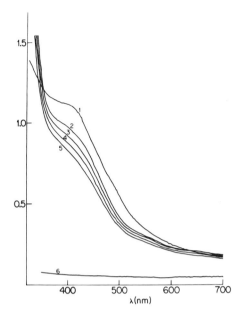

FIGURE 2: Absorption of (7Fe)FdI$_{ox}$ (I) and DT-reduced (7Fe)FdI$_{ox}$ (2-5) in 0.1 M Tris-HCl buffer, pH 9.0. [DT]:[(7Fe)FdI$_{ox}$] $\sim$ 3.5. Scans 2-5 were initiated at 22, 66, 90 and 122 min after addition of DT. Scan time is $\sim$ 10 min. Scan 6 is the buffer baseline. [(7Fe)FdI$_{ox}$] was 0.069 mM before and after DT addition. Cell pathlength was 0.517 cm.

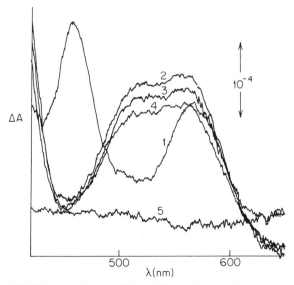

FIGURE 3: CD of (7Fe)FdI$_{ox}$ (1) and DT-reduced (7Fe)FdI$_{ox}$ (2-4) in 0.1 M Tris-HCl buffer, pH 9.0. The solutions and cell were those used for absorption spectroscopy (Figure 2). Scans 2-4 were initiated at 52, 80 and 110 min after addition of DT. Scan time is $\sim$ 15 min. Scan 5 is the buffer base-line. Time constant was 4 sec.

showing that two different "g=1.94" signals are present. The signal
appearing first, signal 1, whose highest g value is 2.07, initially
grows and then diminishes in intensity. Signal 2, whose highest g value
(2.04) is significantly less than that of signal 1, appears subsequently
and over the time monitored only increases in intensity. The changes
in EPR are qualitatively identical at [DT]:[(7Fe)FdI$_{ox}$] $\sim$ 5 and 20, but
occur more rapidly at the higher ratio (Figure 4).

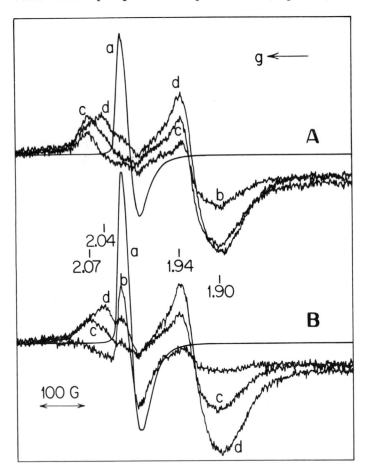

FIGURE 4: EPR at 11°K of DT-reduced (7Fe)FdI$_{ox}$ in 0.1 M Tris-HCl buffer.
pH 9.0. [DT]:[(7Fe)FdI$_{ox}$] $\sim$ 20 (A) and 5 (B). In both A and B, curves a,
b, c and d correspond to incubation times prior to freezing of 5, 30,
60 and 120 min. All spectra were obtained at 2 mW, 9.355 GHz and 10 G
modulation. In both A and B, curves a were at gain 1.25 x 10^3, and
curves b-d were at gain 3.2 x 10^4. g values of interest are indicated.
[(7Fe)FdI$_{ox}$] was 0.068 mM before and after addition of DT. The g $\sim$
2.01 signals in curve a of A, and in curves a and b of B correspond
respectively to 45, 63, and 1% of the g $\sim$ 2.01 intensity of (7Fe)FdI$_{ox}$
prior to addition of DT.

It appears, therefore, that two species exhibiting "g=1.94" EPR are formed, one being the precursor of the other. Further, signal 2 possesses g values very close to those of the DT reduced reconstituted 8Fe protein, (8Fe)FdI[13]. We therefore conclude that the second species is $\{2[4Fe-4S]^{1+}\}$, (8Fe)FdI$_{red}$. The obvious candidate for the species responsible for signal 1 is then the "super-reduced" (7Fe)FdI, $\{[3Fe-3S]^{2+}, [4Fe-4S]^{1+}\}$, (7Fe)FdI$_{superred}$.

These conclusions are consistent with the observed changes in absorption and CD. (7Fe)FdI$_{superred}$ is expected to exhibit lower absorption than (7Fe)FdI$_{red}$, since reduction of the $[4Fe-4S]^{2+}$ cluster to the 1+ oxidation state causes bleaching of the absorption in well-characterised bacterial ferredoxins[14], and it is also not unreasonable that the absorption of (8Fe)FdI$_{red}$ is lower than that of (7Fe)FdI$_{superred}$. The loss of CD amplitude without major change in shape shows that both (7Fe)FdI$_{superred}$ and (8Fe)FdI$_{red}$ have much weaker CD than (7Fe)FdI$_{red}$. We have no independent knowledge of the CD of (7Fe)FdI$_{superred}$. However, our earlier studies of (8Fe)FdI$_{red}$[13] showed that its CD when reduced is indeed extremely weak (the CD of (8Fe)FdI$_{red}$ was consequently not shown in ref. 13).

In the experiments illustrated in Figure 4 at pH 9.0 the intensities of the combined "g=1.94" EPR signals are 0.25-0.30 spin per molecule after 2 hrs at both [DT]:[(7Fe)FdI$_{ox}$] $\sim$ 5 and 20.

The immediate conclusions to be drawn are therefore:

a) the super-reduced state of (7Fe)FdI indeed exists

b) super-reduction of (7Fe)FdI is followed by spontaneous conversion to 8(Fe)FdI.

The former conclusion is consistent with our demonstration that the [4Fe-4S] cluster of (7Fe)FdI is not a HIPIP-type cluster and our deduction that it therefore is a low-potential cluster, whose redox potential is extremely low[7].

The appearance of the EPR of (7Fe)FdI$_{superred}$ at pH 9.0, but not at pH 7.5, is attributable to the greater reducing potential of DT at the higher pH[15], although we cannot exclude the possibility of an increase in redox potential with pH also. The precise redox potential of the $[4Fe-4S]^{1+/2+}$ couple in (7Fe)FdI remains to be determined. At pH 7.5, CD spectroelectrochemical studies in our laboratory have shown no evidence for significant reduction of $[4Fe-4S]^{2+}$ at -600 mV (vs SHE).

The spontaneous conversion of (7Fe)FdI$_{superred}$ to (8Fe)FdI$_{red}$ is analogous to the spontaneous conversion of the reduced 3Fe cluster of beef heart aconitase to a [4Fe-4S] cluster[11,12]. We presume that intermolecular cannibalisation is also involved. We have no explanation for the requirement of prior reduction of the $[4Fe-4S]^{2+}$ cluster to the 1+ oxidation state for conversion of the 3Fe cluster. (We cannot of course rule out the possibility that spontaneous conversion of (7Fe)FdI$_{red}$ to (8Fe)FdI can occur. Our results only show that under the conditions employed, conversion from (7Fe)FdI$_{superred}$ is much faster).

In beef heart aconitase, the conversion of the reduced 3Fe cluster to a [4Fe-4S] cluster is accelerated, and increased in yield, by addition of Fe^{2+}[11,12]. Addition of Fe^{2+}, S^{2-} and DTT in large excess to (7Fe)FdI, either with or without prior DT reduction, at pH 7.5 leads to no change in the CD or EPR attributable to conversion of the 3Fe cluster to a [4Fe-4S] cluster. At pH $\sim$ 9.0, addition of Fe^{2+}, S^{2-} and DTT in large excess to DT reduced (7Fe)FdI has no more than a minor effect on the development of "g=1.94" intensity. It appears, therefore, that if the conversion of (7Fe)FdI to (8Fe)FdI involves initial disintegration of the [3Fe-3S] cluster, giving free Fe^{2+} and S^{2-}, that the reconstitution of the [4Fe-4S] cluster is not the rate limiting step.

Our results show that experiments on (7Fe)FdI, under conditions where superreduction and conversion to (8Fe)FdI can occur, must be carefully interpreted. The amounts of (7Fe)FdI$_{superred}$ and (8Fe)FdI formed will vary significantly with conditions such as pH, temperature, protein and reductant concentrations and incubation time. Previous work on reduced (7Fe)FdI includes EPR[5], Mössbauer[6] and NMR studies [16]. The absence of "g=1.94" EPR was reported after reduction at pH 7.4 using illuminated spinach chloroplasts[5], consistent with our observations on DT reduction at pH 7.5. Mössbauer spectroscopy used (7Fe)FdI reduced by DT and methylviologen at pH 9.0 for 1 hour at 0°C [6]. NMR was carried out on (7Fe)FdI reduced by methyl viologen at pD 8.6[16]. No evidence of more than one species arising from reduction was obtained in either Mössbaer or NMR study. However, in neither case was EPR reported.

Lastly, a further complicating factor in experiments employing DT reduction is introduced by our observation (based on EPR and absorption spectroscopies) that excess DT not only reduces (8Fe)FdI$_{ox}$ to the (8Fe)FdI$_{red}$ level, but also causes destruction of its Fe-S clusters.

Figure 5 summarises the metallated states, oxidation levels and interconversion processes identified to date in Azotobacter vinelandii ferredoxin I.   Since the function of this protein remains unknown, the physiological significance of specific states and processes are yet to be defined.

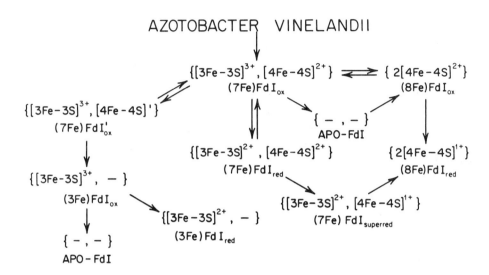

FIGURE 5:   Metallated states, oxidation levels and interconversion processes in Azotobacter vinelandii ferredoxin I.

ACKNOWLEDGEMENTS

    This work was supported by the National Institutes of Health and the National Science Foundation.

REFERENCES

(1) D. Ghosh, W. Furey, S. O'Donnell, C.D. Stout. J. Biol. Chem. 256 (1981) 4185-4192.

(2) D. Ghosh, S. O'Donnell, W. Furey, A.H. Robbins, C.D. Stout. J. Mol. Biol. 158 (1982) 73-109.

(3) E.T. Adman, L.C. Sieker, L.H. Jensen. J. Biol. Chem. 251 (1976) 3801-3806 and references therein.

(4) S.T. Freer, R.A. Alden, C.W. Carter, J. Kraut. J. Biol. Chem. 250 (1975) 46-54 and references therein.

(5) W.V. Sweeney, J.C. Rabinowitz, D.C. Yoch. J. Biol. Chem. 250 (1975) 7842-7847.

(6) M.H. Emptage, T.A. Kent, B.H. Huynh, J. Rawlings, W.H. Orme-Johnson,
     E. Munck. J. Biol. Chem. 255 (1980) 1793-1796.

(7) T.V. Morgan, P.J. Stephens, F. Devlin, C.D. Stout, K.A. Melis,
     B.K. Burgess. Proc. Natl.Acad.Sci. 81 (1984) 1931-1935.

(8) T.V. Morgan, P.J. Stephens, F. Devlin, B.K. Burgess, C.D. Stout.
     FEBS Letters 183 (1985) 206-210.

(9) P.J. Stephens, T.V. Morgan, F. Devlin, J. Penner-Hahn, K.O. Hodgson,
     R.A. Scott, C.D. Stout, B.K. Burgess. Proc. Natl. Acad. Sci. (1985)
     in press.

(10) J.J.G. Moura, I. Moura, T.A. Kent, J.D. Lipscomb, B.H. Huynh,
     J. Le Gall, A.V. Xavier, E. Munck. J. Biol. Chem. 257 (1982)
     6259-6267.

(11) T.A. Kent, J.-L. Dreyer, M.C. Kennedy, B.H. Huynh, M.H. Emptage,
     H. Beinert, E. Munck. Proc. Natl. Acad. Sci. 79 (1982) 1096-1100.

(12) M.C. Kennedy, M.H. Emptage, J.L. Dreyer, H. Beinert. J. Biol. Chem.
     258 (1983) 11098-11105.

(13) T.V. Morgan, P.J. Stephens, B.K. Burgess, C.D. Stout. FEBS Letters
     167 (1984) 134-141.

(14) P.J. Stephens, A.J. Thomson, J.B.R. Dunn, T.A. Keiderling, J.
     Rawlings, K.K. Rao, D.O. Hall. Biochemistry 17 (1978) 4770-4778.

(15) S.G. Mayhew. Eur. J. Biochem. 85 (1978) 535-547.

(16) W.V. Sweeney. J. Biol. Chem. 256 (1981) 12222-12227.

Relevance of Organocobalt B_{12} Models to B_{12} Biochemistry

Luigi G. Marzilli, Wallace O. Parker, Jr., Jean-Pierre Charland, Michael F. Summers

Department of Chemistry, Emory University, Atlanta, Georgia 30322, U.S.A.

Lucio Randaccio, Nevenka Bresciani-Pahor, Ennio Zangrando

Departimento di Scienze Chimiche, Università di Trieste, 34127 Trieste, Italy

SUMMARY

Evidence is presented that the Schiff base saloph ligand system has synergistic cis and trans effects. Consequently, rare five-coordinate organocobalt complexes could be isolated and structurally characterized. The Costa model system has about the same cis effect and cis influence as the relatively poor cobaloxime B_{12} model complexes. There is no evident synergism between the cis and trans effects. The Co-N bond distance trans to the organo group is long and comparable to that in organocobalamins with the Schiff base models but is much shorter in the cobaloximes. The Costa model system bond lengths are only slightly larger than those found for cobaloximes. The role of the putative five-coordinate intermediate in B_{12} dependent enzymic processes is doubtful, since steric strain is relieved in five-coordinate species. Finally, the features of the three model systems are compared in terms of fidelity to cobalamins.

1 INTRODUCTION

Penta-coordinate organocobalt(III) species have been suspected to exist either as reactive intermediates in ligand exchange reactions or, less commonly, as relatively stable species (1). Clear-cut demonstrations of stable penta-coordinate Co(III) complexes are rare but suggestive evidence for such species has been presented for a range of organocobalt(III) B_{12} models as well as for cobalamins (1).

The types of model systems where five-coordinate species have been invoked range from the relatively "electron deficient" cobaloximes ($LCo(DH)_2R$, see scheme next page) to the relatively "electron rich" Schiff-base complexes (e.g. $LCo(saloph)R$, see scheme), where the corrin ring in cobalamins is replaced by two mononegative dioximato ligands or by a tetradentate N_2O_2 dinegative Schiff-base ligand, respectively. These two classes of models, in fact, appear to "bracket" many characteristics of cobalamins (1). Thus, a mixed Schiff base/oxime system would appear worthy of study. Indeed, Costa has explored the chemistry of cobalt complexes with the (DO)(DOH)pn equatorial ligand (2), which has the same charge (-1) and pseudo symmetry as the corrin (see scheme). A closely related equatorial ligand (EMO)(EMOH)pn (3) has ethyl groups rather than methyl groups at the 2 and 10 positions (fig. 1). Compared to other model systems these so called "Costa" complexes may better reflect the electrochemical behavior of cobalamins (4), may better promote reactions characteristic of B_{12} enzymes (3), and may approximate most closely the ^{59}Co NMR shifts of cobalamins (5).

More work is needed on both the Costa model and on the saloph complexes in order to more fully evaluate organocobalt chemistry relevant to B_{12} biochemistry. Since the involvement of Co in the rearrangement reactions appears unlikely (3,6), we are concentrating our efforts on understanding the dynamic, thermodynamic and structural freatures of both models and cobalamins as these may relate to the essential Co-C bond homolysis step in B_{12}-dependent enzyme catalyzed reactions (7).

The suspected penta-coordinate complexes, Co(saloph)R and "base-off" alkylcobalmins, share the behavior that Co-C bond homolysis is less facile than in the counterpart hexa-coordinate complexes, LCo(saloph)R and "base-on" alkylcobalmins (1,8). "Base-off" cobalamins (made by adding acid to protonate the 5,6 dimethylbenzimidazole, BzImd, ring) and cobinamides (which are derived from cobalamins but lack BzImd) are believed to be penta-coordinate when R is a strong electron donor but the evidence is primarily spectroscopic (1). For example, the hexa-coordinate forms are red whereas a yellow color (440 nm absorption) has been interpreted to indicate a penta-coordinate species. It has been suggested that penta-coordinate species are relevant to the mechanism of action of B_{12} dependent enzymes (9), although such species generally are more thermally stable than their hexa-coordinate counterparts.

2 RESULTS

2.1 Structural Comparisons

Costa Models: The X-ray structures of two $[pyCo((DO)(DOH)pn)R]PF_6$ salts have been determined (10). Drawings of the crystallographically independent molecules of (I) (R = CH_3) and (II) (R = neo-C_5H_{11}) with the atom numbering scheme are depicted in

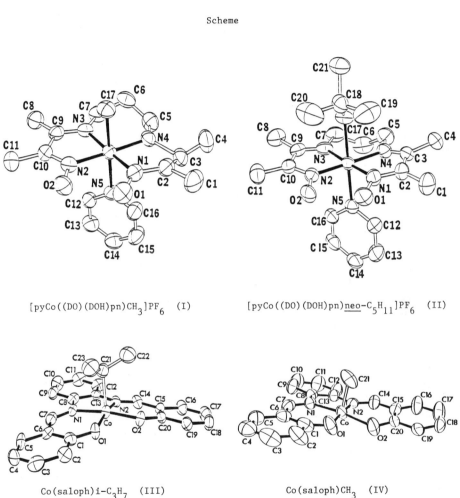

Scheme

[pyCo((DO)(DOH)pn)CH$_3$]PF$_6$ (I)

[pyCo((DO)(DOH)pn)<u>neo</u>-C$_5$H$_{11}$]PF$_6$ (II)

Co(saloph)i-C$_3$H$_7$ (III)

Co(saloph)CH$_3$ (IV)

Figure 1. Molecular structures and atom numbering scheme for the cobalt complexes
(I) to (IV).

Figure 1. In (I) and (II), distortions from planarity of the non-hydrogen atoms of the equatorial moiety (excluding the central atom in the propylene bridge) are larger than those reported for the nearly planar Co(EMO)(EMOH)pn unit (10). The four equatorial N atoms are nearly coplanar. The two chemically equivalent halves of (DO)(DOH)pn with the exclusion of C(6), are approximately planar. These planes have dihedral angles, α, of 6.9° (I) and 14.4° (II) and bend toward the axial alkyl group. The six-membered chelate ring has the expected conformation with the C(6) atom out of the chelate plane on the side of the R group in (I) and of the py in (II). A comparison of α and d (displacement of Co out of the equatorial plane) values, reported in Table I, shows that the equatorial moiety of pyCo(DO)(DOH)pn complexes is more easily distorted than the $Co(DH)_2$ unit. This result may be mainly attributed to the different orientation of the py ligand with respect to the equatorial moiety in the two series of model complexes.

The relevant data for the py-Co-R fragment are reported in Table I. The Co-C bond lengths are significantly affected by the bulk of the alkyl group as already found in cobaloximes (10), but no significant differences are observed with those found for a given R in the latter complexes. The Co-C-C angle of neopentyl derivatives is very similar.

On the contrary, the Co-L bond lengths in (DO)(DOH)pn type compounds are about 0.04Å longer than those found in cobaloximes (Table I). Since the lengthening of the Co-L bond appears to be independent of the nature of the axial ligands (py or H_2O), the structural cis-influence order is $(DO)(DOH)pn > (DH)_2$.

Table I. Structrual Comparisons of B_{12} Models and Cobalamins [a]

R	L	Co-R(Å)[12]	Co-L(Å)	Co-C-C(°)	α(°)	d(Å)
		Costa Models				
(I) CH3	py	2.003(3)	2.106(3)	–	+ 6.9	+0.07
(II) neo-C5H11	py	2.083(4)	2.121(3)	130.4(3)	+14.3	+0.03
CH3	H2O	1.977(4)	2.103(3)	–	+ 2	+0.01
		Cobaloximes				
CH3	py	1.998(5)	2.068(3)	–	+ 3.2	+0.04
neo-C5H11	py	2.060(6)	2.081(4)	130.3(4)	– 5.2	0
CH3	H2O	1.990(5)	2.058(3)	–	– 4.0	0
CH2CH3	4-CH3OC(NH)py	2.035(5)	2.081(3)	117.2(4)	+ 9	+0.05
CH2NO2	py	2.002(3)	2.028(3)	113.2(7)	0	+0.02
		Saloph				
(III) i-C3H7	–	2.031(8)	–	110.5(8)	–15	+0.16
(IV) CH3	–	1.957(13)	–	–	+11	+0.11
CH2CH3	py	2.042(6)	2.215(4)	117.3(5)	–25	+0.03
CH2CN	py	1.999(5)	2.098(5)	114.2(9)	+18	+0.05
		Cobalamins				
CH3	BzImd	1.99(2)	2.19(2)	–	15.8	–
Ado	BzImd	2.03(3)	2.24(3)	124°	14.6	–

[a] Positive values of α and d indicate that the bending of the equatorial ligand is towards the alkyl group and that the displacement of Co out of the N4 equatorial donor set is towards L. See references (1, 10 and 11).

Co(saloph) Models: The X-ray structures of two penta-coordinate Co(saloph)R
complexes have been determined (1).   Drawings of (III) (R = i-C$_3$H$_7$) and (IV)
(R = CH$_3$) with the atom numbering scheme are depicted in Figure 1.

The crystals of (III) are composed of Co(saloph)i-C$_3$H$_7$ distorted square
pyramidal units held together by Van der Waals interactions and by weak hydrogen
bonds.   The atoms of the N$_2$O$_2$ basal set are nearly coplanar and d is 0.16Å with Co
displaced towards the apical i-C$_3$H$_7$ group. The Co-C bond length is only 2.031(8)Å,
whereas the bond lengths and angles in the Co(saloph) moiety are quite normal.

The Co(saloph) unit is significantly distorted from planarity with an
umbrella-shaped conformation and an α value of -15.0°, away from the i-C$_3$H$_7$ ligand,
while the phenylene bridging group is slightly bent towards the apical group.
There are two crystallographically independent molecules of (IV).   Molecules of A
form dimeric units, [Co(saloph)CH$_3$]$_2$ with an O of one unit coordinated to Co of the
other unit (Co-O 2.435(4)Å).   On the contrary, the arrangement of molecule B around
the symmetry center does not permit dimer formation.   For molecule A, the
difference between the Co-O distances is indicative of coordination by O.   In
contrast, no difference is detected for the Co-O distances of molecule B.   The
presence of monomeric and dimeric units in the same crystal of (IV) may be
attributed to the formation of a hydrogen bond between a water molecule and the
O(1) atom of the molecule B.   On the contrary no hydrogen bond is formed with
molecule A (1).

For (IV), the Co-CH$_3$ bond length of 1.957(13)Å in B seems slightly smaller than
those reported for hexa-coordinate saloph complexes (Table 1).   On the contrary,
the d values are significantly larger than the 0.02 to 0.03Å found in pyCo(saloph)R.
The Co-C bond length in (IV) appears significantly shorter than that of 2.031(8)Å
found in (III).   This difference is strongly indicative of the greater steric
intereaction of the i-C$_3$H$_7$ group compared to that of the CH$_3$ group, a relationship
well documented in hexa-coordinate cobaloximes with these R groups (1,10).

2.2 Rate Comparisons

All three series of compounds, (saloph, DO(DOH)pn, (DH)$_2$) undergo ligand
exchange by a S$_N$1 LIM mechanism with the RDS step having a rate constant, k$_1$.

The k$_1$ for 3,5LUTCo(saloph)CH$_3$ exceeds that for 3,5LUTCo(DH)$_2$CH$_3$ by 8 x 10^{10}
(Table II).   This result is an example of the cis effect since only the cis
(equatorial) ligand is changed.   A log log plot of ligand exchange rate constants
for 4CN-py, cobaloximes and 3,5LUT saloph compounds with corresponding R groups
gives a linear relationship, with a slope = 1.3.   A slope greater than unity means

that the relative trans effect of alkyl ligands increases with increasing R electron donation (increasing trans influence and increasing trans effect).

In contrast, the k_1 for [pyCo((DO)(DOH)pn)CH$_3$]ClO$_4$ is only 4.5 times that for pyCo(DH)$_2$CH$_3$. A comparison of log k_1 for [pyCo((DO)(DOH)pn)R]ClO$_4$ vs. log k_1 for 4CN-pyCo(DH)$_2$R gives a slope of 0.996 (Figure 2). Therefore, unlike the LCo(saloph)R comparison, there is no synergism between the cis and trans effects in this comparison.

Table II. Comparison of Ligand Exchange Rates of LCo(chel)R in CH_2Cl_2, 25°C.

Complex	$k_1 (s^{-1})$	Complex	$k_1 (s^{-1})$	Ratio
[pyCo((DO)(DOH)pn)CH$_3$]$^+$	3.6×10^{-2}	pyCo(DH)$_2$CH$_3$	8×10^{-3}	4.5
[pyCo((DO)(DOH)pn)i-C$_3$H$_7$]$^+$	3.3×10^1	pyCo(DH)$_2$i-C$_3$H$_7$	3	11
3,5LUTCo(saloph)CH$_2$CF$_3$	4.3×10^5	3,5LUTCo(DH)$_2$CH$_2$CF$_3$	1.4×10^{-5}	3×10^{10}
3,5LUTCo(saloph)CH$_3$	2.8×10^8	3,5LUTCo(DH)$_2$CH$_3$	3.4×10^{-3}	8×10^{10}

3,5LUT = 3,5 lutidine. See references (1,10).

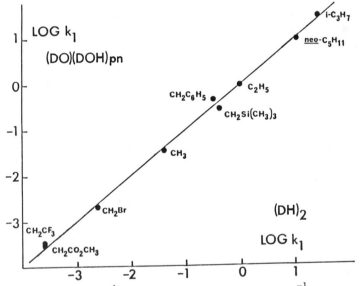

Figure 2.   Log $k_1 (s^{-1})$ for 4CN-pyCo(DH)$_2$R vs. log $k_1 (s^{-1})$ for [pyCo((DO)(DOH)pn)R]ClO$_4$ (25°C, CH$_2$Cl$_2$).

3 DISCUSSION

Five-coordinate cobaloximes are likely to exist only under optimal conditions (in H$_2$O and R = very good electron donor) (1). The similarities in structure and reactivity of the Costa model suggest such species are unlikely to be important in this model system also.

A better model system for comparison to cobalamins is the saloph system. Even with a moderate donor such as CH$_3$, a five-coordinate species exists in the solid. The relative trans influence of alkyl groups is the same in cobalamins as in organocobalt B$_{12}$ models (11,12). Therefore, the present results are consistent with suggestions that five-coordinate cobalamins exist in aqueous solutions of "base off" alkyl cobalamins where R is a good electron donor (1). Similarly, comparison of NMR and X-ray data for methyl B$_{12}$ and 5'-deoxyadenosyl cobalamin (coenzyme B$_{12}$) demonstrate that the 5'-deoxyadenosyl (Ado) ligand has a strong trans influence (11). Thus five coordinate forms of coenzyme B$_{12}$ appear energetically feasible for good e$^-$ donor R groups. Cobalamins containing sterically bulky R groups are thermally unstable and are readily stabilized in the "base off" form. Spectroscopic studies have provided evidence for a change in coordination number. The 440 nm band (9) mentioned above may not necessarily be indicative of five coordination and some other feature of the conformationally distorted coenzyme B$_{12}$ in B$_{12}$ holoenzymes may be the cause of this band. In addition, the species exhibiting this band may not be kinetically competent.

Halpern's work on models demonstrates that poor electron donor ligands trans to R weaken the Co-C bond by destabilizing the Co(III) oxidation state (8). However, removal of the trans ligand altogether stabilizes the Co-C bond. We demonstrate here that, when R is bulky, the Co-C bond <u>does</u> get shorter in a five-coordinate species. These steric effects may be important. On the other hand, comparison of structural and NMR results for methyl B$_{12}$ with Ado B$_{12}$ does not suggest that the Ado moiety is particularly bulky (11).

Nevertheless, estimates of Co-C bond energies in coenzyme B$_{12}$ (8,13) demonstrate that B$_{12}$ enzymes are able to enhance Co-C bond cleavage rates by a factor of $\sim$10^{10}. The recent structural studies and Co-C bond energy estimates lead to a qualitative understanding of the importance of structural changes during the cleavage process.

For the ground state, the strength of axial ligation trans to R should have the effect shown on the left below:

For the activated complex, which we approximate as a cobalt(II) species, the dependence on the above right is likely.

A four coordinate cobalt(II) species is probably relatively unstable. Thus, the
Co–C cleavage process would be most facile in a stituation where the Co–N bond
changes from being a relatively long bond (weak donor) in the still six coordinate
ground state to a relatively stronger bond leading to a five–coordinate Co(II)
species, as illustrated schematically below:

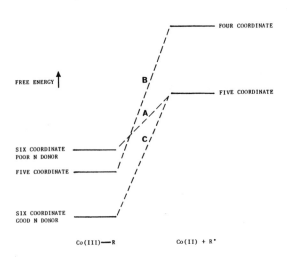

The minimum barrier would involve path A, where the BzImd supports formation of the
five–coordinate Co(II) species without stabilizing the six–coordinate Co(III)
relative to the five–coordinate Co(III) species. In a six–coordinate species with
a weakly bound BzImd, the Co is maintained in the plane defined by the four corrin
N atoms, thereby maintaining steric repulsions between Ado and the corrin. These
steric interactions could be made more severe in the holoenzyme if the protein
distorts the corrin. Path B, between a five–coordinate Co(III)R and a
four–coordinate Co(II) species, is probably the most unfavorable pathway both
because the five–coordinate species is stabilized somewhat by the reduction in
steric interaction but also because a four–coordinate Co(II) species should be
relatively unstable. Path C corresponds to free energy changes expected in models
and in cobalamins in the absence of enzymes.

    The above qualitative picture requires further investigation of both the
energetics and structural changes in models and cobalamins. However, if it
represents a reasonable approximation of the interrelationship between structure,
coordination number and axial bond strengths, then the intermediacy of five–
coordinate Co(III)R species in the enzymic process appears unlikely.

    Finally, the question arises as to which B_{12} model system considered here most
closely reflects the cobalamins. In terms of ligand exchange rates, structures of

the L-Co-R moiety, and five-coordination stability, the saloph system seems to be most similar to organocobalamins. If criteria such as Co-C BDE are considered, the BDE of cobalamins with R = i-C$_3$H$_7$ and CH$_2$C$_6$H$_5$ have been given as 19 and 23 Kcal/mole, respectively (14). The pyCo(saloph)R analogs have values of 19 and 22 Kcal/mole, respectively (15). If criteria such as electrochemistry are considered, methyl B$_{12}$ has a III → II redox potential of -1.6V (16). For [1-methylimidazole Co[(DO)(DOH)pn)CH$_3$]$^+$, the reported value is -1.2V (4). For DMFCo(saloph)CH$_2$CH$_3$, this value is -1.5V (2). For non-alkyl compounds, and II → I reduction, the Costa model is better, however (4).

In summary, except for limited electrochemical data, the structural, dynamic, and thermodynamic properties along the axial direction are best modeled by the saloph ligand system when models employing simple organic equatorial ligands are compared.

ACKNOWLEDGEMENTS

This work was supported by NIH grant 29225 (L.G.M.) and by a grant (to L.R.) from CNR, Rome, Italy. We are grateful to these organization. L.G.M. thanks the Alexander von Humboldt Foundation for a Senior U.S. Scientist Award.

4 REFERENCES

(1) L. G. Marzilli, M. F. Summers, N. Bresciani-Pahor, E. Zangrando, J.-P. Charland, L. Randaccio, J. Am. Chem. Soc. in press, and references therein.

(2) G. Costa, Coord. Chem. Revs., 8 (1972) 63.

(3) R. G. Finke, D. A. Schiraldi, B. J. Mayer, Coord. Chem. Revs., 54 (1984) 1.

(4) C. M. Elliot, E. Hershenhart, R. G. Finke, B. L. Smith, J. Am. Chem. Soc., 103 (1981) 5558.

(5) H. A. O. Hill in G. L. Eichhorn, (ed.) Inorganic Biochemistry, Elsevier Scientific Pubs., Amsterdam (1973) 1067.

(6) S. Wollowitz, J. Halpern, J. Am. Chem. Soc., 106 (1984) 8319.

(7) D. Dolphin, (ed.) B$_{12}$, John Wiley and Sons, New York (1982).

(8) J. Halpern, Science, 227 (1985) 869.

(9) J. M. Pratt, Inorg. Chim. Acta, 79 (1983) 27.

(10) W. O. Parker, Jr., N. Bresciani-Pahor, E. Zangrando, L. Randaccio, L. G. Marzilli, Inorg. Chem., in press, and references therein.

(11) M. Rossi, J. P. Glusker, L. Randaccio, M. F. Summers, P. J. Toscano, L. G. Marzilli, J. Am. Chem. Soc., 107 (1985) 1729 and references therein.

(12) K. L. Brown, J. M. Hakimi, D. W. Jacobsen, J. Am. Chem. Soc., 106 (1984) 7894.

(13) R. G. Finke, B. P. Hay, Inorg. Chem., 23 (1984) 3043.

(14) G. N. Schrauzer, J. H. Grate, J. Am. Chem. Soc., 103 (1981) 541.

(15) F. T. T. Ng, G. L. Rempel, J. Halpern, J. Am. Chem. Soc., 104 (1982) 621.

(16) D. Lexa, J.-M. Saveant, J. Am. Chem. Soc., 100 (1978) 3220.

Proton and Deuteron NMRD Studies of Ca^{2+}-Mn^{2+}-Concanavalin A, PEA, and Lentil Lectins; Evidence for a Common Site of Exchanging Water Molecules

Seymour H. Koenig, Rodney D. Brown, III, Lokesh Bhattacharyya, and C. Fred Brewer

IBM Thomas J. Watson Research Center, Yorktown Heights, NY, USA, (SHK and RDB) and Departments of Molecular Pharmacology, and Microbiology and Immunology, Albert Einstein College of Medicine, Bronx, NY, USA (LB and CFB)

SUMMARY

We have measured the magnetic field dependence of the longitudinal nuclear magnetic relaxation rate $1/T_1$ (NMRD profiles) of solvent protons and deuterons in solutions of Ca^{2+}-Mn^{2+}-Concanavalin A (CMPL), Ca^{2+}-Mn^{2+}-lentil lectin (CMLcH), and Ca^{2+}-Mn^{2+}-pea lectin (CMPSA) from -8 to 35° C. We find that CMPL has two types of solvent binding sites that differ both in the exchange time τ_M of liganded solvent molecules, and in their distance, r, from the Mn^{2+} ions. The "slow" exchange sites with $\tau_M \sim 10^{-5}$ s at 25 °C are assigned to the inner coordination spheres of the Mn^{2+} ions. For the "fast" exchange sites, $\tau_M \sim 5 \times 10^{-9}$ s and r $\sim$ 5 Å. The temperature dependence of the proton NMRD profiles of CMPL is composite, containing two contributions with opposite temperature dependences. The rapidly exchanging waters dominate the paramagnetic NMRD profile of CMPL at -8 °C, while the thermally activated slowly exchanging waters dominate the profile at 35 °C. Only the relaxation contribution of the slowly exchanging waters is altered by binding of monosaccharide to the protein.

Abbreviations: NMRD, nuclear magnetic relaxation dispersion (the magnetic field dependence of the solvent longitudinal magnetic relaxations rate $(1/T_1)$; Con A, concanavalin A with unspecified metal ion content; MP, Con A with Mn^{2+} at S1, in the unlocked conformation; CMPL, Con A with Mn^{2+} and Ca^{2+} at S1 and S2, respectively, in the locked conformation; CZPL, Con A with Zn^{2+} and Ca^{2+} at S1 and S2, respectively, in the locked conformation; LcH, lentil lectin; CMLcH, native LcH containing 1 equivalent of Mn^{2+} and 1.7-2 equivalents of Ca^{2+} per monomer; CZLcH, LcH containing 1 equivalent of Zn^{2+} and 1.5-2 equivalents of Ca^{2+} per monomer; PSA, pea lectin; CMPSA, native PSA containing 1 equivalent of Mn^{2+} and 1.5-2 equivalents of Ca^{2+} per monomer; CZPSA, PSA containing 1 equivalent of Zn^{2+} and 1.5-2 equivalents of Ca^{2+} per monomer.

Similar proton and deuteron measurements of solutions of CMLcH and CMPSA show that these proteins have a common solvent exchange site, which corresponds to the site of rapid exchange for CMPL. These conclusions are reinforced by the inverse temperature dependences of the proton NMRD profiles of CMLcH and CMPSA, with rates similar to those of the fast exchange contribution found for CMPL. We assign the site of rapid solvent exchange to the inner coordination sphere of the Ca^{2+} ions adjacent to the Mn^{2+} ions in all three proteins.

1. INTRODUCTION

Lectins are proteins, generally isolated from the seeds of plants, with diverse and unusual biological properties that derive from their distinct saccharide binding capabilities (1). They are widely used to explore the membrane properties of both normal and transformed cells (2), and can be used to agglutinate malignant cells selectively. They are also potential chemotherapeutic agents in the treatment of transformed cells (1,3). Among the more widely used lectins are Concanavalin A (Con A), and the lentil (LcH) and pea (PSA) lectins.

All three lectins are Ca^{2+}-Mn^{2+}-metalloproteins, and normally require both metal ions for saccharide binding (4). Con A is the most widely studied and, indeed, the X-ray crystal structure of the protein has been determined to 1.75 Å (5). Con A, LcH, and PSA are all classified as D-mannose/D-glucose specific lectins (4), and all three have a high degree of structural similarity (6,7). These lectins also have similar specificities for simple carbohydrates (8), but display significant differences in their affinities toward glycopeptides (9), differences believed to be responsible for their differing biological activities (1,2). Thus, it is of considerable interest to elucidate the molecular properties of these lectins in order to find the basis for their distinct biological activities.

Measurements of the magnetic field dependence of solvent proton relaxation (NMRD) profiles in solutions of Con A and its complexes with Mn^{2+}, Ca^{2+}, and saccharides have yielded a wealth of information concerning the relation between metal ion binding and the saccharide binding activity (10-13). NMRD measurements have also been used to explore the binding of mono- and oligosaccharides to the protein (14), as well as the mechanism of binding of high mannose and more complex glycopeptides, such as those found on the surfaces of normal and transformed cells (15,16). In all of these investigations, the observed NMRD profiles were used primarily as empirical indicators of the chemical state of the Mn^{2+} in the protein; the conformation of the protein; and changes in conformation as a function of time in response to changes in ligands. The details of relaxation theory played little role in the interpretation of the chemistry of Con A, though the nature of the solvent nuclear relaxation and the details of the mechanisms that underlie the NMRD profiles of the various Mn^{2+}-complexes of Can A have remained a subject of continuing interest (17) and are relevant to the present work.

In the present study, NMRD measurements of both solvent protons and deuterons were used to demonstrate the existence of two classes of solvent binding sites in Ca^{2+}-Mn^{2+}-Con A (CMPL). The deuteron NMRD profiles, which are much more sensitive to sites of slowly exchanging solvent molecules than proton profiles, indicated "slow" sites at S1 (the transition metal site), while the proton NMRD data, which are more sensitive to sites of faster exchanging water molecules, indicates "fast" sites about 4.4 Å from the Mn^{2+}, well beyond its inner coordination sphere.

The recent discovery of a method of preparing Ca^{2+}-Zn^{2+}-derivatives of LcH (CZLcH) and PSA (CZPSA) (18-20) has allowed us to study both paramagnetic and diamagnetic metal ion derivatives of these two lectins, and thereby obtain the paramagnetic contribution itself. We find (21) that all three proteins contain a common class of exchange sites characterized by rapidly exchanging solvent molecules, with their protons about 4.4 to 5.5 Å from the Mn^{2+} ions. The location of this site is assigned to the inner coordination sphere of the Ca^{2+} ions at S2 in all three proteins. This is the first time that exchanging water molecules at the diamagnetic ion of a paramagnetic-diamagnetic ion pair have been identified.

2. MATERIALS AND METHODS

The preparation of the samples (10,18) and the NMRD procedures (10,17) have been presented previously, and are not reiterated here, except to note that because of the electric quadrupolar contribution to the relaxation rate of deuterons in D$_2$O, the contribution of the demetallized protein to the deuteron relaxation is about 10-fold greater than that for protons in undeuterated H$_2$O. Coupled with its smaller magnetic moment, the relative paramagnetic effects for deuterons, particularly at low fields, are 400-fold lower than for protons, and become difficult to measure with high accuracy.

All NMRD profiles shown (except Fig. 7) are paramagnetic contributions to the observed relaxation rates, obtained by subtraction of the appropriate diamagnetic controls (10,20,21) and are given in units of relaxivity, the relaxation rate per mM of complexed paramagnetic (Mn^{2+}) ions.

3. RESULTS AND ANALYSIS

3.1 Proton NMRD Profiles of Con A

Fig. 1 shows NMRD profiles of MP and CMPL at 5 and 25 °C (10,22). As previously discussed (10), the MP profiles result from two water molecule ligands of the Mn^{2+} ions in moderately rapid exchange with solvent; a decrease in their exchange rate with a decrease in temperature is responsible for the temperature dependence of these profiles. Addition of Ca^{2+} ions to MP, to generate the native protein CMPL, decreases this exchange rate an order of magnitude or more. In earlier work, the entire difference between the MP and CMPL profiles was attributed to this effect (10). However, as shown recently (22) and discussed below, the large decrease in exchange rate has unmasked another contribution to the profiles of CMPL, a contribution that we assign to waters, in rapid exchange, liganded to the (diamagnetic) Ca^{2+} ions, with their protons relaxed by the Mn^{2+} ions. The major burden of the present paper is to delineate this contribution clearly, since it is the only one observed (so far) in LcH and PSA (21), and is unaltered by saccharide binding, in contrast to the contributions from the water ligands of the Mn^{2+} ions.

3.2 Deuteron NMRD Profiles of Con A

Fig. 2 shows deuteron profiles of MP and CMPL (17), in all aspects analogous to the proton profiles of Fig. 1. No temperature dependence is observed for the deuteron MP data, Fig. 2; the moderate exchange rate of the waters on the Mn^{2+} ions, which leads to a temperature dependence for the proton MP data of Fig. 1, is relatively rapid for deuterons (which have a lower intrinsic paramagnetic relaxation rate). Nonetheless, as for protons, addition of Ca^{2+} reduces the relaxivity substantially, and the temperature dependence of the profiles returns.

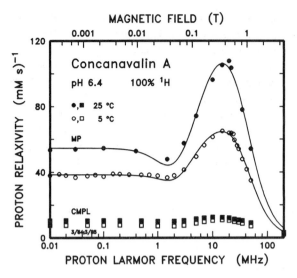

Fig. 1. Paramagnetic contributions to the proton NMRD profiles of the unlocked binary Mn^{2+}-Con A complex (MP) at 5 (O) and 25 (●) °C and the locked ternary Ca^{2+}-Mn^{2+}-Con A (CMPL) complex at 5 (□) and 25 (■) °C, in undeuterated pH 6.4 buffer containing 0.1 M potassium acetate and 0.1 M potassium chloride. The curves through the MP data are visual guides, and have no other significance. After reference (10).

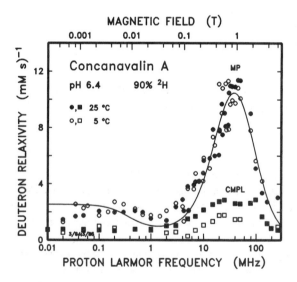

Fig. 2. Paramagnetic contributions to the deuteron NMRD profiles of the unlocked binary complex (MP) at 5 (O) and 25 (●) °C and the locked ternary complex (CMPL) at 5 (□) and 25 (■) °C, in pH 6.4 buffer containing 0.1 M potassium acetate and 0.1 M potassium chloride in 90% deuterated solvent. The curve associated with the MP data is a fit of theory to the data, discussed in detail in reference (17) but not germane here.

From the foregoing, one infers that both the proton and deuteron profiles for CMPL at 5 °C arise from exchange-rate limited interactions of liganded protons with protein-bound Mn^{2+} ions. However, if relaxation occurs for nuclei on water molecules of the same sites for both the proton and deuteron data, their *respective relaxivities should be identical* (cf. 17,22). This clearly is not the case, as seen in Fig. 3, in which the proton and deuteron CMPL profiles are shown in an expanded scale. (It has been previously shown, as a control, that the proton CMPL profiles are independent of the isotopic composition of the solvent (22).)

The only way to explain the differences between the proton and deuteron profiles, Fig. 3, is to postulate an additional contribution to the proton data, which must arise from waters in rapid exchange so that there will be negligible contribution to the deuteron profiles. Additionally, because the proton CMPL relaxivities are small (compared to those for MP, Fig. 1), these waters must be rather remote from the Mn^{2+} ions.

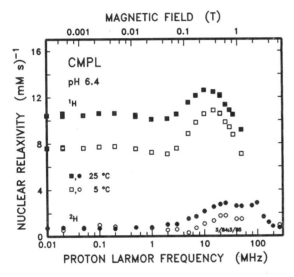

Fig. 3. A comparison of the paramagnetic contributions to the proton NMRD profiles of CMPL at 5 (□) and 25 (■) °C, pH 6.4 (Fig. 1) with the analogous deuteron NMRD profiles of CMPL at 5 (O) and 25 (●) ° C, pH 6.4 in 90% deuterated solvent (Fig. 2).

3.3. Temperature Dependence of Proton NMRD Profiles for CMPL and SCMPL

Evidence for such a composite proton CMPL profile is seen in Fig. 4, in which proton profiles for CMPL from -8 to 35 °C are shown, along with those for SCMPL (CMPL saturated with saccharide). (The low end of the temperature range is made possible by the presence of 5 M NaCl, shown independently to have no influence on the profiles (22).).

The major point to note for the CMPL profiles, Fig. 4, is that there is a reversal in the sign of their temperature dependence; the -8 °C relaxivities are greater than those of the 5 °C profile, as is the range of their variation. This has been explained (22) by invoking two independent contributions to the CMPL profiles: one from water molecules liganded directly to the Mn^{2+} ions and in relatively slow exchange with solvent, and a second from water molecules liganded to the Ca^{2+} ions, about 5 Å from the Mn^{2+} ions, and in relatively rapid exchange. The lowest curve, Fig. 4, is an estimate of the contribution at 25 °C from the slowly exchanging ligands; this contribution becomes negligible at -8 °C. By contrast, exchange from the Ca^{2+} sites

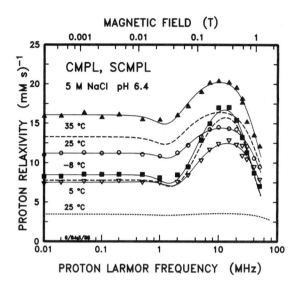

Fig. 4. The paramagnetic contributions to the proton NMRD profiles of Ca^{2+}-Mn^{2+}-Con A (CMPL) at -8 (■), 5 (∇), 25 (O) and 35 (▲) °C, and with 100 mM methyl-α-D-mannopyranoside at the two extremes of temperature (dashed curves). The protein concentration was 0.56 mM, and the bound Mn^{2+} and Ca^{2+} concentrations were each 0.48 mM. The buffer, 0.1 M sodium acetate, contained 5 M NaCl to prevent freezing at -8 °C. The solid lines through the data points are visual guides, and have no other significance. The dotted curve is the approximate contribution of the slowly exchanging class of water molecules to the 25 °C data, computed for protons from the proton and deuteron CMPL profiles, Figs. 1 and 2. After reference (22).

appears sufficiently rapid so that the decrease in its rate at lower temperatures increases the correlation times for the Mn^{2+}-proton interactions, and enhances the range of variation of the low temperature profiles (Table I and reference (20)).

The data for SCMPL, Fig. 4, show that the effect of saccharide binding is rather large at 35 °C, and almost nil at -8 °C. The inference is that saccharide binding influences only the relaxivity contribution of the slowly exchanging waters liganded directly to Mn^{2+} ions (22).

3.4 Application of Relaxation Theory to CMPL

An approach to obtaining reliable values for the various parameters that enter into the theory of NMRD profiles has been developed and evaluated recently (17). Its application to the -8 °C CMPL profile is shown in Fig. 5, and the results are in Table I. The essence of the fit is that, assuming two equivalent exchanging water molecules, their protons are 4.4 Å from the Mn^{2+} centers, with residence times of 5.2 ns.

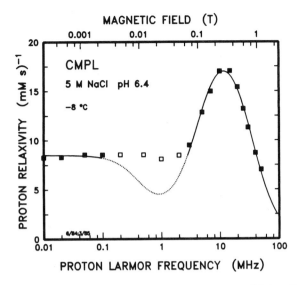

Fig. 5. Results of a least squares comparison of the -8 °C data, Fig. 3, with theory. The open squares, which were excluded from the comparison, are in a region of field for which the theory is expected to give a poor representation of the data (17).

3.5 Proton NMRD Profiles for CMLcH and CMPSA

Fig. 6 shows the paramagnetic contribution to the proton profiles for the lentil and pea lectins at 5 and 35 °C; the results for these two lectins are essentially identical. Moreover, addition of saturating concentrations of saccharide has no observable effect on the profiles. The profiles are similar in form to the low temperature profile of CMPL, Fig. 5, and indeed have the same temperature dependence as the low temperature contribution from waters in rapid exchange, as in the foregoing discussion of the data of Fig. 4. The data of Fig. 7 demonstrate that these waters are indeed in rapid exchange for lentil lectin. (The behavior of pea lectin is identical.)

If the proton NMRD profiles, Fig. 6, arise from rapidly exchanging water molecules, then the deuteron profiles should be about 40-fold lower in magnitude; i.e., never more than about 0.2 (mM s)$^{-1}$. In Fig. 7, profiles of (paramagnetic) CMLcH and (diamagnetic) CZLcH at 5 °C are compared, the former *uncorrected* for the diamagnetic contribution, in this case. It is clear that the paramagnetic contribution is close to zero, within the scatter of the data, and certainly no greater than 0.2 (mM s)$^{-1}$, indicating that the water molecules that produce the proton profiles, Fig. 6, are in rapid exchange.

3.6 The Common Site of the Three Lectins

Fig. 8 shows proton NMRD profiles at -8 °C for CMPL and CMPSA to illustrate the similarity of the contributions from the rapidly exchanging water molecules, here considered to be liganded to the Ca^{2+} ions at the S2 sites of the several lectins. (Results for LcH are essentially the same as for PSA.) Application of theory, as in Fig. 5, gives the results listed in Table I.

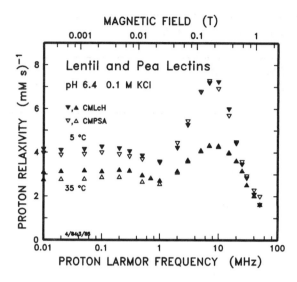

Fig. 6. Paramagnetic contributions to the proton NMRD profiles of Ca^{2+}-Mn^{2+}-lentil lectin (CMLcH) at 5 (▼) and 35 (▲) °C, and Ca^{2+}-Mn^{2+}-pea lectin (CMPSA) at 5 (▽) and 35 (△) °C, both in pH 6.4 buffer, containing 0.1 M potassium acetate and 0.9 M potassium chloride. After reference (21).

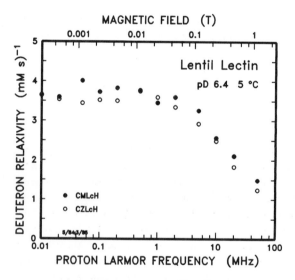

Fig. 7. Deuteron NMRD profiles of Ca^{2+}-Zn^{2+}-LcH (CZLcH) (O) and Ca^{2+}-Mn^{2+}-LcH (CMLcH) (●), at 5 °C in 90% deuterated pH 6.4 buffer, 0.1 M potassium acetate and 0.1 M potassium chloride. Concentrations of CMLcH and CZLcH from which the data were derived were 1.6 mM and 0.95 mM, respectively, and the former (in this instance only) is uncorrected for the diamagnetic contribution. After reference (21).

Table I. Values for the parameters[a] derived from a comparison of relaxation theory with the paramagnetic NMRD profiles of CMLcH at 5 and 35 °C (Fig. 6) and CMPL[b] at -8 °C.

	CMLcH 5 °C	CMLcH 35 °C	CMPL -8 °C
τ_M (ns)	12	8.6	5.2
$T_{1So} = T_{2So}$ (ns)	1.3	1.2	6.5
τ_V (ps)	140	190	100
τ_R (ns)	22	9.4	42
r (Å)	5.5	5.6	4.4

[a] τ_M is the residence time of the exchanging water ligands, T_{1So} and T_{2So} are the longitudinal and transverse relaxation times, respectively, of the unpaired electrons of the Mn^{2+}; τ_V is the correlation time describing the interaction that couples the Mn^{2+} magnetic moment with the protein; τ_R is the appropriate rotational correlation time of the protein and computed from Stokes' Law; r is the distance separating the protons of the exchanging water ligands from the Mn^{2+} ions. The number of exchanging water ligands, q, is assumed to be 2.

[b] From references (21, 22).

4. DISCUSSION

This paper describes the first application of NMRD techniques to the study of water exchange from each of two metal ions of a diamagnetic-paramagnetic ion pair of a metalloprotein, in the present case for three lectins; Con A and the structurally similar lentil and pea lectins. X-ray crystallographic studies of CMPL, to 1.75 Å resolution (5), show two inner-coordinated water molecules as ligands of the Mn^{2+} ions at the S1 sites. These molecules, presumably present and in rapid exchange in MP, are in relatively slow exchange in CMPL, and contribute substantially to the proton NMRD profiles only when thermally activated at the higher temperatures. They are the only waters that contribute to the (paramagnetic) deuteron profiles. For both protons and deuterons, the observed effects of saccharide binding to CMPL arise from alterations of the water ligand exchange rate upon binding saccharide (22). For the lentil and pea lectins, neither a thermally activated relaxivity contribution to the profiles nor a saccharide effect is observed; the analogous ligand positions at S1 are either not occupied by water molecules, or their exchange rate is very slow.

A second class of liganded water molecules was found for CMPL, in rapid exchange with solvent, with a contribution to the NMRD profiles that is unaltered by saccharide binding. The only observed paramagnetic contribution to the lentil and pea lectin profiles is analogous in all ways to that of the rapidly exchanging

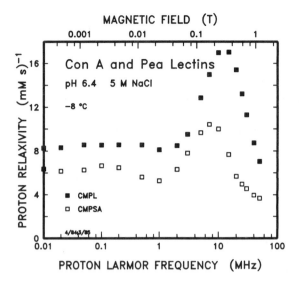

Fig. 8. Paramagentic contributions to the proton NMRD profiles of Ca^{2+}-Mn^{2+}-Con A (CMPL) (■) (from Fig. 4) and Ca^{2+}-Mn^{2+}-PSA (CMPSA) (□) in pH 6.4 buffer containing 0.1 M sodium acetate and 5 M sodium chloride, -8 °C. After reference (21).

ligands of CMPL. Application of theory to the data for all three lectins gives an average distance of 5 Å ± 10% for the relevant Mn^{2+}-proton separations, and a residence time of the order of 5 to 10 ns. We proposed (22) that these waters are ligands of the Ca^{2+} ions, a proposal consistent with the X-ray data for CMPL (5) and the tabulated exchange rates for hydrated Ca^{2+} ions (23).

These findings are the first identification of two sites for solvent exchange from different environments of the same paramagnetic ion of a metalloprotein, as well as the first demonstration of a common site for solvent exchange for a group of related proteins. The procedure should have general applicability to the study of binary metal clusters in a variety of other proteins.

5. ACKNOWLEDGEMENT

Bert Olson and Bernard Gilbert of the IBM T. J. Watson Research Center performed the metal ion analyses. This work was supported in part by Grant CA-16054, awarded to C.F.B. by the National Cancer Institute, Department of Health, Education, and Welfare, and Core Grant P30 CA-13330 from the same agency.

6. REFERENCES

1. cf. H. Lis, N. Sharon, Biochem. Plants 6 (1981) 371-447.

2. J. C. Brown, R. C. Hunt, Int. Rev. Cytol. 52 (1978) 277-349.

3. G. L. Nicolson, in J. K. Koehler, (Ed.), Advanced Techniques in Biological Electron Microscopy, Springer-Verlag, Berlin and New York 1978, pp. 1-38.

4. I. J. Goldstein, C. E. Hayes, Adv. Carbohydr. Chem. Biochem. 35 (1978) 127-340.

5. K. D. Hardman, R. C. Agarwal, M. J. Freiser, J. Mol. Biol. 157 (1982) 69-86.

6. A. Foriers, E. Lebrun, R. van Rapenbusch, R. de Neve, A. D. Strosberg, J. Biol. Chem. 256 (1981) 5550-5560.

7. E. J. Meehan, Jr., J. McDuffie, H. Einspahr, C. E. Buggs, F. L. Suddath, J. Biol. Chem. 257 (1982) 13278-13282.

8. A. K. Allen, N. N. Desai, A. Neuberger, Biochem. J. 155 (1976) 127-135.

9. K. Kornfeld, M. L. Reitman, R. Kornfeld, J. Biol. Chem. 256 (1981) 6633-6640.

10. R. D. Brown, III, C. F. Brewer, S. H. Koenig, Biochemistry 16 (1977) 3883-3986.

11. S. H. Koenig, C. F. Brewer, R. D. Brown, III, Biochemistry 17 (1978) 4251-4260.

12. C. F. Brewer, R. D. Brown, III, S. H. Koenig, Biochemistry 22 (1983) 3691-3702.

13. C. F. Brewer, R. D. Brown, III, S. H. Koenig, J. Biomol. Str. Dyn. 1 (1983) 961-997.

14. C. F. Brewer, R. D. Brown, III, Biochemistry 18 (1979) 2555-2562.

15. C. F. Brewer, Biochem. Biophys. Res. Commun. 90 (1979) 117-122.

16. C. F. Brewer, L. Bhattacharyya, R. D. Brown, III, S. H. Koenig, Biochem. Biophys. Res. Commun. (in press) (1985).

17. S. H. Koenig, R. D. Brown, III, J. Magn. Res. 61 (1985) 426-439.

18. L. Bhattacharyya, C. F. Brewer, R. D. Brown, III, S. H. Koenig, Biochem. Biophys. Res. Commun. 124 (1984) 857-862.

19. L. Bhattacharyya, J. A. Freedman, C. F. Brewer, R. D. Brown, III, S. H. Koenig, Arch. Biochem. Biophys. (in press) (1985).

20. L. Bhattacharyya, C. F. Brewer, R. D. Brown, III, S. H. Koenig, Biochemistry (in press) (1985a).

21. L. Bhattacharyya, C. F. Brewer, R. D. Brown, III, S. H. Koenig, Biochemistry (in press) (1985b).

22. S. H. Koenig, R. D. Brown, III, C. F. Brewer, Biochemistry (in press) (1985).

23. M. Eigen, L. DeMaeyer in A. Weissberger (Ed.), Techniques of Organic Chemistry, Wiley and Sons, Inc., New York 1963, pp. 895-1051.

Can Copper(II) Ions Biologically Activate Small Peptide Molecules

Henryk Kozłowski[a], Grazyna Formicka-Kozłowska[a], Leslie D. Pettit[b] and Ian Steel[b]

a) Institute of Chemistry, University of Wrocław, Joliot-Curie 14,
   50-383 Wrocław, Poland.
b) School of Chemistry, The University, Leeds, LS2 9JT, England.

SUMMARY

Spectroscopic and thermodynamic studies on Cu(II) ion interaction with natural and model oligopeptides lead to the conclusion that metal ion may influence the biological activity of small natural peptides, among other neurohormones. The specific interaction of proline or/and tyrosine containing peptide with cupric ion organizes the peptide conformation which, like e.g. β-turn, are biologically active structures.

INTRODUCTION

Many oligopeptides show very high biological activity, particularly in the central nervous system where many of them act as releasing factors, neurotransmitters or as opiates. Very frequently these peptides contain proline or tyrosine residues in their sequences (1) which have a critical importance in their biological activity. The L-proline (Pro) residue in a peptide chain influences the conformation of the chain, promoting the formation of β-turns, particularly when in the second position (2,3). These β-turns are known to be particularly important in the biologically active conformations of many peptides. The L-tyrosine (Tyr) residue, a component of many neuropeptides (e.g. enkephalins), may influence the conformation of a peptide molecule as well as influencing its interactions as a result of the aromatic ring present in its side-chain and the potentially co-ordinating phenolate oxygen.

Copper is a biologically essential element which is distributed unevenly

throughout the body (50-100 mg per adult), with relatively high concentrations
being found in the liver-gall bladder area and the brain. In many organs copper
complexes can act as intermediates in redox reactions or oxygen transport but,
in the brain, the role of copper is not yet defined. In the body labile copper
is generally present as amino acid or peptide complexes. Below pH 5 Cu(II) bonds
to most peptides via the terminal $-NH_2$ group and the carbonyl oxygen of the vici-
nal peptide bond. This bond is weak, hence the complex formed has only a small
range of existence. Above pH 5 Cu(II) promotes ionization of the adjacent amide
nitrogen to form a Cu-N bond with a 5-membered chelate ring (4,5). Further chelate rings are formed by deprotonation of, and Cu-N bond formation to, successive
peptide nitrogens. In the presence of competitive donor centres in side-chains
(e.g. an imidazole nitrogen of the histidine residue) the binding mode of Cu(II)
to peptides may be changed but small 5- or 6-membered rings are generally
formed (5,6).

THE EFFECT OF THE PROLINE RESIDUE ON THE BINDING ABILITIES OF PEPTIDE LIGANDS.

Proline as an N-terminal residue in acidic solution contains an ionizable
proton on the nitrogen donor atom. This proton is more acidic (7,8) (log K_{HL} =
8.8-9.0) than in proline itself (log K_{HL} = 10.5) so that the nitrogen donor of
the N-terminal of a Pro- residue is comparable to that in a normal primary amino-
group ($-NH_2$). For example, melanostatin (Pro-Leu-Gly-NH_2) behaves, as far as
binding modes are concerned, similarly to prolylglycine although its stability
constants are different (8). In addition, co-ordination of the secondary nitrogen
of a proline residue creates a new chiral centre on the nitrogen atom. This is
seen clearly in the CD spectra of such complexes (9). Since proline contains the
-NH- group rather than $-NH_2$, there is no ionizable amide-NH-proton when it is
inserted in a peptide chain, hence the -Pro- nitrogen is unable to bind metal
ions such as Cu(II). As a result the proline residue in any position other than
the N-terminal position may act as a 'break-point' to metal co-ordination,
allowing the two ends of the chain to behave independently.

We have studied recently the Cu(II) complexes of a range of tri-, tetra-
and octapeptides containing proline and sarcosine (which also contains a secondary nitrogen) residues at various positions in the peptide chain using potentiometric and spectroscopic (absorption, CD and EPR spectroscopy) techniques (6,10-19).
Entirely self-consistent results have been found using all these methods. These
results demonstrate clearly that the proline (or, to a lesser extent, the sarcosine) residue acts as a break-point in metal-peptide equilibria. As a consequence
of this fact large chelate rings can be formed, and these can be readily identified in, for example, the Cu(II) - Gly-Pro-Gly-Gly system (Figure 1). Since neither
-Pro- nor -Sar- in position 2 of a peptide chain possess an ionizable amide pro-

ton, complexes similar to the $CuH_{-1}L$ (or NN) species with tetraglycine or Pro-Gly$_3$ cannot be formed. Two co-ordination schemes are, however, possible: i) formation of a bis-complex, CuL_2, and ii) formation of a $CuH_{-1}L$ species which, while empirically similar to the corresponding complex with tetraglycine, involves ionization of a proton from a peptide nitrogen further along the chain followed by Cu-N bond formation to give an NN complex with an unusually large chelate ring. Formation of this species is delayed to a higher pH as a result of the less favourable entropy change and, once formed, it soon loses further protons to form $CuH_{-2}L$ and $CuH_{-3}L$ complexes. While this large chelate ring is less stable than the normal 5-membered ring it becomes the major species soon above pH 7 as is apparent from a comparison of the formation constants of complexes of Cu(II) with Gly-Pro-Gly-Gly (or Gly-Sar-Gly-Gly) with those of tetraglycine.

log β values

	CuL	$CuH_{-1}L$	$CuH_{-2}L$	$CuH_{-3}L$	CuL_2
Gly-Pro-Gly-Gly	5.46	-2.46	-11.86	-21.34	9.61
Gly-Sar-Gly-Gly	5.18	-1.78	-11.02	-21.90	9.92
tetraglycine[5]	5.08	-0.42	-7.31	-16.60	

Formation of a large chelate ring spanning the two terminal residues of the tetrapeptide chain was also supported by a study of the CD spectra of Phe-Pro-Gly-Gly, Gly-Pro-Phe-Gly and Gly-Pro-Gly-Phe (16) and analogues containing the Tyr residue (15). The formation of macrochelates was also observed in the Cu(II) complexes with -Pro- or -Sar- as the third residue of the peptide chain (11,12).

Studies of octapeptide systems containing -Pro- as the third and seventh residues (analogues of canine tuftsinyltuftsin) have shown that, in these cases also, Cu(II) ions may bring together the N- and C- terminal residues stabilizing a bent conformation for the peptide chain. CD spectra and potentiometric data have both provided reasonable evidence. The CD spectra of the final NNN species show a new intra-ligand transition at 224 nm. Although the precise assignment of this band might be controversial (3,20-23), it is clear that it indicates the organization of the peptide chain into some form of bent structure involving co-ordination of the amide-N of the peptide linkage of the C-terminal glycine.

As a general conclusion, the results of potentiometric and spectroscopic studies of model and natural peptides show that, in the presence of labile Cu(II) ions, these ligands can form stable chelated complexes with the peptide chain locked in a bent conformation. Since the biologically active forms of such molecules are generally the bent, β-conformations, there is a possible role for Cu(II) in the bio-activation of small peptides containing the -Pro- residue (e.g. neuro-

peptides) (24). The formation of such Cu(II)-neuropeptide complexes would require comparatively high local concentrations of the reactants, e.g. at pH 8
and with a 1:1 Cu:Gly-Pro-Gly-Gly ratio, over 30% of the Cu(II) is complexed when
the concentrations exceed 10^{-6} mol dm^{-3}. While it is likely that, on a micro
scale, locally high concentrations exist in the vicinity of active sites in the
central nervous system, it is a difficult fact to establish experimentally.

CAN TYROSINE BE A SPECIFIC RESIDUE IN ITS INTERACTION WITH Cu(II)?

Several studies on the interaction of tyrosine (Tyr) residues with metal ions
have revealed the possibility of interaction between the metal ion and the aromatic ring, or of some form of ring 'stacking' (25-34). This interaction, though
relatively weak, could be of critical importance to the conformations of the aromatic amino acid residues although the exact mechanism is still difficult to
establish (28,32,34). Stacking of the aromatic side-chains (or their interaction
with metal ions) is possible with any aromatic amino acid residue such as tyrosine, phenylalanine or tryptophan. The Tyr residue, however, also contains in its
side-chain a hydroxyl group which, on ionization, can be involved more specifically in metal ion binding.

The phenolic proton of Tyr does not normally ionize until above pH 10 but,
once ionized, it can co-ordinate to Cu(II) ions although, for steric reasons,
it cannot bind to a metal ion which is already co-ordinated to the other amino
acid donor centres (NH$_2$ or COO$^-$). When in a peptide sequence, however, the phenolate oxygen of -Tyr- can co-ordinate to Cu(II) by at least two routes; it can
form dimeric species (15,17,18,35) or macrocyclic chelated complexes (15,18).
This latter mode of co-ordination is seen particularly clearly in complexes with
the tetrapeptides Gly-Pro-Gly-Tyr (15) and Tyr-Pro-Gly-Tyr (18). In both cases
stable complexes with large chelate rings are observed over a large pH range
(about pH 6-9), with the Cu(II) bonded to the phenolate oxygen of the C-terminal
-Tyr and to the N-terminal -NH$_2$ group. As a result a large, 18-membered chelate
ring is formed, holding the peptide in a bent conformation. In both the tetrapeptides studied this mode of co-ordination is a result of the break-point effect
of -Pro- in the second position of the chain. The mutual influence of -Pro- and
-Tyr- residues on the specificity of Cu(II) binding by a peptide is also found
in the Cu(II)-β-casomorphin system (17).

Comparable studies to those described above but using tetrapeptides containing
phenylalanine in place of tyrosine, support our conclusions on Cu(II)-phenolate
oxygen interaction (16), and demonstrate the potential importance in some biolo-
cal processes of interaction of the -Tyr- side-chain with metal ions, as well as
the mutual influence of other amino acid residues (e.g. -Pro-) on the binding

ability of the -Tyr- residue. Under suitable conditions Cu(II)-phenolate bonds are formed at comparatively low pH values (pH 5-6), hence they could be important in many biological processes.

Evidence that Cu(II) can influence the biological activity of other small molecules already exists, e.g. for aspirin (36) and for cimetidine (37). Evidence also exists for dependence of the bioactivity of some oligopeptides on metal ions. For example, it has been shown that the activity of the thyrotropin releasing factor (TRF, L-pyroglutamyl-L-histidyl-L-prolinamide) increases considerably when bound to Ni(II) while it becomes inactive when bound to Cu(II) or Pd(II) (38). Potentiometric and spectroscopic studies of the complexes of TRF provide some explanation of the above observations (6). At pH 7.4 (the pH at which the biological experiments were conducted) TRF bonds to Cu(II) via three N donors, i.e. an imidazole-N (of -His-), the peptide-N (also of -His-) and the pyroglutamyl-N. Such co-ordination appears to block interaction of the neuropeptide with its receptor site making the co-ordinated TRF inactive. However, at this pH, Ni(II) ions are bound to the imidazole-N only, allowing the peptide molecule to bridge to its receptor site so promoting its activity.

Studies on enkephalins have also demonstrated that the biological activity of Met-enkephalin in opiate binding tests is enhanced as a consequence of co-ordination to Cu(II) (39). This phenomenon could be explained as resulting from the strengthening of the biologically active β-turn as a result of metal co-ordination (39,40), although such a suggestion is very difficult to check explicitly.

ACKNOWLEDGEMENTS

Two of the authors (H.K. and G.F.-K.) wish to thank the Polish Academy of Sciences for financial support for some of the work presented here.

REFERENCES

(1)   L.L. Iversen, Ann.Rev.Pharmacol.Toxicol. 23, 1 (1983), F.E. Bloom, ibid, 23, 151 (1983).

(2)   P.Y. Chou and G.D. Fasman, J.Mol.Biol. 115, 135 (1977).

(3)   M. Lisowski, I.Z. Siemion and K. Sobczyk, Int.J.Pept.Protein Res. 21, 439 (1983) and references therein.

(4)   R.B. Martin, in H. Sigel /Ed./ "Metal Ions in Biological Systems", Marcel Dekker, N.Y. 1974, p. 129.

(5) H. Sigel and R.B. Martin, Chem.Rev. 82, 385 (1982), and references therein.

(6) G. Formicka-Kozłowska, M. Bezer and L.D. Pettit, J.Inorg.Biochem. 18, 335-347 (1982).

(7) H. Sigel, Inorg.Chem. 14, 1535 (1975).

(8) G. Formicka-Kozłowska, H. Kozłowski, M. Bezer, L.D. Pettit, G. Kupryszewski and J. Przybylski, Inorg.Chim.Acta 56, 79-82 (1981).

(9) I.Z. Siemion, A. Kubik, M. Jeżowska-Bojczuk and H. Kozłowski, J.Inorg.Biochem. 22, 137-141 (1984) and references therein.

(10) G. Formicka-Kozłowska, H. Kozłowski, I.Z. Siemion, K. Sobczyk and E. Nawrocka, J.Inorg.Biochem. 15, 201-212 (1981).

(11) M. Bataille, G. Formicka-Kozłowska, H. Kozłowski, L.D. Pettit and I. Steel, J.Chem.Soc.Chem.Commun. 1984, 231-232.

(12) L.D. Pettit, I. Steel, G. Formicka-Kozłowska, T. Tatarowski and M. Bataille, J.Chem.Soc.Dalton (1985), 535-539.

(13) M. Bataille, L.D. Pettit, I. Steel, H. Kozłowski and T. Tatarowski, J.Inorg.Biochem. (in press).

(14) G. Formicka-Kozłowska, D. Konopińska, H. Kozłowski and B. Decock-Le-Reverend, Inorg.Chim.Acta 78, L47-L49 (1983).

(15) H. Kozłowski, M. Bezer, L.D. Pettit, M. Bataille and B. Hecquet, J.Inorg.Biochem. 18, 231-240 (1983).

(16) M. Bezer, L.D. Pettit, I. Steel, M. Bataille, S. Djemil and H. Kozłowski, J.Inorg.Biochem. 20, 13-21 (1984).

(17) G. Formicka-Kozłowska, L.D. Pettit, I. Steel, B. Hartrodt, K. Neubert, P. Rekowski and G. Kupryszewski, J.Inorg.Biochem. 22, 155-164 (1984).

(18) L.D. Pettit, I. Steel, T. Kowalik, H. Kozłowski and M. Bataille, J.Chem.Soc.Dalton (in press).

(19) H. Kozłowski, G. Formicka-Kozłowska and L.D. Pettit, Pure and Appl. Chem. 55, 107-113 (1983).

(20) R.W. Woody in "Peptides, Polypeptides and Proteins", Ed. E.R. Blout,
      F.A. Bovey, M. Goodman and N. Lotau, Wiley, N.Y. 1974.

(21) S. Brahms and J. Brahms, J.Mol.Biol. 138, 149 (1980).

(22) J.C. Howard, A. Ali, H.A. Scheraga and F.A. Momany, Macromolecules 8,
      607 (1975).

(23) J.P. Aubert, N. Helbecque and M.H. Loucheux-Lefebvre, Arch.Biochem.
      Biophys. 208, 20 (1981).

(24) L.D. Pettit and G. Formicka-Kozlowska, Neuroscience Letters 50, 53 (1984).

(25) W.A. Franks and D. van der Helm, Acta Cryst. B26, 1299 (1970).

(26) D. van der Helm and C.E. Tatsch, Acta Cryst. B28, 2307 (1972).

(27) H. Kozłowski and M. Jeżowska, Chem.Phys.Lett. 47, 452-456 (1977).

(28) H. Kozłowski, M. Jeżowska and H. Szyszuk, J.Mol.Struct. 50, 73-80 (1978).

(29) H. Kozłowski, G. Formicka-Kozłowska and B. Jeżowska-Trzebiatowska,
      Org.Magn.Resonance 10, 146-150 (1978).

(30) H. Kozłowski, Inorg.Chim.Acta 31, 135-140 (1978).

(31) M.B. Hursthouse, S.A.A. Jayaweera, G.H.W. Milburn and A. Quick,
      J.Chem.Soc.Dalton 1971, 207

(32) D. van der Helm, S.E. Ealick and J.E. Burks, Acta Cryst. B31, 1013 (1975).

(33) P.A. Mosset and J.J. Bonnet, Acta Cryst. B33, 2807 (1977).

(34) P.I. Vestues and R.B. Martin, J.Am.Chem.Soc. 102, 7906 (1980).

(35) R.J.W. Hefford and L.D. Pettit, J.Chem.Soc.Dalton 1981, 1331.

(36) J.R.J. Sorenson, L.W. Oberley, V. Kishore, S.W.C. Leuthauser, T.D. Oberley
      and A. Pezeshk, Inorg.Chim.Acta 79, 45 (1983).

(37) F.T. Greenaway, L.M. Brown, J.C. Dabrowiak, M.R. Thomson and V.M. Day,
      J.Am.Chem.Soc. 102, 7782 (1980).

(38) T. Tonoue, S. Minagawa, N. Kato and K. Ohki, Pharmacol.Biochem.Behav. 10,
      201 (1979).

(39) P. Sharrock, R. Day, S. Lemaire, S. St-Pierre, H. Mazarguil, J.E. Gairin
      and R. Haran, Inorg.Chim.Acta 66, 91-96 (1982).

(40) G. Formicka-Kozłowska, L.D. Pettit, I. Steel, C.E. Livera, G. Kupryszewski
      and K. Rolka, J.Inorg.Biochem. (in press).

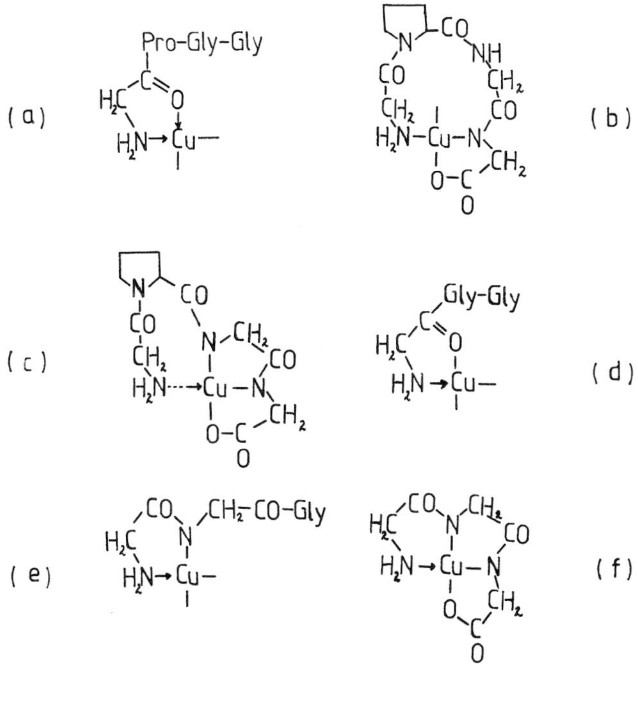

Figure 1. Complexes of Cu(II) with Gly-Pro-Gly-Gly : (CuL) species (a), $(CuH_{-1}L)$
          (b), $(CuH_{-2}L)$ (c), and with triglycine : (CuL) species (d), $(CuH_{-1}L)$
          (e), $(CuH_{-2}L)$ (f).

Electron Transfer
Processes

Long Range Electron Transfer in Pentaammineruthenium(His-48)Myoglobin

Robert J. Crutchley, Walther R. Ellis, Jr., and Harry B. Gray

Contribution No. 7231 from the Division of Chemistry and Chemical
Engineering, California Institute of Technology, Pasadena, California,
91125 USA

SUMMARY

The rate constants for intramolecular electron transfer in
$a_5Ru^{2+/3+}$(His-48)myoglobin($Fe^{3+/2+}$), initiated by flash photolysis
of a solution containing a_5Ru^{3+}(His-48)myoglobin(Fe^{3+})/Ru(bpy)$_3^{2+}$/
EDTA (a = NH_3), are 0.019(2) s^{-1} and 0.041(3) s^{-1} for $Ru^{2+} \rightarrow Fe^{3+}$
and $Fe^{2+} \rightarrow Ru^{3+}$ reactions, respectively. Combining activation enthalpies
with redox thermodynamic parameters for this system places the high-
spin heme reorganizational enthalpy at 20 kcal mol^{-1}; the relatively
high value (the low-spin heme in cytochrome $\underline{c}$ is only 7-8 kcal mol^{-1})
is likely associated with the dissociation of axial water in the
reduction of high-spin Fe^{3+}.

1   INTRODUCTION

Presently known multisite redox metalloenzymes (e.g., nitrogenase,
cytochrome $\underline{c}$ oxidase) typically contain, in addition to a substrate
binding site consisting of one or more metal ions, additional redox

cofactors that function purely as electron transfer agents. Thus, a
key aspect of the turnover of multisite redox enzymes involves electron
transfer over long distances through protein interiors. Unfortunately,
few systems have been extensively studied, and many have proved resistant to detailed kinetic analysis, due (in part) to a lack of structural information. We have therefore focused our efforts on experiments designed to elucidate the factors that determine the rates of
intramolecular electron transfer reactions in proteins and protein
complexes. Factors generally agreed to be of importance include:[1-7]
(1) the thermodynamic driving force ($\Delta G°$); (2) the nature of the
intervening medium between donor and acceptor; (3) the inner-sphere
reorganization (i.e., changes in geometry of the donor and acceptor
upon electron transfer); (4) solvation of the donor and acceptor; (5)
the donor-acceptor distance; and (6) the donor-medium-acceptor orientation.

The philosophy underlying our experimental program of modifying
structurally (i.e., crystallographically) characterized metalloproteins
is rather simple. The attachment of a substitution-inert transition
metal complex to a well characterized metalloprotein is, in our view,
the simplest route to the "synthesis" of a multisite metalloprotein
from which one can extract kinetic and thermodynamic information per-
taining to electron transfer processes in metalloproteins in which the
redox site-to-site distance is fixed and known. In some respects the
protein framework may be simply viewed as that of a bridging ligand.
Recent work from the Hoffman,[8] Isied,[9] and McLendon[10] laboratories
should be consulted for alternative experimental approaches.

Results from two semisynthetic systems, a_5Ru(His-33)cytochrome c
(a = NH_3)[9,11] and a_5Ru(His-83)azurin,[12] have been reported recently.
In each case, the rate constant for intramolecular electron transfer
from the surface-bound a_5Ru^{2+} site to the electron acceptor buried in
the protein interior is very weakly temperature dependent. Both
inner-sphere and outer-sphere contributions to the reorganizational

enthalpy (ΔH^*) associated with the $a_5Ru^{2+/3+}$ center are small and one must conclude that the ΔH^*s for the low-spin heme (cytochrome c) and blue copper (azurin) are also very small. A general picture that has emerged during the last thirty years is that large changes in molecular geometry lead to high activation energies and hence slow electron-transfer rates. With this in mind, we have examined a third protein system, sperm whale myoglobin.[13] Figure 1 displays selected parts of the myoglobin skeleton together with the attachment site of the ruthenium label.[14]

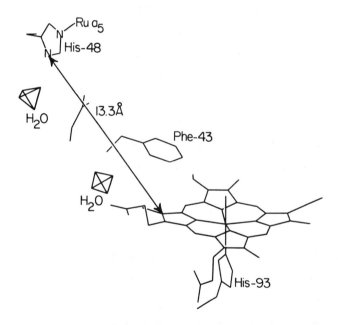

Figure 1. Selected parts of the molecular skeleton of sperm whale myoglobin illustrating the edge-to-edge through space distance from $a_5Ru(His-48)^{3+/2+}$ to the heme($Fe^{3+/2+}$).

2 RESULTS AND DISCUSSION

Chromatographically pure sperm whale myoglobin (Sigma) was reacted with a fifteen-fold excess of $[Ru(NH_3)_5OH_2](PF_6)_2$[15] for thirty minutes

at room temperature (pH 7.0) and the reaction was terminated by passage
of the solution through a Sephadex G-25 gel column. Computer graphics
modeling suggests that four histidine residues (12, 48, 81, and 116)
are sufficiently solvent accessible to react with the aquopentaammine-
ruthenium(II) complex. After oxidation of the mixture of modified
proteins, preparative isoelectric focusing (Figure 2) and cation-
exchange chromatography (Whatman CM-52 resin) yield all four expected
singly modified proteins as well as multiply modified derivatives.
Peptide mapping experiments verified the labeling sites. Peptides T1
through T23 were obtained after digestion of myoglobin with trypsin
(Figure 3). His-12, -48, -81, and -116 are contained in separate
tryptic peptides (T1, T7, T14, and T17).

(-)

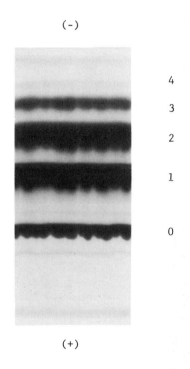

4

3

2

1

0

(+)

Figure 2. Preparative isoelectric focusing on a flat bed gel (LKB
ultrodex, pH 7-11 ampholines) of ruthenium-modified myoglobins. 0,
unreacted $Mb(Fe^{3+})$; 1, $[a_5Ru^{3+}(His)]Mb(Fe^{3+})$; 2, $[a_5Ru^{3+}(His)]_2Mb(Fe^{3+})$;
3, $[a_5Ru^{3+}(His)]_3Mb(Fe^{3+})$; 4, $[a_5Ru^{3+}(His)]_4Mb(Fe^{3+})$, trace amount.

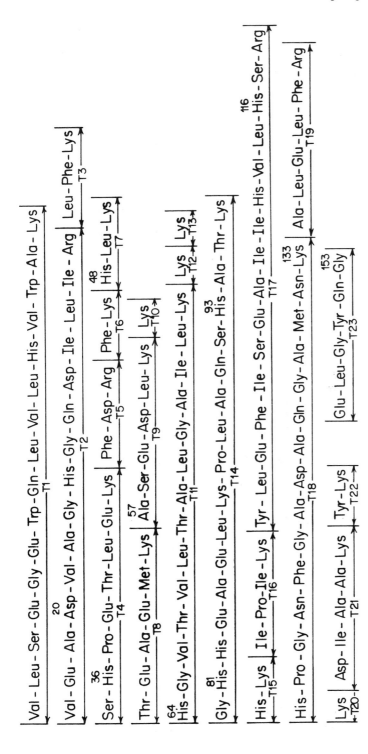

Figure 3.   Tryptic peptides of sperm whale myoglobin.

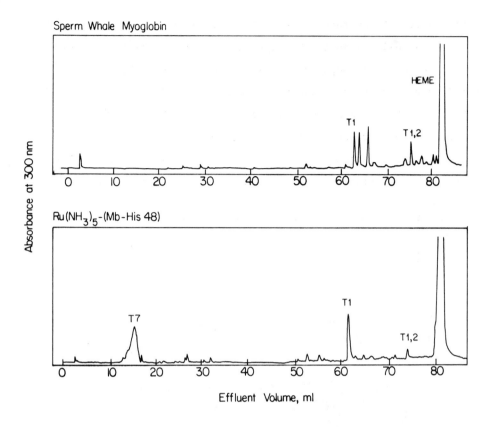

Figure 4.   Reverse-phase HPLC of tryptic digests of native myoglobin and $Ru(NH_3)_5(His-48)^{3+}Mb$ at 300 nm (0.1 O.D. full scale).   A 2 mg sample of hydrolyzed protein was chromatographed (flow rate 2 mL/min) with a linear gradient between 0% and 55% CH_3CN in which both the initial aqueous developer and the CH_3CN contained 0.1% CF_3COOH.

One of the singly modified derivatives, $a_5Ru(His-48)^{3+}Mb$, was selected for complete characterization[16] and kinetic studies.   The tryptic peptides of this derivative and native myoglobin were separated by reverse-phase HPLC and the eluate was monitored at 300 nm (Figure 4). Only the peaks corresponding to the T1 and T1,2 (tryptophan-containing) peptides and heme are present in the chromatogram of the native myo-globin tryptic peptides.   (The two peaks between T1 and T1,2 are artifacts.)   A new peak at an elution volume of 15 mL appears in the chromatogram of the ruthenium-modified protein; it was identified by amino acid analysis as the T7 peptide.[16] The attachment of $Ru(NH_3)_5^{3+}$ to His-48 in the T7 peptide generates a chromophore that makes it possible to detect T7 at 300 nm. The spectrum of the $Ru(NH_3)_5His^{3+}$ complex exhibits a maximum at 300 nm (ε = 2100 M^{-1} cm^{-1}).[17]

Spectroscopic measurements (UV-vis, CD, EPR, and ^{1}H NMR)[16,18] indicate that the heme site is virtually unperturbed by the a_5Ru^{3+} label. This conclusion is supported by electrochemical results.

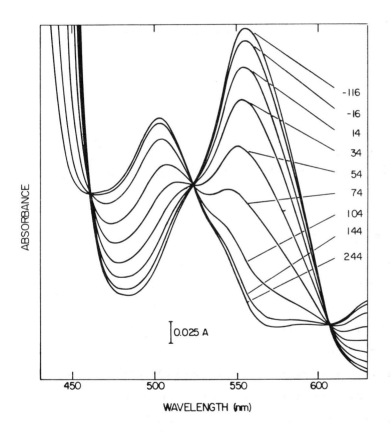

Figure 5. Thin-layer spectroelectrochemistry of native sperm whale myoglobin (25°C; I = 0.1, pH 7.0, phosphate buffer). Redox mediator: $Ru(NH_3)_6Cl_3$. Overlay spectra and absorbance changes at different values of the applied potential in mV vs. NHE.

Figure 5 illustrates a typical set of overlay absorbance spectra obtained during a spectroelectrochemical titration of native myo-globin. Electrolysis to equilibrium was accelerated by the addition of a redox mediator, $Ru(NH_3)_6^{3+/2+}$. The corresponding Nernst plot is displayed in Figure 6. The heme chromophore interfered with the spectroelectrochemical determination of the $a_5Ru^{3+/2+}$ reduction potential; consequently, differential pulse polarography was used (4,4'-bipyridine was present as a redox promoter). In the differen-tial pulse polarography experiments, no current attributable to the heme iron was observed when native myoglobin was run as a control. Variable-temperature electrochemical measurements (5-45°C) yielded the entropy and enthalpy changes associated with reduction of the metal sites (Table 1).

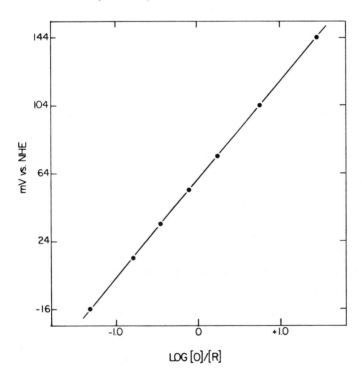

Figure 6. Nernst plot of the data in Figure 5. The line is a least-squares (58 mV slope) fit to the data at 556 nm.

Table 1. Thermodynamic parameters[13,16] for the reduction of a_5Ru^{3+}
          and the heme site in native and modified myoglobin(Mb).[a]

Thermodynamic Parameter	Native Mb $Fe^{3+/2+}$	Modified Mb $Fe^{3+/2+}$	$a_5Ru^{3+/2+}$
$E°$, mV vs. NHE (25°C)	58.8 ± 2	65.4 ± 2	85.8 ± 2
$\Delta G°$, kcal mol^{-1} (25°C)	-1.26 ± 0.05	-1.51 ± 0.05	-1.98 ± 0.05
$\Delta S°$, e.u.	-39.2 ± 1.2	-37.6 ± 1.2	4.2 ± 1.2
$\Delta H°$, kcal mol^{-1} (25°C)	-13.0 ± 0.4	-12.7 ± 0.4	-0.7 ± 0.4

[a]pH 7.0, I = 0.1 M phosphate buffer.

Since the reduction potentials (at 25°C) for the ruthenium and heme
sites in the modified protein differ by only 20 mV, the observed rate
constant (equation 1) for intramolecular electron transfer between
these sites is expected to follow reversible first-order behavior (i.e.,
$k_{obs} = k_1 + k_{-1}$).

$$a_5Ru^{3+}\text{-}Mb(Fe^{3+}) \xrightarrow[e^-]{\text{fast}} a_5Ru^{2+}\text{-}Mb(Fe^{3+}) \underset{k_{-1}}{\overset{k_1}{\rightleftharpoons}} a_5Ru^{3+}\text{-}Mb(Fe^{2+}) \quad (1)$$

Production of a_5Ru^{2+}(His-48)Mb(Fe^{3+}) was achieved by flash photolysis
of a solution of the fully oxidized protein derivative and Ru(bpy)$_3^{2+}$
(bpy = bipyridine). EDTA was present in solution to scavenge Ru(bpy)$_3^{3+}$
produced by oxidative quenching.[11] The flash trace (Figure 7a) shows
a rapid increase in absorbance, corresponding to the generation of
Mb(Fe^{2+}), followed by a much slower increase that continues long after
the flash for the modified protein but not for native myoglobin (Figure
7b); this slow step is attributable to intramolecular electron transfer.

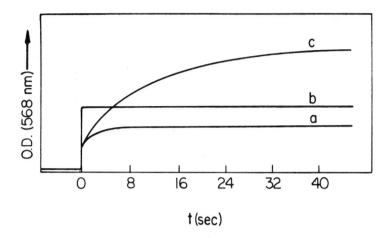

Figure 7. The change in optical density at 568 nm upon flash photolysis of protein solutions. Solution (a), $a_5Ru^{3+}(His-48)Mb(Fe^{3+})$;
solution (b), native sperm whale myoglobin; solution (c), solution
(a) in the presence of approximately 2 atm CO. Conditions: 5 x 10^{-6} M
protein, 6.6 x 10^{-5}M Ru(bpy)$_3$Cl$_2$, 5.0 x 10^{-3}M EDTA, pH 7.0 phosphate
buffer (I = 0.1M), 45°C. An isosbestic point for the Mb and MbCO
absorption spectra occurs at 568 nm.

Figure 7b is an important control experiment that shows that the partial
reduction of the ferric heme by EDTA-derived radicals is very rapid and
does not interfere with the collection of intramolecular electron
transfer data. The observed electron transfer rate closely follows
first-order behavior (Figure 8) and is independent of protein concentration (5 - 50 μM range). A residuals plot (Figure 9) supports our
contention that the system is in first-order electron transfer

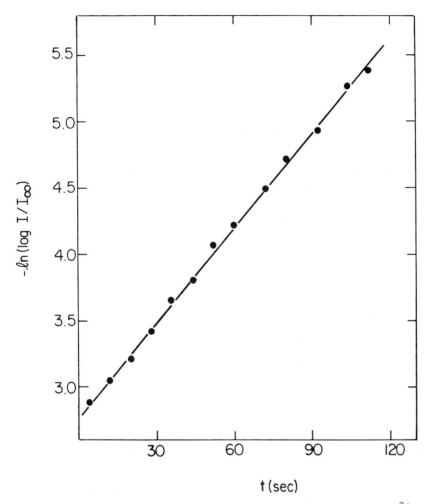

Figure 8. First-order kinetic plot for the reduction of Fe^{3+} in flash-generated $a_5Ru^{2+}(His-48)Mb(Fe^{3+})$ at 15°C; $t = 0$ taken at 1 ms after the flash. The line drawn is a least-squares fit to the data.

equilibrium. Finally, when the flash solution of modified protein is saturated with CO (Figure 7c), a large increase in absorbance at the monitoring wavelength (568 nm) is observed. CO binds to the ferrous heme generated in step k_1 and prevents back electron transfer to produce the ferric heme. The equilibrium step in Equation 1 is thus transformed into a dead-end reaction, yielding $a_5Ru^{3+}(His-48)Mb(Fe^{2+}-CO)$.

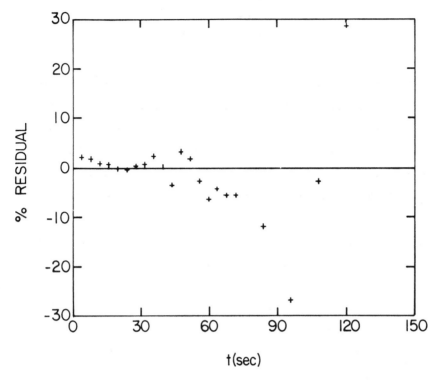

Figure 9.   Residuals plot (data minus fit) for the first-order fit in Figure 8.   (More data points are used here than are displayed in Figure 8).

The equilibrium constant for Equation 1 and k_{obs} determine the forward and reverse rate constants.   Thus, at 25°C, the forward rate (k_1) is 0.019 ± 0.002 s^{-1}, while the reverse rate (k_{-1}) is 0.041 ± 0.003 s^{-1}.   The temperature dependences (5-45°C range) of the forward and reverse rate constants yield $\Delta H_1^{\ddagger}$ and $\Delta H_{-1}^{\ddagger}$ values of 7.4 ± 0.5 kcal mol^{-1} and 19.5 ± 0.5 kcal mol^{-1}, respectively.

The reorganization enthalpy associated with the reduction of the high-spin heme in myoglobin can be estimated using an expression derived by Marcus and Sutin:[19]

$$\Delta H^*_{12} = \tfrac{1}{2}(\Delta H^*_{11} + \Delta H^*_{22})(1 - 4\alpha^2) + \tfrac{1}{2}\Delta H^\circ_{12}(1 - 2\alpha) \qquad (2)$$

$$\text{where } \alpha = \frac{\Delta G^{\circ}_{12}}{4(\Delta G^*_{11} + \Delta G^*_{22})}.$$

In the following calculation, we neglect α since ΔG°_{12} is very small. The reactions of interest are <u>intramolecular</u>; therefore, the translational enthalpy component ($-RT/2$) of ΔH^*_{12} is of no importance and $\Delta H^*_{12} = \Delta H^{\ddagger}_{12}$. Brown and Sutin[20] have estimated the reorganization free energy (ΔG^*_{22}) associated with the $Ru(NH_3)_5py^{3+/2+}$ self-exchange reaction to be 6.92 kcal mol^{-1}. This quantity should closely approximate that for electron exchange in the $Ru(NH_3)_5His^{3+/2+}$ system. Furthermore, both inner-sphere and outer-sphere contributions to the reorganization entropies for ruthenium-ammine complexes are very small. ΔH^*_{22}, the reorganization enthalpy for $a_5Ru(His-48)^{3+/2+}$, is therefore taken to be 6.9 kcal mol^{-1}. Using $\Delta H^*_{12} = 7.4$ kcal mol^{-1} and $\Delta H^{\circ}_{12} = -12$ kcal mol^{-1} (data for the forward reaction, $a_5Ru^{2+}-Fe^{3+} \rightarrow a_5Ru^{3+}-Fe^{2+}$), we estimate ΔH^*_{11}, the reorganization enthalpy for the Mb-($Fe^{3+/2+}$) system to be 20 kcal mol^{-1}.

In contrast, the enthalpic reorganization[11] for the low-spin heme in horse heart cytochrome <u>c</u> is only 7-8 kcal mol^{-1}. We attribute this difference in ΔH^* to a ligation change that accompanies the reduction of metmyoglobin to deoxymyoglobin. Takano's x-ray crystallographic studies[21] indicate that the axial water molecule dissociates from the myoglobin ferriheme upon reduction. Reduction of cytochrome <u>c</u> is not accompanied by a large inner-sphere reorganization as the axial Met and His ligands are retained.[22] Studies of myoglobin,[23] cytochrome <u>c</u>,[24] and iron porphyrin[25,26] cross reactions have led to the suggestion that electron transfer reactions involving high-spin porphyrins are more sluggish than those of low-spin porphyrins. The intramolecular rate constants and the enthalpic barriers reported here are clearly in accord with this view.

3 ACKNOWLEDGMENTS

We thank Steve Mayo for Figure 1 and Lorne Reid for Figure 8. R.J.C. acknowledges the receipt of a postdoctoral fellowship from the Natural Sciences and Engineering Research Council of Canada. This research was supported by Grant CHE82-18502 from the U.S. National Science Foundation.

4 REFERENCES AND NOTES

(1) R. A. Marcus, N. Sutin, Biochim. Biophys. Acta, submitted for publication.

(2) S. Wherland, H. B. Gray in D. Dolphin et al. (Eds.), "Biological Aspects of Inorganic Chemistry," Wiley, New York 1977, pp 289-368.

(3) R. A. Scott, A. G. Mauk, H. B. Gray, J. Chem. Educ., submitted for publication.

(4) D. DeVault, Quantum Mechanical Tunnelling in Biological Systems, 2nd ed., Cambridge Univ. Press, Cambridge 1984.

(5) B. Chance, D. DeVault, H. Frauenfelder, R. A. Marcus, J. R. Schrieffer, N. Sutin (Eds.), Tunneling in Biological Systems, Academic Press, New York 1979.

(6) S. S. Isied, Prog. Inorg. Chem. 32 (1984) 443-517.

(7) J. L. Dreyer, Experientia 40 (1984) 653-776.

(8) S. E. Peterson-Kennedy, J. L. McGourty, P. S. Ho, C. J. Sutoris, N. Liang, H. Zemel, N. V. Blough, E. Margoliash, B. M. Hoffman, Coord. Chem. Revs. 64 (1985) 125-133.

(9) S. S. Isied, C. Kuehn, G. Worosila, J. Am. Chem. Soc. 106 (1984) 1722-1726.

(10) G. McLendon, T. Guarr, M. McGuire, K. Simolo, S. Strauch, K. Taylor, Coord. Chem. Revs. 64 (1985) 113-124.

(11) D. G. Nocera, J. R. Winkler, K. M. Yocom, E. Bordignon, H. B. Gray, J. Am. Chem. Soc. 106 (1984) 5145-5150.

(12) R. Margalit, N. M. Kostic, C.-M. Che, D. F. Blair, H.-J. Chiang, I. Pecht, J. B. Shelton, J. R. Shelton, W. A. Schroeder, H. B. Gray, Proc. Nat. Acad. Sci. USA 81 (1984) 6554-6558.

(13) R. J. Crutchley, W. R. Ellis, Jr., H. B. Gray, J. Am. Chem. Soc. 107 (1985) in press.

(14) Generated using an Evans and Sutherland computer graphics system and Caltech software. Myoglobin coordinates supplied by the Brookhaven Protein Data Bank.

(15) R. W. Callahan, G. M. Brown, T. J. Meyer, Inorg. Chem. 14 (1975) 1443-1453.

(16) R. J. Crutchley, W. R. Ellis, Jr., J. B. Shelton, J. R. Shelton, W. A. Schroeder, H. B. Gray, Proc. Nat. Acad. Sci. USA, to be submitted for publication.

(17) R. J. Sundberg, G. Gupta, Bioinorg. Chem. 3 (1973) 39-48.

(18) H. Toi, G. N. La Mar, R. Margalit, C.-M. Che, H. B. Gray, J. Am. Chem. Soc. 106 (1984) 6213-6217.

(19) R. A. Marcus, N. Sutin, Inorg. Chem. 14 (1975) 213-216.

(20) G. M. Brown, N. Sutin, J. Am. Chem. Soc. 101 (1979) 883-892.

(21) T. Takano, J. Mol. Biol. 110 (1977) 537-568; 659-584.

(22) T. Takano, R. E. Dickerson, J. Mol. Biol. 153 (1981) 79-84; 95-115.

(23) A. G. Mauk, H. B. Gray, Biochem. Biophys. Res. Commun. 86 (1979) 206-210.

(24) K. M. Kadish, J. Jordan, J. Electrochem. Soc. 125, (1978) 1250-1257.

(25) R. F. Pasternack, E. G. Spiro, J. Am. Chem. Soc. 100 (1978) 968-972.

(26) D. W. Dixon, M. Barbush, A. Shirazi, Inorg. Chem. 24 (1985) 1081-1087.

Electron Self-Exchange Reactions of Blue Copper Proteins

G.W. Canters and C.M. Groeneveld

Gorlaeus Laboratories
State University
P.O.Box 9502
2300 RA Leiden
THE NETHERLANDS

1. INTRODUCTION

In this contribution a brief review is given of what is presently
known about electron self-exchange reactions of blue copper proteins.
Although reactions of this kind in most cases probably have no physiological function, their study is relevant for several reasons. Firstly,
until now biological electron transfer has been studied primarily by
looking at electron transfer between different redox partners. Clearly,
the study of electron exchange between identical partners offers advantages. The effect of a non-zero driving force is absent, for instance,
and for a proper interpretation of the experimental results the structural details of only one protein need to be known in detail.

Secondly, electron self-exchange rates figure prominently in Marcus
theory, according to which the rate of electron transfer between
different partners can be related to the individual self-exchange rates
and the driving force of the reaction.

Most of what is known at the moment about self-exchange reactions of
type I copper proteins is the result of Marcus analyses of redox reactions between blue copper proteins and a variety of reaction partners.
The latter can be divided into two classes: i) small coordination complexes of the 3d-transition metals, and ii) redox proteins (mostly cytochromes). It is only recently that the blue-copper self-exchange
rates have been determined directly by experiment for a few cases.

In the following the results of these experiments are reviewed for a number of blue-copper proteins and copper coordination compounds. It appears that inconsistency between the results of the different types of experimental approach is the rule rather than the exception.

Special attention will be given to the case of azurin from Pseudomonas aeruginosa. There is a debate in the literature about the redox activity of this protein as a function of pH and the measurement of the self-exchange rate at different pH's is of direct relevance for this question.

For a recent review of earlier work on the electron transfer properties of the blue copper proteins we refer to (1). Structural information on blue copper proteins has been reviewed in (2).

2. ELECTRON TRANSFER WITH 3d-TRANSITION METALS

Electron-transfer reactions of redox proteins (not only blue-copper proteins) with 3d-transition metal complexes have been studied extensively by Gray and coworkers (3-6). The electron self-exchange rates of the metal complexes are known and by measuring the rates of electron transfer between these compounds and various redox proteins, the self-exchange rates of the latter were found with the help of the Marcus relation. Representative examples are azurin and stellacyanin, of which the k_{11} values have been collected in Table 1.

Table 1.: Electron self-exchange rates of stellacyanin and azurin (Ps. aeruginosa) at room temperature corrected for electrostatic effects, as calculated from a Marcus analysis of the electron transfer reaction with various coordination compounds.

Reaction partner	Self-exchange rate M^{-1}, s^{-1}		Reference
	azurin	stellacyanin	
$Co(ox)_3^{3-}$	2.6×10^{-3}	2.5×10^{4}	3
$Fe(EDTA)^{2-}$	1.1×10^{-2}	2.7×10^{5}	4
$Fe(CN)_6^{3-}$	7.6×10^{0}		5
$Co(4,7\ dmp)_3^{3-}$	2.0×10^{3}		5
$Ru(NH_3)_5py^{3+}$	2.7×10^{3}	1.6×10^{5}	6
$Co(phen)_3^{3+}$	1.7×10^{4}	3.1×10^{5}	4
$Co(5-Cl-phen)_3^{3+}$	1.4×10^{5}		5
$Co(5,6-dmp)_3^{3}$	6.3×10^{5}	5.8×10^{5}	5

Table 1, continued

ox   = oxalate

dmp = dimethylphenanthroline

py   = pyridine

phen = phenanthroline

The most conspicuous feature of Table 1 is the large variation in self-exchange rates of azurin and the much smaller spread in rates of stellacyanin. Consistency would require k_{11} to be constant for a particular protein and independent of the reaction partner. The variation in rates has been interpreted by Gray et al (3-6) as signalling specific interactions (for instance, of a hydrophobic or an electrostatic nature) between protein and transition metal complex.

To analyse the data in Table 1 numerically, Gray et al (3-6) devised a "kinetic accessibility scale" for the active site of redox proteins, two blue copper proteins incidentally being at the extreme ends of the scale: azurin (P.aeruginosa) with the least accessible site and stellacyanin with the most accessible site. The inference about the accessibility of the copper site in azurin has been borne out by experiment (2). Crystallographic data have shown that the copper site is buried inside this protein indeed, at a distance of about 7.5 Å from the surface. For stellacyanin no structural details are available as yet.

3. ELECTRON TRANSFER WITH REDOX PROTEINS

The kinetics of the reactions of blue copper proteins with other redox proteins have been studied by a number of groups. Notably Pecht and coworkers (1,7) have performed a Marcus analysis of the rate data and extracted self-exchange rates. The values for a number of copper proteins are presented in Table 2.

Table 2.: Electron self-exchange rates in $M^{-1}s^{-1}$ of various blue-copper proteins as determined from a Marcus analysis of electron transfer reactions with the cytochromes - c_{551}, - c_{553}, c and f (azurin, plastocyanin) and the cytochromes - c_{551} and c (stellacyanin) at room temperature.

azurin	Ps. aeruginosa	9.9×10^5
	Alc. faecalis	2.6×10^5
	Alc. spp	2.6×10^5

Table 2, continued

plastocyanin	Phas. vulgaris	6.6×10^2
	Scen. acutus	6.6×10^2
	Parsley	--- *)
stellacyanin		5.3×10^3

*) no consistent results obtained

Data from references 1 and 7.

One of the main results of this work is a set of self-exchange rates which is much more consistent than the rates obtained from the electron transfer reactions with the 3d-metal complexes. The reason for this may be that in the cases studied association between the redox partners is governed by the same type of interaction (possibly hydrophobic forces). If the reaction rates are biased to the same extent by these interactions, a Marcus analysis will still give mutually consistent results. For plastocyanin, however, no consistent values for the self-exchange rate were obtained for all instances (see Table 2). This protein reacts fast with its natural partner cytochrome-f, but often much slower with non-fysiological partners. It is known that the redox activity of plastocyanin is determined to a large extent by electrostatic effects. It has a high net negative charge at neutral pH and it exhibits several highly charged patches on its surface (2). The importance of electrostatic interactions is highlighted by the way small ions (Na^+, Mg^{2+}) are able to modulate its reactivity (8). Application of Marcus theory in this case will give less satisfactory results as in the other cases in Table 2, as long as no way is found to take these specific interactions into account.

It is interesting to compare the data for azurin and stellacyanin (Table 2) in view of the opposite positions they occupy on the kinetic accessibility scale mentioned in 3. Azurin, with the kinetically least accessible site, exhibits a higher self-exchange rate than stellacyanin, although the latter was inferred to have the most accessible site.

4. SELF-EXCHANGE RATES; EXPERIMENTAL METHODS

In view of the variation in rates encountered in the previous two sections direct determinations of electron self-exchange rates are desirable. One of the methods to do this is to label reduced and oxidized species with different isotopes and to measure the rate at which the label is scrambled when mixing the two species. Dahlin et al (9) used $^{63}Cu/^{65}Cu$ isotopes to establish the self exchange rate of stellacyanin at room temperature by this method.

   Instead of isotopic labels also a "magnetic quantum label" corresponding with either the electronic spin or the nuclear spins, can be used. Provided it is sufficiently fast (i.e., pseudo first order rates of 10^7 s^{-1} and higher), electron self-exchange will lead to broadening or even collapse of the hyperfine structure in the EPR spectrum of the paramagnetic species and from this the self-exchange rate can be determined. Biological electron transfer is usually too slow to be studied in this way, but examples of this method are well known from the work of Weissman and coworkers on organic free radicals in solution (see for example ref (10)), where the bimolecular exchange rate is nearly diffusion controlled (10^8-$10^9 M^{-1}s^{-1}$).

   A preferable alternative is NMR spectroscopy. The NMR spectra of blue copper proteins in the reduced (diamagnetic) form are usually fairly well resolved. In the presence of a small amount of the oxidized (paramagnetic) Cu(II) form, electron exchange between the reduced and oxidized species may selectively broaden some of the peaks in the spectrum (11). From the paramagnetic effect on the T_1 or T_2 NMR relaxation times of these peaks the electron self-exchange rates can be extracted. The method is suited for measuring bimolecular exchange rates in the range of from 10^3-$10^6 M^{-1}s^{-1}$, and has been succesfully applied to proteins as well as copper coordination complexes. A summary of results is presented in Table 3.

Table 3.: Experimentally determined Cu^{2+}/Cu^+ electron exchange rates of
          a number of Cu coordination compounds and blue copper proteins at room temperature.

Ligand	Self-exchange rate M^{-1}, S^{-1}	Reference
plastocyanin	$<< 2 \times 10^4$	19
stellacyanin	1.2×10^5	9
azurin	0.1×10^7	11
aqua 2)	2×10^{-4}	14
	1×10^{-5}	13
various tripeptides	$(0.4-5.5) \times 10^4$	20
2,9-dimethyl phenanthroline 2)	4×10^4	14
tri-α-aminoisobutyric acid 1)	5.5×10^4	15
TAAB in methanol	5.5×10^5	21
Cl^- in 12 M HCl	0.5×10^8	22
various N_2S_2 ligands 2)	$(0.07-4.5) \times 10^1$	23

Table 3, continued

2,2'-bipyridine 2)	2.8×10^1	14
	4.4×10^3	24
1,10-phenanthroline 2)	1.6×10^4	24

1) Cu^{3+}/Cu^{2+} couple
2) determined from a Marcus analysis

5. SELF-EXCHANGE RATES; DISCUSSION

5.1. Cu coordination compounds

Electron transfer between Cu(II) and Cu(I) will in general be accompanied by a change in coordination geometry and often also in coordination number of the metal. It has been postulated that no such changes occur for the metal site in the type I copper proteins and that the more or less rigid frame work of the protein fixes the Cu site in a geometry in between the customary geometries of the Cu(I) and the Cu(II) state (12). This "frozen transition state" would lower the kinetic barrier for electron transfer and form an adaptation of the copper protein to its function as an electron transfer agent. It is therefore of interest to look at the self-exchange rates of copper complexes, which do not have this "kinetic advantage" (see Table 3).

For the Cu^+/Cu^{2+} couple in 12 M HCl the rate is unusually high possibly because we are dealing here with inner sphere electron transfer (13). For the same couple in H_2O, on the other hand the rate is very low; in this case the highly symmetrical 6-coordinate Cu(II) state must undergo substantial reorganization upon reduction to form the 4-coordinate Cu(I) state (14). For the remaining cases in Table 3 the geometry of the copper is not fixed either. Especially the water ligands in the Cu(II) or Cu(III) state may have to reorganize upon reduction of the metal (15). Nevertheless as the data in Table 3 show, the self-exchange rates are comparable with those exhibited by some of the blue copper proteins.

5.2. Blue copper proteins

Although as yet no detailed structural data have been published on a blue copper protein in the reduced as well as the oxidized form, there is sufficient circumstantial evidence to substantiate the idea of a "frozen transition state". Structural data on various blue copper proteins in the oxidezed state or in the apo form show that the coordination geometry of the metal is that of a tetrahedron distorted midway

between the usual tetrahedral coordination of Cu(I) and the square planar conformation of Cu(II) (2). The small enthalpy of reorganization
of the Cu site accompanying a change in oxidation state likewise is
indicative of only small changes in coordination geometry.

Although reorganizational effects must therefore be small, large
variations in the self-exchange rates do still occur (see Table 3). The
self-exchange rate of azurin from Ps. aeruginosa is in good agreement
with the rate calculated from a Marcus treatment of the electron transfer rates between azurin and various cytochromes (see Table 2 and 3).
That this agreement may be fortuitous is illustrated by the case of
stellacyanin for which the experimental self-exchange rate differs by
more than an order of magnitude from the "Marcus" rate of Table 2.

The low self-exchange rate of plastocyanin is in accordance with the
purported preponderance of electrostatic interactions for the redox activity of this protein. The high net charge of plastocyanin and the
presence of highly charged surface patches apparently hinder the formation of an association complex in which electron transfer can proceed
at a substantial rate.

Little is known about the thermodynamic parameters of self-exchange
reactions. The only case studied in some detail so far is azurin from
Ps. aeruginosa (16). Its electron self-exchange rate is rather insensitive to variations in buffer, ionic strength and pH. Its high self-
exchange rate is mainly due to a favourable (high) entropy of activation. Hydrophobic interactions probably play an important role in promoting association of azurin molecules along their so-called hydrophobic patch (16). In an association complex of this type the Cu-Cu distance in minimized to 15 Å and electron transfer is facilitated by a
favourable mutual orientation of the His-117 ligands of the Cu centres.
This would explain why the self exchange rate of azurin is high even
though the Cu site is buried well inside the protein.

A point of special interest is the pH dependence of the redox activity of azurin. T-jump studies of the redox equilibrium between this
protein and various cytochromes have led different research groups to
propose the occurrence of azurin in a redox active (low pH) and a redox
inactive (high pH) form (17). The self-exchange rates, however, do not
show the expected pH dependence. It is not clear, yet, how this finding
can be reconciled with the results of earlier T-jump experiments. It is
possible, for instance, that different pathways or different mechanisms
of electron transfer are operative in the two types of experiment, and
that they exhibit a different pH dependence. Further experiments are
needed to decide on this point.

About the detailed mechanism of electron transfer very little is
known at the moment. For azurin a lower limit of 3×10^3 s^{-1} has been

found for the unimolecular electron transfer rate within the encounter complex of two azurin molecules (11). This is of the same order of magnitude as the rate observed in a complex of cytochrome c and cyt-c oxidase (18). Further, hydrophobic channels or networks of overlapping aromatic Π-systems have been postulated as pathways for electron transfer in redox proteins (2). It has been concluded from NMR experiments, that if a pathway of the latter type would be operative in azurin, the time of residence of the electron on a particular aromatic residue would have to be less than 3×10^{-7}s (11).

6. CONCLUSION

Electron self-exchange rates of blue copper proteins have been determined indirectly by studying their electron transfer reactions with transition metal complexes and redox proteins and subsequently and applying Marcus theory. Direct experimental determinations have been performed for a few cases by isotopic labeling techniques and NMR measurements.

In general the rates determined by different methods disagree considerably. The complexity and peculiarities of biological macromolecules often compromise the consistency of a Marcus analysis and additional considerations must be introduced to assist in the treatment of the experimental data. An example is the concept of kinetic accessibility of the redox centre of redox proteins. The available evidence indicates that this idea can be succesfully applied to the study of redox reactions between proteins and transition metal compounds. It remains to be seen whether it is equally useful for the study of protein/protein electron transfer.

As the examples in Table 3 demonstrate, reorganization of the coordination sphere around the metal upon a change in oxidation state does not necessarily form an impediment to rapid electron transfer. On the other hand, protein conformational changes often occur on a much longer time scale than conformational changes in coordination compounds of copper. The presence of a rigid protein environment thus prevents this kind of reorganizational effect to become the rate determining step in biological electron transfer.

ACKNOWLEDGEMENTS

During the 2nd ICBIC conference the authors have benefitted from useful discussions with profs. H.B. Gray, M. Brunori, I. Pecht and G. Sykes, and Drs. G.F. Moore and F.A. Armstrong. They thank Prof. J. Reedijk for his continuous interest in this work.

REFERENCES

(1) O. Farver and I. Pecht, in "Copper Proteins", T.G. Spiro, Ed., Wiley, 1981, Ch. 4, page 151-192.

(2) E.T. Adman, in "Metalloproteins", P.M. Harrison, Ed., Verlag Chemie, 1985, Ch. 1, page 1-42.

(3) R.A. Holwerda, D.B. Knaff, H.B. Gray, J.D. Clemmer, R. Crowley, J.M. Smith and A.G. Mauk, J. Am. Chem. Soc. 102 (1980) 1142-1146.

(4) H.B. Gray et al, Adv. Chem. Series 162. Am. Chem. Soc. 1977, Ch. 8, page 145-155.

(5) S, Wherland and H.B. Gray, in: "Biological Aspects of Inorganic Chemistry", A.W. Addison et al, Eds., Wiley, 1977, Ch. 10, page 289-368.

(6) A.G. Mauk, R.A. Scott and H.B. Gray, J. Am. Chem. Soc. 102 (1980) page 4360-4363.

(7) S.Wherland and I. Pecht, Biochemistry 17 (1978) page 2585-2591.

(8) T. Takabe, S. Niwa, H. Ishikawa and M. Miyakawa, J. Biochem. 87 (1980) page 111-115; S. Niwa, H. Ishikawa, S. Nikai and T. Takabe, Ibid., 88 (1980) page 1177-1183; T. Takabe, H. Ishikawa, S. Niwa and S. Itoh, Ibid., 94 (1983) page 1901-1911; K. Takenaka and T. Takabe, Ibid., 96 (1984) page 1813-1821.

(9) S. Dahlin, B. Reinhammar and M.T. Wilson, Biochem. J., 218 (1984) page 609-614.

(10) R.L. Ward and S.I. Weissman, J. Am. Chem. Soc. 79 (1957) page 2086-2090.

(11) G.W. Canters, H.A.O. Hill, N.A. Kitchen and E.T. Adman, J. Magn. Res., 57 (1984) page 1-23.

(12) B.I. Vallee and R.J.P. Williams, Proc. Natl. Ac. Sc. 59 (1968) page 498-505.

(13) M.A. Hoselton, C.-T. Lin, H.A. Schwarz and N. Sutin, J. Am. Chem. Soc. 100 (1978) page 2383- 2388.

(14) K.M. Davies, Inorg. Chem. 22 (1983) page 615-619.

(15) C.A. Koval and D.W. Margerum, Ibid. 20 (1981) page 2311-2318.

(16) C.M. Groeneveld and G.W. Canters, submitted for publication.

(17) P. Rosen and I. Pecht, Biochemistry 15 (1976) page 775-786; M.C. Silvestrini, M. Brunori, M.T. Wilson and V.M. Darley-Usmar, J. Inorg. Biochem. 14 (1981) page 327-338.

(18) P.S. Ho, C. Sutoris, N. Liang, E. Margoliash and B.M. Hoffman, J. Amer. Chem. Soc. 107 (1985) page 1070-1071.

(19) J.K. Beattie, D.J. Fensom, H.C. Freeman, E. Woodcock, H.A.O. Hill and A.M. Stokes, Biochim. Biophys. Acta 405 (1975) page 109-114.

(20) J.M. Anast, A.W. Hamburg and D.W. Margerum, Inorg. Chem. 22 (1983) page 2139-2145.

(21) E.J. Pulliam and D.R. McMillin, Ibid. 23 (1984) page 1172-1175.

(22) H.M. McConnell and H.E. Weaver, J. Chem. Phys. 25 (1956) page 307-311.

(23) K.D. Karlin and J.K. Yandell, Inorg. Chem. 23 (1984) page 1184-1188.

(24) C.W. Lee and F.C. Anson, J. Phys. Chem. 87 (1983) page 3360-3362.

Initial Characterization of Two New Model Systems Designed to Probe The Effect of Distance and Thermodynamic Driving Force on The Rates of Electron Transfer Between Metals

John H. Dawson, Maureen J. Kendrick Geno, Elisabeth T. Kintner

Department of Chemistry, University of South Carolina, Columbia, South Carolina 29208 U.S.A.

SUMMARY

Two new model systems designed to study the mechanism of electron transfer and in particular to delineate the roles that distance and thermodynamic driving force play in determining the rates of electron transfer are described. In both cases, alkanedione dioxime bridging ligands are employed to provide a non-conjugated spacer of variable distance to separate the two metals. In the first approach, three mixed valence diruthenium complexes have been prepared and spectroscopically characterized. The energy of the intervalence charge transfer (IT) transition has been found to increase as the distance between the metals increases while the molar absorptivity of the IT band as well as the degree of delocalization and the electronic splitting of the mixed valence states decrease. The separation in the reduction potentials of the two metals has also been found to decrease with increasing distance. In the second approach, the rates of intramolecular electron transfer from cobalt to osmium within two heteronuclear dimer complexes have been measured and found to proceed at rates comparable to those of related metal-containing adducts. The current system has the advantage that both metals display reversible electrochemistry, thus allowing the thermodynamic driving force for the electron transfer reaction to be accurately determined for the first time in a system of this nature. In addition, simple extensions of the present approach will make it possible to systematically vary the driving force of the reaction.

Abbreviations: BPY: Bipyridine; IT: Intervalence charge transfer; SCE: Saturated calomel electrode.

1 <u>INTRODUCTION</u>

The transfer of electrons between two metals is one of the most
fundamental reactions in chemistry.   Nonetheless, there is still much to
be learned concerning the contributions that distance, driving force,
solvent, molecular structure, and the potential of the reductant make
to the observed rates of such reactions.   In biological systems, the
systematic variation of the above-mentioned parameters is difficult,
and in some cases impossible, to achieve.   Thus the study of electron
transfer in a properly designed series of dinuclear metal complexes
would provide a more thorough understanding of how the process works in
metalloproteins.   To that end, we have developed two model systems; this
report contains a description of our progress to date in studying the
chemistry of electron transfer using these model systems.   Our first
approach has been to <u>indirectly</u> examine the distance dependence of
intramolecular electron transfer through non-conjugated barriers in a
series of dinuclear bipyridyl ruthenium alkanedione dioxime complexes
having the monocyclic (1), bicyclic, and tetracyclic bridging ligand
structures shown in Fig. 1.   This series of ligands allows the distance
of separation between the two metals to be varied from 3 to 9 Å.   Our

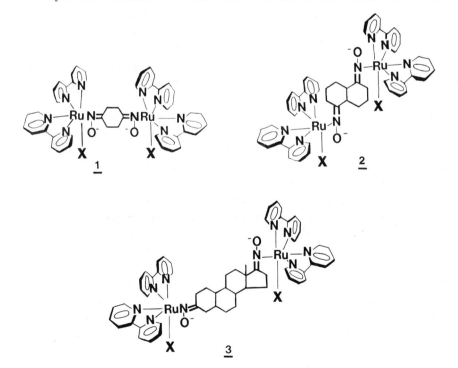

Fig. 1. Ruthenium Dimers

second model system is designed to <u>directly</u> measure the rate of thermal
intramolecular electron transfer between two metals (osmium and cobalt)
bridged by the same non-conjugated ligands as have been employed for
the first approach. As with the diruthenium system, we are using bis-
bipyridyl-coordinated metal centers. However, we have only examined the
monocyclic system (2) and the related 1,4-benzoquinone dioxime-bridged
dimer at present.

2 THE STUDY OF MIXED-VALENCE RUTHENIUM DIMERS

   The relevant physical properties of the ruthenium dioxime dimers are
shown in Table 1. Infrared spectroscopic studies using ^{15}N-labeled
cyclohexanone oxime have shown that coordination of the oximes to the
Ru(II) centers occurs via the oxime nitrogen atom (1). The monocyclic
Ru dimer (<u>1</u>) displays two reversible cyclic voltammetric waves centered
at 0.685 and 0.214 V (vs SCE). The wide separation between the two redox
couples (444 mV) illustrates the effect of oxidation/reduction at one
site on the redox behavior at the second metal. For the series of
dimers, the difference in potential decreases as the distance between
metal centers increases (Table 1) thereby suggesting that as the metal
centers are further separated they behave more and more independently
of one another. The comproportionation constant (K_{com}) (3) also
decreases as the distance of separation increases.

TABLE 1. Physical Data for Ru Dimers[a].

DIMER		ELEMENTAL ANALYSIS[b]			$E_{1/2}$[c]		$\Delta E_{1/2}$	log
		% C	% H	% N	V, vs SCE			K_{com}[d]
<u>1</u>	Calc	42.74	3.42	10.83				
	Found	42.88	3.25	10.74	0.685	0.241	0.471	7.98
<u>2</u>	Calc	41.28	4.12	9.62				
	Found	41.20	3.72	9.59	0.960	0.770	0.190	3.22
<u>3</u>	Calc	48.24	4.12	9.53				
	Found	48.39	4.35	9.89	0.900	0.827	0.073	1.24

(a) PF_6^- salts.
(b) C,H,N analyses provided by Robertson Laboratory, Florham Park, N.J.
(c) Electrochemical system used: Pt disk working electrode, Pt wire
    auxiliary electrode and saturated calomel reference electrode.
    Experiments were performed under nitrogen at 25° C in acetonitrile
    in the presence of 0.1 M tetra-n-butylammonium perchlorate.
(d) See Reference 3.

As a further test of the interaction of the two metal sites in our
model system, we have generated the mixed valence [Ru(II)--Ru(III)]
dimers which are expected to display characteristic intervalence charge
transfer (IT) electronic absorption bands in the near-infrared region
(4). In the case of the monocyclic (1) and steroid (3) dimers, we have
been able to observe weak IT bands centered at 910 (1) and 718 nm,
respectively. Preliminary data suggest that the 1,5-bicyclic
diruthenium (2) mixed valence species displays an IT band near 830 nm.
No bands are observed in the near-infrared region in any case for the
doubly-reduced (II,II) or doubly-oxidized (III,III) ions. From Table 2,
it can be seen that as the distance between the ruthenium centers is increased,
the band energy increases and the molar absorptivity decreases.

According to Hush (4), for symmetrical mixed-valence complexes, the
band-width of the IT band at half-height ($\nu_{1/2}$, in cm^{-1}) should be a
function of the maximum band energy (ν_{max}, in cm^{-1}). A lower limit for
$\nu_{1/2}$ at room temperature can be calculated from equation 1 (4). The

$$\nu = [(\nu_{max})(2300)]^{1/2} \qquad \text{(eq. 1)}$$

theoretical value of $\nu_{1/2}$ for the steroid dimer (3) is only slightly
lower than is observed (Table 2). On the other hand, the IT band for
the monocyclic dimer (1) is much narrower than predicted. For this
reason, we conclude that the monocyclic dimer is not behaving according
to Hush theory perhaps because some other mechanism (possibly involving
the bipyridine rings) is operative in the electron transfer process.

TABLE 2. Properties of intervalence Charge Transfer Bands in
Ruthenium Dimers[a].

DIMER	ν_{max}	$\nu_{1/2}$ obs[b]	$\nu_{1/2}$ th[b]	ε_{max} $M^{-1}cm^{-1}$	α^2 $M^{-1}cm^{-1}/A^2$	J eV	d Å
1	10,900 (910 nm)	1450	5017	42	3.8×10^{-4}	2.6×10^{-2}	4.6
2	12,020 (830 nm)	--[c]	5269	--[c]	--[c]	--[c]	5.8
3	13,900 (718 nm)	6740	5666	3.4	6.6×10^{-6}	4.4×10^{-3}	9.4

(a) Spectra were recorded (Cary 14 or 2390 spectrophotometers) at 25° C
in 0.2 M DCl. All values are in cm^{-1} unless otherwise noted.
(b) obs., observed; th., theoretical.
(c) To be determined.

The extent of delocalization of the exchanging electron (α^2) can be estimated from the properties of the IT band according to the theory of Hush (4). The α^2 parameter is a measure of the delocalization in both the ground and excited state and can be calculated according to equation 2 where d is the internuclear separation between the ruthenium atoms

$$\alpha^2 = \frac{4.2 \times 10^{-4} \; \varepsilon_{max} \; \nu_{1/2}}{\nu_{max} \; d^2} \qquad \text{(eq. 2)}$$

(using the N to N distance of the dioximes from crystal structure data) (5), ε_{max} is the molar absorptivity at the wavelength maximum and $\nu_{1/2}$ is the bandwidth at half-height (3). Values of α^2 for the monocyclic (1) and tetracyclic (3) dimers are shown in Table 2. The difference of two orders of magnitude between the two values suggests that the degree of delocalization of the electron in the monocyclic dimer is far greater than in the rigid steroid.

Using Hush theory (4,6), it is also possible to determine the degree of electronic coupling (J) between the two metal sites according to equation 3 (6), where ε_{max}, $\nu_{1/2}$, ν_{max} and d are the same as in

$$J = \frac{2.06 \times 10^{-2} \; (\varepsilon_{max} \; \nu_{1/2} \; \nu_{max})^{1/2}}{\alpha d} \qquad \text{(eq. 3)}$$

equation 2 and α is a factor which, following Hush, we assume to be 1. The values of J for the monocyclic (1) and tetracyclic (3) dimers (Table 2) show that as the distance between the metals increases, the magnitude of the electronic coupling decreases. It should be noted that both α^2 and J provide a means of comparing systems and that the values are essentially meaningless outside of that context.

In summary, these $Ru_2(bpy)_4$-dioxime dimers represent a new series of ligand complexes with which to study the distance dependence of intramolecular electron transfer through non-conjugated barriers. As the distance between the ruthenium ions increases, the difference in reduction potential of the two metal centers decreases as do the degree of delocalization (α^2), the comproportionation constant (K_{com}) and the electronic coupling (J) of the mixed-valence state. At the same time, the energy of the IT band increases with a concomitant decrease in molar absorptivity.

3 THE STUDY OF COBALT-OSMIUM DIMERS

Using our second strategy, we have directly measured the rate of intramolecular electron transfer between two metals across a non-conjugated barrier. Miller, Closs and Calcaterra (7) have observed extremely rapid intramolecular electron transfer across a known distance using strongly reducing organic free radicals. Isied and Vassilian (8), Anderes and Lavallee (9), and Wieghardt and coworkers (10) have developed model systems for electron transfer using cobalt and ruthenium as the metal centers. However, in all three of the metal-containing systems, the mixed valence dimer is generated from the doubly-oxidized [Ru(III)--Co(III)] species by selectively reducing the Ru(III) center. Intramolecular electron transfer to the cobalt is irreversible because the resulting Co(II) is unstable, rapidly hydrating with concomitant scission of the bond between the cobalt and the bridging ligand. Thus, the driving force of the reaction can only be estimated.

Our system is designed to directly measure the rate of thermal intramolecular electron transfer between two metals bridged by a non-conjugated ligand under conditions where both metals (osmium and cobalt) exhibit reversible electrochemical behavior. Consequently, accurate reduction potentials are measurable for both metals and the driving force of the reaction can be determined. As in our work with ruthenium, we have used cyclic alkanedione dioxime ligands to bridge the two metals as in (4); the analogous mononuclear osmium and cobalt complexes, (5) and (6), have also been prepared. Elemental analysis data as well as the spectroscopic and electrochemical characteristics of the Os-Co dimer and of Os and Co monomers containing bipyridyl ligands are shown in Table 3. A cyclic voltammogram of the dimer (4) shows reversible waves at 0.617 and 0.314 V (vs SCE) for the osmium and cobalt centers, respectively.

$$[H_2O(bpy)_2CoN \overbrace{}^{} NOs(bpy)_2Cl]^{3+} \quad (bpy = 2,2'\text{-bipyridine})$$

4

$$[Cl(bpy)_2OsN \overbrace{}^{} N]^{n+}$$

5a, n=1
b, n=2

$$[H_2O(bpy)_2CoN \overbrace{}^{} N]^{n+}$$

6a, n=1
b, n=2

TABLE 3. Physical Data for the Os-Co Dimer and for Os and Co Monomers
Containing Bipyridyl Ligands.

COMPLEX	ELEMENTAL ANALYSIS[a][b]				$E_{1/2}$	EPR
		% C	% H	% N	V, vs SCE[b]	g value[c]
4·H$_2$O	Calc	35.28	3.04	9.20	0.617, 0.314	1.998
	Found	36.52	3.04	8.77		
5a	Calc	37.84	3.18	10.18	0.597	silent
	Found	37.68	2.64	9.88		
6a	Calc	38.01	3.44	10.23	0.304	1.998
	Found	38.13	2.70	9.46		
6b·H$_2$O	Calc	31.27	3.07	8.54	0.300	silent
	Found	31.54	2.68	8.37		

(a) PF_6^- salts.
(b) See Table 1 for experimental details.
(c) EPR spectra were recorded at 9.018 GHz in the solid state at room
     temperature as well as in frozen dimethylsulfoxide at -77 K.
     2,2'-Diphenyl-1-picrylhydrazyl hydrate was used as a standard.
(d) "Silent" indicates that no EPR signal was seen at -77 K.

Addition of one equivalent of Ce(IV) to the doubly reduced ion
generates the thermodynamically-unstable Os(III)-Co(II) dimer which, in
a slow intramolecular electron transfer step (k_{et} = 7.2 x 10^{-5} s^{-1}),
produces the thermodynamically-stable Os(II)-Co(III) complex (2). The
overall reaction sequence is outlined in Fig. 2. The electron transfer
reaction can be monitored by observing the reappearance of the Os(II)-
oxime charge transfer bands (Fig. 2). It should also be possible to
study the process by following the disappearance of the g = 1.998 EPR
signal for Co(II). The electron transfer reaction is clearly shown to
be intramolecular based upon (a) the lack of dependence of the observed
rate on the concentration of the dimer and (b) measurement of the
intermolecular electron transfer rate between the mononuclear complexes
(6b and 7a). The latter rate constant can then be used to calculate
that intermolecular electron transfer contributes negligibly to the
observed rate of reaction in the dimer (Fig. 2).

The rate observed for this system, the first model system of this
type (11) for which the electrochemical driving force is known, is
within the same order of magnitude (Table 4) as the intramolecular
electron transfer rates estimated by Anderes and Lavallee (9) and
measured by Isied and Vassilian (8). We have also measured the rate of

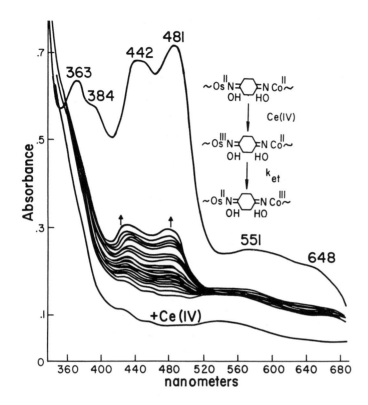

Fig. 2. Intramolecular Electron Transfer Reaction.   The UV-visible
         absorption spectrum (top) of the Os(II)-Co(II) dimer bleaches
         rapidly upon addition of one equivalent of Ce(IV) to give the
         bottom spectrum of the Os(III)-Co(II) dimer.   The Os(II) charge
         transfer bands return slowly as the Os(II)-Co(III) dimer is
         formed.

Table 4. Rate Constants for Intramolecular Electron Transfer in

         Bimetallic Model Systems.

COMPLEX	RATE CONSTANT (s^{-1})	REFERENCE
~RuN≡C—⟨⟩—C≡NCo~	3.6×10^{-6} (est.)	9
~RuN⟨O⟩—C—(proline)—C—OCo~	10.4×10^{-5}	8
~CoN=⟨⟩=NOs~ OH HO	7.2×10^{-5}	This work, 2
~CoN=⟨⟩=NOs~ OH HO	6.3×10^{-3}	This work

intramolecular electron transfer for a 1,4-benzoquinone dioxime-bridged
Os(III)-Co(II) dimer (Table 4). As expected, with a conjugated bridging
ligand separating the metals, the rate of electron transfer increases
although only by a factor of 100. These rather slow rates of electron
transfer between cobalt and either ruthenium or osmium (Table 4)
contrast dramatically with the extremely rapid (10^5 - 10^9 s^{-1})
intramolecular rates observed with strongly reducing organic free
radicals by Miller, Closs and Calcaterra (7). As recently discussed by
Sandrini et al (12), numerous factors contribute the slow rates of
electron transfer of cobalt complexes as in these dinuclear metal
systems. Clearly more work is necessary with both metal- and free
radical-containing systems in order to experimentally determine the
effect of distance and of thermodynamic driving force on the rates of
intramolecular electron transfer. A distinct advantage of our model
system is that it can easily be extended to completely rigid bridging
dioxime ligands having variable metal-metal separations. In addition,
the reduction potentials of both metals and therefore the driving force
of the reaction can be readily varied by addition of substituents on the
bipyridyl ligands. A systematic study of the rate of thermal
intramolecular electron transfer between metals across a non-conjugated
barrier as a function of the distance of separation is now possible.

4 ACKNOWLEDGEMENT

   We wish to thank the donors of the Petroleum Research Fund,
administered by the American Chemical Society, and the University of
South Carolina Venture Fund for support of this work. J.H.D. is a
Camille and Henry Dreyfus Teacher-Scholar, an Alfred P. Sloan Foundation
Research Fellow, and the recipient of a NIH Research Career Development
Award.

5 REFERENCES

(1) M. J. K. Geno, J. H. Dawson, Inorg. Chem. $\underline{23}$ (1984) 1182-1183.

(2) M. J. K. Geno, J. H. Dawson, Inorg. Chem. $\underline{24}$ (1985) 1731-1732.

(3) Determined according to the procedure of K. A. Goldsby, T. J. Meyer,
    Inorg. Chem. $\underline{23}$ (1984) 3002-3010.

(4) N. S. Hush, Prog. Inorg. Chem. $\underline{8}$ (1967) 391-444.

(5) P. Roth, Acta Chem. Scand. $\underline{22}$ (1968) 128-142.

(6) N. S. Hush, Coord. Chem. Rev., 64 (1985) 135-157.

(7) J. R. Miller, L. T. Calcaterra, G. L. Closs, J. Am. Chem. Soc. 106 (1984) 3045-3047.

(8) S. S. Isied, A. Vassilian, J. Am. Chem. Soc. 106 (1984) 1732-1736.

(9) B. Anderes, D. K. Lavallee, Inorg. Chem. 22 (1983) 2665-2666.

(10) A. Neves, W. Herrmann, K. Weighardt, J. Am. Chem. Soc. 106 (1984) 5532-5537.

(11) Elegant experiments by Isied, Gray, and coworkers have measured rates of intramolecular electron transfer with known driving forces in "semisynthetic" metalloproteins, see for example: K. M. Yocom, J. B. Shelton, J. R. Shelton, W. A. Schroeder, G. Worosila, S. S. Isied, E. Bordignon, H. B. Gray, Proc. Natl. Acad. Sci. U.S.A. 79 (1982) 7052.

(12) D. Sandrini, M. T. Gandofi, F. Boletta, V. Balzani, Inorg. Chem. 23 (1984) 3017-3023.

The Effect of pH on Electron Redistributions in Cytochrome c Oxidase

R. Wever, R. Boelens[*] and A.C.F. Gorren.

Laboratory of Biochemistry, University of Amsterdam, P.O. Box 20151,
1000 HD Amsterdam, The Netherlands

* Present address: Laboratory of Physical Chemistry, State University
of Groningen, The Netherlands

SUMMARY

Upon photodissociation of mixed-valence carboxy-cytochrome $\underline{c}$ oxidase
($\underline{a}^{3+}\underline{a}_3^{2+} \cdot CO$) intramolecular electron transfer reactions occur,
resulting in an oxidation of cytochrome $\underline{a}_3$ and a reduction of other
redox sites in the enzyme. These electron redistributions are
explained by the decrease in the apparent midpoint potential of
cytochrome $\underline{a}_3$ when CO photodissociates from reduced cytochrome $\underline{a}_3$.

Static steady-state illumination experiments on mixed-valence
carboxy-cytchrome $\underline{c}$ oxidase at various pH values show that above pH
8.0 more cytochrome $\underline{a}_3$ gets oxidized with a concomitant change in spin
state of the heme iron from high to low-spin. Upon recombination of CO
with the mixed-valence enzyme after photodissociation above pH 8.0 two
phases are observed. The first phase is the recombination of CO with
unligated cytochrome $\underline{a}_3$ while the second slower phase is ascribed to a
slow ($k=2s^{-1}$) dissociation reaction of a cytochrome $\underline{a}_3^{3+} \cdot OH^-$ complex
foloed by recombination of cytochrome $\underline{a}_3$ with CO.

The experiments demonstrate that above pH 8.0, OH^- ligates to the
heme iron of cytochrome $\underline{a}_3$. This step should be considered in studies
of the effect of pH on redoxpotentials of the various redox sites and
on steady-state kinetics of cytochrome $\underline{c}$ oxidase.

INTRODUCTION

Cytochrome c oxidase, the terminal enzyme of the respiratory chain contains 4 redox centres, 2 heme a groups and 2 copper ions. The 2 heme a groups differ structurally with cytochrome a being low-spin while cytochrome a_3 is high-spin and in the oxidized enzyme is anti-ferromagnetically coupled to one of the copper ions (Cu_B)[1,2]. The heme iron in cytochrome a_3 and Cu_B are involved in the binding and reduction of dioxygen to water. The other heme a group in cytochrome a and Cu_A are involved in the uptake of electrons from cytochrome c and the intramolecular transfer to the dioxygen binding site [3]. Little is still known about the pathways during turnover via which electron are transferred from cytochrome a and Cu_A to the cytochrome a_3-Cu_B pair. This pair not only binds dioxygen but also nitric oxide and carbon monoxide [2,4-6]. These cytochrome a_3^{2+} ligand complexes are photodissociable [7-9] and upon illumination the redoxpotential of the binding site which is increased with respect to the unligated state will decrease to its original values [10]. Thus, the light-induced dissociation of the heme iron-CO bond is coupled to a change in the apparent midpoint potential of cytochrome a_3 and in the mixed-valence enzyme $(a^{3+}a_3^{2+}CO)$ this will lead to electron redistributions [10, 11]. These light-induced changes in the redox state of the various components can be studied optically by a steady-state illumination technique or by laser photolysis of the CO compound [10,12].

Little is known about the effect of pH on these redistributions in such a system. Since in the mitochondrial membrane the enzyme is not only involved in the reduction of dioxygen to water but also during this process pumps protons accross the mitochondrial membrane [13] the electron transfer reactions should be coupled to proton uptake or release. However, the redox components involved in this have not yet been identified. Therefore, we have carried out experiments to settle whether the electron redistributions induced by photolysis are affected by pH. It is shown that at higher pH values oxidation of cytochrome a_3 is accompanied by ligation of OH^- to the heme iron of cytochrome a_3.

MATERIALS AND METHODS

Cytochrome c oxidase was isolated by the method developed in our laboratory as described in Ref. 14 and dissolved in 50 mM potassium phosphate/0.5% Tween 80 or 50 mM Trissulphate/0.5% Tween 80. Concentrations were determined optically with an absorbance coeffi-cient (reduced minus oxidized) of 24.0 $mM^{-1}.cm^1$ at 605 nm [15].

Mixed-valence carboxy-cytochrome $\underline{c}$ oxidase was prepared as described [6]. Optical absorbance spectra were measured with a Cary-17 recording spectrophotometer.

RESULTS AND DISCUSSION

As has been shown in detail in [10] steady-state illumination of fully reduced carboxy-cytochrome $\underline{c}$ oxidase ($\underline{a}^{2+}\underline{a}_3^{2+}$.CO) led in the light-minus-dark difference spectrum to a trough at 428 nm which could be assigned to photodissociation of the cytochrome $\underline{a}_3^{2+}$.CO complex (Fig. 1)

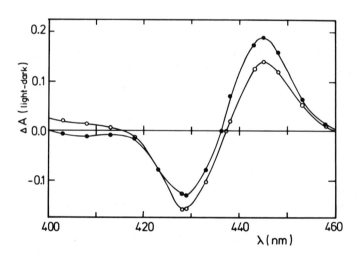

Fig. 1. Light minus dark difference spectra of fully ($\bullet$——$\bullet$) and partially reduced (o——o) carboxy-cytochrome $\underline{c}$ oxidase. 8 μM cytochrome $\underline{c}$ oxidase in 50 mM potassium phosphate (pH 7.4) and 0.5% Tween 80, pCO, 30 kPa.

Also a peak was formed at 445 nm corresponding to formation of unligated cytochrome $\underline{a}_3^{2+}$. A somewhat similar spectrum was found when the mixed-valence carboxy-cytochrome $\underline{c}$ oxidase ($\underline{a}^{3+}\underline{a}_3^{2+}$.CO) was illuminated. However, as table I and Fig. 1 show the light-induced peak at 445 nm was less intense than in fully reduced enzyme species.

Table I. Effect of pH on the photodissociation spectra of
mixed-valence carboxy-cytochrome c oxidase.

enzyme species	pH	$\Delta A_{445nm}/\Delta A_{428nm}$	$\Delta A_{412nm}/\Delta A_{427nm}$
$a^{2+} a_3^{2+} \cdot CO$	7.4	1.40	-0.06
$a^{3+} a_3^{2+} \cdot CO$	7.4	0.78	+0.06
$a^{3+} a_3^{2+} \cdot CO$	6.4	0.84	+0.05
$a^{3+} a_3^{2+} \cdot CO$	7.8	0.76	+0.06
$a^{3+} a_3^{2+} \cdot CO$	8.2	0.71	+0.05
$a^{3+} a_3^{2+} \cdot CO$	8.5	0.59	+0.05
$a^{3+} a_3^{2+} \cdot CO$	8.9	0.50	+0.05

Experimental conditions. 8 µM cytochrome c oxidase in 100 mM potassium
phosphate (pH 8.2-8.9) and 1% Tween 80; pCO, 30 kPa.

In addition, in the mixed-valence enzyme an absorbance increase was
observed around 412 nm. These differences between the two enzyme
species were explained by oxidation of cytochrome a_3 in the
mixed-valence enzyme. This oxidation of cytochrome a_3 will result in a
less intense band at 445 nm and formation of a band absorbing around
412 nm assigned [10,16] to cytochrome a_3^{2+} in a high-spin state. As
judged from the ratio $\Delta A_{445nm}/\Delta A_{427nm}$ which decreases at high pH it is
clear that at these pH values cytochrome a_3 gets more oxidized. This
observation is in line with a decrease in the differences between the
apparent midpoint potentials of the various components at pH values
above 7 [17-20]. However, it is expected that concomitantly with a
decrease of the band of reduced cytochrome a_3 at 445 nm, the band at
412 nm assigned to oxidized cytochrome a_3 would increase in intensity
at higher pH values and as table I shows this was not observed. There
is some evidence from EPR studies [20-23] that cytochrome a_3 at these
pH values is converted from a high into a low-spin state and in which
hydroxide is bound to the heme iron. This spin-state transition may
account for this discrepancy, since low-spin cytochrome a_3 will absorb
around 430 nm.

During this static illumination experiments it was noted that the
recombination of CO after dissociation was also affected by pH. At
neutral pH the rate of recombination of CO with cytochrome a_3 in the
mixed-valence enzyme is 5.10^4 $M^{-1} \cdot s^{-1}$ in line with [12] and the
reaction is first order in enzyme. However at pH 8.5 the recombination

was biphasic. The first phase corresponded to the normal recombination reaction; the second phase was a slower non-exponential with a rate constant of about 2 s^{-1} (not shown).

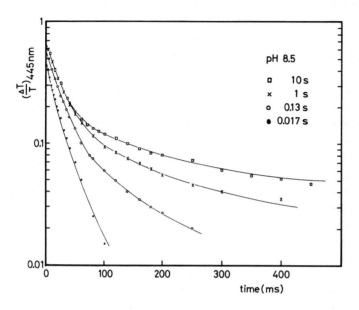

Fig. 2. Effect of illumination period on subsequent recombination of cytochrome $\underline{a}_3$ with CO. 8 μM cytochrome $\underline{c}$ oxidase in 100 mM Trissulphate(pH 8.5)/0.5% Tween 80.

To our surprise the extent of the non-exponential phase was a function of the period of illumination (Fig. 2). When the sample was illuminated only shortly the second phase was nearly absent. However, when the sample was illuminated for a longer period of time (10 s) the second phase got more pronounced. These observations suggest that during illumination, another ligand is bound to the heme iron of cytochrome $\underline{a}_3$ which in the dark upon recombination is slowly expelled by CO. It is conceivable that some protein group binds strongly to the heme iron at high pH, but it is more likely that the ligand involved is OH^-. The slow phase then could correspond to the slow dissociation reaction (k=2 s^{-1}) of OH^- in the cytochrome $\underline{a}_3^{3+}.OH^-$ complex. From the effect of time of illumination on the second phase it is possible to estimate the association rate constant. This leads to a value of about $2 \cdot 10^6 M^{-1} \cdot s^{-1}$ and combination of both association and dissociation rate constants gives a dissociation constant of about 1 μM.

Scheme 1 summarises the sequence of events:

$$\underline{a}^{2+}\underline{a}_3^{3+}\cdot OH^- \xrightleftharpoons[OH^-]{} \underline{a}^{2+}\underline{a}_3^{3+} \xrightleftharpoons[]{CO} \underline{a}^{3+}\underline{a}_3^{2+}\cdot CO \qquad (1)$$

In the dark the equilibria will shift to the right, whereas upon illumination the equilibria are shifted to the left. The value of 1 μM for the dissociation constant shows that this ligand has an affinity for the enzyme which is not very different from that observed for CO [10].

Most studies [17-20] on the effect of pH on redox equilibria do not consider the possibility that at higher pH values OH$^-$ ligates to the heme iron of cytochrome $\underline{a}_3$. Wikström et al. [20] introduced three acid-base groups to explain the redox behaviour of cytochrome $\underline{c}$ oxidase. One of these in the partially or fully reduced state had a pk_a of 8.0-8.2. It is conceivable that the group involved is the heme iron, which binds the hydroxyl ion but the similarity may be accidental. Two detailed studies [24,25] have appeared on the steady-state kinetics of cytochrome $\underline{c}$ oxidase. In the model derived three sites were involved which upon protonation leads to an increase in activity. The pk_a of one of the sites had a value of 7.8 -8.0. It was suggested by Wilms et al. [24] that binding of an hydroxyl ion to the site with a pk_a of 8.0 causes cytochrome $\underline{c}$ oxidase to became inactive with a K_i of 1 μM. Our present study does support this notion. The results can be explained by the assumption that at high pH the hydroxyl ion is bound to the enzyme and this binding inhibits the ligation of CO to the heme iron of cytochrome $\underline{a}_3$.

REFERENCES

(1) B.F. Van Gelder and H. Beinert, Biochim. Biophys. Acta 189 (1969) 1-24

(2) T.H. Stevens, G.W. Brudvig, D.F. Bocian and S.I. Chan, Proc. Natl. Acad. Sci. USA 76 (1979) 3320-3324

(3) B.C. Hill and C. Greenwood, FEBS Lett. 166 (1984) 362-366

(4) G.W. Brudvig, T.H. Stevens and S.I. Chan, Biochemistry 19 (1980) 5275-5285

(5) M.F.J. Blokzijl-Homan and B.F. Van Gelder, Biochim. Biophys. Acta 234 (1971) 493-498

(6) C. Greenwood, M.T. Wilson and M. Brunori, Biochem. J. 137 (1974) 205-215

(7) O.Warburg and E. Negelein, Biochem. Z. 214 (1929) 64-100

(8) S. Yoshida, H. Hori and Y. Orii, J. Biochem. 88 (1980) 1623-1627

(9) R. Boelens, H. Rademaker, R. Pel and R. Wever, Biochim. Biophys. Acta 679 (1982) 84-94

(10) R. Boelens and R. Wever, Biochim. Biophys. Acta 547 (1979) 296-310

(11) R. Boelens and R. Wever, FEBS Lett. 116 (1980) 223-226

(12) R. Boelens, R. Wever and B.F. Van Gelder, Biochim. Biophys. Acta 682 (1982) 264-272

(13) M.K.F. Wikström and K. Krab, Biochim. Biophys. Acta 549 (1979) 177-222

(14) C.R. Hartzell, H. Beinert, B.F. Van Gelder and T.E. King, Methods Enzymol 53 (1978) 54-66

(15) B.F. Van Gelder, Biochim. Biophys. Acta 118 (1966) 36-46

(16) R. Wever, J.H. van Drooge, G.Van Ark and B.F. Van Gelder,
     Biochim. Biophys. Acta 347 (1974) 215-223

(17) B.F. Van Gelder, J.L.M.L. van Rijn, G.J.A. Schilder and J. Wilms
     in K. van Dam and B.F. Van Gelder(eds.), Structure and Function
     of Energy-Transducing Membranes, BBA Library 14, Elsevier
     Amsterdam 1977, pp.61-68

(18) V. Yu. Artsatbanov, V.A. Grigor'ev and A.A. Konstantinov,
     Biokhimiya 48 1983, 46-53

(19) D.F. Wilson, J.G. Lindsay and E.S. Brocklehurst, Biochim.
     Biophys. Acta 256 (1972) 277-286

(20) M. Wikström, K. Krab and M. Saraste, Cytochrome c oxidase,
     Academic Press, London-New York 1981, 111-116

(21) C.R. Hartzell and H. Beinert, Biochim. Biophys. Acta 368 (1974)
     318-338

(22) R. Wever, G. Van Ark and B.F. Van Gelder, FEBS Lett. 84 (1977)
     388-390

(23) B. Lanne, B.G. Malmström and T. Vänngård, Biochim. Biophys. Acta
     545 (1979) 205-214

(24) J. Wilms, J.L.M.L. van Rijn and B.F. Van Gelder, Biochim.
     Biophys. Acta 593 (1980) 17-23

(25) P-E. Thörnström, B. Soussi, L. Arvidson and B.G. Malmström, Chem.
     Scrip. 24 (1984) 230-235.

Electron/Proton Transfer Mechanisms in The Tetraheme Cytochrome c_3

A.V.Xavier

Centro de Química Estrutural and FCT,UNL, Complexo I, I.S.T., Av.
Rovisco Pais, 1000 Lisboa, Portugal

SUMMARY

Proton NMR studies of the tetraheme cytochrome c_3 from *Desulfovibrio gigas* have shown that: i) the overall microscopic midpoint redox potentials of its hemes are pH dependent; and ii) there is a redox interaction between the hemes. These results are analysed in terms of the potential use of these properties for electron/proton energy transduction as well as for two-electron transfer steps.

1 INTRODUCTION

Cytochrome c_3 (M_r 13,000) is a multiheme protein found in anaerobic sulfate reducing bacteria belonging to the genus *Desulfovibrio*. Each molecule contains four hemes with an unusually low redox potential. They are covalently attached to the polypeptide chain by thioether linkages provided by cysteinyl residues and two histidines are used as axial ligands.

NMR is a very convenient technique for the study of the electron exchange mechanism in cytochrome c_3. In fact, each redox center can be probed through the behaviour of the different resonances of methyl groups belonging to different hemes and the experiments can be performed at temperatures close to the physiological values. From recent NMR studies on the electron transfer mechanisms of *D.gigas* cytochrome c_3, five main conclusions can be extracted (1): 1) The heme microscopic midpoint redox potentials are different. 2) The intramolecular electron exchange rate is faster than 10^5 s^{-1}.   3) There is a redox interaction between the different hemes - the interacting potentials are not negligible.   4) Some heme midpoind redox potentials are pH dependent. 5) At least two of the interacting potentials also change with the pH.

2 REDOX-BOHR EFFECT

The observation that the heme midpoint redox potential is sensitive to the pH of the solution and that there are interactions between the hemes, supports the idea that cytochrome c_3 plays a complex role in the electron transfer chain of *Desulfovibrio* spp. which has to be carried out at different redox potentials and possibly also involves proton transfer. Although a mechanism for the interaction between the different hemes in cytochrome c_3 cannot yet be anticipated, it is reasonable to speculate that a conformational change induced by the redox stage of the protein can influence the different heme midpoint redox potentials and also the pK_a of dissociable groups.

There are two ways in which the observed Redox-Bohr effect can play an important role: 1) the binding of the energized protons can temporarily increase the midpoint redox potential of the hemes favouring the subsequent acceptance of electrons, which will be followed by the release of protons and energized electrons; and 2) the possibility of performing a fine tuning of the midpoint redox potential in order to optimize the interaction with other electron transfer partners in different physiological situations, which would require a broad range of redox potentials. This can be achieved by the modulation of the midpoint redox potentials by different interacting potentials and different responses to the solution pH, enabling the transfer of electrons in a very wide range of redox potentials (2).

3 COUPLED TWO-ELECTRON TRANSFER

The need for a two-electron transfer process is a recurrent and elusive problem in biochemistry (3). Analysis of the relative microscopic midpoint redox potentials for the four hemes of *Desulfovibrio gigas* cytochrome c_3 (1) shows that this molecule has the potential properties to optimize this function (4).

The oxidation of cytochrome c_3 can be considered to involve five steps which are obtained by successive loss of one electron (1): Step 0 (all hemes reduced) through Step IV (all hemes oxidized). A full description of the redox equilibria involves 16 oxidation states and

32 microscopic midpoint redox potentials, e_i^{jkl} (the presence of the upperscripts, j, k, l, indicates those hemes which are oxidized). The relative values, $e_{ij} = e_i - e_j$, as well as the heme-heme interacting potentials, $I_{ij} = e_i - e_i^j = e_j - e_j^i$, where obtained for *D.gigas* cytochrome $\underline{c}_3$ by a thorough NRM study (see Table III of reference 1). The microscopic redox potentials are such that for a dynamic equilibrium (e.g., in an electron transfer chain) a situation optimized for a two--electron transfer can be generated. In order to explain the mechanism by which this phenomenum is achieved, let us follow the successive alterations of the microscopic midpoint redox potentials of each heme throughout the oxidation at pH = 7.2, starting with the fully reduced protein (Δe_{12} = -35 mV, Δe_{13} = -36 mV and Δe_{14} = -61 mV). Oxidation of the heme with lowest midpoint redox potentials (heme 1, e_1) modifies the microscopic midpoint redox potential of the other hemes (e_i^1, i = = 2, 3 or 4). It is important to notice that although I_{12} is positive (+19 mV), I_{13} is negative (-29 mV), altering the values of e_2 and e_3 in such way that $e_2^1 < e_2$, $e_3^1 > e_3$ and $e_3^1 \gg e_2^1$. Heme 2 is now easier to oxidize and heme 3 becomes more difficult to oxidize. Subsequent oxidation of heme 2 has a similar but even more drastic effect on heme 3 (I_{23} = +42 mV) and heme 4 (I_{24} = -24 mV). I_{23} is so large and positive that e_3^{12} becomes equal to e_3^1, within experimental error. Thus, oxidation of heme 2 impels the concominant oxidation of heme 3. Heme 4 is now more difficult to oxidize (I_{34} = -18 mV). Using the values given in the Table cited above (1), it is easily seen that a similar situation is also observed both for the reduction at pH = 7.2 as well as for the oxidation/reduction at pH = 9.6 of *D.gigas* cytochrome $\underline{c}_3$.

4 CONCLUSIONS

The above analysis depicts a situation of strong cooperativity (coupling) between the redox centers of *Desulfovibrio gigas* cytochrome $\underline{c}_3$, where oxidation (reduction) of heme 1 (heme 4) triggers a process by which two electrons are selected to be released (captured) in an essentially simultaneous way (4).

It is worth stressing that by purely electrostatic considerations, the values of the interacting potentials, I_{ij}, should be always negative and could never be of use for a similar mechanism. Redox linked conformational modifications must be involved. A further implication of this redox-linked conformational changes is their effect on the pK_a of dissociable groups (see Section 2). These conformational changes result in the presence of regulatory redox centers as well as redox centers actually implicated in the electron transfer chain.

This regulatory role may be quite general. In particular, the present knowledge of *D.gigas* hydrogenase (2) for which cytochrome c_3 is a coupling protein, suggests the use of redox centers with a similar role.

Furthermore, the postulation of these centers makes it possible to reconcile the need for fast electron transfer with that of avoiding "short-circuits" (5). The ready state for the redox centers involved in the electron transfer chain, e.g., an entatic state (6) can only be generated after a signal has been emitted by the dispatcher redox center.

ACKNOWLEDGEMENTS

I should like to thank J.LeGall, I.Moura, J.J.G.Moura and H.Santos with whom the work reviewed in the present article has been carried out. This work was supported by INIC, JNICT and USAID.

REFERENCES

(1) H.Santos, J.J.G.Moura, I.Moura, J.LeGall, A.V.Xavier, Eur. J. Biochem. 141 (1984) 283-296.

(2) M.Teixeira, I.Moura, A.V.Xavier, B.H.Huynh, D.V.DerVartanian, H.D. Peck,Jr., J.LeGall and J.J.G.Moura, J.Biol. Chem. 260 (1985) 8942--8950.

(3) R.J.P.Williams, Biochim. Biophys. Acta 505, (1978) 1-14.

(4) A.V.Xavier, H.Santos, J.J.G.Moura, I.Moura and J.LeGall, Rev. Port. Quim. 27 (1985) 149-150.

(5) J.Kraut, Biochem. Soc. Trans., 9 (1981) 197-202.

(6) B.L.Vallee and R.J.P.Williams, Proc. Natl. Acad. Sci., USA 59 (1968) 498-505.

Index

Author Index

Subject Index